CATALOGUE OF
EARLY BOOKS
ON MUSIC
(BEFORE 1800)

Da Capo Press Music Reprint Series

GENERAL EDITOR

FREDERICK FREEDMAN

VASSAR COLLEGE

CATALOGUE OF

EARLY BOOKS
ON MUSIC

(BEFORE 1800)

By

JULIA GREGORY

and

HAZEL BARTLETT

DA CAPO PRESS • NEW YORK • 1969

A Da Capo Reprint Edition

This Da Capo Press edition of *Catalogue of Early Books on Music (Before 1800)* is an unabridged republication, in one volume, of the 1913 *Catalogue* published in Washington, D.C., and of the 1944 *Supplement,* also published in Washington, D.C.

Library of Congress Catalog Card Number 69-12684

Published by Da Capo Press
A Division of Plenum Publishing Corporation
227 West 17th Street
New York, N.Y. 10011

Printed in the United States of America

LIBRARY OF CONGRESS

CATALOGUE

OF

EARLY BOOKS ON MUSIC

(BEFORE 1800)

BY

JULIA GREGORY

OF THE CATALOGUE DIVISION

PREPARED UNDER THE DIRECTION OF

O. G. SONNECK

CHIEF OF THE DIVISION OF MUSIC

WASHINGTON
GOVERNMENT PRINTING OFFICE
1913

Table of Contents

L. C. card, 12–35008

PREFATORY NOTE

The "musical renaissance" movement is placing ever increasing treasures of olden time music before us in the form of "Denkmäler" and similar, more or less, monumental publications, edited by competent musical scholars. Thus the old masters of music are again accessible to libraries which could not and can not acquire them in the very costly and scarce original editions, and this remark applies for obvious reasons to practically all American libraries.

While therefore the evolution of modern music may be fairly well reconstructed through the medium of these modern editions of old music, it is entirely different with the old books *on* music in which there lies stored such a great wealth of historical suggestion and fact. They are not accessible in reprint, if we except certain works by standard authors—I mention at random Altenburg, Agricola, St. Augustine, Bach, Blankenburgh, Boethius, Diruta, Glarean, Hawkins, Mattheson, Parfaict, Praetorius, Quantz, Ramos de Pareja, Schlick, Virdung, Zacconi. Confronted by this fact, the Library of Congress, immediately after the reorganization of the Music Division in 1902, undertook systematically to collect the old books on music in the original (because practically, only available) editions. In the short space of ten years it was, of course, impossible to acquire every rare book of moment and in some instances this was due less to rarity than to prohibitive cost. Fortunately, a few such books are available either in modern reprints at the Library of Congress, or they found their way years ago, when prices were less exasperating, to other American libraries, principally the Boston Public, the New York Public and the Newberry Library of Chicago. It would be unsafe to assume that an old book on music is not to be found in America because it happens to be wanting here in the largest American collection of the kind.

Possibly, if fortune favors us, certain annoying gaps in our own collections, annoying because of the otherwise comprehensive character of the collections, will gradually disappear. But, whether or not fortune will so favor us, it was felt that the publication of a catalogue of the old books on music already in the Library of Congress—probably more than a third of the entire output before 1800—had become advisable in the interest of musicology at home and abroad. One point, however, should not be overlooked. It has not been the policy of the Library of Congress to collect every or even many edi-

3

tions of a rare book, much less every known translation. The matter embodied in the edition–usually decided our choice of edition. Nor did first editions without distinguishing matter tempt us, merely because they were *first* editions. Such a complete representation of the typographical history of a book may be and is a legitimate desideratum in special collections, but is not necessarily an essential in a general collection as planned by the Library of Congress.

This catalogue is practically the work of Miss Julia Gregory of the Catalogue Division, and, with revisions and certain modifications, represents the catalogue cards prepared since 1902. The adoption of the Anglo-American code of rules some years later will account for occasional slight variations in form between earlier and later entries. Suggestions that would naturally be offered from time to time by the chief of the Music Division, in whose custody the books are kept, have not materially affected the character of Miss Gregory's work. He assumes, however, the full responsibility for the form of this book, and for a few minor deviations from the code of "Catalogue rules, compiled by Committees of the American Library Association and the (British) Library Association," published 1908 with the modifications in force in the Catalogue Division of the Library of Congress. In case of doubt as to the meaning of a collation, etc., the user of the Catalogue is referred to that publication.

To avoid misunderstanding, it may be stated that the entries have as a rule been restricted to books dealing exclusively or in an essential degree with music. Many of the latter are not shelved in the Music Division, but elsewhere, and this accounts for classification symbols other than M, ML and MT to be found in this catalogue. Books dealing only incidentally with music, such as Forkel, for instance, enumerates, have been excluded for practical reasons, though their incidental musical matter may possess a greater scientific value than treatises devoted exclusively to music. Finally, a subject index has been dispensed with after mature reflection, principally because the old books do not lend themselves satisfactorily to modern subject headings, and because a really useful subject index would have involved analytical labor of such magnitude as to be clearly out of proportion to its usefulness for the musicological expert, the person for whom alone it could possess a practical value. At the end of the volume will be found an "Index to anonymous works, including references to special contents" as compiled by me, and entries for books received too late for insertion in the main alphabet.

O. G. SONNECK
Chief, Music Division

HERBERT PUTNAM
Librarian of Congress
Washington, D. C., May, 1913

EARLY BOOKS ON MUSIC

A.

See SENDSCHREIBEN an die herren verfasser der Freyen urtheile, 1750.

A., J. A.

See KEINSPECK, M. Liliũ musice plane [1506]

A B C Dario musico. Bath, Printed for the authors, and sold at the rooms; [etc., etc.] 1780.

1 p. l., iii, [5]–51 p. 21½^{cm}.

Critical notices of the principal musicians of the period, resident in England.

ML105.A2A2

Aaron, Pietro.

Compendiolo di molti dvbbi, segreti et sentenze intorno al canto fermo, et figvrato, da molti eccellenti & consumati musici dichiarate, raccolte dallo eccellente & scienzato autore frate Pietro Aron del ordine de Crosachieri & della inclita citta di Firenze. In memoria eterna erit Aron, et nomen eius nunquam destruetur. In Milano, Per Io. Antonio da Castelliono stampatore [*ca.* 1545]

[76] p. 21½^{cm}.

Printer's mark on t.-p. Signatures: 4 l. unsigned, A–C, A–D in fours, E in six.

ML171.A11

Libri tres de institvtione harmonica editi a Petro Aaron Florentino interprete Io. Antonio Flam. Foro Cornelite. [*Colophon:* Impressum Bononiæ in aedibus Benedicti Hectoris bibliopolæ bononiensis. Tempore pontificatus domini nostri Leonis pape decimi. MCCCCXVI]

62 numb. l. 20½^{cm}.

Title within ornamental border; printer's mark at end. Leaf 39 numbered 38.

ML171.A15

Lvcidario in mvsica di alcvne oppenioni antiche, et moderne con le loro oppositioni, & resolutioni, con molti altri secreti appresso, & questioni da altrui anchora non dichiarati, composto dall' eccellente, & consumato musico Pietro Aron del ordine de Crosachieri, & della citta di Firenze. [*Colophon:* In Vinegia appresso Girolamo Scotto. Nel M.D.XLV]

12 unnumb. l., 41 numb. l. illus. (port.) 21½ x 15½^{cm}.

ML171.A16

Toscanello in mvsica di messer Piero Aron . . . nvovamente stampato con laggivnta da lvi fatta et con diligentia corretto . . . [*Colophon:* Stampato in Vinegia per maestro Bernardino & maestro Matheo de Vitali Venitiani el di v. de iulii mille cinquecento. XXIX.]

[124] p. illus. 29^{cm}.

Initials. Signatures: a, A–K in fours, L in six, M–N in fours, O in six. On verso of [a iiii] is a full page illustration representing Aaron in his lecture room which appears also in his "Trattato," 1525. In this copy the signature L 6, originally blank, contains in contemporary (?) hand "Versus de ligaturis ĩ musica" and commentary.

ML171.A13

5

Aaron, Pietro—*Continued.*

Trattato della natvra et cognitione di tvtti gli tvoni di canto figvrato non da altrvi piv scritti, composti per Messer Piero Aaron mvsico fiorentino canonico in Rimini maestro di casa del reve^do et magnifico cavaliere hierosolimitano Messer Sebastiano Michele priore di Vinetia. [*Colophon:* Impresso in Vinegia per Maestro Bernardino de Vitali Venitiano el di qvarto di agosto. M.CCCCC.XXV. Con privilegio]

[48] p. illus. 30½^cm.

Signatures: 3 l. unsigned, a in three, b–d in twos, e–g in fours.
Title within ornamental border, consisting of an architectural design supported by columns, with portraits of famous classical authors, and at foot the Muses in two groups; initials.
Bound with L. of C. copy of the author's Toscanello in musica, is a supplement to the present work, comprising 12 p., sig. aa–[aa6], with colophon "Stampato in Vinegia per Bernardino de Vitali Venetiano. M.D.XXXI," but without title.

ML171.A14

Abbé *le fils.*

See SAINT-SÉVIN, JOSEPH BARNABÉ.

Abercorn, James Hamilton, *7th earl of,* 1685–1744.

See PEPUSCH, J. C. A short treatise on harmony, 1730.

Abguerbe, Quentin Godin d'.

See GODIN D'ABGUERBE, QUENTIN.

Abhandlung von den pantomimen, historisch und critisch ausgeführt. Hamburg, C. S. Geissler, 1749.

6 p. l., 81 p. 18½^cm.

Preface dated: Hamburg, im jennermonate, 1749.
Attributed to Johann Mattheson by Paul Trommsdorff (Zeitschrift für bücherfreunde x 3 beiblatt p. 7) on the authority of the Gesamtkatalog der preussischen bibliotheken. In the British museum catalogue the work is ascribed to Johann Christoph Strodtmann.

ML3460.A2A14

Abreu, Antonio.

Escuela para tocar con perfeccion la guitarra de cinco y seis ordenes, con reglas generales de mano izquierda y derecha. Trata de las cantorias y pasos dificiles que se pueden ofrecer, con método fácil de executarlas con prontitud y limpieza por una y otra mano. Compuesta por D. Antonio Abreu ... Ilustrada y aumentada con varios divertimientos honestos y útiles para los aficionados á este instrumento: por el P. F. Victor Prieto ... La da a luz su apasionado N. N. Salamanca, En la imprenta de la Calle del prior, 1799.

107 p. 3 pl. (music) 20^cm.

MT582.A2A2

Academy of ancient music, *London.*

Letters from the Academy of ancient musick at London, to Sig^r Antonio Lotti of Venice: with his answers and testimonies. London, Printed by G. James, 1732.

1 p. l., 41 p. 20^{cm}.

The letters are given in the original Latin, French or Italian, with English translation on opposite pages.

ML410.L88A2

R. Accademia filarmonica, *Bologna.*

Statuti ovvero costituzioni de' signori accademici filarmonici di Bologna promulgati sotto gli auspicj dell' eminentissimo, e reverendissimo principe il Sig. cardinale Pietro Ottoboni . . . degnissimo protettore di detta accademia. Bologna, G. B. Bianchi, 1721.

4 p. l., 52 p. 23^{cm}.

ML290.8.B68A3

Adami *da Bolsena,* **Andrea,** 1663–1742.

Osservazioni per ben regolare il coro de i cantori della Cappella pontificia, tanto nelle funzioni ordinarie, che straordinarie, fatte da Andrea Adami da Bolsena, tra gl'Arcadi Caricle Piseo, maestro della medesima cappella . . . Roma, A. de' Rossi, 1711.

10 p. l., xlvj, 215, [3] p. illus. (ports.) port. 24½ x 17^{cm}.

Title vignette; tail-pieces. Added t.-p., engr.

MT88.A2A19

Adgate, Andrew, *d.* 1793.

See INTRODUCTORY lessons, practised by the Uranian society [1785]

Adlung, Jacob, 1699–1762.

M. Jacob Adlungs . . . Anleitung zu der musikalischen gelahrtheit; theils vor alle gelehrte, so das band aller wissenschaften einsehen; theils vor die liebhaber der edlen tonkunst überhaupt; theils und sonderlich vor die, so das clavier vorzüglich lieben; theils vor die orgel- und instrumentmacher. Mit kupfern und einer vorrede des . . . herrn Johann Ernst Bachs . . . Erfurt, J. D. Jungnicol, 1758.

30, 814, [34] p. VIII pl. 18^{cm}.

Pages 551 and 623 numbered 581 and 62 respectively.

ML100.A2A2

—— M. Jacob Adlungs . . . Anleitung zur musikalischen gelahrtheit, worinn von der theorie und praxis der alten und neuen musik, von den musikalischen instrumenten, besonders der orgel, nachricht gegeben, und die in jedes fach gehörigen bücher bekannt gemacht werden. 2. aufl., besorgt von Johann Adam Hiller. Dresden und Leipzig, Breitkopfische buchhandlung, 1783.

8 p. l., 976 p. VIII pl. 18^{cm}.

The plates, numbered "tab. I–VIII," are on 4 folding leaves.

ML100.A2A23

Adlung, Jacob—*Continued.*

Musica mechanica organoedi. Das ist: Gründlicher unterricht von der struktur, gebrauch und erhaltung, &c. der orgeln, clavicymbel, clavichordien und anderer instrumente, in so fern einem organisten von solchen sachen etwas zu wissen nöhtig ist. Vorgestellet von M. Jakob Adlung . . . Aus der hinterlassenen handschrift des seel. hrn. verfassers in ordnung gebracht, mit einigen anmerkungen und einer vorrede versehen, und zum drucke befördert von M. Johann Lorenz Albrecht . . . Nebst zwey tabellen und vielen figuren. Berlin, F. W. Birnstiel, 1768.

2 v. in 1 (v. 1: 3 p. l., [3]–291 p.; v. 2: 4 p. l., xx, 185, [13] p., 1 l.) illus., 11 diagr. on ii pl. 21½ x 18ᶜᵐ.

Title of v. 2 varies slightly.
Contains additions by J. F. Agricola, and an autobiography of Adlung (v. 2, p. ii–xiv)

ML550.A2A2

M. Jakob Adlungs . . . Musikalisches siebengestirn. Das ist: Sieben zu der edlen tonkunst gehörige fragen, welche derselbe, auf erhaltenen befehl der Churfürstl. maynzischen akademie nützlicher wissenschaften in Erfurt, anfänglich in lateinischer sprache beantwortet, nachgehends aber ins deutsche übersetzet hat. Aus der hinterlassenen eigenen deutschen handschrift des seel. herrn verfassers mit einer vorrede ans licht gestellet von M. Johann Lorenz Albrecht . . . Nebst einer noten-tabelle. Berlin, F. W. Birnstiel, 1768.

x, [11]–34 p., 1 l. illus. 22½ x 18½ᶜᵐ.

MT50.A2A3

Affillard, Michel l'.

See L'AFFILLARD, MICHEL.

Agricola, Johann Friedrich, 1720–1774.

See ADLUNG, J. Musica mechanica organoedi, 1768.

Agricola, Johann Friedrich, 1720–1774, *translator.*

See TOSI, P. F. Anleitung zur singkunst, 1757.

Agricola, Martin, 1486–1556.

Musica ‖ Chora- ‖ lis ‖ Deudsch. ‖ Mart. Agricola. ‖ 1533. [*Colophon:* Gedruckt zu Wittemberg durch ‖ Georgen Rhaw]

[96] p. 14½ᶜᵐ.

Title within historiated border, the sides formed by two figures playing the flute and drum, with the first notes of a Te Deum for four parts above and below.
Signatures: A–F in eights (Eij and Eiij signed Dij and Diij respectively)

ML171.A24

Musica ‖ Figu- ‖ ralis ‖ Deudsch. ‖ Mart. Agricola. [*Colophon:* Gedruckt zu Wit ‖ temberg durch ‖ Georgen Rhaw ‖ M. D. xxxij]

[240] p. tables, diagr. 15½ᶜᵐ.

Agricola, Martin—*Continued.*

Title in red and black, within historiated border with printer's mark.
On verso of t.-p.: Musica figuralis mit ihren zugehörenden exempeln / sampt einem besunderlichen schönen büchlein von den proportionibus / welche allen gemeinen sengern / instrumentisten vnd anhebern dieser kunst / gantz nützbarlich zu wissen / auffs einfeltigst vnd vorstentlichst jns deudsche verfasset.
In two parts. The second part has special t.-p. with ornamental border: Von den ‖ Propor- ‖ cionibus. ‖ Wie dieselbigen inn ‖ die Noten wircken / vnd ‖ wie sie im figural ge- ‖ sang gebraucht ‖ werden. ‖ Mart. Agricola. [*Colophon:* Gedruckt zu Wittemberg ‖ durch Georgen ‖ Rhaw]
Signatures: A–M in eights, N in four, A–B in eights, C in four (for Cii is printed Bii)

ML171.A25

Musica instru- ‖ mētalis deudsch ‖ ynn welcher begrif- ‖ fen ist / wie man ‖ noch dem gesange auff mancherley ‖ Pfeiffen lernen sol / Auch wie auff ‖ die Orgel / Harffen / Lauten / Gei- ‖ gen / vnd allerley Instrument vnd ‖ Seytenspiel / noch der recht- ‖ gegründten Tabelthur ‖ sey abzusetzen. ‖ Mart. Agricola. [*Colophon:* Gedrückt zu Wittemberg ‖ durch Georgen Rhaw. M.D.XXX.]

lvi numb. l., 4 l. illus., 4 fold. pl. 15^cm.

In verse.
Title in red and black. Leaves and first three plates printed on both sides.
Leaves xxxviij, xlvij, liij numbered xxxvi, 47, liiij respectively. Part of plate 2 torn off.
Ms. note on fly-leaf (by A. Wotquenne?): Edition originale, quoiqu'en dise Eitner, I, 60–61, qui confond toutes ces éditions.

ML171.A26

Rvdimenta ‖ mvsices, qvibvs canen- ‖ di artificivm compen- ‖ diosissime complexum, pue- ‖ ris vna cum Monochor- ‖ di dimensione ‖ traditur, ‖ per ‖ Mar. Agricolam. ‖ Vitebergæ apud ‖ Geor. Rhaw. ‖ Anno. ‖ 1539.

[62] p. 14½^cm.

Title within ornamental border.
Signatures: A–C in eights, D in seven (Diiij signed Ciiij)˙ According to Weckerlin's catalogue of the library of the Conservatoire national, Paris, 1885, the work should comprise 40 leaves, the last part being a eulogy of the science of music in Latin verse by Johann Spangenberg.

ML171.A27

Aiguino, Illuminato,· *b.* 1520?

La illvminata de tvtti i tvoni di canto fermo, con alcvni bellissimi secreti, non d'altrui piu scritti, composta per il reverendo padre frate Illuminato Aiguino da Bressa . . . Venetia, A. Gardano, 1562.

58 numb. l., [4] p. 22^cm.

Title vignette (port.) initials; printer's mark at end.

ML171.A28

Il tesoro illvminato di tvtti i tvoni di canto figvrato, con alcvni bellissimi secreti, non da altri più scritti: nuouamente composto dal reuerendo padre frate Illuminato Aijguino Bresciano . . . Venetia, G. Varisco, 1581.

2 p. l., 88 numb. l., [8] p. port. 22½ x 17^cm.

MT55.A2A8

Alard, Lambert, 1602–1672.

Lamp. Alardi . . . De veterum musica liber singularis: in fine accessit Pselli sapientissimi Musica è græco in latinum sermonem translata, autore eodem . . . Schleusingæ, sumtibus H. Grosii jun., excusus typis P. Fabri, 1636.

11 p. l., 203 p. fold. tab. 12½ᶜᵐ.

"Ψελλοῦ Τῆς μουσικῆς σύνοψις ἠκριβωκένη[!]*"*: p. 177–189. "Pselli De musica compendium exactissimum. Interprete Lamperto Alardo": p. 189–203.

ML169.A2A6

Albar . . . , *Comte* d', *pseud.*

Lettre familiere de M. le comte d'Albar . . . a Mᵐᵉ. la duchesse de L * * *. Sur l'opéra. [n. p., ca. 1790]

15 p. 21½ᶜᵐ.

Caption title.

ML1727.3.A2A52

Alberti, J., *editor.*

See REICHARDT, J. F. Geist des Musikalischen kunstmagazins, 1791.

Albrecht, Johann Lorenz, 1732–1773.

M. Johann Lorenz Albrecht. Abhandlung über die frage: ob die musik bey dem gottesdienste der christen zu dulden, oder nicht . . . Berlin, F. W. Birnstiel, 1764.

32 p. 20½ x 17ᶜᵐ.

ML3001.A5

Gründliche einleitung in die anfangslehren der tonkunst. Zum gebrauche musikalischer lehrstunden nebst einer erklärung der vornehmsten sowohl in der vokal- als instrumentalmusik vorkommenden kunstwörter, und einem kurzen abrisse einer musikalischen bibliothek, abgefasset von m. Johann Lorenz Albrecht . . . Langensalza, J. C. Martini, 1761.

8 p. l., 136 p. 21½ x 17½ᶜᵐ.

MT6.A2A34

Albrecht, Johann Lorenz, 1732–1773, *editor.*

See ADLUNG, J. Musica mechanica organoedi, 1768.
Musikalisches siebengestirn, 1768.

Albrecht, Johann Wilhelm, 1703–1736.

Tractatus physicus de effectibus musices in corpus animatum, authore D. Jo. Wilh. Albrecht . . . Lipsiæ, apud J. C. Martini, 1734.

4 p. l., 136 p. 15½ᶜᵐ.

ML3820.A2A6

Albrechtsberger, Johann Georg, 1736–1809.

Johann Georg Albrechtsbergers . . . Gründliche anweisung zur composition; mit deutlichen und ausführlichen exempeln, zum selbstunterrichte, erläutert; und mit einem anhange: von der beschaffenheit und anwendung aller jetzt üblichen musikalischen instrumente. Leipzig, J. G. I. Breitkopf, 1790.

2 p. l., 440 p. 24½ x 20ᶜᵐ.

MT40.A2A34

Kurzgefasste methode den generalbass zu erlernen, von herrn G. Albrechtsberger . . . Wien und Mainz, Artaria compagnie [1792]

1 p. l., 36 p. 24½ x 35ᶜᵐ.

Engraved throughout.
"Beispiele über alle intervalla": p. 17–36.

MT49.A2A5

Alembert, Jean Le Rond d', 1717–1783.

Élémens de musique, theorique et pratique, suivant les principes de M. Rameau. Paris, David l'aîné [etc.] 1752.

xvj, 171, [1] p., 1 l. 10 fold. pl. (partly music) 20½ᶜᵐ. (*With* Gresset, Jean B. L. Discours sur l'harmonie. Paris, 1737)

ML3815.A2A5

—— Élémens de musique, théorique et pratique, suivant les principes de M. Rameau, éclaircis, développés et simplifiés, par M. d'Alembert . . . Nouv. éd., rev., cor. & considérablement augm. Lyon, J.-M. Bruyset, 1762.

2 p. l., xxxvj, 236, [3] p. 10 fold. pl. (partly music) 20ᶜᵐ.

"Réponse à une lettre imprimée de M. Rameau" (p. 211–231) was first pub. in Le Mercure, March, 1762, as "Lettre à M. Rameau, pour prouver que le corps sonore ne nous donne et ne peut nous donner par lui-même aucune idée des proportions."

ML3815.A2A52

—— Élémens de musique, théorique et pratique, suivant les principes de M. Rameau, éclaircis, développés et simplifiés, par M. d'Alembert . . . Nouv. éd., rev., cor. & considérablement augm. Lyon, J.-M. Bruyset, 1766.

2 p. l., xxxvj, 236, [2] p., 1 l. 10 fold. pl. (partly music) 20ᶜᵐ.

ML315.8A2A53

—— Élémens de musique, théorique et pratique, suivant les principes de M. Rameau, éclaircis, développés et simplifiés, par M. d'Alembert . . . Nouv. éd., rev., cor. & considérablement augm. Lyon, J. M. Bruyset, 1772.

2 p. l., xxxvj, 236, [3] p. 10 fold. pl. (partly music) 20½ᶜᵐ. (*With* Kalkbrenner, Christian. Histoire de la musique. Paris [etc.] 1802)

ML160.K14

—— Hrn. d'Alembert . . . Systematische einleitung in die musicalische setzkunst, nach den lehrsätzen des herrn Rameau. Aus dem französischen übersetzt und mit anmerkungen vermehret von Friedr. Wilh. Marpurg. Leipzig, J. G. I. Breitkopf, 1757.

6 p. l., 136 p. 22½ x 18½ᶜᵐ.

ML3815.A2A54

See also Bâton, C. Examen de la lettre de M. Rousseau, 1753.

[Alexis de Sainte Anne, *brother*]

Methode du chant ecclesiastique, qui contient les vraies regles de la bonne modulation, & les premiers elemens de la composition . . . [Paris] Impr. de C. J. F. Ballard, 1752.

iv, 62, [2] p. 17½ᶜᵐ.

Signed: Frere Alexis de Sainte Anne, religieux carme de la province de Touraine.

MT860.A2A36

Algarotti, Francesco, *conte,* 1712–1764.

Saggio sopra l'opera in musica . . . Livorno, M. Coltellini, 1763.

157 p. 18ᶜᵐ.

Title vignette. The author's name occurs in the caption of the dedication.
Includes the texts of Algarotti's librettos "Enea in Troja" and "Iphigenie en Aulide."
1st edition 1755.

ML3858.A37

—— An essay on the opera. Written in Italian by Count Algarotti . . . Glasgow, R. Urie, 1768.

iv, [3]–124, [2], 125–182 p. 16ᶜᵐ.

ML3858.A39

Allacci, Leone, 1586–1669.

Drammaturgia di Lione Allacci, accresciuta e continuata fino all'anno MDCCLV. Venezia, G. Pasquali, 1755.

4 p. l., 1016 col. 24ᶜᵐ.

Rev. and continued by Giovanni Cendoni, Apostolo Zeno and others.
1st edition Rome, 1666.

Z2354.D7A4

Allgemeine musikalische zeitung . . . 1.–50. jahrg., oct. 1798–1848; neue folge 1.–3. jahrg., 1863–65; [3. folge] 1.–17. jahrg., 1866–82. Leipzig, Breitkopf and Härtel; [etc., etc., 1798]–1882.

70 v. illus., plates, ports. 25½–30ᶜᵐ. weekly.

Engraved title-pages. "Beylagen" (music) on separate sheets. With the first series was issued "Intelligenz-blatt zur Allgemeinen musikalischen zeitung."
Founded by Friedrich Rochlitz and ed. by him till 1818; ed. by G. W. Fink, 1827–41; C. F. Becker, 1842; Moritz Hauptmann, 1843; J. C. Lobe, 1846–48.
Publication suspended from 1849 to 1862, inclusive.
Ed. by Selmar Bagge and others, 1863–68; Friedrich Chrysander, 1869–June 1871; Joseph Müller, July 1871–1874; Friedrich Chrysander, 1875–82.
From 1866–68 title reads: Leipziger allgemeine musikalische zeitung.

—— Register zu den ersten zwanzig jahrgängen . . . (1798–1818.) Leipzig, Breitkopf und Härtel [1819?]

1 p. l., 140 p. 25½ᶜᵐ.

ML5.A43

Almanach des theaters in Wien. Nebst einer abhandlung von der kunst und dem stande des schauspielers, nach dem englischen übersetzt. [Wien] 1774.

[188] p. 6 pl. 17ᶜᵐ.

"Gönnern und freunden des theaters gewidmet von allen mitgliedern der K. K. National-schauspielergesellschaft."

PN2616.V5A6

Almeida Campos, João Ribeiro de.

See RIBEIRO DE ALMEIDA CAMPOS, JOÃO.

Alsted, Johann Heinrich, 1588–1638.

Templvm mvsicvm: or, The musical synopsis, of the learned and famous Johannes-Henricus-Alstedius, being a compendium of the rudiments both of the mathematical and practical part of musick: of which subject not any book is extant in our English tongue. Faithfully translated out of Latin by John Birchensha . . . London, P. Dring, 1664.

7 p. l., 93 (*i. e.* 94) p. front. 16½^{cm}.

A translation of the 6th part (Elementale musicum) of the author's Elementale mathematicum, Frankfort, 1611.

MT6.A2A46

Altenburg, Johann Ernst, 1736–1801.

Versuch einer anleitung zur heroisch-musikalischen trompeter- und pauker-kunst, zu mehrerer aufnahme derselben historisch, theoretisch und praktisch beschrieben und mit exempeln erläutert von Johann Ernst Altenburg . . . Halle, J. C. Hendel, 1795.

ix, [1] p., 1 l., 144 p. 20 x 18^{cm}.

Pages 133–144 ("Concerto a VII clarini con tymp.," "Marsch" and "Minuetto") printed on leaves 20 x 35½^{cm}.

MT440.A2A6

Alypius.

See MEIBOM, M., *translator.* Antiqvæ mvsicæ avctores, 1652.
MEURS, J. VAN, *editor.* Aristoxenvs, 1616.

Alypius *junior, pseud.*

Qvid sit mvsice aetatem agere ex Plavti Mostellaria act. III. sc. II. v. 40. Ad componendam controversiam de vita mvsica inter viros mvsicos nvper ortam exponit Alypivs ivnior. [n. p.] 1751.

xvi p. 21½ x 17½^{cm}.

The controversy referred to was occasioned by the publication of a pamphlet by J. G. Biedermann, entitled De vita musica ex Plaut. Mostellar. act. III. sc. II.

ML64.A5

Amiot, Joseph Marie, 1718–1793.

Mémoire sur la musique des Chinois, tant anciens que modernes, par M. Amiot . . . avec des notes, des observations & une table des matieres, par M. l'abbé Roussier . . . faisant partie du tome sixième des Mémoires concernant les Chinois. Paris, Nyon l'aîné, 1779.

3 p. l., 254 p. xxx pl. (partly fold.) incl. tables, diagrs. 26½^{cm}.

Printer's mark on t.-p. Plate XXIX is in two states, the figures of the first being reversed on the second.
One of a few copies printed with separate title. This copy belonged originally to the Abbé Roussier, and contains many notes in Roussier's handwriting. *cf.* Matthew, J. E., The literature of music

ML336.A2A16

Analyse critique de Tarare. A Ormutz, et se trouve a Paris, Hôtel de Mesgrigny, 1787.

26 p. 20^{cm}.

Text has caption: A Monsieur de * * * qui réside en province.
A criticism of the libretto of the opera Tarare, which was written by Beaumarchais (music by Salieri)

ML410.S16A2

[Ancelet,   ]

Observations sur la musique, les musiciens, et les instrumens. Amsterdam [*i. e.* Paris] Aux dépens de la Compagnie, 1757.

40 p. 18½^{cm}.

ML270.3.A59

[André, Yves Marie] 1675–1764.

Essai sur le beau, ou l'on examine en quoi consiste précisément le beau dans le physique, dans le moral, dans les ouvrages d'esprit, & dans la musique. Paris, H.-L. Guerin, & J. Guerin, 1741.

viij, 302, [2] p. 17½ x 10^{cm}.

N63.A55

Andrea *di Modena.*

Canto harmonico in cinqve parti diviso, col quale si può arriuare alla perfetta cognitione del canto fermo, del p. f. Andrea di Modona . . . Modana, Per gli eredi Cassiani stampatori episcopali, 1690.

228, 90, [2] p. pl., 3 fold. tab. 24½^{cm}.

MT45.A2A6

Andrien, J. F.

See KURTZE anführung zum general-bass, 1733.
KURTZE und gründliche anleitung zum generalbasse, 1744.

Angelo *da Picitono.*

Fior ange- ‖ lico di Mvsica: ‖ Nuouamente dal R. P. frate ‖ Angelo da Picitono, Conuen ‖ tuale, dell' ordine minore, ‖ Organista preclarissi- ‖ mo, composto. ‖ Nelqual si contengono alcune bellissime ‖ dispute contra quelli che dicono, la ‖ Musica non esser scienza: Con al ‖ tre molte questioni, & solu- ‖ tioni di varii dubbii: ‖ Pur hora da lui da- ‖ to in luce. ‖ MDXLVII. [*Colophon:* In Vinegia per Agostino Bindoni. ‖ MDXLVII]

[199] p. illus., diagrs. 20½^{cm}.

Title within ornamental border; printer's mark on last page. Signatures: ⬛, A–Z, &, in fours (versos of ⬛ 2, P 4, & 4, blank) N and Niv transposed in binding.

ML171.A58

Angelo da Conceição.

See DOMINGOS DO ROSARIO. Theatro ecclesiastico, 1774.

Angiolini, Gasparo.

Lettere di Gasparo Angiolini a Monsieur Noverre sopra i balli pantomimi. [Milano, G. B. Bianchi, 1773]

112 p. 20½^{cm}.

ML3460.A2A58

Angleria, Camillo, *d.* 1630.

La regola del contraponto, e della mvsical compositione . . . Con due ricercari l'vno à 4. e l'altro à 5. dell' autore, & vn ricercare, e canoni à 2. 3. e 4. da cantarsi in vari modi del Signor Gio. Paolo Cima, al quale la presente opera è dedicata, e nuouamente data in luce dal rever. padre fr. Camillo Angleria . . . Milano, G. Rolla, 1622.

4 p. l., 117, [7] p. 1 illus. 24 x 18^{cm}.

Title within ornamental border. Title vignette, St. Cecilia at the organ, appears again on last page, somewhat altered and enlarged. Signature O, p. 105–112, irregularly imposed and folded.

MT55.A2A6

L'anti-scurra, ou Préservatif contre les Bouffons italiens. [n. p., 1753]

7, [1] p. 19^{cm}.

Caption title. Dated "6 février 1753." In verse.
See also Caux de Cappeval.

ML1727.33.A1

Antoniotto, Giorgio, 1692–1776.

L'arte armonica; or, A treatise on the composition of musick, in three books; with an introduction, on the history, and progress of musick, from it's beginning to this time, written in Italian by Giorgio Antoniotto, and translated into English . . . London, Printed by J. Johnson, 1760.

2 v. (v. 1: 5 p. l., 109 p.; v. 2: 1 p. l., 62 pl., partly fold.) 33^{cm}.

Engr. t.-p. Vol. 2, containing the examples, has engr. half-title only.

MT40.A2A6

Antonius, Johann Ephraim, 1702–1749.

Principia musices, oder Ersten anfänge der music, hat . . . seinen unterhabenden schülern des lateinischen Pædagogei bremensis zu mehrerm nutzen und besserm anwachs in derselben entworffen Joh. Ephr. Antonius . . . Bremen, Gedruckt bey sel. H. C. Jani, E. Löbl. gymnasii buchdruckers, wittwe, 1743.

71 p. 17^{cm}.

Interleaved. "Scala in dur durch alle thone" and "Scala in moll durch alle thone," in ms., inserted opposite pages 25 and 26 respectively.

MT7.A2A7

Apligny,   Le Pileur d'.

See LE PILEUR D'APLIGNY.

Apthorp, East, 1732 *or* 3–1816.

Of sacred poetry and music. A discourse at Christ-church, Cambridge, at the opening of the organ, on Tuesday, XXI August, MDCCLXIV. By East Apthorp . . . Boston, Printed by Green and Russell, 1764.

vii, 22 p. 23½ x 18½^{cm}.

Arbeau, Thoinot, *pseud.*

See TABOUROT, JEAN.

Aristides Quintilianus.

See MEIBOM, M., *translator.* Antiqvæ mvsicæ avctores. 1652.

Aristoteles.

See GOGAVA, A. H., *translator.* Aristoxeni . . . Harmonicorvm
elementorvm libri III, 1562.

Aristoxen *der jüngere, pseud.*

See MATTHESON, JOHANN.

Aristoxenus.

See GOGAVA, A. H., *translator.* Aristoxeni . . . Harmonicorvm
    elementorvm libri III, 1562.
    MEIBOM, M., *translator.* Antiqvæ mvsicæ avctores, 1652.
    MEURS, J. VAN, *editor.* Aristoxenvs, 1616.

Armonici erudimenti nei quali si contengono le regole e suoi
    esempj per imparare accompagnare sul cimbalo il basso continovo,
    il modo di trasportarlo in altri tuoni, un esempio dal quale si conosce
    qual sia il metodo da praticarsi per acquistare un buon portamento
    di mano sopra detto strumento, scale dimostrative per bene impos-
    sessarsi della proprieta' de' tuoni si di terza maggiore come di terza
    minore, e tutto per maggiore facilita' e comodo di chi desidera appli-
    carsi a tale studio . . .   Firenze, Stamperia di A. G. Pagani, e comp.,
    si vende da G. Chiari, 1790.

2 p. l., 24 p.   illus.   25ᶜᵐ.

Ornamental borders; title vignette; head and tail piece.

MT49.A2A7

[Arnaud, François] 1721–1784.

Lettre sur la musique, a Monsieur le comte de Caylus, académicien
honoraire de l'Académie royale des inscriptions & belles-lettres, & de
celle de peinture.   [Paris] 1754.

1 p. l., 36 p.   17½ᶜᵐ.

Signed: L'abbé Arnaud.
Intended to serve as a preface for a work which was never written.
An Italian translation of the letter is given by Arteaga in v. 3 of his Rivoluzioni
del teatro musicale italiano.

ML3800.A2A6

La soirée perdue a l'Opéra.   A Avignon, et se trouve à Paris, chez
Esprit, 1776.

26 p.   19½ᶜᵐ.

Attributed also to Pascal Boyer

ML1727.35.A7

See also RIEDEL, F. J.   Ueber die musik des ritters Christoph von
Gluck, 1775.

Arnobat, Charles Pierre Coste d'.

See COSTE D'ARNOBAT, CHARLES PIERRE.

Arrhenius, Laurentius, 1680–1730, *praeses.*

. . . Dissertatio mythologico-historica de primis musicæ inventoribus, quam . . . in illustri Upsal. lycæo, sub præsidio . . . dn. Laurentii Arrhenii . . . publicæ censuræ modeste subjicit . . . Johannes Christiern. Duræus . . . Upsaliæ, literis Wernerianis [1729]

3 p. l., 32 p. 14½ᶜᵐ.

ML3800.A2A7

L'art du plein-chant, ou Traité théorico-pratique sur la façon de le chanter: dans lequel on propose aux églises de province les regles & le goût reçus dans la capitale du royaume pour le chant des offices. Villefranche-de-Rouergue, P. Vedeilhié, 1764.

6 p. l., xvj, 204, 226 p. 16ᶜᵐ.

"Pieces de plein-chant choisies, et relatives à cet ouvrage": 226 p.

MT860.A2A7

—— **L'art** du plein-chant, ou Traité théorico-pratique sur la façon de le chanter: dans lequel on propose aux églises de province les regles & le goût reçus dans la capitale du royaume pour le chant des offices. Villefranche-de-Rouergue, P. Vedeilhié, 1765.

6 p. l., xvj, 214 p., 1 l., 226 p. 16ᶜᵐ.

"Pieces de plein-chant choisies, et relatives à cet ouvrage": 226 p.

MT860.A2A72

[L'arte del detto contrapûto] Per imparare ciascheduno, che desidera approfittarsi nel contrapûto, è necessario sapere tutte le cose appartenenti all' esecuzione di ben registrare, e modulare. L'arte del detto contrapûto.

3–156 p. 22½ x 16ᶜᵐ.

Manuscript of the 18th (?) century, arranged in the form of a printed book. In 2 parts, "Libro primo" and "Libro secôdo." At end: Fine delle disposizioni a tre uoci.

MT55.A2A65

Arteaga, Stefano, 1747–1799.

Le rivoluzioni del teatro musicale italiano dalla sua origine fino al presente; opera di Stefano Arteaga . . . Bologna, Stamperìa di C. Trenti, 1783–88.

3 v. in 2. fold. pl. (music) 19½ᶜᵐ.

"Osservazioni intorno ad un estratto del tomo secondo della presente opera inserito nel Giornale enciclopedico di questa città n. xiii. . . . 1786, colle repliche fatte a queste osservazioni dallo stesso autor dell' estratto [V. Manfredini], e intitolate Difesa della musica moderna": v. 2, 207 p. at end.
"Lettera sopra la musica indirizzata al Sig. co. di Caylus e stampata l' anno 1754" (translation of the Abbé Arnaud's Lettre sur la musique): v. 3, p. 56–91.

ML1733.3.A7

—— Le rivoluzioni del teatro musicale italiano dalla sua origine fino al presente; opera di Stefano Arteaga . . . 2. ed. accresciuta, variata, e corretta dall' autore . . . Venezia, Stamperia di C. Palese, 1785.

3 v. 6. pl. on 3 fold. l. (music) 20½ᶜᵐ.

Arteaga, Stefano—*Continued.*

Plates printed on both sides.
"Lettera d'un celebre scrittore francese che contiene l' idea d' un' opera eccellente da farsi intorno alla musica" (translation of the Abbé Arnaud's Lettre sur
la musique, Paris, 1754): v. 3, p. 243–284.
"Osservazioni intorno ad un estratto del tomo 2°. della presente opera inserito
nel Giornale enciclopedico di Bologna n. xiii. del mese d'aprile del corrente
anno": v. 3, p. [285]–391.

ML1733.3.A71

—— Stephan Arteaga's . . . Geschichte der italiänischen oper von
ihrem ersten ursprung an bis auf gegenwärtige zeiten . . . Aus dem
italiänischen übersetzt und mit anmerkungen begleitet von Johann
Nicolaus Forkel . . . Leipzig, Schwickert, 1789.

2 v. (v. 1: x, [2], 344 p.; v. 2: vi, [3]–532 p.)   17½ᶜᵐ.

ML1733.3.A72

Artusi, Giovanni Maria, *d.* 1613.

L'arte del contraponto ridotta in tavole da Gio: Maria Artvsi . . .
Dove brevemente si contiene i precetti à quest' arte necessarij . . .
Venetia, G. Vincenzi, & R. Amadino, 1586.

2 p. l., 46 p., 1 l.   30ᶜᵐ.
Title within ornamental border; title vignette.   L. of C. copy has ms. notes.

ML171.A78

—— L'arte del contraponto, del rever. d. Gio. Maria Artvsi . . .
nella quale con ordine, e modo facilissimo si insegnano tutte quelle
regole, che à questa arte sono necessarie.   Nouamente ristampata, &
di molte nuoue aggiunte, dall' auttore arrichita.   Con due tauole, vna
de capitoli, & l' altra delle cose piu notabili.   Venetia, G. Vincenti,
1598.

6 p. l., 80 p.   28½ᶜᵐ.
Title within ornamental border.

ML171.A79

—— Seconda parte dell' Artvsi ouero Delle imperfettioni della
moderna mvsica, nella quale si tratta de' molti abusi introdotti da
i moderni scrittori, & compositori.   Nuouamente stampata.   Venetia, G. Vincenti, 1603.

6 p. l., 56, 54 p.   30ᶜᵐ.   (*With his* L'arte del contraponto.   Venetia, 1586)
Title vignette.   Corrections in ms.   Author's autograph presentation copy.
"Considerationi mvsicali, del r. p. d. Gio. Maria Artvsi . . .": 54 p. at end.

ML171.A78

Au petit prophête de Boesmischbroda, au grand prophête Monet,
&c.   [Paris, 1753]

13 p.   19ᶜᵐ.
Dated: A Paris, ce 21. février 1753.
No. 7 in a volume of pamphlets lettered Quere[lle] des Bouffo[ns]
Attributed to Diderot by Poulet-Malassis and in the catalogue of the Bibliothè-
que nationale, Paris.

ML1727.33.A1

[Aubert, Jean Louis] 1731-1814.

Réfutation suivie et détaillée des principes de M. Rousseau de Genève, touchant la musique françoise. Adressée à lui-même, en réponse à sa Lettre ... Paris, Chaubert [etc.] 1754.

2 p. l., iii-vi, 7-98, [3] p. 17 x 10^{cm}.

ML1727.33.A88

Aulnaye, François Henri Stanislas de l'.

See L'AULNAYE, FRANÇOIS HENRI STANISLAS DE.

Avella, Giovanni d'.

Regole di mvsica, divise in cinqve trattati, con le quali s'insegna il canto fermo, e figurato, per vere, e facili regole. Il modo di fare il contrapvnto. Di comporre l'vno, e l'altro canto. Di cantare alcuni canti difficili, e molte cose nuoue, e curiose. Composte dal padre fra Giovanni d'Avella ... Roma, Nella stampa di F. Moneta, 1657.

2 p. l., 167, [1] p. illus. 32½^{cm}.

MT860.A2A94

Aventinus *i. e.* **Johannes Turmair,** *of Abensberg,* 1477-1534, *editor.*

See FABER, N. Mvsicae rvdimenta [1516]

Ávila, Gerónimo Romero de.

See ROMERO DE ÁVILA, GERÓNIMO.

Avison, Charles, *d.* 1770.

An essay on musical expression. By Charles Avison ... London, C. Davis, 1752.

4 p. l., 138 p. 16½^{cm}.

ML3847.A95

Azopardi, Francesco, 1748-1809.

Le musicien pratique, ou Leçons qui conduisent les elèves dans l'art du contrepoint, en leur enseignant la manière de composer correctement toute espèce de musique; ouvrage composé dans les principes des conservatoires d'Italie ... par il Signor Francesco Azopardi ... Tr. de l'italien, par M. Framery ... avec des notes du traducteur pour en faciliter l'intelligence ... Paris, Le Duc, 1786.

2 v. 20^{cm} (v. 2: 21½^{cm})

Collation: v. 1, 127 p.; v. 2 ("Exemples") 1 p. l., 120 p.
"Published in the form of a French translation only."—Grove, Dict. of music.

MT55.A2A97

Bacchini, Bernardino, *in religion* **Benedetto,** 1651-1721.

D. Benedicti Bacchini De sistris, eorumque figuris, ac differentia, ad illustrissimum d. d. Leonem Strozza dissertatio. Jacobus Tullius Dissertatiunculam & notulas adjecit, & perillustri Velthusio consecravit. Trajecti ad Rhenum, ex officina Francisci Halma, 1696.

36 p. fold. pl. 24½ x 18½^{cm}.

Title vignette.
2d edition. 1st edition Bologna, 1691.

ML1040.A2B13

Bacchius, *senior.*

See MEIBOM, M., *translator.* Antiqvæ mvsicæ avctores, 1652.

Bach, Carl Philipp Emanuel, 1714–1788.

Versuch über die wahre art das clavier zu spielen, mit exempeln und achtzehn probe-stücken in sechs sonaten erläutert von Carl Philipp Emanuel Bach . . . Berlin, In verlegung des auctoris, gedruckt bey C. F. Henning, 1753.

2 v. (v. 1: 4 p. l., 135 p.; v. 2: 1 p. l., 26 pl. on 14 l.)   22½ x 18½ᶜᵐ (v. 2: 40½ᶜᵐ)

Vol. [2] has title: Exempel nebst achtzehn probe-stücken in sechs sonaten zu Carl Philipp Emanuel Bachs Versuche über die wahre art das clavier zu spielen auf XXVI. kupfer-tafeln.

MT224.A2B10

—— Carl Philipp Emanuel Bachs Versuch über die wahre art das clavier zu spielen, mit exempeln und achtzehn probe-stücken in sechs sonaten erläutert . . . Berlin, In verlegung des auctoris, gedruckt bey G. L. Winter, 1759–62.

2 v. in 1 (v. 1: 4 p. l., 118 p.; v. 2: 5 p. l., 341, [1] p.)   pl.   21 x 17ᶜᵐ.

Errors in paging. "Exempel," same as in 1753 edition, wanting.
Part 1: 2. aufl.   Part 2 is here issued for the first time; title reads: . . . Versuch . . . zweyter theil, in welchem die lehre von dem accompagnement und der freyen fantasie abgehandelt wird . . . Nebst einer kupfertafel.

MT224.A2B11

—— Carl Philipp Emanuel Bachs . . . Versuch über die· wahre art das clavier zu spielen, mit exempeln und achtzehn probe-stücken in sechs sonaten erläutert . . . Leipzig, Schwickert, 1787–97.

3 v. in 2.   23 x 19ᶜᵐ (v. 3: 40½ᶜᵐ)

Part 1: 3. mit zusätzen und sechs neuen clavier-stücken verm. aufl.
Part 2: . . . Zweiter theil, in welchem die lehre von dem accompagnement und der freyen fantasie abgehandelt wird. Nebst einer kupfertafel. 2. vom verfasser verb., und mit zusätzen verm. aufl.
Part [3] has title: Exempel nebst achtzehn probe-stücken in sechs sonaten zu Carl Philipp Emanuel Bachs Versuche über die wahre art das clavier zu spielen, mit sechs neuen clavier-stücken vermehrt auf XXXI. kupfer-tafeln.

MT224.A2B12

Verzeichniss des musikalischen nachlasses des verstorbenen capell-meisters Carl Philipp Emanuel Bach, bestehend 1) aus instrumental-compositionen . . . 2) aus sing-compositionen . . . 3) aus vermischten stücken, 4) aus compositionen von Johann Sebastian Bach, W. F. Bach, J. C. F. Bach, J. C. Bach (dem Londner), J. Bernhard Bach, 5) aus dem altbachischen archive, 6) aus musikalien von verschiedenen meistern, 7) aus instrumenten, 8) aus einer sammlung bildnisse von berühmten tonkünstlern, und 9) aus einer sammlung dergleichen silhouetten, nebst angehängtem verzeichnisse verschiedener vorhandenen zeichnungen des . . . Joh. Sebast. Bach, und einiger andern . . . Hamburg, Gedruckt bey G. F. Schniebes, 1790.

1 p. l., 142 p.   17½ᶜᵐ.

ML134.B15A1

Bach, Johann Christian, 1735–1782.

Methode ou recueil de connoissances elementaires pour le forte-piano ou clavecin; œuvre melé de theorie et de pratique, divisé en deux parties, composé pour le conservatoire de Naple par J. C. Bach et F. P. Ricci . . . Paris, Le Duc [17—]

1 p. l., 12, 45 p.; 1 p. l., 48–75 p. 25½ x 32½^{cm}.

Engraved, with the exception of the text, which occupies only 12 pages.

MT222.A2B12

Bach, Johann Ernst, 1722–1777.

See ADLUNG, J. Anleitung zu der musikalischen gelahrtheit, 1758.

Bach, Johann Michael, *b.* 1754?

Kurze und systematische anleitung zum general-bass, und der tonkunst überhaupt, mit exempeln erläutert. Zum lehren und lernen entworfen von J. M. Bach . . . Cassel, Gedruckt in der Way-senhaus-buchdruckerey, 1780.

3 p. l., 47, [1] p. 17 x 20½^{cm}.

MT49.A2B16

Bacilly, Bénigne de, *b.* 1625?

L'art de bien chanter de M. de Bacilly. Augmenté d'un discours qui sert de réponse à la critique de ce traité, et d'une plus ample instruction pour ceux qui aspirent à la perfection de cet art. Ouvrage tres-utile, non seulement pour le chant, mais même pour la decla-mation. Paris, Chez l'autheur, 1679.

7 p. l., 32, 428, [2] p. 15^{cm}.

Preceding the printed t.-p. is an engraved t.-p.: "Remarques curieuses sur l'art de bien chanter et particulierement pour ce qui regarde le chant françois, par le sieur B. D. B." According to Fétis this is the title of the 2d issue of the 1st edition, 1668, the title of the 1st issue not containing the words "par le sieur B. D. B." The main part of work, which follows the Discours, has caption and running title: Remarques sur l'art de bien chanter (caption title adds "et particulierement pour ce qui regarde le chant françois") Colophon: A Paris, De l'imprimerie de C. Blageart, rue S. Iacques, à la Cloche rouge, 1668. Last leaf has on recto "Extrait du priuilege du roy," dated "le 23. mars 1668"; on verso, "Errata."

MT820.A2B2

Bähr, Johann, 1652–1705.

Johann Beerens . . . Musicalische discurse durch die principia der philosophie deducirt, und in gewisse capitel eingetheilt, deren innhalt nach der vorrede zu finden. Nebst einem anhang von eben diesem autore, genannt Der musicalische krieg zwischen der composition und der harmonie. Nürnberg, P. C. Monath, 1719.

7 p. l., 116 (*i. e.* 216) p. front. 17½^{cm}.

Last signature paged incorrectly, 109–116. Edited by Peter Wenig?

ML60.B27

Bagatella, Antonio.

Regole per la costruzione de' violini, viole, violoncelli e violoni; memoria presentata all' Accademia di scienze, lettere ed arti di Padova al concorso del premio dell' arti dell' anno MDCCLXXXII. Dal Signor Antonio Bagatella . . . Padova, A spese dell' Accademia, 1786.

xxiv p.   illus., 2 fold. pl.   29 x 22½ᶜᵐ.

Title vignette.

ML802.A2B14

Bagnall, Gibbons, 1719–1800.

The antiquity of music, and the propriety of admitting it into divine worship, asserted from the example of beings above us, and the custom of all the wisest and politest nations.   A sermon preached in the cathedral-church of Hereford, at the anniversary meeting of the Three choirs of Worcester, Glocester, and Hereford, on Wednesday, September 15, 1762.   By Gibbons Bagnall . . . Glocester, Printed by R. Raikes [1762]

22 p.   22½ᶜᵐ.

ML3001.B13

Bailleux, Antoine, d. 1791.

Methode pour apprendre facilement la musique vocale et instrumentale, ou tous les principes sont developés avec beaucoup de clarté, et cent leçons dans le gout nouveau à une et à deux parties, ce qui enseigne en très peu de tems a solfier sur toutes les clefs, toutes les mesures et tous les tons . . . Composée par M.ʳ Bailleux . . . Paris [etc.] L'auteur [1770]

2 p. l., 127 p.   34 x 26½ᶜᵐ.

Engraved throughout.

MT870.A2B2

Bailleux, Antoine, d. 1791, editor.

See ROUSSIER, P. J.   L'harmonie pratique [1775]

Baïls, Benito, d. 1797, translator.

See BEMETZRIEDER, A.   Lecciones de clave, 1775.

Ballière de Laisement, Charles Louis Denis, 1729–1800.

Théorie de la musique, par M. Balliere . . . Paris, P. F. Didot le jeune; [etc., etc.] 1764.

1 p. l., viij, 177 p., 1 l.   diagrs. on 5 fold. pl.   26 x 20½ᶜᵐ.

ML3805.A2B15

Banchieri, Adriano, d. 1634.

Cartella mvsicale nel canto figvrato, fermo, & contrapunto. Del . p. d. Adriano Banchieri . . . Nouamente in questa terza impressione ridotta dall' antica alla moderna pratica . . . Venetia, G. Vincenti, 1614.

8 p. l., 4, [2], 248 (i. e. 244) p.   illus.   20ᶜᵐ.

Banchieri, Adriano—*Continued.*

No. 77–80 omitted in paging.
Imperfect, wanting leaf preceding text, and p. 247–248 (supplied in ms.)
In 7 parts; each part, except the first, has special t.-p., dated 1613. (2)
Brevi et primi docvmenti mvsicali a gli figliuoli, & altri, che desiderano assicurarsi sopra il canto figurato . . . (3) Dvo in contrapvnto sopra vt, re, mi, fa,
sol, la . . . (4) Altri docvmenti mvsicali nel canto fermo . . . (5) Dvo spartiti
al contrapvnto in corrispondenza trà gli dodeci modi, & otto tuoni . . . (6)
Canoni mvsicali a qvatro voci . . . (7) Moderna pratica mvsicale, opera
trentesima settima . . .

MT860.A2B2

. . . Direttorio monastico di canto fermo, per vso particolare della
Congregatione Oliuetana in preuenire l'offitio diurno al choro; nuouamente registrato dalli libri chorali alla riforma del breuiario impresso
sotto la santità di N. S. papa Paolo V. dal p. d. Adriano Banchieri
. . . Bologna, Per gli heredi di G. Rossi, 1615–16.

407, [1] p. illus. 15^{cm}.

Title vignette. Composed of 2 "books" containing together 4 parts. Each
part has special t.-p., as has an appendix to book I.
2d edition, Bologna, 1622, has title: Il cantore Olivetano.

MT860.A2B21

Organo svonarino del p. d. Adriano Banchieri . . . In questa
quarta impressione accordato con ogni diligenza e diuiso in cinque
registri, libro vtilissimo à qual si voglia organista per alternare in
voce chorista alli canti fermi di tutto l'anno nelle chiesi secolari,
regolari, monache, e confraternità à secondo l'vso di santa madre
chiesa. Et nel fine dopò la tauola generale di tutta l'opera aggiuntoui
il sesto registro . . . Opera XXXXIII. Venetia, A. Vincenti, 1638.

2 p. l., 159, [1] p. 24^{cm}.

Errors in paging.

MT190.A2B17

Bandeira, Jeronymo da Cunha.

See CUNHA BANDEIRA, JERONYMO DA.

Bandini, Angelo Maria, 1726–1803.

Ang. Maria Bandini Commentariorvm de vita et scriptis Ioannis
Bapt. Doni patricii florentini olim Sacri cardinal. collegii a secretis
libri qvinqve, adnotationibvs illvstrati ad Silvium Valenti . . .
Accedit eivsdem Doni literarivm commercivm nvnc primvm in lvcem
editvm. Florentiae, Typis caesareis, 1755.

2 v. in 1 (v. 1: xx, cxvi p.; v. 2: xii p., 272 col.) front. (port.) vign. 37^{cm}.

Title vignette; initials; tail-pieces.
Vol. [2] has title: Io. Baptistae Donii . . . Commercivm litterarivm nvnc
primvm collectvm, digestvm editvmqve stvdio et labore Ant. Francisci Gorii
. . . Florentiae, in Typographio caesareo, 1754.
"Autorum omnium nomina . . . qui de Donio nostro honorifice meminerunt,
& quorum potissimum testimonio usi fuimus": v. [1] p. xj–xiiij.
"Index opervm qvorvm partim Io. Bapt. Donivs evvlgavit, partim absolvit,
partim incepit": v. [1] p. cxi–cxvi.

ML423.D6B2

Barca, Alessandro, 1741–1814.

Introduzione a una nuova teoria di musica, memoria prima del p. d. Alessandro Barca. (Letta il dì xxiii. gennajo MDLXXXIII.)

(*In* R. Accademia di scienze, lettere ed arti in Padova. Saggi scientifici e letterarj. Padova, 1786. 29ᶜᵐ. t. I, p. 365–418)

Detached copy.

ML3800.A2B2

Introduzione ad una nuova teoria di musica, memoria seconda del p. d. Alessandro Barca C. R. S. (Letta il dì xx. dicembre MDCCLXXXVI.)

(*In* R. Accademia di scienze, lettere ed arti in Padova. Saggi scientifici e letterarj. Padova, 1789. 29ᶜᵐ. t. I, p. 329–362)

AS222.P21

Barnickel,

See KURTZGEFASSTES musicalisches lexicon.

Baron, Ernst Gottlieb, 1696–1760.

Ernst Gottlieb Barons . . . Abriss einer abhandlung von der melodie. Eine materie der zeit. Berlin, A. Haude und J. C. Spener, 1756.

12 p. 21½ x 17½ᶜᵐ.   ML3851.B18

Ernst Gottlieb Barons . . . Historisch-theoretisch und practische untersuchung des instruments der lauten / mit fleiss aufgesetzt und allen rechtschaffenen liebhabern zum vergnügen herausgegeben. Nürnberg, J. F. Rüdiger, 1727.

15 p. l., 218, [4] p. illus. 16½ᶜᵐ.

ML1010.A2B2

Barradas Muitopão e Morato, João Vaz.

See VAZ BARRADAS MUITOPÃO E MORATO, JOÃO.

[Barthélemy, Jean Jacques] 1716–1795.

Entretiens sur l'état de la musique grecque, vers le milieu du quatrieme siecle, avant l'ere vulgaire. À Amsterdam, et se trouve a Paris, chez les freres de Bure, 1777.

110 p., 1 l. 21ᶜᵐ.   ML169.A2B15

Bartholin, Caspar, 1655–1738.

Caspari Bartholini Thom. fil. De tibiis vetervm & earum antiquo vsu libri tres . . . Romæ, ex typographia P. Monetæ, sumptibus B. Carraræ, 1677.

8 p. l., 235, [5] p. 3 fold. pl. 17½ᶜᵐ.

ML169.A2B2

——— Casp. Bartholini Thom. fil. De tibiis veterum, et earum antiquo usu libri tres. Editio altera, figuris auctior. Amstelædami, apud JHenr. Wetstenium, 1679.

12 p. l., 415, [5] p. illus. (incl. port.) 5 fold. pl. 14ᶜᵐ.

Added t.-p., engr.

ML169.A2B28

Bartl, Franz Konrad, 1750–1813.

Abhandlung von der tastenharmonika, von Franz Konrad Bartl . . . Mit 5 kupfertafeln. Brünn, L. Haller, 1798.

8 p. l., [15]–75 p. v pl. 25½ x 20^{cm}.

Engr. t.-p.

ML1055.A2B18

Bartoli, Daniello, 1608–1685.

Del svono de' tremori armonici e dell' vdito. Trattati del p. Daniello Bartoli . . . Roma, A spese di N. A. Tinassi, 1679.

9 p. l., 330 p. diagrs. 21^{cm}.

ML3805.A2B29

Bartolus, Abraham.

Mvsica mathematica, das ist: Das fundament der allerlieblichsten kunst der musicæ, wie nemlich dieselbe in der natur stecke / vnd jhre gewisse proportiones, das ist / gewicht vnd mass habe / vnd wie dieselben in der mathematica, fürnemlich aber in der geometria, vnd astronomia beschrieben seind: sonsten genennet die beschreibung des instrumentes magadis oder monochordi . . . in deutzsch gegeben / durch M. Abrahamum Bartolum . . .

(In Zeising, Heinrich. Theatrum machinarum. Altenburg, 1614. 16½ x 19^{cm}. v. 6, p. [89]–174. pl. 21–24)

ML3805.A2B19

Baryphonus, Heinrich, 1581–1655.

Henrici Baryphoni . . . Pleiades musicae, qvæ in certas sectiones distributæ præcipuas quæstiones musicas discutiunt, & omnia, quæ ad theoriam pertinent, & melopœiæ plurimùm inserviunt ex veris fundamentis mathematicis exstructa, theorematis septenis proponunt, exemplis illustrant, & coram judicio rationis & sensus examinant, studiosis non solùm musices, verûm etiam matheseos scitu necessariæ & lectu jucundæ . . . Halberstadi, ex officinâ typographicâ J. A. Cotenii, 1615.

8 p. l., 95, [1] p. 14^{cm}.

ML3805.A2B3

Basili, Domenico Andrea, d. 1775?

Musica universale armonico pratica dettata dall' istinto, e dalla natura, illuminata dai veri precetti armonici; opera utile per i studiosi di contrapunto, e per i suonatori di grave cembalo, ed organo. Esposta in ventiquattro esercizi da Andrea Basili . . . [Venezia, 1776?]

1 p. l., [1], 54, 77 p. 24 x 35^{cm}.

Title within ornamental border. Engraved throughout. "L'incisione de rami è fatiha di Innocente Aleśandri, e Pietro Scattaglia Veneziani."

MT55.A2B18

Bassi, Antonio Benedetto.

Lettre adressée a la Société olympique de Paris, a l'occasion de l'opéra bouffon italien de Versailles. Par M. Bassi . . . [Paris] 1787.

2 p. l., 24 p. 21½^{cm}.

ML1727.3.A2B18

[Bâton, Charles] *d.* 1758.

Examen de la lettre de M. Rousseau, sur la musique françoise. Dans lequel on expose le plan d'une bonne musique propre à notre langue. Par M. B. * * * [Paris] 1753.

2 p. l., 36 p. 17½ᶜᵐ.

Georges Cucuel in his Notes sur Jean-Jacques Rousseau (Zeitschrift d. In*ernat. musikgesellschaft XIII, 9) cites from a contemporary ms. (Bibl. nat. ms. français 22158 in 4° fol. 100 à 203. 1753–1754) a passage to the effect that Bâton merely lent his name to the author of the present brochure, who was thought by some to be Rousseau himself, by others, D'Alembert.

ML1727.33.B17

Bauderon de Sénecé, Antoine.

See Sénecé, Antoine Bauderon de.

Baumann, Johann Gottfried.

Schediasma historico-theologicvm de hymnis et hymnopoeis veteris et recentioris ecclesiae, verae atqve christianae religioni promovendae ac propagandae inservientibvs, avtore Ioan. Godofr. Bavmann . . . Bremae, apvd I. H. Cramer, 1765.

54 p. 18½ᶜᵐ.

Ch. 17. 1896

Bayly, Anselm, 1718 *or* 19–1794.

The alliance of musick, poetry and oratory. Under the head of poetry is considered the alliance and nature of the epic and dramatic poem, as it exists in the Iliad, Æneid and Paradise lost. By Anselm Bayly . . . London, J. Stockdale, 1789.

iv, [1], 384 p. 22½ᶜᵐ.

Engr. t.-p. PN1066.B3

A practical treatise on singing and playing with just expression and real elegance. Being an essay on I. Grammar. II. Pronunciation; or, The art of just speaking. III. Singing—its graces—their application.—On cathedral compositions. By Anselm Bayly . . . London, J. Ridley, 1771.

v, 16, 99 p. 21½ᶜᵐ.

MT830.A2B3

Beauford, William.

See Walker, J. C. Historical memoirs, 1786.

[Beaumarchais, Pierre Augustin Caron de] 1732–1799.

Discours préliminaire de l'opéra de Tarare, appauvri de notes. Par une société d'indifférens. À Ormus [*i. e.* Paris] 1787.

2 p. l., 24 p. 21ᶜᵐ.

Caption title: Aux abonnés de l'Opéra, qui voudraient aimer l'opéra.

ML410.S16B3

Beaumont, Saunier de.

See Saunier de Beaumont.

Beauveset, Pierre Honoré Robbé de.

See ROBBÉ DE BEAUVESET, PIERRE HONORÉ.

[Bêche,   ]

Abrégé de l'histoire de la Ménestrandie, dans lequel on rapporte les différents arrêts du Conseil & lettres-patentes rendus en faveur de l'art musical, contre la Communauté de Saint-Julien des menétriers. [Versailles ? 1774 ?]

36 p. 16ᶜᵐ.

Caption title. Line borders.

ML270.8.P2B3

Bedford, Arthur, 1668–1745.

The great abuse of musick. In two parts. Containing an account of the use and design of musick among the antient Jews, Greeks, Romans, and others; with their concern for, and care to prevent the abuse thereof. And also an account of the immorality and profaneness, which is occasioned by the corruption of that most noble science in the present age. By Arthur Bedford . . . London, Printed by J. H. for J. Wyatt, 1711.

2 p. l., 276 p. 20½ᶜᵐ.

"A canon of four parts in one, according to Mr. Purcell's rule of fuging": p. [269]–276.

ML285.3.A2B41

The Temple musick: or, An essay concerning the method of singing the Psalms of David in the Temple, before the Babylonish captivity. Wherein, the musick of our cathedrals is vindicated, and supposed to be conformable, not only to that of the primitive Christians, but also to the practice of the church in all preceding ages. By Arthur Bedford . . . London, H. Mortlock; [etc., etc.] 1706.

8 p. l., 253, [1] p. 19½ᶜᵐ.

ML3001.B41

Bedos de Celles, François, 1706–1779.

L'art du facteur d'orgues. Par D. Bedos de Celles, Bénédictin. [Paris, Impr. de L. F. Delatour] 1766–[78]

1 p. l., xxxii p., 1 l., 676 p. cxxxvii pl. (partly fold.) 43ᶜᵐ.

Paging irregular. This copy imperfect, wanting plates LXXVII and LXXIX and a portion of each of plates XXX, XXXII, and XXXIII. Issued in 4 parts.

Forms part of a series, Description des arts et métiers, published by the Académie des sciences, Paris.

ML555.A2B41

Bekuhrs, Gottlob Friedrich Wilhelm, *d.* 1795.

Ueber die kirchen-melodien . . . von Gottlob Friedrich Wilhelm Bekuhrs . . . Halle, J. C. Hendel, 1796.

1 p. l., 154 p. 20ᶜᵐ.

ML3184.A2B2

Belli, Lazaro Venanzio.

Dissertazione sopra li preggi del canto gregoriano e la necessità che hanno gli ecclesiastici di saperlo, con le regole principali, e più importanti per bene apprenderlo, lodevolmente pratticarlo, ed in esso ancora comporre. Opera diretta alli signori chierici del V. Seminario vescovile tuscolano . . . da Lazaro Venanzio Belli . . . Frascati, Stamperia dello stesso Seminario, 1788.

xvi, 230 p., 1 l., xxxii, [2] p.   25½ x 19½ᶜᵐ.

Special t.-p. precedes the rules: Regole le principali . . . per bene apprendere . . . il canto ecclesiastico gregoriano, con i precetti di ben comporre nuovi soggetti . . . Same title with slight alterations is prefixed to the appendix.

MT860.A2B44

[Belz, Urban Nathanael] *d.* 1776.

Dissertation sur le son et sur l'ouie, qui a remporté le prix proposé par l'Académie royale des sciences et belles-lettres de Prusse, pour l'année MDCCLXII. adjugé en MDCCLXIII. Berlin, Haude et Spener, 1764.

viii, 139 p.   21½ x 18ᶜᵐ.

Half-title: Abhandlung vom schalle . . . von herrn Urban Nathanael Beltz . . . Text in German.

QC222.B5

Bemetzrieder, Anton, *d.* 1817.

Leçons de clavecin, et principes d'harmonie, par Mʳ Bemetzrieder. Paris, Bluet, 1771.

viii, 362 p., 1 l.   24 x 18ᶜᵐ.

Preface by Diderot.

MT224.A2B42

—— . . . Music made easy to every capacity, in a series of dialogues; being practical lessons for the harpsichord, laid down in a new method, so as to render that instrument so little difficult, that any person . . . may play well; become a thorough proficient in the principles of harmony; and will compose music . . . in less than a twelvemonth. Written in French by Monsieur Bemetzrieder . . . And pub. at Paris, (with a preface) by the celebrated Monsieur Diderot, the whole tr. and adapted to the use of the English student, by Giffard Bernard . . . London, Printed by R. Ayre and G. Moore, and sold by W. Randall, 1778.

vi, iv, 249 p.   29½ x 22½ᶜᵐ.

In 3 parts. Parts 2 and 3 have each special t.-p., not included in paging: Music made easy to every capacity. Part II[-III] London, Printed by R. Ayre, 1779.
"Subscribers to this work", vi p., inserted after t.-p.

MT224.A2B44

—— Music made easy to every capacity, in a series of dialogues; being practical lessons for the harpsichord, laid down in a new method, so as to render that instrument so little difficult, that any person may . . . play well; become a thorough proficient in the principles of harmony; and will compose music . . . in less than a twelvemonth. Written in French by Monsieur Bemetzrieder . . . And pub. at

Bemetzrieder, Anton—*Continued.*

Paris, (with a preface) by the celebrated Monsieur Diderot. The whole tr., and adapted to the use of the English student, by Giffard Bernard . . . [London] Printed by G. Bigg for Messrs. Birchall and Andrews, 1785.

viii, iv, 249 p. 27 x 21½^{cm}.

In 3 parts. Parts 2 and 3 have each special t.-p., not included in paging: Music made easy to every capacity. Part II[-III] London, Printed by R. Ayre, 1779.

MT224.A2B45

—— Lecciones de clave, y principios de harmonía. Por D. Benito Bails . . . Madrid, Por D. J. Ibarra, impresor, 1775.

4 p. l., vi, 291 p. 1 illus., fold. pl. 22½^{cm}.

A free translation of Bemetzrieder's Leçons de clavecin.

MT224.A2B47

Lettre de M. Bemetzrieder a MM. * * * musiciens de profession: ou, Réponse a quelques objections qu'on a faites à sa méthode, pratique, sa théorie & son ouvrage sur l'harmonie. Paris, Pissot-1771.

48 p. 24 x 18^{cm}. (*With his* Leçons de clavecin. Paris, 1771)

MT224.A2B42

Nouvel essai sur l'harmonie, suite du Traité de musique . . . Par M. Bemetzrieder. Paris, Chez l'auteur, et chez Onfroy, 1779.

286 p. 20 pl. on 10 fold. l. 21^{cm}.

"Approbation" dated 1780.

MT50.A2B45

Précis d'une nouvelle méthode de musique. Les différentes branches du savoir musical sont séparées, definies, eclaircies & arrangées suivant l'ordre naturel. Par M. Bemetzrieder. Londres, Se vend chez l'auteur, 1783.

65 p. 20^{cm}.

MT35.A2B47

Réflexions sur les leçons de musique; méthode pour enseigner la lecture musicale, l'accompagnement, l'exécution & les élémens de la composition, par M. Bemetzrieder . . . A Amsterdam, et se trouve à Paris, chez Onfroy, 1778.

iv, [5]-66 p. 19½^{cm}.

MT35.A2B3

—— Méthode et réflexions sur les leçons de musique. Nouv. éd. . . . Par M. Bemetzrieder . . . Paris, Chez l'auteur, et chez Onfroy, 1781.

2 p. l., 127, [3] p. vi pl. on 3 fold. l. 21½^{cm}.

Plates printed on both sides.

MT35.A2B33

Le tolérantisme musical, par M. Bemetzrieder. Paris, Chez l'au-teur, et chez Onfroy, 1779.

1 p. l., [5]-32 p. 21^{cm}.

ML3916.B33

Bemetzrieder, Anton—*Continued.*

Traité de musique, concernant les tons, les harmonies, les accords et le discours musical; 2. éd. Par M. Bemetzrieder . . . Paris, Chez l'auteur, et chez Gueffier, 1780.

viij, 254, [2] p.; 1 p. l., 80 p. (engr.)   20ᶜᵐ.

"Exemples du Traité de musique": 30 p.

MT50.A2B43

Bendeler, Johann Philipp, *b. ca.* 1660.

Organopoeia, oder Unterweisung / wie eine orgel nach ihren haupt-stücken / als mensuriren / abtheilung derer laden / zufall des windes / stimmung oder temperatur &c., aus wahren mathematischen gründen zu erbauen / samt einer zugabe / wie alle übel-klingende spinette / clavicimbel &c. zu einem lieblichen klange / ohne veränderung der decke / zu bringen; ingleichen / wie sie wohl zu bekielen . . . neu ausgearb. / und an den tag gegeben von Johann Philipp Bendelern . . . Franckfurt und Leipzig, In verlegung T. P. Calvisii, Merseburg, druckts C. Gottschick [1690 ?]

4 p. l., 48 p., 1 l.   diagrs.   19½ x 15½ᶜᵐ.

ML552.A2B4

—— Orgel-bau-kunst, oder: Unterweisung, wie eine orgel nach ihren haupt-stücken, als mensuriren, abtheilung derer laden, zufall des windes, stimmung oder temperatur &c. aus wahren mathematischen gründen zu erbauen, sammt einer angabe, wie alle übel-klingende spinette, clavicimbel &c. zu einem lieblichen klange, ohne veränderung der decke, zu bringen; ingleichen wie sie wohl zu bekielen . . . neu ausgearb., und an den tag gegeben von Johann Philipp Bendelern . . .   Franckfurt, 1739.

52 p.   diagrs.   19½ x 16ᶜᵐ.

ML552.A2B42

Benzoni, Donato, 1587–1664, *translator.*

See SECCHI, A.   Della hinnodia, 1643.

Bérard, Jean Antoine, 1710–1772.

L'art du chant, dedié a Madame de Pompadour, par M. Berard. Paris, Dessaint & Saillant [etc.] 1755.

9 p. l., 158, [6], 34 p.(engr.)   pl.   22ᶜᵐ.

The 34 p. contain musical examples.
Authorship claimed by the Abbé Blanchet, who afterward published his "L'art, ou les principes philosophiques du chant" (Paris, 1756) as "2. édition, corrigée & augmentée."

MT820.A2B3

Berardi, Angelo, *d.* 1693 ?

Arcani mvsicali suelati dalla vera amicitia, ne' quali appariscono diuersi studij artificiosi, molte osseruationi, e regole concernenti alla tessitura de componimenti armonici, con vn modo facilissimo per sonare trasportato.   Dialogo del can. Angelo Berardi . . .   Bologna, P.-M. Monti, 1690.

32 p.   22½ x 16½ᶜᵐ.   (*With his* Miscellanea mvsicale.   Bologna, 1689)

MT55.A2B50

Berardi, Angelo—*Continued.*

Docvmenti armonici di D. Angelo Berardi . . . nelli quali con varij discorsi, regole, & essempij si dimostrano gli studij arteficiosi della musica, oltre il modo di vsare le ligature, e d'intendere il valore di ciascheduna figura sotto qual si sia segno . . . Bologna, G. Monti, 1687.

178 (*i. e.* 180) p. 24^{cm}.

Title vignette: coat of arms; initials; tail-pieces. Errors in paging; p. 67, 97, 132, 133 numbered 76, 95, 130, 131 respectively; no. 95 and 96 repeated.

MT55.A2B48

Miscellanea mvsicale di D. Angelo Berardi . . . divisa in tre parti doue con dottrine si discorre delle materie più curiose della musica: con regole, & essempij si tratta di tutto il contrapunto con l'intreccio di bellissimi secreti per li professori armonici . . . Bologna, G. Monti, 1689.

6 p. l., 210, [6] p. 22½ x 16½^{cm}.

Title vignette: coat of arms.

MT55.A2B50

Il perche mvsicale, overo Staffetta armonica nella quale la ragione scioglie le difficoltà, e gli esempi dimostrano il modo d'isfuggire gli errori, e di tessere con artificio i componimenti musicali; opera del canonico D. Angelo Berardi . . . Bologna, P.-M. Monti, 1693.

60 p. 22½ x 16½^{cm}. (*With his* Miscellanea mvsicale. Bologna, 1689)

Title vignette: coat of arms.

MT55.A2B50

Ragionamenti mvsicali composti dal Sig. D. Angelo Berardi . . . Dedicati all' illustriss. e reuerendiss. Sig. il Sig. abbate Carlo Antonio Sampieri da Givseppe Orsolini . . . Bologna, G. Monti, 1681.

190 p. 14 x 7½^{cm}.

A résumé of lessons given by Berardi, written by Orsolini.

MT6.A2B48

—— Aggivnta di D. Angelo Berardi . . . alli svoi Ragionamenti mvsicali, nella quale si pruoua, che la musica è vera, e reale scienza . . . Bologna, G. Monti, 1681.

34 p. 14 x 7½^{cm}. (*With his* Ragionamenti mvsicali. Bologna, 1681)

MT6.A2B48

Berlin, Johann Daniel, 1711–1787.

Anleitung zur tonometrie, oder wie man durch hülfe der logarithmischen rechnung nach der geometrischen progressionsrechnung die so genannte gleichschwebende musikalische temperatur leicht und bald ausrechnen kann; nebst einem unterrichte von dem 1752. erfundenen und eingerichteten monochordum, von Johann Daniel Berlin . . . Kopenhagen und Leipzig, F. C. Pelt, 1767.

1 p. l., 2, 5–48 p. ɪɪɪ fold. pl. 17½^{cm}.

ML3809.A2B36

Berlinische musikalische zeitung. Historischen und kritischen inhalts. Mit funfzig musikstücken von verschiedenen meistern. Hrsg. von Carl Spazier . . . 1.–52. stück; 9. feb. 1793–4. jan. 1794. Berlin, Im verlage der neuen musikhandlung, 1794.

210 p. 25 x 21ᶜᵐ. weekly.

2 numbers issued for Oct. 19, 26, Nov. 2 and Jan. 4 respectively.

ML4.B4

Bermudo, Juan, *b.* 1510?

Comiença el libro llamado Declaraciõ de instumẽtos[!] musicales . . . cõpuesto por el muy reuerendo padre fray Iuã Bermudo . . . en el qual hallarã todo lo que en musica dessearẽ, y cõtiene seys libros . . . 1555. [*Colophon:* Fin delos cinco libros dela declaracion delos instrumento [!] musicales los quales compuso el muy reuerẽdo padre fray Iuã Bermudo . . . y fuerõ impressos ẽla villa de Ossuna por Iuan de Leõ . . . Y acabarõse de imprimir a treze dias del mes de iulio siendo bispera de Sanct Buenauentura año de. M.D.L.V.]

8 p. l., cxlij numb. l. illus. 29ᶜᵐ.

Title within ornamental border; title vignette: coat of arms. The 1st edition, 1548, comprised only the first "book." The sixth was not published.

ML171.B52

Bernard, Giffard, *translator.*

See BEMETZRIEDER, A. Music made easy.

Bernardo da Conceição.

O ecclesiastico instruido scientificamente na arte do canto-chaõ, composta pelo P. P. Fr. Bernardo da Conceiçaõ . . . e dada a' luz por Jeronymo da Cunha Bandeira . . . .Lisboa, F. L. Ameno, 1788.

3 p. l., xii p., 1 l., 1091 (*i. e.* 1094), [1] p. incl. pl., tables. 20½ᶜᵐ.

"Alguns hymnos selectos, tirados do Psalterio romano": p. 341–360.
"Vario canto-chaõ pratico, para uso dos principiantes": p. 361–1028.
"Psalmos, e lições dos tres officios da Semana santa; e tambem do Officio dos defuntos" (text only): p. 1029–1086.

MT860.A2B4

Bertalotti, Angelo Michele, *b.* 1665?

Regole facilissime per apprendere con facilità, e prestezza li canti fermo, e figvrato, dati alle stampe per comodo delli putti delle scvole pie di Bologna. Bologna, M. Silvani, 1698.

54 p. 21ᶜᵐ.

Tail-piece.

MT860.A2B5

—— Regole facilissime, per apprendere il canto fermo, con vn dialogo che può servire tanto per esaminare li scolari, che per esser esaminato, ed una spiegazione de' tuoni per chi volesse comporre antifone, o altro in canto fermo; nuovamente per la quinta volta ristampate, e ricorrette . . . da Angelo Michele Bertalotti . . . Bologna, Stamperìa di L. dalla Volpe, 1756.

44 p. illus. 24½ᶜᵐ.

MT860.A2B53

Bertalotti, Angelo Michele—*Continued.*

Solfeggi a canto, e alto, dati già alle stampe per comodo delle scuole pie di Bologna da Angelo Bertalotti . . . Nuova ed. con aggiunta degli elementi, del solfeggio, e de' terzetti. Bologna, Stamperìa di L. dalla Volpe, 1764.

72 p. 20½ x 26½ᶜᵐ.

MT870.A2B4

Bertezén, Salvatore.

Principj di musica teorico-prattica, di Salvatore Bertezén. Roma, Stamperìa Salomoni, 1780.

350, [2] p. 16½ x 9ᶜᵐ.

MT6.A2B5

—— Principj della musica, di Salvatore Bertezen . . . Londra, E. Reynell, 1781.

iv, xiii, 14–189, [2] p. xviii pl. 20ᶜᵐ.

MT6.A2B52

—— Extract of the work entitled Principles of music by Salvatore Bertezèn. Estratto dell' opera de' Principj della musica, &c. London, Printed for the author, 1782.

1 p. l., 5–46 p. iv pl. 20ᶜᵐ.

Italian and English in parallel columns.

MT6.A2B53

[Berthet, Pierre]

Leçons de musique, ou Exposition des traits les plus necessaires pour apprendre à chanter sa partie à livre ouvert. P. L. S. B. Paris, C. Ballard, imprimeur, 1691.

47, [1] p. 12 x 19ᶜᵐ.

145 p. of music in ms., by Berthet and others, appended. On fly-leaf at end: "Le 14 avril 1693. P. Berthet."

MT870.A2B5

Bertouch, Georg von, 1668–1743.

See STRYK, E. A. Disputatio juridica [1693]

Béthisy, Jean Laurent de, 1702–1781.

Exposition de la théorie et de la pratique de la musique, suïvant les nouvelles découvertes. Par M. de Bethizy. 2. éd. Cor. & augm. par l'auteur. Paris, F. G. Deschamps, 1764.

xvj, 331, [4] p., 60 p. (music, engr.) 20ᶜᵐ.

MT6.A2B56.

Beuf, Jean le.

See LEBEUF, JEAN.

Beurhusius, Friedrich, 1536–1609.

Erotematum mvsicæ libri dvo, ex optimis hvivs artis scriptoribvs vera perspicvaqve methodo descripti, per Fredericvm Bevrhvsivm ... Cum præfatione d. Ioannis Thomæ Freigii. Noribergæ, 1580.

[126] p. 16cm.

Colophon: Noribergæ, imprimebatvr in officina typographica Catharinæ Gerlachin, & hæredum Ioannis Montani.
Signatures: A–G in eights, H in seven.
The first edition quoted is that of Dortmund, 1573.

ML171.B55

[Bianchi, Giovanni Antonio] 1686–1758.

De i vizj, e de i difetti del moderno teatro e del modo di correg-gergli, e d'emendarli, ragionamenti vi. di Lauriso Tragiense pastore arcade. Roma, N., e M. Pagliarini, 1753.

xii, 345, [1] p. illus., 4 pl. (1 fold.) 2 plans. 27 x 20cm.

Title vignette; initials; head and tail pieces.

Ch.34.3018

Bianchini, Francesco, 1662–1729.

Francisci Blanchini Veronensis . . . De tribus generibus instru-mentorum musicæ veterum organicæ dissertatio. Romæ, impensis Fausti Amidei, 1742.

xi, 58 p. viii pl. 25½cm.

Title vignette; head-pieces; initials.

ML162.A2B6

Bicknell, John Laurence, 1740–1787.

See VEAL, G. Musical travels through England.

Biedermann, Johann Gottlieb, 1705–1772.

M. Johann Gottlieb Biedermanns . . . Abgenôthigte ehren-rettung wider die unverschâmten lâsterungen ûber seine einladungsschrifft De vita mvsica. Leipzig, M. C. F. Mûller, 1750.

15 p. 21½ x 17½cm.

ML64.B4

See also NACHGEDANKEN herrn m. Joh. Gottl. Biedermanns, 1750.

Birchensha, John.

See SALMON, T. An essay, 1672.

Birchensha, John, *translator.*

See ALSTED, J. H. Templvm mvsicvm, 1664.

Bisse, Thomas, *d.* 1731.

Musick the delight of the sons of men. A sermon preached at the cathedral church of Hereford, at the anniversary meeting of the three choirs, Glocester, Worcester, Hereford, September 7. 1726. By Tho. Bisse . . . London, W. and J. Innys, 1726.

52 p. 20cm.

ML63.B62

Blainville, Charles Henri, 1711–1769.

L'esprit de l'art musical, ou Réflexions sur la musique, et ses différentes parties, par C. H. Blainville. Genêve, 1754.

2 p. l., 126, [2] p. front. 21½ᶜᵐ.

A German translation, taken from "Vermischte beyträge zur philosophie und den schönen wissenschaften", was pub. by J. A. Hiller in his "Wöchentliche nachrichten", 1767.

ML1727.33.B63

Harmonie theorico-pratique, divisee en six parties . . . Paris, Chez l'auteur [etc.] 1751.

iv, 55, [1] p. 20½ x 27½ᶜᵐ.

Caption title: Regles de composition.
Blainville is given as author in the privilege.
An earlier edition was published by Ballard in 1746.

MT50.A2B5

Histoire générale, critique et philologique de la musique . . . par M. de Blainville. Paris, Pissot, 1767.

xj, [1], 189, [3] p. LXIX (i. e. 61) pl. (incl. front.) 27½ x 21ᶜᵐ.

Plates (partly music) numbered irregularly and in part printed on both sides.

ML159.B63

Blanc, Hubert le.

See LE BLANC, HUBERT.

Blanchet, Jean, 1724–1778.

L'art, ou les principes philosophiques du chant: par M. Blanchet. 2. ed., cor. & augm. . . . Paris, A. M. Lottin [etc.] 1756.

xlviij, 148, [4] p. pl. 16½ᶜᵐ.

For the 1st edition of this work see Bérard, J. A., L'art du chant.

MT820.A2B4

Bland, John.

. . . Catalogue of subjects or beginnings of the several works, for the harpsichord, piano forte, & organ, which are printed & sold by J. Bland, n.º 45, Holborn, London . . . Catalogue thematique, ou commencement de chaque ouvrage pour le clavecin, forte piano ou l'orgue qui sont publiés & vendus par J. Bland . . . London [1790]

18 p. 25ᶜᵐ.

At head of title: Nº 2. Decemʳ· 1790.

ML145.A2B41

Blankenburg, Christian Friedrich von, 1744–1796, editor.

See SULZER, J. G. Allgemeine theorie der schönen künste, 1792–99.

Blankenburg, Quirinus van, *b.* 1654.

Elementa musica, of Niew licht tot het welverstaan van de musiec en de bas-continuo. Door regelen, met reden en bewys, gebouwd op een klare ontledinge der eerste beginselen; na een voorafgaande wederlegging van de dwalingen dezes tyds. Waar nevens de vinding en opkomst der konst; de musiec der ouden; de redenmaat der klanken; de ontdekking van een wiskunstige cirkel, waar in de wet der nature al de toonen verdeelt; de stelkonst; de speeltuigen en de grondlegging van de zangkunst. Door Quirinus van Blankenburg . . . 's Gravenhage, L. Berkoske, 1739.

15 p. l., 200 p., 1 l.　front. (port.) 29 pl. (partly fold.)　26 x 20½ᶜᵐ.

MT49.A2B64

Blewitt, Jonas, *d.* 1805.

A complete treatise on the organ, to which is added a set of explanatory voluntaries composed expressly for the purpose of rendering theory and practice subservient to mutual elucidation. By Jonas Blewitt . . . Op: 4 . . . London, Printed by Longman and Broderip [17—]

1 p. l., 9, 59 p.　24 x 32½ᶜᵐ.

Engraved, except the treatise (9 p.) which is followed by the dedication (p. 1), 12 voluntaries (p. 2–42) and psalm-tunes with preface (p. 43–59)

MT182.A2B6

Bocchi, Francesco, 1548–1618.

Discorso di Francesco Bocchi sopra la musica, non secondo l'arte di quella, ma secondo la ragione alla politica pertinente. Fiorenza, 1581.

39 p.　16ᶜᵐ.

Colophon: In Fiorenza, Nella stamperia di Giorgio Marescotti . . . MDLXXX.
Title within ornamental border; printer's mark at end.

ML171.B57

Boch, Jean, 1555–1609.

See STRAET, J. VAN DER.　Enconivm mvsices [ca. 1600]

Boecklin von Boecklinsau, Franz Friedrich Siegmund August von, *reichsfreiherr zu Rust,* 1745–1813.

Beyträge zur geschichte der musik, besonders in Deutschland; nebst freymüthigen anmerkungen über die kunst. Von F. F. S. A. von Boecklin. Freyburg im Breisgau, Gedruckt bey N. A. Zehnder, 1790.

150 p.　19ᶜᵐ.

A second title precedes the text: xviii. briefe über die tonkunst.

ML275.3.B73

Boethius, Anicius Manlius Severinus.

Arithmetica, geometria et musica Boetii. Venetiis, Johannes et Gregorius de Gregoriis, 1492.

32ᶜᵐ.

From Opera Boetii, 1492, '91 (2 v.) v. 1, 1 p. l., numb. l. 156–220 (*i. e.* 222) (According to Hain: 157–222; according to Pellechet: 157–220 (*i. e.* 175–242))
In Pellechet, f. 157ᵇ, col. 1: "table"; in Hain and this copy, col. 1: ℂ Incipiunt duo libri de Arithmetica.
Book-plate of James E. Matthew.
Complete work listed as follows: Hain *3351, Pellechet 2490, Proctor 4517 (3 Venice 45–16, 17, 20)

Incun.1492.B67

Boethius, Anicius Manlius Severinus—*Continued.*

Opera. [Venetiis, Johannes et Gregorius de Gregoriis, fratres, 1497–99]

3 v. in 1. 32^{cm}.

Hain *3352; Proctor 4555, 4559; Pellechet 2491.

Incun.1499.B6

—— Anitii Manlii Severini Boethi . . . opera omnia . . . Accesservnt Ioannis Murmelij in v. lib. De consolatione philosophiæ commentaria. et in eosdem Rodolphi Agricolæ enarrationes. Item, Gilberti Porretæ, episcopi pictauiensis, in IIII. lib. De trinitate commentarij, antè nunquam æditi. Præter reliquos doctiss. uiros, Henricvs Loritvs Glareanvs, Arithmeticam & Musicam demonstrationibus & figuris auctiorem redditam, suo pristino nitori restituit . . . et Martianvs Rota, opus de tota disserendi ratione, hoc est, Organum . . . illustrauit. et huius autoris uitam . . . descripsit. Basileæ, ex officina Henricpetrina [1570]

23 p. l., 1546, [2] p. diagrs. 31½^{cm}.

Printer's mark on t.-p. and on last page; initials.

Ch.40

Bogatzky, Carl Heinrich von, 1690–1774.

See Der EITLE musicant, 1760.

Boiseul, Jean.

Traitté contre les danses. Par Jean Boiseul. La Rochelle, Les heritiers de Hierosme Havltin, 1606.

50 p. 16^{cm}.

Printer's mark on t.-p.

GV1740.B7

Boissy, M. A. Laus de.

See LAUS DE BOISSY, M. A.

Bollioud-Mermet, Louis, 1709–1793.

De la corruption du goust dans la musique françoise. Par M. Bollioud de Mermet . . . Lyon, Impr. d'A. Delaroche, 1746.

53, [1] p. 16½^{cm}.

Title vignette.

ML270.3.B68

—— Herrn Bollioud von Mermet abhandlung von dem verderben des geschmacks in der französischen musik. Aus dem französischen übersetzt und mit einigen historischen anmerkungen versehen von F[riedrich] G[otthilf] F[reytag] Altenburg, Bey P. E. Richtern, 1750.

78 p. 17½^{cm}.

Title vignette.
"A. G. Kästners . . . schreiben an den uebersetzer, die ursachen, warum man in den künsten auf das unnatürliche verfällt, betreffend": p. 69–78.

ML270.3.B69

Bologna. R. Accademia filarmonica.

See ACCADEMIA FILARMONICA, *Bologna.*

Bona, Giovanni, *cardinal,* 1609–1674.

De divina psalmodia, eivsqve cavsis, mysteriis, et disciplinis, deque variis ritibus omnium ecclesiarum in psallendis diuinis officiis, tractatvs historicvs, symbolicvs, asceticvs. Sive Psallentis ecclesiæ harmonia, opus nouum, & curiosum, ac multiplici eruditione illustratum. Auctore d. Ioanne Bona . . . Ed. 2. avctior et emendatior. Nunc primùm prodit in Galliis. Parisiis, apud Lvdovicvm Billaine, 1663.

12 p. l., 534 p. 23½ᶜᵐ.

"Notitia avctorvm, et librorvm, qvi in hoc opere citantvr, notantvr, illvstrantvr": p. 1–48.

ML3270.A2B6

Bona, Valerio.

Essempi delli passaggi delle consonanze, et dissonanze, et d'altre cose pertinenti al compositore. Del r. p. Valerio Bvona . . . Milano, Appresso li heredi di F.. & S. Tini, 1596.

28 p. 19 x 14½ᶜᵐ.

ML171.B69

Bonaventura *da Brescia.*

Regula musice plane. [Venetia, Jacomo di Penci da Lecho, 1500]

16 l. 21½ᶜᵐ.

Proctor 5589 (3 Venice 136—8, 9, 11) Copinger 1200. Not in Hain or Pellechet.

ML171.B7

—— Regula musice pla ‖ ne Venerabilis fratris Bo ‖ nauenture de Bri- ‖ xia ordinis ‖ mino- ‖ rū. [*Colophon:* ⊄ Impressum Mediolani per Joannem Angelum Scinzenze ‖ ler. Anno dñi. M.cccc.xiiij. Die xxvij. Mensis Septēbris]

[40] p. 1 illus. 20½ᶜᵐ.

Title within woodcut border; printer's mark on t.-p. above title; Guidonian hand on recto of third leaf. Gothic type. Signatures: a in eight, b–d in fours. 1st edition pub. at Brescia in 1497 under title: Breviloquium musicale.

ML171.B71

—— Regula musice plane vene- ‖ rabilis fratris Bonauen ‖ ture de brixia ordinis ‖ Minorum. [*Colophon:* ⊄ Stampato in Venetia per Giouanni An- ‖ drea Valuaflore detto Guadagnino ‖ M.D.L.]

[45] p. 1 illus. 15½ᶜᵐ.

Signatures: A–B in eights, C in seven. Woodcut on t.-p., Guidonian hand on recto of A iii, printer's mark on last leaf.

ML171.B73

Bonlini, Giovanni Carlo, 1673–1731.

Le glorie della poesia, e della musica contenute nell' esatta notitia de teatri della città di Venezia, e nel catalogo purgatissimo de drami musicali quiui sin' hora rapresentati. Con gl' auttori della poesia, e della musica, e con le annotationi a suoi luoghi proprij. In Venezia [C. Bonarigo stampatore, 1730]

1 p. l., 264, [2] p., 1 l. 18 x 10ᶜᵐ.

ML1733.8.V4B5

Bonnet, Jacques, 1644–1724.

Histoire de la musique, et de ses effets, depuis son origine jusqu'à present . . . Paris, J. Cochart [etc.] 1715.

8 p. l., 487, [1] p. 17cm.

Dedication signed: Bonnet.
The work was begun by the Abbé Bourdelot, continued by his nephew, Pierre Bonnet, and completed and pub. by the brother of the latter, Jacques Bonnet.

ML159.B7

—— Histoire de la musique et de ses effets, depuis son origine jusqu'à présent: & en quoi consiste sa beauté . . . Amsterdam, C. Le Cene, 1726.

4 v. in 2. 16cm.

Vol. 2–4 of this edition are a reprint of the "Comparaison de la musique italienne et de la musique françoise" of J. L. Le Cerf de La Viéville.

ML159.B8

Histoire generale de la danse, sacrée et prophane; ses progrès & ses révolutions, depuis son origine jusqu'à présent. Avec un supplement de l'Histoire de la musique, & le Paralele de la peinture & de la poésie . . . Par M. Bonnet . . . Paris, D'Houry fils, 1724.

xl, 269 p. 15½cm.

Based upon material left in manuscript by the Abbé Bourdelot.

GV1601.B71

Bonnet-Bourdelot, Pierre, 1638–1708.

See BONNET, J. Histoire de la musique.

Bonnot de Mably, Gabriel.

See MABLY, GABRIEL BONNOT DE.

Bononcini, Giovanni Maria, 1640–1678.

Mvsico prattico che breuemente dimostra il modo di giungere alla perfetta cognizione di tutte quelle cose, che concorrono alla composizione de i canti, e di ciò ch' all' arte del contrapunto si ricerca. Opera ottava di Gio. Maria Bononcini . . . Bologna, G. Monti, 1673.

5 p. l., 164 p. front. 20½cm.

MT55.A2B71

—— Johannis Mariæ Bononcini . . . Musicus practicus. Welcher in kûrtze weiset die art / wie man zu vollkommener erkântniss aller der jenigen sachen / welche bey setzung eines gesangs unterlauffen / und was die kunst des contra-puncts erfordert / gelangen kan. Stutgart / P. Treu / 1701.

1 p. l., 101, [1] p. 20 x 16cm.

Translation of the second part of his "Mvsico prattico."

MT55.A2B73

Bontempi Angelini, Giovanni Andrea, 1624–1705.

Historia mvsica, nella quale si ha piena cognitione della teorica, e della pratica antica della mvsica harmonica; secondo la dottrina de' Greci . . . e come dalla teorica, e dalla pratica antica sia poi nata la pratica moderna, che contiene la scientia del contrapunto . . . Di Gio: Andrea Angelini Bontempi . . . Pervgia, Pe'l Costantini, 1695.

6 p. l., 278, [2] p., 1 l.   diagrs.   30ᶜᵐ.

Title vignette.

ML159.B85

Borde, Jean Baptiste de la.

See LA BORDE, JEAN BAPTISTE DE.

Borde, Jean Benjamin de la.

See LA BORDE, JEAN BENJAMIN DE.

Bordier, Louis Charles, *d.* 1764.

Nouvelle methode de musique, par Mr. Bordier . . . Paris, Des Lauriers [1760]

1 p. l., 118 p.   33½ x 25¼ᶜᵐ.

Engraved throughout.   Label mounted over imprint on t.-p.: Chez Mᵉˡˡᵉ Castagnery . . .
A new edition was published in 1781 under title: Méthode pour la voix.

MT870.A2B71

Traité de composition, par feu M. Bordier . . . mis au jour par M. Boüin . . . Paris, Chez l'éditeur; [etc., etc., 1770 ?]

2 p. l., 86 p.   24½ᶜᵐ.

Engraved throughout.

MT40.A2B78

Borghese, Antonio D. R.

L'art musical ramené a ses vrais principes; ou, Lettres d'Antoine D. R. Borghese, a Julie, tr. de l'italien par l'auteur . . . Paris, Hardouin & Gattey, 1786.

1 p. l., 16, 178, [2] p.   21ᶜᵐ.

Gaspari gives also a volume of 17 plates, published 1785, containing the musical examples for the work.

MT6.A2B73

[Borjon, Charles Emmanuel] 1633–1691.

Traité de la mvsette, avec vne novvelle methode, pour apprendre de soy-mesme à joüer de cét instrument facilement, & en peu de temps.   A Lyon, Chez Iean Girin, & Barthelemy Riviere, 1672.

5 p. l., 39, 19 p. incl. illus., pl.   front., 2 pl.   29¼ᶜᵐ.

Title vignette; head-pieces; historiated initials.   In two parts; the second part, "Livre de tablature," engraved throughout, consists of arias and dance music in tablature with transcription in modern notation on opposite pages, followed by the words of the songs.

MT530.B78

Borromeo, Carlo, *Saint.*

See CARLO BORROMEO, *Saint.*

Borromeo, Federico, *cardinal,* 1564–1631.

See REGOLE d'alcuni capi, 1795.

Bos, Jean Baptiste du.

See DUBOS, JEAN BAPTISTE.

Bossler, Heinrich Philipp Carl, *d.* 1812, *editor.*

See MUSIKALISCHE real-zeitung [1788–90]

Bottrigari, Ercole, 1531–1612.

Il Patricio, overo De' tetracordi armonici di Aristosseno, parere, et vera dimostratione dell' illustre Signor caualiere Hercole Bottrigaro. Bologna, V. Benacci, 1593.

47, [1] p. 21 x 15½ᶜᵐ.

ML171.B75

Bourdelot, Pierre, *originally* **Pierre Michon,** 1610–1685.

See BONNET, J. Histoire de la musique.
Histoire generale de la danse, 1724.

Boyer, Pascal, *b.* 1743.

Lettre a Monsieur Diderot, sur le projet de l'unité de clef dans la musique. Et la réforme des mesures, proposés par M. l'abbé La Cassagne, dans ses Élémens du chant. Par M. Boyer ... A Amsterdam, et se trouve, a Paris, chez Vente, 1767.

1 p. l., ij, 70 p., 1 l. fold. pl. 19½ᶜᵐ.

ML432.A2B6

See also ARNAUD, F. La soirée perdue a l'Opéra, 1776.

Bradbury, Thomas, 1677–1759.

See PRACTICAL discourses, 1708.

Bravo, José de Torres Martínez.

See TORRES MARTÍNEZ BRAVO, JOSÉ DE.

Breitkopf, Johann Gottlob Immanuel, 1719–1794.

Catalogo ... [Lipsia] 1762–65.

6 pt. in 1 v. 22½ᶜᵐ.

Thematic catalogue of ms. music only.
Each part has special t.-p. (1) Catalogo delle sinfonie che si trovano in manuscritto nella officina musica di Giovanno Gottlob Immanuel Breitkopf, in Lipsia. Parte ıma. 1762. (2) Catalogo dei soli, duetti, trii e concerti per il violino [etc.] chi si trovano in manuscritto nella officina musica di Breitkopf in Lipsia. Parte ııda. 1762. (3) Catalogo de' soli [etc.] per il flauto traverso [etc.] ... Parte ıııza. 1763. (4) Catalogo de' soli [etc.] per il cembalo e l'harpa ... Parte ıvta. 1763. (5) Catalogo de' qvadri, partite, divertimenti, cassat. scherz. ed intrade ... a diversi stromenti ... Parte va. 1765. (6) Catalogo delle arie, duetti, madrigali e cantate, con stromenti diversi e con cembalo solo ... Parte vıta. 1765.

Breitkopf, Johann Gottlob Immanuel—*Continued.*

—— Svpplemento I[-XII] dei catalogi delle sinfonie, partite, ouverture, soli, duetti, trii, quattri e concerti per il violino, fl^auto traverso, cembalo ed altri stromenti, che si trovano in manoscritto nella officina musica di Breitkopf in Lipsia. [Lipsia] 1766–78.

12 pt. in 2 v. 22½^{cm}.

Supplements XIII–XVI wanting in L. of C. set.

ML145.A2B83

Bremner, Robert, *d.* 1789.

The rudiments of music: or, A short and easy treatise on that subject. To which is added, a collection of the best church-tunes, canons, and anthems. By Robert Bremner. Edinburgh, Printed for the author, 1756.

2 p. l., [iii]–ix, [1], 35 p. 12, 52 p .(music, engr.) 2 fold. pl. 16^{cm}.

Page 52 and 4 unnumb. p. following are ruled but otherwise blank.

MT7.A2B8

—— The rudiments of music: or, A short and easy treatise on that subject. The 3d ed. With considerable additions; particularly, Instructions for song; and, A plan for teaching a number of persons collectively the four parts of psalmody. By Robert Bremner. To which is annexed, a collection of the best church-tunes, canons, and anthems. London, Printed for the author, 1763.

1 p. l., [v]–xix, [1], 59 p., 1 l., 72 p. (music, engr.) 3 fold. pl. 17^{cm}.

MT7.A2B83

[Bretagne, Pierre de] *b. ca.* 1666.

De excellentia musicæ antiquæ Hebræorum et eorum instrumentis musicis tractatus ex S. Scriptura, ss. patribus, & antiquis authoribus illustratus . . . Monachii, sumptibus Joannis J. Remy, 1718.

6 p. l., 100 p. fold. pl. 16^{cm}.

Dedication signed: F. P. de Bretagne, A. S. E. B. C. & T.
According to Fétis this is a reprint of the 1st edition, Paris, 1707.

ML166.A2B8

Brett, John, *d.* 1785, *translator.*

See FEIJÓO Y MONTENEGRO, B. J. Three essays, 1778.

Briefwechsel über Danziger musik und musiker. Berlin, 1785.

71 p. 16^{cm}.

Letters to H. W. Gulden (*cf.* Reichardt) concerning a pamphlet by J. G. Hingelberg, published anonymously, " Ueber Danziger musik und musiker."

ML279.8.D16

Brijon, C. R., *b. ca.* 1720.

L'Apollon moderne, ou Le développement intellectuel par les sons de la musique. Nouvelle dévouverte [!] de premiere culture, aisée & certaine pour parvenir à la réussite dans les sciences, & nouveau moyen d'apprendre facilement la musique. Par C. R. Brijon . . . Deuxieme œuvre . . . Lyon [A. A. Belion] 1782.

xxxij, 264, [7], 64 p. 22½^{cm}.

In two parts. The second part has special t.-p.: L'Apollon moderne. Ou, Principes, exemples et leçons de musique. Gravé par Meunier graveur du roy, 1782 a Lyon.

MT6.A2B84

Brijon, C. R.—*Continued.*

Réflexions sur la musique, et la vraie maniére de l'exécuter sur le violon. Par M. Brijon ... Paris, Chez l'auteur [etc.] 1763.

2 p. l., 32, v, 11 p. 26½ x 20½ᶜᵐ.

In two parts. The second part, "Principes de musique, pour parvenir à jouer du violon," is engraved throughout.

MT260.A2B85

Brocarte, Antonio de la Cruz.

See CRUZ BROCARTE, ANTONIO DE LA.

[Brocklesby, Richard] 1722-1797.

Reflections on antient and modern musick, with the application to the cure of diseases. To which is subjoined, an essay to solve the question, wherein consisted the difference of antient musick, from that of modern times ... London, M. Cooper, 1749.

1 p. l., 82 p., 1 l. 19ᶜᵐ.

ML3920.A2B76

Brookbank, Joseph, *b.* 1612.

See The ORGANS fvnerall [1642?]

Brossard, Sébastien de, *d.* 1730.

Dictionaire de musique, contenant une explication des termes grecs, latins, italiens, & françois les plus usitez ... A l'occasion desquels on rapporte ce qu'il y a de plus curieux, & de plus necessaire à sçavoir; tant pour l'histoire & la theorie, que pour la composition, & la pratique ... de la musique ... Ensemble, une table alphabetique des termes françois qui sont dans le corps de l'ouvrage ... Un traité de la maniere de bien prononcer, sur tout en chantant, les termes italiens, latins, & françois. Et un catalogue de plus de 900. auteurs qui ont écrit sur la musique ... Par Mᵉ Sebastien de Brossard ... Paris, C. Ballard, 1703.

[112] p. 37ᶜᵐ.

ML108.A2B6

See also GRASSINEAU, J. A musical dictionary, 1740.

Brouncker, William Brouncker, *2d viscount,* 1620 *or* 21-1684, *editor.*

See DESCARTES, R. Excellent compendium of musick, 1653.

Brown, John, 1715-1766.

A dissertation on the rise, union, and power, the progressions, separations, and corruptions, of poetry and music. To which is prefixed, The cure of Saul. A sacred ode. Written by Dr. Brown ... London, L. Davis and C. Reymers, 1763.

iv, [5]-244 (*i. e.* 248) p. 26½ x 20½ᶜᵐ.

Last page numbered 244 for 248.

ML3849.A2B87

Brown, John—*Continued.*

—— Dr. Brown's Betrachtungen über die poesie und musik, nach ihrem ursprunge, ihrer vereinigung, gewalt, wachsthum, trennung und verderbniss. Aus dem englischen übersetzt, mit anmerkungen und zween anhängen begleitet, von Johann Joachim Eschenburg. Leipzig, Weidmanns erben und Reich, 1769.

7 p. l., 494, [2] p., 1 l. front. 18ᶜᵐ.

"Die heilung Sauls, eine ode von dr. Brown": p. [395]–431.

ML3849.A2B871

—— Dell' origine, unione e forza, progressi, separazioni, e corruzioni della poesia, e della musica, dissertazione del dottor Giovanni Brown, tr. in lingua italiana dall' originale inglese, ed accresciuta di note dal dottor Pietro Crocchi ... A cui si aggiunge La cura di Saule, ode sacra dell' istesso autore, tr. fedelmente in poesia italiana di metre irregolare a confronto del testo inglese da Oresbio Agieo P. A.... Firenze, Stamperia Bonducciana, 1772.

2 p. l., 248 p. 22ᶜᵐ.

"Oresbio Agieo," academic name of Francesco Corsetti.

ML3849.A2B872

Brown, John, 1752–1787.

Letters upon the poetry and music of the Italian opera; addressed to a friend. By the late Mr. John Brown, painter. Edinburgh, Bell and Bradfute; [etc., etc.] 1789.

2 p. l., [iii]–xx, 141 p. 16ᶜᵐ.

ML3858.B87

—— Letters on the Italian opera: addressed to the Hon. Lord Monboddo. By the late Mr. John Brown. 2d ed. London, T. Cadell, 1791.

xviii, 141 p., 1 l. 17ᶜᵐ.

ML3858.B872

Browne, Richard.

Medicina musica: or, A mechanical essay on the effects of singing, musick, and dancing, on human bodies. Revis'd and corrected. To which is annex'd a new essay on the nature and cure of the spleen and vapours. By Richard Browne ... London, J. Cooke, 1729.

xv, 125 p. 14½ᶜᵐ.

1st edition 1674.

ML3920.A2B75

Bruce, Thomas.

The common tunes; or, Scotland's church musick made plain. By Mr. Thomas Bruce ... Edinburgh, Printed for the author, 1726.

3 p. l., viii, 46 p. front., 21 pl. (music) 17ᶜᵐ.

Caption title and running title: The gam-ut, or scale of musick explain'd.

MT7.A2B92

[Brumbey, Carl Wilhelm] *b.* 1757.

Briefe über musikwesen, besonders Cora in Halle. Quedlinburg, In commission bey C. A. Reussner, 1781.

109 p. 18ᶜᵐ.

ML410.N29B8

Brunnelius, Eric, *b. ca.* 1708.

See BURMAN, E. Elementa musices planæ [1728]

Bulyovszky, Mihály, *d.* 1711.

Michaelis Bvliowski . . . Brevis de emendatione organi musici tractatio. Kurtze vorstellung von verbesserung des orgelwercks. Argentorati, apud J. E. Zetznervm, 1680.

6 p. l., 121, [11] p. 18^{cm}.

Text in Latin and German on opposite pages; "Register," Latin and German in parallel columns.
"Lobspruch dieses gründlichen berichts von verbesserung des orgelwercks," poem, signed Jo. Ernestus Saur: [4] p. preceding p. [1]

ML552.A2B9

Buonanni, Filippo, 1638–1725.

Gabinetto armonico pieno d'istromenti sonori, indicati, e spiegati dal padre Filippo Bonanni . . . Roma, Stamperìa di G. Placho, 1722.

8 p. l., 177, [1] p. front., cxlviii (*i. e.* 149) pl. 25^{cm}.

Plates numbered irregularly.

ML460.A2B61

—— Descrizione degl' istromenti armonici d'ogni genere, del padre Bonanni. 2. ed. riv., cor., ed accrescivta dall' abbate Giacinto Cervti. Ornata con cxl. rami incisi d'Arnoldo Wanwesterout. Roma, A spese di V. Monaldini, 1776.

xvi, xxiij, [1], 114 (*i. e.* 214), [2] p. cxl (*i. e.* 142) pl. (1 fold.) 26½^{cm}.

Title and text in Italian and French, arranged in parallel columns. The t.-p. (engr. and folded) is counted as 4 pages in numbering. Page 214 wrongly numbered 114.

ML460.A2B62

Burette, Pierre Jean, 1665–1747.

Dissertation, où l'on fait voir, que les merveilleux effets, attribuez à la musique des anciens, ne prouvent point, qu'elle fust aussi parfaite que la nôtre. Par M. Burette.

(*In* Académie des inscriptions et belles-lettres, *Paris.* Mémoires. Paris, 1729. 25½ x 19^{cm}. [i. sér.] t. v [2. ptie.] p. 133–151)

Detached copy.

ML169.A2B8

—— Paragone dell' antica colla moderna musica. Dissertazione del Signor Burette. In cui si dimostra, che i maravigliosi effetti attribuiti alla musica degli antichi non provano in niun modo, ch' essa fosse più perfetta della nostra. N°. xiv. Venezia, A. Groppo, 1748.

12 p. 22½^{cm}.

Title vignette.

ML169.A2B82

Dissertation sur la mélopée de l'ancienne musique. Par M. Burette.

(*In* Académie des inscriptions et belles-lettres, *Paris.* Mémoires. Paris, 1729. 25½ x 19^{cm}. [i. sér.] t. v [2. ptie.] p. 169–199)

Detached copy.

ML169.A2B8

Burette, Pierre Jean—*Continued.*

—— Addition a la Dissertation sur la mélopée . . .

(*In* Académie des inscriptions et belles-lettres, *Paris.* Mémoires. Paris, 1729.
[I. sér.] t. v [2. ptie.] p. 200–206)

Detached copy.

Dissertation sur la symphonie des anciens. Par M. Burette.

(*In* Académie des inscriptions et belles-lettres, *Paris.* Mémoires. Paris,
1746. 25½ x 19^{cm}. [I. sér.] t. iv, p. 116–131)

Detached copy.

               ML169.A2B8

Dissertation sur le rhythme de l'ancienne musique. Par M.
Burette.

(*In* Académie des inscriptions et belles-lettres, *Paris.* Mémoires. Paris,
1729. 25½ x 19^{cm}. [I. sér.] t. v. [2. ptie.] p. 152–168)

Detached copy.

               ML169.A2B8

Extrait d'une lettre écrite aux auteurs du Mercure, suivie d'un
memoire qui répond à la question proposée dans celui du mois de juin
dernier, au sujet du plainchant &c. [Paris ? 1733 ?]

19 p. 16½^{cm}.

Caption title.
The memoir has caption title "Memoire sur l'autorité des musiciens en
matiere de plainchant," and is signed: Burette. et Falconnet, fils.

               ML3082.A2B8

Prima, e seconda memoria per servire alla istoria del ballo degli
antichi, del Signor Burette. n°. II. Venezia, 1746.

1 p. l., 33–44, 33–42 p. 25 x 19^{cm}.

Title vignette.
The French original was printed in "Histoire de l'Académie royale des inscriptions et belles-lettres", Paris, 1717.

               GV1787.B8

Burette, Pierre Jean, 1665–1747, *translator.*

See PLUTARCHUS. Περὶ μουσικῆς, 1735.

Burman, Erik, 1692–1729, *praeses.*

. . . Dissertatio musica, De basso fundamentali . . . Upsaliæ, literis Wernerianis [1728]

4 p. l., 15, [1] p. 15½^{cm}.

Diss.—Upsala (A. Löfgrön, respondent and author)

               MT49.A2B92

. . . Elementa musices planæ exercitio academico . . . Upsaliæ,
typis Wernerianis [1728]

4 p. l., 40, [4] p. 15½^{cm}.

Diss.—Upsala (E. Brunnelius, respondent and author)

               MT44.A2B78

Burmeister, Joachim, *b. ca.* 1560.

Musica *αὐτοσχεδιαστικῇ* qvae per aliquot accessiones in gratiam philomusorum quorundam ad tractatum de hypomnematibus musicæ poëticæ ejusdem auctoris *σποράδην* quondam exaratas, in unum corpusculum concrevit, in quâ redditur ratio I. Formandi & componendi harmonias; II. Administrandi & regendi chorum; III. Canendi melodias modô hactenùs non usitatô. Edita studiô & labore M. Joachimi Burmeisteri Lunæburgensis. Rostochii, excudebat C. Reusnerus, 1601.

[244] p. illus., 2 fold. l. (music) $18\frac{1}{2} \times 14\frac{1}{2}^{cm}$.

Title within ornamental border.

MT6.A2B96

Musica poetica: definitionibus et divisionibus breviter delineata, quibus in singulis capitibus sunt hypomnemata præceptionum instar *συνοπτικῶς* addita, edita studiô & operâ, M. Joachimi Bvrmeisteri . . . Rostochii, excudebat S. Myliander, 1606.

4 p. l., 76, [4] p. $18\frac{1}{2} \times 14\frac{1}{2}^{cm}$. (*With his* Musica *αὐτοσχεδιαστικῇ*. Rostochii, 1601)

Title within ornamental border.

MT6.A2B96

Burney, Charles, 1726–1814.

An account of the musical performances in Westminster-abbey, and the Pantheon, May 26th, 27th, 29th; and June the 3d, and 5th, 1784. In commemoration of Handel. By Charles Burney . . . London, Printed for the benefit of the musical fund, and sold by T. Payne and son [etc.] 1785.

[237] p. vii pl. (incl. front.) $27\frac{1}{2} \times 22^{cm}$.

Various paging.
"Sketch of the life of Handel": p. [1]–38. "Chronological list of Handel's works": p. [42]–46. "Abstract of the laws and resolutions of the Fund for the support of decayed musicians and their families": p. 129–136.

ML410.H13B9

—— Dr. Karl Burney's Nachricht von Georg Friedrich Hândel's lebensumstânden und der ihm zu London im mai und juni 1784 angestellten gedâchtnissfeyer. Aus dem englischen ûbersetzt von Johann Joachim Eschenburg . . . Mit kupfern. Berlin und Stettin, F. Nicolai, 1785.

14 p. l., [iii]–lii, 102 p., 1 l. front., 1 illus., fold. plan. 25×20^{cm}.

ML410.H13B93

A general history of music, from the earliest ages to the present period. By Charles Burney . . . London, Printed for the author, 1776–89.

4 v. fronts. (v. 1: port.), illus., 10 pl. (4 fold.) 28×22^{cm}.

In L. of C. copy v. 1 is of the 2d edition, 1789. Engraved musical illustrations throughout text. "Chronological list of the principal books published on the subject of music in England, during the present century": v. 4, p. [687]–688.

ML159.B96.

Burney, Charles—*Continued.*

Memoirs of the life and writings of the Abate Metastasio. In which are incorporated, translations of his principal letters. By Charles Burney . . . London, G. G. and J. Robinson, 1796.

3 v. front. (port.) 21ᶜᵐ.

ML429.M4B9

The present state of music in France and Italy: or, The journal of a tour through those countries, undertaken to collect materials for a general history of music. By Charles Burney . . . London, T. Becket and co., 1771.

vii, 396, [10] p., 2 l. 21ᶜᵐ.

ML195.B96

The present state of music in Germany, the Netherlands, and United Provinces. Or, The journal of a tour through those countries, undertaken to collect materials for a general history of music. By Charles Burney . . . London, T. Becket and co., 1773.

2 v. (v. 1: viii, 376 p.; v. 2: 1 p. l., v–vi, 352 p.) 21½ x 12½ᶜᵐ.

ML195.B962

—— The present state of music in Germany, the Netherlands, and United Provinces. Or, The journal of a tour through those countries, undertaken to collect materials for a general history of music. By Charles Burney . . . 2d ed., cor. London, T. Becket [etc.] 1775.

2 v. (v. 1: viii, 380 p.; v. 2: 2 p. l., 352 p.) 21½ᶜᵐ.

ML195.B963

Busby, Thomas, 1755–1838.

A complete dictionary of music. To which is prefixed, a familiar introduction to the first principles of that science. By Thomas Busby, LL. D. London, R. Phillips [1786]

xxxiii, [294] p. 18½ x 10½ᶜᵐ.

Scheme of staves ("Treble stave," "Soprano stave," etc.) on one folding leaf, takes the place of p. [xxi–xxii] of the Introduction.

ML108.A2B9

Butler, Charles, *d.* 1647.

The principles of musik, in singing and setting: vvith the two-fold use therof, <ecclesiasticall and civil.> By Charles Butler . . . London, Printed by J. Haviland, for the author, 1636.

viii, 135 p. illus. 18 x 14ᶜᵐ.

Imperfect, wanting pages 13–14.

MT6.A2B995

Buttstett, Johann Heinrich, 1666–1727.

Ut, re, mi, fa, sol, la, tota musica et harmonia æterna, oder Neu-eröffnetes, altes, wahres, eintziges und ewiges fundamentum musices, entgegen gesetzt dem Neu-eröffneten orchestre, und in zweene partes eingetheilet. In welchen / und zwar im ersten theile / des herrn authoris des Orchestre irrige meynungen . . . wiederleget / im andern theile aber das rechte fundamentum musices gezeiget . . . von Johann

Buttstett, Johann Heinrich—*Continued.*

Heinrich Buttstett . . . Erffurt, Gedruckt bey O. F. Werthern, zu finden in Leipzig, bey J. H. Kloss [1717]

5 p. l., 176 p., 1 l. 26 pl. on 25 l. (partly fold.), fold. tab. 20 x 16½^{cm}.

Added t.-p., engr. The plates contain musical examples.

MT44.A2B98

Der wieder Das beschützte orchestre ergangenen oeffentlichen erklårung zweyte auflage. Von dem verfasser nachgesehen / mit anmerckungen erläutert / und mit seinem angebohrnen insiegel bekråfftiget; auch an vielen orten weit vollståndiger / anders / besser und wahrhafftiger als die erste vom 21. sept. 1718. [Erffurth? 1718]

broadside. 20 x 17½^{cm}.

Dated: Erffurth, den 21. oct. 1718. Signed: J. H. Buttstett.

MT44.A2B982

C., G. M.

See MATTEI, S. Se i maestri di cappella son . . . artigiani [1785?]

Cahusac, Louis de, 1706–1759.

La danse ancienne et moderne, ou Traité historique de la danse. Par M. de Cahusac . . . A La Haye [*i. e.* Paris] Chez J. Neaulme, 1754.

3 v. 13½^{cm}.

GV1600.C2

Calderón, Manuel Pérez.

See PÉREZ CALDERÓN, MANUEL.

Calendrier musical universel, contenant l'indication des cérémonies d'eglise en musique; les découvertes et les anecdotes de l'année . . . la notice des pièces en musique représentées . . . sur les différens théatres de l'Europe . . . le relevé des ouvrages sur la musique et des productions musicales pub. à Londres et à Paris . . . &c. &c. &c. Pour l'année 1788. Paris, Prault [etc., 1788]

3 p. l., 3–288, [4] p. 15½^{cm}.

By N. E. Framery, who is given as author in the privilege.

Framery issued a second calendar, for 1789, after which the publication was discontinued.

ML20.C15

Callcott, John Wall, 1766–1821.

Explanation of the notes, marks, words, &^c, used in music, by I. W. Callcott . . . London, Printed for the author [1792]

2 p. l., 29 p. 26 x 32½^{cm}.

Engraved, with the exception of the 2d prelim. leaf and pages 27–29.

MT7.A2C2

Calmet, Augustin, 1672-1757.

Trésor d'antiquitez sacrées et profanes, tirées des Commentaires du R. P. D. Augustin Calmet . . . sur l'Écriture Sainte . . . Amsterdam, P. Marret, 1723.

2 v. in 1 (v. 1: xl, 131 p.; v. 2: 1 p. l., 190 p.) fold. pl. 17 x 9^cm.

General t.-p. wanting; title supplied from the Catalogue général of the Bibliothèque nationale, Paris.
Added t.-p.: Dissertations sur la poesie et la musique des anciens en général et des Hébreux en particulier, avec les figures des instrumens de musique. Tome premier. Premiere [–seconde] partie. Amsterdam, D. P. Marret, 1723. (Part 2 has special t.-p.: Dissertations sur le Livre des Pseaumes . . .) No more pub. of this edition. Edition of Paris, 1720, in 3 vols., appeared under title: Dissertations qui peuvent servir de prolégomènes de l'Écriture Sainte . . .

ML166.A2C2

Calsabigi, Ranieri de', 1714 *or* 15-1795.

Risposta che ritrovo' casualmente nella gran citta' di Napoli il licenziato Don Santigliano di Gilblas, y Guzman, y Tormes, y Alfarace, discendente per linea paterna, e materna da tutti quegli insigni personaggi delle Spagne; alla critica ragionatissima delle poesie drammatiche del C. de' Calsabigi, fatta dal baccelliere D. Stefano Arteaga . . . Venezia, Stamperia Curti, 1790.

224 p. 20½^cm.

ML429.C14A8

Calvisius, Seth, 1556-1615.

Exercitationes musicæ duæ. Qvarvm prior est, de modis mvsicis, qvos vulgò tonos vocant, rectè cognoscendis, & dijudicandis. Posterior, de initio et progressv mvsices, alijsᵭ rebus eo spectantibus. Institutæ à Setho Calvisio . . . Lipsiæ, impensis I. Apelij, 1600.

1 p. l., 138 (*i. e.* 139), [1] p. 15^cm.

Number 75 repeated in paging, p. 77 wrongly numbered 78.
Colophon: Lipsiæ, Franciscvs Schnelboltz excvdebat. Typis hæredum Beyeri. Anno M.DC.

MT45.A2C18

—— Exercitatio mvsica tertia Sethi Calvisii de præcipuis quibusdam in arte musicâ quæstionibus, quibus præcipua ejus theoremata continentur; instituta ad . . . Hippolytum Hubmeierum . . . Lipsiæ, impensis T. Schüreri, M. Lantzenberger excudebat, 1611.

1 p. l., 180 p. 24½^cm.

MT45.A2C182

Campion, Thomas, 1575-1620.

See PLAYFORD, J. An introduction to the skill of musick.

Campos, João Ribeiro de Almeida.

See RIBEIRO DE ALMEIDA CAMPOS, JOÃO.

Cantorinus. Ad eorum instructionem: qui cantum ad chorum ptinentem: breuiter & q̄ facillime discere concupiscunt: & non clericis modo: sed omnibus etiam diuino cultui deditis, perq̄ utilis, & necessarius. In quo facilis modus est additus ad discendam manū: ac tonos psalmorum: vt sequens tabula indicabit. Nouissime castigatus, cui etiam addite sunt Letanie. Venetiis, 1550.

8 p. l., 104 numb. l.   illus.   17½ᶜᵐ.

Rubricated; printer's mark on t.-p. The illustrations are (1) Guidonian hand on verso of 3d prelim. leaf, (2) the Crucifixion, on verso of 8th prelim. leaf, (3) the Annunciation, on verso of leaf 55. Colophon: Explicit Cantorinus ad commodum nouitiorum cleiicorū factus: nouissime impressus & diligētissime reuisus. In officina heredū Luceantonij Junte. Venetijs anno salutis. 1550. mense januario.
"Compendium musice:" p. l. [3] v°–p. l. [8] r°.

ML171.C32

—— **Cantorinvs** pro his, qui cantum ad chorum pertinentem, breuiter et q̄ facillime discere concupiscunt: & non clericis modo, sed omnibus etiam diuino cultui deditis, perquam vtilis, et necessarius. In quo facilis modus est additus ad discendam manum: ac tonos psalmorum, vt sequens tabula indicabit. Nouissime castigatus. Venetiis, 1566.

8 p. l., 104 numb. l.   17½ᶜᵐ.

Rubricated. Printer's mark on t.-p., Guidonian hand on verso of 2d prelim. leaf. Colophon: Venetijs in officina hęredum Luceantonij Juntę anno Domini.1566.
"Compendium musicę": p. l. [2] –p. l. [7]

ML171.C34

See also COMPENDIŪ musices [1513]

Cantus diversi ex Graduali romano, pro singuliş solemnitatibus, dominicis, festis & feriis per annum. Lugduni, ex officina Petri Valfray, 1724.

190, 105, [5] p.   14½ᶜᵐ.

In two parts. The second part contains: (1) Trois methodes faoiles pour apprendre le plein chant, (2) Les divers tons ou intonations des chants communs de l'eglise, (3) Cantus diversi ad usum ecclesiæ lugdunensis, (4) Maniere pour bien chanter dans un chœur.
An earlier edition was published at Lyons by Claude Moulu in 1700.

M2150.A2C23

Capalti, Francesco.

Il contropuntista pratico, o siano Dimostrazioni fatte sopra l'esperienza da Francesco Capalti . . . Terni, A. Saluzj, stampator vescovile [1788]

2 p. l., 242 p., 1 l.   18½ᶜᵐ.

MT55.A2C2

Capella, Martianus.

See MARTIANUS CAPELLA.

Cappeval, N. de Caux de.

See CAUX DE CAPPEVAL, N. DE.

Cardano, Girolamo, 1501–1576.

See SPANGENBERG, J.   Qvaestiones mvsicæ [1536]

52 LIBRARY OF CONGRESS

Carissimi, Giovanni Giacomo, *d.* 1674.

Ars cantandi; das ist: Richtiger und aussführlicher weg / die jugend aus dem rechten grund in der sing-kunst zu unterrichten; durch weiland den welt-berühmten musicum, herrn Giovan Giacomo Carissimi, in welscher sprach aufgesetzt; nunmehro aus derselben aber von einem music-freund in unsere mutter-sprach gebracht / und / so vil möglich / deutlich gegeben . . . Augspurg, J. Koppmayer, 1693.

16 p. 16 x 20½^{cm}.

MT35.A2C22

See also VERMEHRTER . . . wegweiser, 1693.

Carl, Johann Georg, *editor.*

See WERCKMEISTER, A. Cribrvm mvsicvm, 1700.

Carlo Borromeo, *Saint,* 1538–1584.

S. Caroli Borromaei . . . Opvscvlvm de choreis et spectaculis in festis diebus non exhibendis, accedit collectio selectarum sententiarum ejusdem adversus choreas, et spectacula, ex ejus statutis, edictis, institutionibus, homiliis. Romæ, apud fratres Palearinos, 1753.

xii, 93, [1] p. 16½^{cm}.

GV1740.C3

—— Traitté contre les danses et les comedies. Composé par S. Charles Borromée . . . Paris, G. Soly, 1664.

7 p. l., 198 p. 14½ x 8^{cm}.

"Lettre de l'evesque d'Agnani, pour la défense d'vne ordonnance synodale, par laquelle il auoit défendu de danser les iours des festes:" p. 154–176.

GV1740.C32

[Carlos de Jesus Maria] 1713–1747.

Resumo das regras geraes mais importantes, e necessarias para a boa intelligencia do cantocham, com huma breve instrucçam para os presbyteros, diaconos, e subdiaconos conforme o uso romano. [n. p., n. d.]

47 p. 21½ x 16^{cm}.

Caption title. Title-page wanting?
Perhaps identical with the edition of Coimbra, 1726 (!) described by Vasconcellos.

MT860.A2J58

—— Resumo das regras geraes mais importantes, e necessarias para a boa intelligencia do cantocham, com huma instrucçam para os presbyteros, diaconos, e subdiaconos, conforme o uso romano. Dado novamente ao pre'lo pelo P. Luis da Maia Croesse'r [*pseud.*] . . . Com varios accrescentamentos, que vam notados com este signal*. Coimbra, Na officina de A. S. Ferreyra, impressor, 1741.

1 p. l., 92, [2] p. 22½^{cm}.

L. of C. has also an issue with the following variations: cantochaõ for cantocham in title; different arrangement of type on p. 28 and 29, with a paragraph of text at foot of p. 29 which in the present issue appears on last page, following index; alterations in four lines of index; paragraph 2 of p. 52 in corrected form, the correction being found at foot of last page in this issue.

MT860.A2J59

Caron de Beaumarchais, Pierre Augustin.
See BEAUMARCHAIS, PIERRE AUGUSTIN CARON DE.

Caroso, Marco Fabrizio.

Il ballarino di M. Fabritio Caroso ... diuiso in due trattati; nel primo de' quali si dimostra la diuersità de i nomi, che si danno à gli atti, & mouimenti, che interuengono ne i balli: & con molte regole si dichiara come debbano farsi. Nel secondo s'insegnano diuerse sorti di balli, & balletti sì all' vso d'Italia, come à quello di Francia, & Spagna. Ornato di molte figure. Et con l'intauolatura di liuto nella sonata di ciascun ballo, & il soprano della musica alla maggior parte di essi. Opera nuouamente mandata in luce ... Venetia, F. Ziletti, 1581.

2 v. in 1 (v. 1: 7 p. l., 16 numb. l.; v. 2: 184 numb. l., [8] p.) illus., port. 23 x 18ᶜᵐ.

Title vignettes; head and tail pieces; initials.
Vol. 2 has title: Trattato secondo del Ballarino ... nel quale s'insegnano varie sorti di balletti, cascarde, tordiglione, passo e mezo, pauaniglia, canario, & gagliarde all' vso d'Italia, Francia, & Spagna ...

GV1600.C35

Carré, Rémi, *b.* 1706.

Le maistre des novices dans l'art du chanter: ou, Regles ... pour apprendre parfaitement le plein-chant; pre'ce'de'es de quelques motifs & exemples édifians ... de quelques observations sur la formation, conservation, destruction, enrouement, extinction de la voix ... suivies d'un ample recueil d'antiennes, répons, & messes ... Par frere Remy Carre' ... Paris, Le Breton, 1744.

xij, 54 p., 1 l., lxxxiv p. 27½ x 20½ᶜᵐ.

MT860.A2C31

Casali, Lodovico, *b.* 1594.

Generale inuito alle grandezze, e marauiglie della mvsica oue per ogni raggion tanto diuina, come naturale, e positiua, si mostra la sua antichità, e valore; e come sia necessaria à chi di religion professa; e quanto di buono apporta, à chi ciuilmente l'apprende. All' illvstr.ᵐᵒ Sig.ʳᵉ il Sig.ʳ conte Alessandro Rangoni ... Lodovico Casali ... consacra, e dona. Opera qvarta. Modana, G. B. Gadaldino, 1629.

9 p. l., 211, [1] p. 20ᶜᵐ.

ML3920.A2C3

[Case, John] *d.* 1600.

The praise of mvsicke: wherein besides the antiquitie, dignitie, delectation, & vse thereof in ciuill matters, is also declared the sober and lawfull vse of the same in the congregation and church of God ... Oxenford, Printed by I. Barnes, 1586.

4 p. l., 152 p. 13½ᶜᵐ.

ML3001.C28

Caselli, Domenico Antonio.

Il canto fermo in prattica per vso di qual si voglia sorte di religiosi, e religiose, che bramano con un metodo facilissimo, e breve imparare il canto gregoriano per il buon concerto, e regolamento de' cori. Del p. fr. Domenico Antonio Caselli . . . Roma, Stamperia del Chracas, 1724.

32 p. coat of arms. 20ᶜᵐ.

MT860.A2C38

Castagnères, François de, abbé de Châteauneuf.

See CHÂTEAUNEUF, FRANÇOIS DE CASTAGNÈRES, abbé DE.

Castel, Louis Bertrand, 1688–1757.

Beschreibung der augen-orgel oder des augen-clavicimbels, so der berühmte mathematicus und Jesuit zu Paris, herr pater Castel, erfunden und ins werk gerichtet hat; aus einem französischen briefe übersetzet von Telemann. Hamburg, Gedruckt mit Piscators schriften, 1739.

[8] p. 22 x 18ᶜᵐ.

Written in the 3d person and only in part translated from Castel's "Nouvelles expériences". (Mémoires de Trévoux, Dec. 1735) Published also in Mizler's "Musikalische bibliothek."

ML1055.A2C3

Réponse critique d'un académicien de Rouen, à l'académicien de Bordeaux, sur le plus profond de la musique. [Paris? 1754]

36 p. 16½ᶜᵐ.

Caption title. At foot of p. [1]: Tome 1. No more published.
A pretended reply to his own "Lettres d'un académicien de Bordeaux sur le fond de la musique, à l'occasion de la lettre de M. R. * * * [i. e. Rousseau] contre la musique françoise."

ML1727.33.C34

Catalisano, Gennaro, d. 1793.

Grammatica-armonica fisico-matematica ragionata su i veri principj fondamentali teorico-pratici per uso della gioventù studiosa, e di qualunque musicale radunanza. Composta dal m. r. p. Gennaro Catalisano . . . Roma, Nella stamperia di S. Michele a Ripa, per P. Giunchi, 1781.

xxxii, 166 p. illus., xv fold. pl., tables (1 fold.) 28ᶜᵐ.

Title vignette.

ML3805.A2C3

[Cattaneo, Giovanni, conte]

La libertà del cantare. Lucca, F. M. Benedini, 1752.

204 p. 17½ᶜᵐ.

Letters to "Madama N. N." chiefly on philosophical subjects, but including several on music. Pages 175–204 contain "Ragionamento sopra il medico, impropriamente attaccato da un autore spagnolo."

ML63.C35

Caus, Salomon de, *d.* 1626.

Institvtion harmoniqve, diuisée en deux parties; en la premiere sont monstrées les proportions des interualles harmoniques, et en la deuxiesme les compositions dicelles. Par Salomon de Caus ... Francfort, En la boutique de J. Norton, 1615.

4 p. l., 23 numb. l.; 1 p. l., [2], 47 (*i. e.* 59) p. illus., diagrs. 38½ x 25^{cm}.

Engr. t.-p. with architectural border; red line borders. Leaves 6 and 16 numbered 8 and 13 respectively; p. 59 numbered 47.

MT40.A2C19

Les raisons des forces movvantes auec diuerses machines tant vtilles que plaisantes aus quelles sont adioints plusieurs desseings de grotes et fontaines. Par Salomon de Cavs ... Francfort, En la boutique de I. Norton, 1615.

3 v. in 1. illus., plates, diagrs. (1 double) 37½^{cm}.

The general t.-p. and the special t.-p. of "livre" 2 are illustrated and engraved.
Vol. 2 has special t.-p.: Livre second ov sont desseignées plusieurs grotes et fontaines propres pour l'ornement des palais, maisons de plaisances et iardins. par Salomon de Cavs ... Francfort ... 1615.
Vol. 3 has special t.-p.: Liure troisiesme traitant de la fabriqve des orgves. Par Salomon de Cavs ... Francfort ... 1615.
"Mesures de madrigal, Che sera sed al cielo, d' Alessandro Strigio, mis en tablature par Pierre Filippe": vol. 1, l. 38 v°–l. 39 r°.

TJ144.C4

[Caux de Cappeval, N. de] *d.* 1774.

Apologie du goût françois, relativement à l'opéra: poeme, avec un Discours apologetique, et des Adieux aux Bouffons. [n. p.] 1754.

2 p. l., 3–80 p. 20^{cm}.

Engr. t.-p. The "Adieux aux Bouffons" is a revised version of "L'anti-scurra" (*see* title)

ML1727.33.C37

Cavazza, Manuel, *d.* 1790.

El musico censor del censor no musico, ó Sentimientos de Lucio Vero Hispano, contra los de Simplicio Greco, y Lira. Discurso unico publicale D. Manuel Cabazza ... Madrid, A. Lopez [etc., 178– ?]

2 p. l., 176, [4] p. 14^{cm}.

The work was completed in 1786, but was published somewhat later (*cf.* Note preceding p. 1)
"Es contestación al discurso 97 de El Censor que, abundando en las ideas de Eximeno, había ridiculizado los artificios de los contrapuntistas."—Pedrell, Diccionario de músicos.

ML63.C37

Cavelier, Louise.

See Lévesque, *Mme.* Louise (Cavelier)

[Cazotte, Jacques] 1719–1792.

La nouvelle Raméide, poëme, revu, corrigé, et presque refondu; par M. Rameau, fils & neveu de deux grands hommes, qu'il ne fera pas revivre. A Amsterdam [i. e. Paris] 1766.

vj p., 1 l., [9]–30 p. 18½^{cm}.

A parody on Jean François Rameau's "La Rameïde."

ML410.R2C3

[Cazotte, Jacques]—*Continued.*

Observations sur la lettre de J. J. Rousseau au sujet de la musique françoise . . . [n. p.] 1753.

1 p. l., 19 p.   16½ x 9½ᶜᵐ.

ML1727.33.C38

La guerre de l'opera. Lettre ecrit a une dame en province, par quelqu'un qui n'est ni d'un coin, ni de l'autre. [n. p., 1753]

24 p.   19ᶜᵐ.

No. 2 in a volume of pamphlets lettered Quere[lle] des Bouffo[ns]

ML1727.33.A1

Celles, François Bedos de.

See BEDOS DE CELLES, FRANÇOIS.

Celma, Gaspar Francisco Bartolomé Sanz y.

See SANZ Y CELMA, GASPAR FRANCISCO BARTOLOMÉ.

Cendoni, Giovanni.

See ALLACCI, L. .Drammaturgia, 1755.

Cépède, Bernard Germain Étienne de La Ville sur Illon, comte de la.

See LACÉPÈDE, BERNARD GERMAIN ÉTIENNE DE LA VILLE SUR ILLON, *comte* DE.

Cephise, *pseud.*

See LÉVESQUE, *Mme.* LOUISE (CAVELIER)

Cerf de La Viéville, Jean Laurent le.

See LE CERF DE LA VIÉVILLE, JEAN LAURENT, *seigneur de Freneuse.*

Cerone, Domenico Pietro, *b.* 1566.

. . . El melopeo y maestro. Tractado de mvsica theorica y pratica: en que se pone por extenso, lo que vno para hazerse perfecto musico ha menester saber: y por mayor facilidad, comodidad, y claridad del lector, esta repartido en XXII. libros . . . Compuesto por el R. D. Pedro Cerone . . . Napoles, Por I. B. Gargano, y L. Nucci, impressores, 1613.

8 p. l., 1160 p., 1 l.   illus., diagrs.   30½ᶜᵐ.

Title in red and black within line border; title vignette. On verso of 2d leaf an illustration representing the Virgin and Child; on verso of 3d leaf, coat of arms of Philip III of Spain; on verso of 4th leaf, port. of Cerone.
Errors in paging; no. 294–295, 375–376 repeated; no. 371–372, 1157–1158 omitted.
"A work . . . founded on the system of Zarlino; indeed there is some reason to believe that it is a mere redaction of a work with the same title which Zarlino speaks of as having completed in ms., but which has totally disappeared."— Grove, Dict. of music (*cf. also* Fétis)

MT6.A2C3

See also GUZMÁN, J. DE. Cvriosidades del cantollano, 1709.

Cerreto, Scipione, *b.* 1551.

Scipione Cerreto Napolitano. Della prattica mvsica vocale, et strvmentale, opera necessaria a coloro, che di musica si dilettano. Con le postille poste dall' avtore à maggior dichiaratione d'alcune cose occorrenti ne' discorsi. Napoli, G. I. Carlino, 1601.

4 p. l., 335, [1] p.   illus. (port.) diagr.   21cm.

Head and tail piece; initials; side-notes.   On t.-p. is a short four part song without key (Omnes per ostium intrant) each part forming the side of a square.

MT6.A2C38

Ceruti, Giacinto, *b.* 1737 ?   *translator.*

See Buonanni, F.   Descrizione degl' istromenti armonici, 1776.

Chabanon, Michel Paul Gui de, 1730–1792.

Éloge de M. Rameau, par M. Chabanon . . . Paris, Impr. de M. Lambert, 1764.

63, [1] p.   19cm.

"Ouvrages de musique, par M. Rameau": p. 58–59.   "Ouvrages de theorie": p. 60–63.

ML410.R2C4

Observations sur la musique, et principalement sur la metaphysique de l'art . . .   Paris, Pissot, père & fils, 1779.

2 p. l., xx, 215, [1] p.   19½cm.

At end: "Fin de la première partie."   No more published of this edition.

ML3800.A2C4

—— De la musique considérée en elle-même et dans ses rapports avec la parole, les langues, la poésie, et le théatre . . .   Paris, Pissot, 1785.

2 p. l., 459, [1] p.   20½cm.

A rev. edition of the "Observations sur la musique," with an additional part, "Des propriétés musicales des langues" and "Considérations sur les langues."

ML3800.A2C5

—— Ueber die musik und deren wirkungen, mit anmerkungen hrsg. von Johann Adam Hiller.   Leipzig, F. G. Jacobäer und sohn, 1781.

xxviii, 228 p.   18 x 10½cm.

A translation of Chabanon's "Observations sur la musique."

ML3800.A2C43

Chagas, Luiz das, *d.* 1640.

See Raymundo da Converção.   Manval de tvdo o qve se canta fora do choro, 1675.

[Chastellux, François Jean, *marquis* **de]** 1734–1788.

Essai sur l'union de la poesie et de la musique.   A La Haye, et se trouve à Paris, chez Merlin, 1765.

1 p. l., iv, 94 p.   17cm.

ML3849.A2C5

[Châteauneuf, François de Castagnères, *abbé* de] *d.* 1709.

Dialogue sur la musique des anciens. A Monsieur de * * *. Paris, N. Pissot, 1725.

4 p. l., 126, [4] p., 1 l.   vii pl.   17 x 9½^{cm}.

Published, with a preface, by Jacques Morabin.

ML169.A2C4

Chauncey, Nathaniel, 1681–1756.

Regular singing defended, and proved to be the only true way of singing the songs of the Lord; by arguments both from reason and Scripture: having been heard and approved of, by the General association at Hartford, May the 12th. 1727. with their recommendation of it to the publick. By Nathaniel Chauncey . . . N. London, T. Green, 1728.

2 p. l., 54 p.   15½^{cm}.

Half-title: Mr. Chauncey's arguments for regular singing.
George Hood, Hist. of music in New England, Boston, 1846, quotes Chauncey's arguments at some length, apropos of the discussion which was going on at the time concerning a reform in church music.

ML3001.C49

[Chevrier, François Antoine] 1721–1762.

Constitution du Patriarche de l'Opera.   Qui condamne cent une propositions extraites de deux ecrits intitulés: Reflexions sur les vrais principes de l'harmonie, & Lettre sur l'origine & les progrès de l'Académie royale de musique.   Cytheropolis [*i. e.* Paris] 1754.

32 p.   16½^{cm}.

Author's pseud. follows caption title (Pancrace . . . archevêque de Cytheropolis, & patriarche de l'Opera)
Reprint of "La constitution de l'Opéra," Amsterdam [Paris?] 1736. Attributed to Chevrier.

ML1727.33.C39

Chiavelloni, Vincenzo.

Discorsi della mvsica, composti da Vincenzo Chiavelloni . . . Roma, I. de Lazeri, 1668.

8 p. l., 556 p.   25^{cm}.

Added t.-p., engr.; printer's mark (?) on t.-p.

ML3920.A2C4

Chiodino, Giovanni Battista.

Arte prattica & poëtica, das ist: Ein kurtzer unterricht / wie man einen contrapunct machen und componiren sol lernen (in zehen bûcher abgetheilet) sehr kûrtz- und leichtlich zu begreiffen: so vor diesem von Giov. Chiodino latein- und italienisch beschrieben worden.   Dessgleichen: ii. Ein kurtzer tractat und vnterricht / wie man einen contrapunct à mente, non à penna . . . componiren und setzen solle: vnd letzlichen: iii. Corollarii loco: eine instruction und vnterweisung zum general-bass . . . in die hochteutsche sprach versetzet . . . anjetzo publiciret und zum truck verfertiget / durch Johann-Andream Herbst . . . Getruckt zu Franckfurt / bey A. Hummen, in verlegung / T. M. Gôtzens, 1653.

4 p. l., 48 p.   20 x 16½^{cm}.

The last part (p. 43–47) has caption: . . . Corollarii loco, eine kurtze instruction . . . zum general-bass: vor diesem von Wolff Ebner . . . lateinisch beschrieben / nun aber . . . in die teutsche sprach versetzet durch J. A. H.

MT55.A2H51

[Choquel, Henri Louis] *d.* 1767.

La musique rendue sensible par la méchanique, ou Nouveau systeme pour apprendre facilement la musique soi-même. Ouvrage utile et curieux. Nouv. éd. . . . Paris, C. Ballard, 1762.

3 p. l., 19, 10, [xi]–xiv, 213, [4] p.   2 fold. tab., diagrs.   20^{cm}.

Title vignette. Dedication signed: Choquel.

"La méthode de Choquel consiste à enseigner l'intonation par l'usage du monocorde, et la mesure par le chronomètre."—Fétis, Biog. univ. des musiciens.

MT7.A2C54

Christmann, Johann Friedrich, 1752–1817, *editor.*

See MUSIKALISCHE real-zeitung [1788–90]

Cizzardi, Liborio Mauro.

Il tutto in poco, overo Il segreto scoperto; composto da Liborio Mauro Cizzardi . . . diviso in cinque libri, ne' quali si mostra un modo facilissimo, per imparare il vero canto fermo con le giuste regole, e con alcune altre osservazioni necessarie ad un cantore . . . Parma, G. Rosati, 1711.

6 p. l., 166, [2] p.   illus., 3 pl.   30½^{cm}.

Title vignette: coat of arms.

MT860.A2C54

[Clagget, Charles] 1740?–1820?

Musical phænomena, founded on unanswerable facts; and a proof that musical instruments have been hitherto fabricated on [!] the most uncertain, therefore the most improper materials . . . This work will extend to several numbers. No. I. contains an account of the aiuton, and the cromatic trumpets and the French horns, capable of fine tune and regular harmony in all the keys in use, minor as well as major. London, Printed for the author, 1793.

4 p. l., [7]–22, 4 p.   illus.   29½ x 23^{cm}.

Added t.-p.: No. 1 of Musical phænomena. An organ, made without pipes, strings, bells, or glasses ... a cromatic trumpet, capable of producing just intervals and regular melodies in all keys . . . without undergoing any change whatever; a French horn, answering the above description of the trumpet . . . The above instruments . . . may be seen and heard at the Musical museum, Greek street, Soho . . .

Prefixed is a portrait of Clagget, which according to Grove was published with his "Discourse on musick," 1793. An advertisement of Clagget's Musical museum is appended.

ML1055.A2C5

Clemens XIII, *pope,* 1693–1769.

Sanctissimi in Christo patris, et domini nostri domini Clementis divina providentia papæ XIII. constitutio svper regimine & directione Collegii cantorum Pontificiæ cappellæ; cvm opportunis ordinationibus. Romæ, ex typographia reverendæ Cameræ apostolicæ, 1762.

xii p.   25 x 19^{cm}.

Title vignette; head-piece. Signed: N. card. Antonellus.

ML291 I762

Clément, Charles François, *b.* 1720?

Essai sur l'accompagnement du clavecin, pour parvenir facilement & en peu de tems à accompagner avec des chiffres ou sans chiffres par les principes les plus clairs & les plus simples de la composition. Par M. Clément. Paris, Impr. de C. Ballard, 1758.

22 p.   20 x 25½^{cm}.   MT68.A2C6

—— Essai sur la basse fondamentale; pour servir de supplément à l'Essai sur l'accompagnement du clavecin, & d'introduction à la composition-pratique . . . Par M. Clément . . . Paris, Impr. de C. Ballard, 1762.

35 p.   20 x 25½^{cm}.   (*With his* Essai sur l'accompagnement du clavecin. Paris, 1758)

MT68.A2C6

[Clément, Jean Marie Bernard] 1742–1812.

Anecdotes dramatiques . . .   Paris, Veuve Duchesne, 1775.

3 v.   17½^{cm}.

By Clément and the Abbé de Laporte.

Title in full: Anecdotes dramatiques, contenant, 1°. Toutes les pieces de théatre, tragédies, comédies, pastorales, drames, opéra, opéra-comiques, parades, proverbes, qui ont été joués à Paris ou en province, sur des théatres publics, ou dans des sociétés particulieres, depuis l'origine des spectacles en France, jusqu'à l'année 1775, rangés par ordre alphabétique. 2°. Tous les ouvrages dramatiques qui n'ont été représentés sur aucun théatre, mais qui sont imprimés, ou conservés en manuscrits dans quelques bibliotheques. 3°. Un recueil de tout ce qu'on a pu rassembler d'anecdotes imprimées, manuscrites, verbales, connues ou peu connues; d'evénements singuliers, sérieux, ou comiques; de traits curieux, d'épigrammes, de plaisanteries, de naïvetés & de bons-mots, auxquels ont donné lieu les représentations de la plupart des pieces de théatre, soit dans leur nouveauté, soit à leurs reprises. 4°. Les noms de tous les auteurs, poëtes ou musiciens, qui ont travaillé pour tous nos theatres; de tous les acteurs ou actrices célebres qui ont joué à tous nos spectacles, avec un jugement de leurs ouvrages & de leurs talents, un abrégé de leur vie, & des anecdotes sur leurs personnes. 5°. Un tableau, accompagné d'anecdotes, des théatres de toutes les nations.

ML102.O6C6

—— Bibliothèque des theatres, dictionnaire dramatique . . . Paris, Veuve Duchesne, 1784.

3 v.   front. (port.)   17^{cm}.

Caption title: Anecdotes dramatiques.

PN2208.C4

[Cleonides]

Εὐκλείδου Εἰςαγωγὴ ἁρμονική. Τοῦ αὐτοῦ Κατατομὴ κανόνος. Euclidis Rudimenta mvsices. Eiusdem Sectio regulæ harmonicæ. E Regia bibliotheca desumpta, ac nunc primùm græcè & latinè excusa, Ioanne Pena regio mathematico interprete . . . Parisiis, apud A. Wechelum, sub Pegaso, 1557.

2 p. l., 5–16, 10 numb. l.   20^{cm}.

Printer's mark on t.-p.
The Rudimenta musices is now attributed to Cleonides.

ML171.E9

See also MEIBOM, M., *translator.* Antiqvæ mvsicæ avctores, 1652.

Clerc, Jean Baptiste le.

See LECLERC, JEAN BAPTISTE.

Cochlaeus *i. e.* **Johannes Dobnek,** *of Wendelstein,* 1479–1552.

Tetrachordū musices Joannis Coclei Norici . . . Nurnbergæ æditum: pro iuuentute laurentiana in primis: dein pro ceteris quoq̨ musarum tyrunculis . . . Hvivs tetrachordi qvatvor tractatus, quorū quilibet decem capita complectitur. Primus, De musices elementis; secundus, De musica gregoriana; tertius, De octo tonis meli; quartus, De musica mensurali. [*Colophon:* ☾ Finis Tetrachordi musices Nurnbergæ impressi in officina excusoria Friderici Peypus anno salutis 1514]

[59] p. 20½ᶜᵐ.

1st edition, Nuremberg, 1511. Said to be based on his "Musica," Cologne, 1507.

ML171.C66

Coferati, Matteo.

Il cantore addottrinato, ovvero Regole del canto corale, oue con breue, e facil metodo s'insegna la pratica de' precetti più necessarj del canto fermo; il modo di mantenere il coro sempre alla medesima altezza di voce; di ripigliare doue resta l'organo; d'intonare molte cose, che fra l'anno si cantano; ed in particolare tutti gl' inni. Con varie aggiunte dell' autore in questa seconda impressione. Opera di Matteo Coferati . . . Firenze, Il Vangelisti [1691]

xvj, 391 p. illus. 15ᶜᵐ.

MT860.A2C67

Manvale degli invitatorj cò suo' salmi da cantarsi nell' ore canoniche per ciascuna festa, e feria di tutto l'anno: nell' Vfizio paruo della Beatissima Vergine, e de' morti. Coll' aggiunta delle sequenze, e lor canto, e antifone da cantarsi alla distribuzione delle candele, e delle palme. Opera raccolta da Matteo Coferati . . . Firenze, V. Vangelisti stamp., 1691.

vij, 196 p. 15ᶜᵐ.

MT860.A2C39

Coll, Antonio Martín y.

See MARTÍN Y COLL, ANTONIO.

Colle, Francesco Maria, 1744–1815.

Dissertazione sopra il quesito: *Dimostrare, che cosa fosse, e quanta parte avesse la musica nell' educazione de' Greci. qual era la forza di una siffatta istituzione, e qual vantaggio sperar si potesse, se fosse introdotta nel piano della moderna educazione,* presentata dal Signor Francesco Maria Colle de' nobili di S. Bartolommeo de Colle, e de' conti di Cesana, Bellunese, socio dell' Accademia letteraria, e georgica di Belluno al concorso dell' anno 1774 . . . Mantova, Per l'erede di A. Pazzoni, stampatore, 1775.

140 p. 27½ x 20ᶜᵐ.

"Coronata dalla Reale accademia di scienze e belle lettere di Mantova."

ML169.A2C6

Collier, Joel, *pseud.*

See VEAL, GEORGE.

Colonna, Fabio, 1567–1650.

La sambvca lincea, overo Dell' istromento mvsico perfetto lib. iiɪ. di Fabio Colonna Linceo, ne' quali oltre la descrittione, et costruttione dell' istromento si tratta della diuisione del monacordo: della proportione de tuoni, semituoni, et lor minute parti. Della differenza de tre geni di musica, de gradi enarmonici et chromatici: et in che differiscano da quelli de gli antichi l'osseruati et descritti dall' autore; con gli esempi di numeri, di musica, et di segni . . . Con l'organo hydraulico di Herone Alessandrino dichiarato dall' istesso autore . . . Napoli, C. Vitale, 1618.

3 p. l., 116 p.   illus., port., tables.   21ᶜᵐ.

Title within architectural border.

ML697.A2C75

Comes y de Puig, Bernardo.

Fragmentos musicos. Caudalosa fuente gregoriana, en el arte de canto llano. Cuyos fundamentos, teorica, reglas, practica, y exemplos, copiosamente se explican sobre los ocho tonos, con sus entradas, clausulaciones finales, y diversidad de seculorums, que en la obra se manifiestan. Con la addicion de las processiones mas solemnes, que en la santa iglesia se practican. Por el P. Fr. Berardo Comes, y de Pvig . . . Barc[elona] Herederos de J. Pablo, y M. Martì, 1739.

11 p. l., 197, [3] p.   fold. tab.   20ᶜᵐ.

MT860.A2C7

[Compan, Charles] *b. ca.* 1740.

Dictionnaire de danse, contenant l'histoire, les règles & les principes de cet art, avec des réflexions critiques, & des anecdotes curieuses concernant la danse ancienne & moderne; le tout tiré des meilleurs auteurs qui ont écrit sur cet art . . . Paris, Cailleau [etc.] 1787.

1 p. l., [v]–xvj, 395, [2] p.   17ᶜᵐ.

Dedication signed: Compan.

GV1585.C7

Compendiŭ musices ‖ confectū ad faciliorē instructionē can- ‖ tum choralē discentiū: necnō ad intro- ‖ ductionē huius libelli: qui Cātorinus ‖ intitulatur: omnibus diuino cultui de- ‖ ditis ɡutilis ⱬ necessarius: vt in tabula ‖ hic immediate sequēti latius apparet. [wdct.] [*Colophon:* ⟨ Finis Cantorini Romani: impressi ‖ Venetijs ɡ dñm Lucantoniū de ‖ Giunta Florentinuȝ: Anno ‖ dñi millesimo ɋngente ‖ simo tertiodecimo ‖ die v̇o tertia ‖ decēbris. ‖ . ▩ . ‖ Registrum. ‖ A . . . P. ‖ Omnia sunt quaterna.] ‖ [Printer's mark of Lucantonio Giunta, in red]

t.-p., [2]–120 numb. l. incl. 2 diagr., wdcts.   14½ᶜᵐ.

Printed in red and black; gothic type; initials.   Sig. Aij and Bij are wrongly signed Pij, and for Biiij stands Aiiij.
The Compendium ends with l. 16, rº.   At foot of page: ⟨ Hic modus cantãdi revelat' fuit a dño iesu chri- ‖ sto sancte Brigide vidue: vt habet in suo volumine ⱬ ‖ in libro extrauaganti caɡ. iiij.
The Cantorinus begins with l. 17, and has caption: Cātorinus. ‖ ⟨ Romani cantus vtilissimū cōpēdi- ‖ olū: oïa diuino officio ɡsoluēdo ꝗcernē ‖ tia ī se includēs: clericis oïbus ⱬ diuino ‖ cultui dedicatis ɡmaxime necessariū.

MT860.A2C73

Compendiū musices—*Continued*.

—— **Tractatvs** mvsices . . . [*Colophon:* Impressum Venetijs per Joannem Baptistam Sessa]

8 l. 20½ᶜᵐ.

Guidonian hand on t.-p. with the letters I. B. S.; printer's mark at end; gothic type. Signatures: a–b in fours.

"Il presente trattatello è fedelissima copia del *Compendium musices* posto nelle prime carte di tutti gli antichi *Cantorini*. L'operetta qui citata fu per certo data in luce nel principio del sec. xvi."—Gaspari, Catalogo d. bibl. d. Liceo musicale di Bologna.

ML171.T81

See also CANTORINUS.

Compendium regularum generalium cantus ecclesiastici regularis, seu plani. Pro instrvctione novitiorvm secundum usum FF. ordinis Prædicatorum. Romæ, ex typographia H. Mainardi, 1736.

28 p. 18ᶜᵐ.

MT860.A2D67

Compleat instructions for the German flute, containing the easiest & most modern methods for learners to obtain a proficiency, carefully corrected by the most eminent masters. To which is added, a favourite collection of minuets, marches, song tunes & duetts, properly dispos'd for that instrument . . . London, J. Bland [178– ?]

1 p. l., 36 p. front. 17 x 24ᶜᵐ. (*With* Entire new . . . instructions for the fife. London [17—])

Caption title: New instructions for the German flute and the method of double tongueing with proper examples. Engraved throughout.

MT356.A2E62

—— **New** instructions for the German flute and the method of double tongueing, with proper examples &c. [n. p., n. d.]

32 p. 23ᶜᵐ.

Caption title. Title-page wanting?

MT342.A2N5

—— **New** instructions for the German flute, containing the easiest and most modern methods for learners to play. To which is added a favorite collection of minuets, marches, song tunes, duets, &c. Also the method of double tongueing. And a complete scale and description of the German-flute with all the additional keys, invented by Mʳ Tacet. London, Longman & Broderip [17—]

1 p. l., 42 p. front. 17 x 24ᶜᵐ. (*With* Entire new . . . instructions for the fife. London [17—])

Engraved throughout. Frontispiece colored by hand.

MT356.A2E62

Compleat instructions for the violin [*ca.* 1790?]

See GEMINIANI, F.

The **compleat** tutor for the fife, containing easy rules for learners after a new method, with a choice collection of all the celebrated marches that are played upon that instrument which all are in proper keys for the German flute. London, D. Rutherfoord [1756 ?]

1 p. l., 21 p. 23ᶜᵐ.

Engraved throughout.

MT356.A2E6

The **compleat** tutor for the fife—*Continued.*

—— **New** and complete instructions for the fife, containing the best and easiest directions to learn that instrument, with a collection of the most celebrated marches, airs, &c. performed in the Guards and other regiments . . .   London, G. Goulding [17—]

1 p. 1., 26, [6] p.   17 x 24^{cm}.   (*With* Entire new . . . instructions for the fife. London [17—])

Engraved throughout.

MT356.A2E62

—— **Entire** new and compleat instructions for the fife; containing the best and easiest directions to learn that instrument, with a collection of the most celebrated marches, airs &c perform'd in the Guards & other regiments.   N. B. The tunes in this book are proper for the German flute.   London, J. Preston [1780?]

1 p. 1., 32 p.   front.   17½ x 25½^{cm}.

Engraved throughout.

MT356.A2E61

—— **Entire** new and compleat instructions for the fife, containing the best and easiest directions to learn that instrument, with a collection of the most celebrated marches, airs &c perform'd in the Guards & other regiments.   N. B. The tunes in this book are proper for the German flute.   London, Printed by Longman and Broderip [17—]

1 p. 1., 36 p.   front.   17 x 24^{cm}.

Engraved throughout.   Frontispiece colored by hand.

MT356.A2E62

The **compleat** tutor for the German flute, containing the best and easiest instructions for learners to obtain a proficiency.   Translated from the French.   To which is added a choice collection of ye most celebrated Italian, English, & Scotch tunes, curiously adapted to that instrument.   London, J. Simpson [17—]

30, 2 p.   front.   21½^{cm}.

Engraved throughout.
Apparently a much altered edition of "The newest method for learners on the German flute" which forms the third part of Peter Prelleur's "Modern musick-master," London, 1738.   The "Newest method" is itself a free translation from Hotteterre's "Principes de la flute traversière," Amsterdam, 1708.

MT342.A2C76

—— The **compleat** tutor, for the German flute; containing the best and easiest instructions for learners to obtain a proficiency.   Translated from the French.   To which is added a choice collection of ye most celebrated Italian, English & Scotch tunes; curiously adapted to that instrument.   London, J. Fentum [n. d.]

32 p.   25½^{cm}.

MT342.A2C7

—— The **compleat** tutor for the German flute, containing the best and easiest instructions for learners to obtain a proficiency.   Translated from the French.   To which is added a choice collection of ye most celebrated Italian, English, & Scotch tunes curiously adapted to that instrument.   London, J. Johnson [17—]

1 p. 1., 36 p.   front., fold. pl.   22^{cm}.

Engraved throughout.

MT342.A2C78

The **compleat** tutor for the German flute—*Continued*.

—— The **compleat** tutor for the flute. Containing the best and easiest instructions for learners to obtain a proficiency. To which is added a choice collection of the most celebrated Italian, English, and Scotch tunes. Curiously adapted to that instrument. London, J. Johnson [17—]

1 p. l., 36 p. front. 22ᶜᵐ.   MT342.A2C79

The **compleat** tutor for the harpsichord or spinnet; wherein is shewn the Italian manner of fingering, with suits of lessons for beginners & those who are already proficients on that instrument & the organ: with rules for tuneing the harpsichord or spinnet. London, P. Thompson [175–]

2 p. l., 33 p. front. 21½ᶜᵐ.

Engraved throughout.
Forms the sixth part of Peter Prelleur's "Modern musick-master," London, 1738, where it appears under title "The harpsichord illustrated and improv'd." In the present edition the "Rules for attaining to play a thorough bass" are omitted and a part of the musical examples of the earlier edition have been replaced by others.

—— —— Copy 2. 23½ᶜᵐ.

Imperfect, wanting last leaf.

MT252.A2C76

See also The HARPSICHORD illustrated [174—]

Conceição, Angelo da.
See ANGELO DA CONCEIÇÃO.

Conceição, Bernardo da.
See BERNARDO DA CONCEIÇÃO.

Conceição, Manuel da.
See MANUEL DA CONCEIÇÃO.

Contamine,   Cousin de.
See COUSIN DE CONTAMINE.

[Contant d'Orville, André Guillaume] 1730 ?–1800.
Histoire de l'opera bouffon, contenant les jugemens de toutes les pieces qui ont paru depuis sa naissance jusqu'à ce jour. Pour servir à l'histoire des théâtres de Paris . . . À Amsterdam, et se trouve a Paris, chez Grange', 1768.

2 v. (v. 1: 4 p. l., 266, [2] p.; v. 2: 2 p. l., 214, [2] p.) 17ᶜᵐ.

Vol. 2 dated 1748 by printer's error.
"Cet ouvrage est l'amusement de deux freres, qui . . . toujours séparés l'un de l'autre, se sont rendu compte des bagatelles qui . . . fixoient l'attention du public."—Avertissement.

ML1727.3.A2C6

Contant de La Molette, Philippe du.
See DU CONTANT DE LA MOLETTE, PHILIPPE.

Converção, Raymundo da.
See RAYMUNDO DA CONVERÇÃO.

[Coquéau, Claude Philibert] *d.* 1794.

Entretiens sur l'état actuel de l'opéra de Paris.   Amsterdam, et se trouve à Paris, chez Esprit, 1779.

vi, [7]–174 p.   21ᶜᵐ.

ML1727.35.C67

—— Suite des Entretiens sur l'état actuel de l'opéra de Paris, ou Lettres à M. S. . . . [*i. e.* Suard] auteur de l'extrait de cet ouvrage dans le Mercure.   [Paris, 1779]

iv, [5]–48 p.   19½ᶜᵐ.

ML1727.35.C672

Corrette, Michel.

Le maitre de clavecin pour l'accompagnement, methode theorique et pratique, qui conduit en très peu de tems a accompagner à livre ouvert.   Avec des leçons chantantes ou les accords sont notés pour faciliter l'etude des commençans.   Ouvrage utile a ceux qui veulent parvenir a l'excelence de la composition.   Le tout selon la règle de l'octave et de la basse fondamentale.   Par Monsieur Corrette . . . Paris, L'auteur [etc.] 1753.

3 p. l., 94 p.   30ᶜᵐ.

Engraved throughout.

MT68.A2C7

Methode pour apprendre aisément à joüer de la flute traversiere. Avec des principes de musique, et des brunettes a i. et ii. parties. Ouvrage utile et curieux, qui conduit en très peu de tems à la parfaite connoissance de la musique et a joüer a livre ouvert les sonates et concerto.   Par Mʳ. Corrette . . .   Paris, Chez l'auteur; [etc., etc., 177– ?]

2 p. l., 50 p.   front.   26 x 19ᶜᵐ.

Engraved throughout.

MT342.A2C8

Methode, théorique et pratique.   Pour apprendre en peu de tems le violoncelle dans sa perfection.   Ensemble des principes de musique avec des leçons a i, et ii, violoncelles.   La division de la corde pour placer s'il on veut dans les commencemens, des lignes traversalles sur le manche du violoncelle.   Plus une petite methode particuliere pour ceux qui joüent de la viole, et qui veullent joüer du violoncelle. Composée par Michel Corrette.   xxiv.ᵉ ouvrage . . .   Paris, Chez l'auteur; [etc., etc.] 1741.

3 p. l., 46 p.   front., illus.   29 x 22ᶜᵐ.

Engraved throughout.
"Catalogue des ouvrages de Mʳ. Corrette": [1] p. preceding p. 1.

MT302.A2C824

Le parfait maitre a chanter, methode pour apprendre facilement la musique vocale et instrumentale, ou tous les principes sont dévelopés nettement et distinctement.   Avec des leçons dans le gout nouveau à une et à deux parties, ce qui enseigne en très peu de tems à solfier toutes sortes de musique à livre ouvert, et des régles invariables pour ceux qui veulent se servir de la transposition . . .   Par

Corrette, Michel—*Continued.*

Michel Corrette . . . Nouv. ed. auguementée de nouveaux signes de musique et d'airs à chanter. Paris, Chez l'auteur [1782]

1 p. l., A–B, 61 p. front. 29ᶜᵐ.

Engraved throughout; line borders. Label of Melle. Castagnery mounted over imprint.

MT6.A2C56

Corsetti, Francesco, *d.* 1774, *translator.*

See BROWN, J. Dell' origine . . . della poesia, 1772.

Corvinus, Johannes Michaelis.

See RAVN, HANS MIKKELSEN.

[Coste d'Arnobat, Charles Pierre] *b.* 1732. .

Doutes d'un Pyrronien, proposés amicalement a J. J. Rousseau . . . [Paris] 1753.

1 p. l., 36 p. 17½ᶜᵐ.

ML1727.33.C68

[Couppé, Marie Angélique] *b.* 1723.

Requeste de deux actrices d'Opera a Momus, avec son ordonnance. A la Haye [*i. e.* Paris] 1743.

1 p. l., [5]–21 p. 15½ᶜᵐ.

In verse.
Caption title: Requeste présentée à Momus par les Demoiselles Coupée & Desgranges, actrices de l'Opéra, tant pour elles que pour celles de leurs compagnes qui se trouvent dans le cas de l'article xx. du Code lyrique, ou reglement pour l'Opera, imprimé au mois de juin 1743.

ML1727.8.P2R35

[Cousin de Contamine,   ] *b.* 1704.

Traité critique du plain-chant, usité aujourd'hui dans l'eglise; contenant les principes qui en montrent les défauts, & qui peuvent conduire à le rendre meilleur. Paris, P. G. Le Mercier, 1749.

xxiv, 69, [3] p. 8 (*i. e.* 9) fold. pl. 16 x 8½ᶜᵐ.

Imperfect, wanting plates 2 and 6; plate 8 (in 2 parts) supplied in ms.

ML3082.A2C6

[Coxe, William] 1747–1828.

Anecdotes of George Frederick Handel, and John Christopher Smith. With select pieces of music, composed by J. C. Smith, never before published. London, Printed by W. Bulmer and co., sold by Cadell and Davies; [etc., etc.] 1799.

4 p. l., iv, 64, 34 p. 2 port. (incl. front.) 27½ x 21½ᶜᵐ.

ML410.H13C87

Cramer, Carl Friedrich, 1752–1807, *editor.*

See MAGAZIN der musik [1783–86]

Crivellati, Cesare.

Discorsi mvsicali, nelli qvali si contengono non solo cose pertinenti alla teorica, ma etiandio alla pratica; mediante le quali si potrà con facilità peruenire all' acquisto di così honorata scientia. Raccolti da diuersi buoni autori da Cesare Criuellati . . . Viterbo, Agostino Discep., 1624.

196, [3] p.   15½ᶜᵐ.

Title in red and black; title vignette: ecclesiastical coat of arms.

MT6.A2C8

Crocchi, Pietro, *translator.*

See BROWN, J.   Dell' origine . . . della poesia, 1772.

Croesse'r, Luis da Maia, *pseud.*

See CARLOS DE JESUS MARIA.

Croix, A. Phérotée de la.

See LA CROIX, A. PHÉROTÉE DE.

Crousaz, Jean Pierre de, 1663–1750, *praeses.*

Systematis physici disputatio decima quinta. Quam . . . præside N. J. P. de Crosa . . . defendere conabitur Gabriel Jacobus Ballivus Lucinensis.   In publico Academiæ lausanensis auditorio . . . Bernæ, ex officina illustris. Reipubl. bernensis, 1713.

67 p.   19 x 15ᶜᵐ.

ML3809.A2C95

Crudeli, Tommaso, 1703–1745.

In lode del Signor Carlo Broschi detto Farinello, musico celebre, ode di Tommaso Crudeli.   Firenze, A. M. Albizzini, 1734.

18 p. incl. port.   20½ᶜᵐ.

ML420.B8C8

Crüger, Johann, 1598–1662.

Synopsis musica continens ratιonem constituendi & componendi melos harmonicvm. Conscripta, varijsq, exemplis illustrata a Johanne Crügero . . . [Berolini] sumtibus Iohannis Kally, 1630.

[127] p.   19½ x 15ᶜᵐ.

Engr. t.-p., illustrated (allegorical figures of the seven liberal arts) with printer's mark.   Signatures: A–Q in fours.
Several authorities cite an earlier edition, Berlin, 1624, but Fétis considers the present the first edition.

MT55.A2C75

Cruz, João Chrysostomo da, 1707–1748.

Methodo breve, e claro, em que sem prolixidade, nem confusaõ se exprimem os necessarios principios para inteligencia da arte da musica . . . por Joaõ Chrysostomo da Cruz . . . Com hum appendix dialógico que servirá de index da obra, e liçaõ dos principiantes. Lisboa, I. Rodrigues, 1745.

9 p. l., 75, [33] p.   tables, diagr.   20ᶜᵐ.

MT7.A2C95

Cruz Brocarte, Antonio de la.

Medula de la mvsica theorica. Cuya inspeccion manifiesta clara-
mente la execucion de la practica, en division de quatro discursos;
en los quales se dà exacta noticia de las cosas mas principales, que
pertenecen al canto llano, canto de organo, contrapunto, y composicion, con toda brevedad, y claridad. Por Don Antonio de la Crvz
Brocarte . . . Salamanca, E. A. Garcia, 1707.

9 p. l., 234 p. illus. 15^{cm}.

Paging irregular.

MT6.A2C95

Cuisse,   de la.

See LA CUISSE,   DE.

Cunha Bandeira, Jeronymo da, *editor*.

See BERNARDO DA CONCEIÇÃO. O ecclesiastico instruido, 1788.

D. * * *, M.

See DISSERTATIONS en forme de lettres, 1788.

The **dancing-master:** or, Directions for dancing country dances,
with the tunes to each dance for the treble-violin. The 10th ed.
cor.; with the addition of several new dances and tunes never before
printed. [London] Printed by J. Heptinstall, for H. Playford, 1698.

2 v. in 1 (v. 1 : 4 p. l., 215 p.; v. 2 : 2 p. l., 48 p.) 11 x 19½^{cm}.

Vol. 2 has title: The second part of the Dancing master: or, Directions for
dancing country dances, with the tunes to each dance for the violin or flute. The
2d ed., with additions. [London] Printed for H. Playford, 1698.
    The 1st edition, comprising vol. 1 only, was published by John Playford in
1651, under title: The English dancing-master.

MT950.A2D3

Dard,

Nouveaux principes de musique, qui seuls doivent suffire, pour
l'apprendre parfaitement. Auxquels l'auteur a joint l'histoire de la
musique et de ses progressions, depuis son origine jusqu'à présent . . .
par Mr Dard . . . Gravés par Melle Girard . . . Paris, Chez l'auteur
[1769]

1 p. l., 149, 19 p. 24 x 19½^{cm}.

Title within ornamental border, text within line borders.
    Forms the second part of his "Nouveaux principes de musique, avec histoire
suivi du paralelle de Lully et de Rameau et du catalogue de tous les opéras
représ. depuis 1671," Paris, 1768. *cf.* Eitner, Biog.-bibl. quellen-lexikon.

MT6.A2D2

Daube, Johann Friedrich, 1730–1797.

Anleitung zur erfindung der melodie und ihrer fortsetzung. Von
Johann Friedrich Daube . . . Wien, Gedruckt bey C. G. Täubel,
1797–98.

2 v. in 1 (v. 1: 4 p. l., [5]–51, [1] p.; v. 2: 2 p. l., [3]–68 p.) illus. 22½ x 17½^{cm}.

Vol. 2 (Zweyter theil, welcher die composition enthält) has imprint: Wien, In
commission der Hochenleitterschen buchhandlung, 1798.
    Published also under title: Anleitung zum selbstunterricht in der musika-
lischen composition, sowohl für die instrumental- als vocalmusik.

MT47.A2D2

Daube, Johann Friedrich—*Continued.*

General-bass in drey accorden, gegründet in den regeln der alt- und neuen autoren, nebst einem hierauf gebaueten unterricht: wie man aus einer jeden aufgegebenen tonart, nur mit zwey mittels-accorden, in eine von den drey und zwanzig tonarten die man begehret, gelangen kann, und der hierauf gegründeten kunst zu präludiren, wie auch zu jeder melodie einen bass zu setzen, dass also durch diese neue und leichte anleitung, zugleich auch zur composition unmittelbar der weg gebahnet wird, von Johann Friedrich Daube ... Leipzig, J. B. Andrä, Frankfurt am Mayn, 1756.

xxii, [2], 215, [1] p.   fold. pl.   21½ᶜᵐ.

MT49.A2D23

Der musikalische dilettant: eine abhandlung der komposition, welche nicht allein die neuesten setzarten der zwo- drey- und mehrstimmigen sachen: sondern auch die meisten künstlichen gattungen der alten kanons: der einfachen und doppelfugen, deutlich vorträgt, und durch ausgesuchte beyspiele erkläret. Von Johann Friederich Daube ... Wien, Gedruckt bey Johann Thomas edlen von Trattnern, 1773.

3 p. l., [3]–333, [1] p.   22½ x 18ᶜᵐ.

MT40.A2D23

See also Der MUSIKALISCHE dillettante, 1770.

David, François.

Methode nouvelle ov principes generaux pour apprendre facilement la musique, et l'art de chanter. Par M.ʳ David ... Paris, M.ᵉ la v.ᵉ Boivin; [etc., etc.] 1737.

1 p. l., 142 p.   16 x 24½ᶜᵐ.

Engraved in part.

MT835.A2D3

Davy, Charles, 1722–1797.

Letters, addressed chiefly to a young gentleman, upon subjects of literature: including a translation of Euclid's Section of the canon; and his treatise on harmonic; with an explanation of the Greek musical modes, according to the doctrine of Ptolemy. By Charles Davy ... Bury St. Edmunds, Printed for the author, by J. Rackham, 1787.

2 v. (2 p. l., iii–xii, 423 p., 1 l.; 2 p. l., 541, [1] p., 1 l.)   plates, tables, diagrs. 23ᶜᵐ.

"Balaam: an attempt towards an oratorio, for a private concert. 1769" (words only): v. 1, p. [341]–352. "Ruth: an attempt towards an oratorio, for a private concert. 1769" (words only): v. 1, p. [353]–368.

PN45.D3

De veteris Græcorum musices in omnes scientias usu, et energia divinatio. *Rem tibi Socraticæ poterunt ostendere chartæ.* Venetiis, typis Antonii Zatta, 1762.

1 p. l., xxxv p.   30ᶜᵐ.

Title vignette.

ML169.A2D3

Declaration du public, au sujet des contestations qui se sont élevées sur la musique. [n. p., 175–]

7 p. 19cm.

Caption title.
No. 13 in a volume of pamphlets lettered Quere[lle] des Bouffo[ns]

ML1727.33.A1

—— Copy 2.

ML1727.33.D2

Dedekind, Henning, *d.* 1628?
See GOETTING, V. Compendium mvsicæ [1587]

Deimling, Ernst Ludwig, *b. ca.* 1760.

Beschreibung des orgelbaues und der verfahrungsart bei untersuchung neuer und verbesserter werke. Ein buch für organisten, schulmeister und orts-vorgesetzte. Von Ernst Ludwig Deimling. 2. aufl. Offenbach, Gedruckt bei C. L. Brede [1796]

1 p. l., x, [13]–216 p., 1 l. 19½cm.

"Etwas vom choral-gesang": p. 193–216.

ML555.A2D3

Dellain,

Nouveau manuel musical, contenant les élémens de la musique, des agrémens du chant et de l'accompagnement du clavessin . . . Par M. Dellain. Paris, Veuve Ballard & fils; [etc., etc.] 1781.

viij, 52, [2] p. 27 x 20½cm.

Given by Fétis as Charles Henri, by Michel Brenet as Charles Louis Joseph, Dellain.

MT7.A2D35

Demantius, Johann Christoph, 1567–1643.

Isagoge artis musicæ ad incipientium captum maxime accommodata. Kurtze anleitung recht und leicht singen zu lernen / neben kurtzer / doch grûndlicher erklårung / der griechischen / lateinischen und italiânischen wôrtlein / so bey den neotericis oder ietzigen neuen musicis hin und wieder ûblichen [!] und in gebrauch seyn. Auctore Christophoro Demantio . . . Ed. 9. & ultima, prioribus multò auctior & correctior . . . Freibergæ, impensis G. Beutheri, 1656.

[192] p. 16cm.

Colophon: Jenæ, typis Samuelis Krebsi. Anno M.DC.LVII.
Text in Latin and German on opposite pages.

MT870.A2D37

[Démotz de La Salle, Jean François] *d. ca.* 1741.

Methode de musique selon un nouveau systême très-court, très-facile & très-sûr, approuve' par messieurs de l'Academie royale des sciences, & par les plus habiles musiciens de Paris. Dediée a la reine. Par M. * * * prêtre. Paris, P. Simon, 1728.

6 p. l., 3–216, [4] p. 1 illus. 20cm.

ML432.A2D3

Denis, Jean.

Traité de l'accord de l'espinette, auec la comparaison de son ciauier à la musique vocale. Augmenté en cette edition des quatre chapitres suiuants. I. Traité des sons & combien il y en a. II. Traité des tons de l'eglise & de leurs estenduës. III. Traité des fugues & comme il les faut traiter. IV. La maniere de bien jouër de l'espinette & des orgues . . . Par I. Denis . . . Paris, Par R. Ballard, imprimeur, et se vendent chez l'autheur, 1650.

40 p. fold. tab. 19½ᶜᵐ.

MT252.A2D36

Denis, Pierre.

Nouvelle methode pour apprendre en peu de tems la musique et l'art de chanter, avec un nombre de leçons dans plusieurs genres. Par Mʳ Denis . . . Paris, De La Chevardiere [17—]

72 p. 20½ x 25½ᶜᵐ.

"Gravé par Mᵉˡˡᵉ Vendôme."

MT6.A2D4

Denis, Pierre, *translator.*

See Fux, J. J. Traité de composition musicale [17—]
TARTINI, G. Traité des agrémens de la musique [1782]

Dennis, John, 1657–1734.

An essay on the opera's after the Italian manner, which are about to be establish'd on the English stage: with some reflections on the damage which they may bring to the publick. By Mr. Dennis . . . London, J. Nutt, 1706.

4 p. l., 15, [1] p. 23 x 17ᶜᵐ.

ML1731.3.A2D3

Dentice, Luigi.

Dvo dialoghi della mvsica del Signor Lvigi Dentice . . . Delli quali l'uno tratta della theorica, & l'altro della pratica: raccolti da diuersi autori greci, & latini. Nuouamente posti in luce. Roma, V. Lucrino, 1553.

[79] p. diagrs. 19ᶜᵐ.
Title vignette. Signatures: A in two, B–K in fours, L in two.

ML171.D47

[Desboulmiers, Jean Auguste Julien, *known as*] 1731–1771.

Histoire anecdotique et raisonnée du Théâtre italien, depuis son rétablissement en France jusqu'à l'année 1769. Contenant les analyses des principales pièces, & un catalogue de toutes celles tant italiennes que françaises, données sur ce théâtre, avec les anecdotes les plus curieuses & les notices les plus intéressantes de la vie & des talens des auteurs & acteurs . . . Paris, Lacombe, 1769.

7 v. 18ᶜᵐ.

PN2633.D4

Histoire du théatre de l'Opéra comique . . . Paris, Lacombe, 1769.

2 v. (v. 1: 1 p. l., 497, [5] p., 1 l.; v. 2: 1 p. l., 558, [2] p.) 17ᶜᵐ.

Desboulmiers, Jean Auguste Julien—*Continued.*

An analysis of pieces represented 1712 to 1761, followed by "Catalogue raisonné des auteurs, des acteurs, et des piéces, qui n'ont point été compris dans l'Histoire de l'Opéra comique" (v. 2, p. 133–558)

ML1727.8.P2D44

Desbout, Luigi.

Ragionamento fisico-chirurgico sopra l'effetto della musica nelle malattie nervose, dedicato all' illustriss. Sig. dottore Giorgio de Lagusius ... da Luigi Desbout ... Livorno, Calderoni, e Faina, 1780.

40 p. 18½ᶜᵐ.

ML3920.A2D4

—— Dissertation sur l'effet de la musique dans les maladies nerveuses, par Louis Desbout ... St. Pétersbourg, Impr. de Breitkopf, 1784.

3 p. l., 75 p., 1 l. 20ᶜᵐ.

ML3920.A2D42

Descartes, René, 1596–1650.

Renati ‖ Des-Cartes ‖ Musicæ ‖ Compendium. ‖ Trajecti ad Rhenum,‖ Typis Gisberti à Zÿll, & Theodori ab Ackersdÿck, ‖ cɪɔɪɔcl.

58 p. diagrs. 18½ x 15ᶜᵐ.

ML3805.A2D2

—— Renati Des-Cartes Musicæ compendium. Francofvrti ad Moenvm, sumptibus F. Knochii, 1695.

48 p. diagrs. 19½ x 16ᶜᵐ.
Title vignette.

ML3805.A2D3

—— Renatus Des-Cartes excellent compendium of musick: with necessary and judicious animadversions thereupon. By a person of honour. London, Printed by T. Harper, for H. Moseley, 1653.

8 p. l., 94 p., 1 l. diagrs. 19½ x 15ᶜᵐ.
The "Animadversions," p. [59]–94, have special t.-p.
A person of honour: William viscount Brouncker.

ML3805.A2D32

Desessarts, Nicolas Toussaint Lemoyne, 1744–1810.

Les trois théatres de Paris, ou Abrégé historique de l'établissement de la Comédie françoise, de la Comédie italienne & de l'Opéra; avec un précis des loix, arrêts, réglemens & usages, qui concernent chacun de ces spectacles. Par M. Des Essarts ... Paris, Lacombe, 1777.

3 p. l., 300, [3] p. 20½ᶜᵐ.

PN2636.P3D4

[Desforges,   ]

Memoires anecdotes pour servir a l'histoire de M. Duliz. Et la suite de ses avantures, après la catastrophe de celle de Mademoiselle Pelissier, actrice de l'Opera de Paris. Londres, S. Harding, 1739.

1 p. l., 206 p., 1 l., 75 p.   front.   16ᶜᵐ.

Title vignette.
"Le triomphe de l'interêt. Comedie. [Par Laus de Boissy]": 1 l., 75 p.

ML429.D88

[Desgranges, *Mlle.*]

Requeste de deux actrices d'Opera a Momus,ₐavec son ordonnance. A la Haye [*i. e.* Paris] 1743.

1 p. l., [5]–21 p.   15½ᶜᵐ.

In verse.
Caption title: Requeste présentée à Momus par les Demoiselles Coupée & Desgranges, actrices de l'Opera, tant pour elles que pour celles de leurs compagnes qui se trouvent dans le cas de l'article xx. du Code lyrique, ou reglement pour l'Opera, imprimé au mois de juin 1743.

ML1727.8.P2R35

Despériers, Bonaventure, *d.* 1544?

See DISCOURS non plus melancoliqves qve divers, 1557.

Dibdin, Charles, 1745–1814.

The musical tour of Mr. Dibdin; in which—previous to his embarkation for India—he finished his career as a public character . . . Sheffield, Printed for the author by J. Gales, 1788.

3 p. l., iv, 443, [1] p.   19 pl. on 15 l. (music)   26 x 20ᶜᵐ.

ML410.D44D5

Diderot, Denis, 1713–1784, *editor.*

See AU petit prophête de Boesmischbroda [1753]
BEMETZRIEDER, A.   Leçons de clavecin, 1771.
      Music made easy.

Dingley, William, 1672 *or* 3–1735.

Cathedral service decent and useful. A sermon preach'd before the University of Oxford at Sᵗ Mary's on Cecilia's day, 1713. By W. Dingley . . . Oxford, A. Peisley, 1713.

2 p. l., 19 p.   19ᶜᵐ.

ML64.D4

Dionigi, Marco.

Primi tvoni, overo introdvzione del canto fermo, con l'aggiunta d'altri tuoni; del Sig. dottor Marco Dionigi . . . Parma, M. Vigna, 1667.

112 p. illus. 28ᶜᵐ.

Dedication, p. 3–4, wanting in this copy.
The present is the 2d edition; the 1st edition was published at Parma in 1648.

MT860.A2D59

Discours non plus ‖ melancoliqves qve divers, ‖ de choses mesmement, qui appartiennent ‖ a notre France: & a la fin La maniere de ‖ bien & iustement entoucher les lucs & ‖ guiternes. ‖ A Poitiers,‖ De l'imprimerie d'Enguilbert de Marnef. ‖ 1557 ‖ Auec priuilege du roy.

4 p. l., 112 p. incl. tab., diagr. 19½ᶜᵐ.

Title, with printer's mark.—Priuilege du roy, donné a Enguilbert de Marnef. t.-p. verso.—Engvilbert de Marnef imprimevr av lectevr salvt. [3] p.—Table des choses contenues en ce liure. [2] p.—Fautes aduenues en l'impression de ce liure. [1] p.—Text, followed by colophon: Acheué d'imprimer a Poitiers, le 13 de may 1556 par Enguilbert de Marnef. 112 p.
The table (Les noms des jours de la semaine) which is counted as page 9, is wanting in L. of C. copy, being replaced by a printed facsimile.
Attributed to B. Despériers by some authorities, by others to Jacques Peletier and Élie Vinet. cf. Notice by L. Lacour in Œuvres fr. de B. Des Periers, 1856, v. 1.

ML171.D58

Dissertations en forme de lettres sur différens sujets de littérature et des beaux-arts: ouvrage divisé en deux parties. Par M. D. * * * de Dijon . . . A Londres, et se trouve a Paris, chez Brunet, 1788.

150, [2] p. 16½ᶜᵐ.

CONTENTS.—Entretien d'un musicien françois avec un gentilhomme russe, sur les effets de la musique moderne; ou, Tableau des concerts de province.—Lettre à M. d'Alembert, sur la seconde édition de ses Elémens de musique.—Lettre à M. de Marmontel, sur les nouveaux spectacles de l'Opéra.—Lettre à M. Rousseau, dans laquelle on fait le paralelle de ce célebre Genevois, mentor d'Emile, avec son illustre compatriote Lefort, le mentor de Pierre le Grand.—Lettre à messieurs de l'Académie des sciences de Dijon, sur la graisse du vin.—Lettre à M. de Voltaire, sur son histoire de la guerre de 1741.—Lettre à M. Bé * * * sur la force de l'imagination.—Dissertation, ou lettre adressée à M. d'Alembert, sur les honneurs rendus à Rome aux comédiens.

ML3877.A2D45

Doane, Joseph, *editor.*

See A MUSICAL directory [1794]

Dodwell, Henry, 1641–1711.

A treatise concerning the lawfulness of instrumental musick in holy offices. By Henry Dodwell, M. A. To which is prefixed, a preface in vindication of Mr. Newte's sermon, concerning the lawfulness and use of organs in the Christian church, &c., from the exceptions of an anonymous letter to a friend in the country, concerning the use of instrumental musick in the worship of God, &c. The 2d ed., with large additions. London. W. Haws, 1700.

1 p. l., 84, [3], 143, [1] p. 20ᶜᵐ.

ML3001.D64

Domenjoud, Jean Baptiste.

De la préférence des vis aux chevilles, pour les instrumens de musique. Et un Essai sur la maniere de changer l'A, mi, la, en tendant ou détendant toutes les cordes à la fois, sans détruire l'harmonie. Ce qui donne lieu à des manches d'une forme nouvelle, beaucoup plus commodes que les anciens. Présenté à l'Académie royale des sciences, le 13 août 1756, par M. Domenjoud . . . Paris, Thiboust, 1757.

22, [2] p. fold. pl. 16½ᶜᵐ.

ML845.A2D6

Domingos do Rosario.

Theatro ecclesiastico, em que se acham muitos documentos de cantochão para qualquer pessoa dedicada ao culto divino nos officios do coro, e altar . . . ordenado por seu author o padre fr. Domingos do Rosario . . . novamente disposto com melhor ordem, correcto, e accrescentado com todas as missas de Nossa Senhora, e as que em todos os dias festivos do anno se cantam, &c. pelo padre fr. Angelo da Conceicaõ. 5. impressaõ. Lisboa, Officina de M. Coelho Amado, 1774.

xi, 580 p. 21ᶜᵐ

MT860.A2D77

Doni, Giovanni Battista, 1593 or 4–1647.

Compendio del trattato de' generi e de' modi della mvsica. Di Gio. Battista Doni. Con vn discorso sopra la perfettione de' concenti. Et vn saggio à due voci di mutationi di genere, e di tuono in tre maniere d'intauolatura: et d'vn principio di madrigale del principe, ridotto nella medesima intauolatura . . . Roma, A. Fei, 1635.

20 p. l., 171, [1] p. 5 fold. diagr. 22ᶜᵐ.

Title vignette: ecclesiastical coat of arms.
Abstract of a larger work which was never published. The present work was completed by the publication of "Annotazioni sopra il Compendio," Rome, 1640.

ML3805.A2D7

Io: Baptistae Doni . . . De præstantia musicæ veteris libri tres totidem dialogis comprehensi, in quibus vetus ac recens musica, cum singulis earum partibus, accurate inter se conferuntur. Adiecto ad finem onomastico selectorum vocabulorum, ad hanc facultatem cum elegantia, & proprietate tractandam, pertinentium . . . Florentiæ, typis A. Massæ Foroliuien., 1647.

4 p. l., 266 p. 24½ᶜᵐ.

ML169.A2D6

Io. Baptistae Doni . . . Lyra Barberina ἀμφίχορδος. Accedvnt eivsdem opera, pleraqve nondvm edita, ad veterem mvsicam illvstrandam pertinentia, ex avtographis collegit, et in lvcem proferri cvravit Antonivs Franciscvs Gorivs . . . Absolvta vero stvdio et opera Io. Baptistae Passeri . . . Florentiae, Typis caesareis, 1763.

2 v. (v. 1: xii, 424 p.; v. 2: xii, 306 p., 1 l., iv, 100 p.) front. (port.) plates (partly fold.) diagrs. 37½ᶜᵐ.

Title vignette; head and tail pieces; initials.
Vol. 2 has title: De' trattati di mvsica di Gio. Batista Doni . . . tomo secondo, ne' qvali si esamina e dimostra la forza e l'ordine della mvsica antica e per qval via ridvr si possa alla pristina efficacia tla moderna; raccolti e pvbblicati per opera di Anton Francesco Gori . . . Aggiuntovi un lessico delle voci musiche, e l'indice generale, per opera e studio del p. maestro Gio. Batista Martini . . . Firenze, Stamperia imperiale, 1763.
"Index aliorvm opervm Io. Baptistae Donii ad mvsicam spectantium": v. 1, p. 180.

ML60.D68

See also BANDINI, A. M. Commentariorvm de vita . . . Ioannis Bapt. Doni, 1755.

[Dorat, Claude Joseph] 1734–1780.

Euterpe; or, Remarks on the use and abuse of music, as a part of modern education . . . London, J. Dodsley [1779]

2 p. l., 28 p. 25½ x 20cm.

ML63.D77

Douwes, Klaas, *b.* 1668.

Grondig ondersoek van de toonen der musijk: zijnde een klaare betooninge van de wijdte of grootheit van octaven, quinten, quarten en tertien, geheele en halve toonen: van de imperfecte, ende valsche spetien. Als mede of in een goed musijk de octaven, ende hoe veel malen de quinten, quarten en tertien met malkanderen mogen gaan. Van de twaalf toonen der musijk; ende eenige exempelen om de musijk-nooten te componeren. Met een tweede deel; handelende van verscheidene musijk-instrumenten. Alles kort en klaar aange-weesen, door Klaas Douwes . . . Franeker, A. Heins, 1699.

5 p. l., 3–132 p. fold. pl. 16cm.

Added t.-p., illustrated.

MT6.A2D68

Dowland, John, 1563–1626, *translator.*

See ORNITHOPARCUS, A. Micrologvs, 1609.

Draghetti, Andrea, 1736–1825.

Replica del padre Andrea Draghetti . . . alla Risposta del padre D. Giovenale Sacchi . . . Milano, G. Galeazzi, 1772.

94 p., 1 l. diagr. 18½cm.

Half-title: Della legge di continuità nella scala musica.

ML3809.A2D7

Drechssler, Johann Gabriel, *d.* 1677, *praeses.*

כנור לדוד sive De cithara Davidica . . . Ed. 3. ob defectum exem-plarium denuo excusa . . . Lipsiæ, literis Colerianis, 1675.

[48] p. 19½ x 15½cm.

Diss.—Leipzig (Casparus Felmerius, respondent)

ML166.A2D7

Dressler, Ernst Christoph, 1734–1779.

Fragmente einiger gedanken des Musikalischen zuschauers die bes-sere aufnahme der musik in Deutschland betreffend . . . Gotha, C. Mevius seel. erben, 1767.

2 p. l., 8, 36 p. 23½ x 18cm.

Title vignette; head-pieces.

ML66.A2D7

Dressler, Ernst Christoph—*Continued.*

Ernst Christoph Dresslers Theater-schule fûr die Deutschen, das ernsthafte singe-schauspiel betreffend. Hannover und Cassel, J. W. Schmidt, 1777.

4 p. l., 200, [14] p. 17^{cm}.

ML3858.D77

Dressler, Gallus, *b. ca.* 1530.

Mvsicæ practicæ elementa in vsum Scholæ magdeburgensis edita, a M. Gallo Dreslero ... Magdebvrgi, excudebat VVolffgangus Kirchner, 1571.

[205] p. 14^{cm}.

Signatures: A–M in eights, N in seven. Ms. notes.

ML171.D72

Drewis, F. G.

Freundschaftliche briefe ûber die theorie der tonkunst und composition. Von F. G. Drewis ... Halle, J. C. Hendel, 1797.

iv, 88 p. pl. 20½^{cm}.

MT6.A2D77

Dubos, Jean Baptiste, 1670–1742.

Reflexions critiques sur la poesie et sur la peinture ... Nouv. ed. rev. & cor. ... Utrecht, E. Neaulme, 1732–36.

3 v. 16^{cm}.

Vol. 3 has caption title: Supplement aux Reflexions critiques ... Dissertation sur les répresentations théatrales des anciens.

N63.D8

—— Réflexions critiques sur la poësie et sur la peinture. Par M. l'abbé Du Bos ... 6. éd. ... Paris, Pissot, 1755.

3 v. 16^{cm}.

Vol. 3 has caption title: Réflexions critiques ... Troisième partie. Qui contient une dissertation sur les représentations théatrales des anciens.

N63.D83

—— Critical reflections on poetry, painting and music. With an inquiry into the rise and progress of the theatrical entertainments of the ancients. Written in French by the Abbé Du Bos ... Tr. into English by Thomas Nugent, gent. From the 5th ed. rev., cor., and inlarged by the author ... London, J. Nourse, 1748.

3 v. 21½^{cm}.

Vol. 2 has title: Critical reflections on poetry and painting ...

N63.D88

Dubreuil, Jean, *d.* 1775.

Manuel harmonique, ou Tableau des accords pratiques, pour faciliter à toutes sortes de personnes, l'intelligence de l'harmonie & de l'accompagnement, avec une partie chiffrée pour le clavessin, & deux nouveaux menuets en rondeau. Par M. Dubreuil ... Paris, Lacombe [etc.] 1767.

viii, 60 p., 2 l., [2] p. 21^{cm}.

Four folding leaves of music included in paging.

MT50.A2D81

Du Contant de La Molette, Philippe, 1737–1793.

Traité sur la poésie et la musique des Hébreux, pour servir d'introduction aux Pseaumes'expliqués . . . par M. l'abbé du Contant de La Molette . . . Paris, Moutard, 1781.

2 p. l., 251, [1] p. 18½ᶜᵐ.

ML166.A2C67

Dünkelfeind, Caspar, *pseud.*

See LEOPOLD, G.

Dufayel, Sophie.

Mémoire pour la Dⁿˡᵉ Dufayel l'ainée, actrice de la Comédie italienne, pensionnaire du roi. [n. p., 1779?]

29 p. 19½ᶜᵐ.

Written to refute the accusation that she had tried to poison her sister.
"Reflexions sur le mémoire ci-dessus": p. 17–29.

ML420.D93

Dufort, Giovanni Battista.

Trattato del ballo nobile di Giambatista Dufort, indirizzato all' eccellenza delle signore dame, e de' signori cavalieri napoletani. Napoli, Stamperia di F. Mosca, 1728.

12 p. l., 160 p. diagrs. 17½ᶜᵐ.

GV1600.D8

Dumas, Antoine Joseph, *b.* 1705.

L'art de la musique enseigné et pratiqué par la nouvelle methode du bureau typografique etablie sur une seule clé, sur un seul ton, et sur un seul signe de mesure . . . par Mʳ Dumas. Gravé par Mᵉˡˡᵉ Vandôme. Paris, Chez l'auteur [1753]

3 p. l., 427, 10 p., 1 l. incl. 7 fold. pl. fold. pl. 20½ x 26ᶜᵐ.

"Le bureau typografique musical est composé de trente colonnes contenant huit cases chacunes. Trois de ces colonnes . . . contiennent l'exposition des elemens de la musique. Dix huit autres partagées en trois octaves . . . enseignent au moyen de l'arrangement des cartes . . . une lecture de la musique prompte et facile. Les neuf dernieres colonnes . . . donnent une parfaite connoissance des transpositions Diézées et Bmolées, et mettent en état de chanter dans la partition."—Avertissement.

MT6.A2D86

[Dumont,]

Le vol plus haut, ou L'espion des principaux théatres de la capitale; contenant une histoire abrégée des acteurs & actrices de ces mêmes théâtres, enrichie d'observations philosophiques & d'anecdotes récréatives. Dédié aux amateurs . . . A Memphis, chez Sincere, libraire réfugié au Puits de la Vérité. [Paris] 1784.

viij, [9]–142 p. 17½ᶜᵐ.

"Je ne . . . présente que l'histoire du Concert spirituel & de l'Opéra."—Avis de l'éditeur.
Attributed also to François Marie Mayeur de Saint-Paul.

ML1727.3.A2D88

Dupont, Henri Bonaventure.

Principes de musique, par demande et par reponce, par lequel toutes personnes, pouront aprendre d'eux même a connoître toutte la musique . . . Par le S.ʳ Dupont . . . Paris, L'Hauteur, 1718.

2 p. l., 45, [1] p.   25½ x 19½ᶜᵐ.

Engraved throughout.

MT7.A2D93

Duræus, Johannes Christiern.

. . . Dissertatio mythologico-historica de primis musicæ inventoribus, quam . . . in illustri Upsal. lycæo, sub præsidio . . . Dn. Laurentii Arrhenii . . . publicæ censuræ modeste subjicit . . . Johannes Christiern. Duræus . . . Upsaliæ, literis Wernerianis [1729]

3 p. l., 32 p.   14½ᶜᵐ.

ML3800.A2A7

[Durey de Noinville, Jacques Bernard] 1683–1768.

Histoire du théatre de l'opera en France.   Depuis l'établissement de l'Académie royale de musique, jusqu'à présent . . .   Paris, J. Barbou, 1753.

2 v. in 1 (v. 1: 4 p. l., 264 p.; v. 2: 1 p. l., 221, [3] p.)   20ᶜᵐ.

Vol. 2 dated M.LCC.LIII.
Dedication signed: D * * *
By Durey de Noinville and Louis Travenol.

ML1727.3.A2D8

—— Histoire du théatre de l'Académie royale de musique en France, depuis son établissement jusqu'à présent. 2. éd., cor. & augm. des pieces qui ont été représentées sur le théâtre de l'Opera par les musiciens italiens, depuis le premier août 1752. jusqu'à leur départ en 1754. avec un extrait de ces piéces & des ecrits qui ont paru à ce sujet . . .   Paris, Duchesne, 1757.

2 v. in 1 (v. 1: 6, [8], 320 p.; v. 2: 1 p. l., 221, [3], 221–222 p., 1 l., 11 p.)   20ᶜᵐ.

Dedication signed: D * * *

ML1727.3.A2D82

[Du Roullet, François Louis Gaud Lebland, *marquis*] 1716–1786.

Lettre sur les drames-opera.   A Amsterdam, et se trouve a Paris, chez Esprit, 1776.

55 p.   19½ᶜᵐ.

ML3858.D96

Duval, *abbé, d.* 1781.

Principes de la musique pratique.   Par demandes et par reponses. De M. l'abbé Duval.   Paris, Cailleau [etc.] 1764.

x, [11]–66, [3] p.   4 fold. pl.   19½ᶜᵐ.

In the "Catalogue général" of the Bibliothèque nationale, Paris, this is ascribed to the Abbé Pierre Duval (1730–1797)

MT7.A2D98

Dwight, Josiah, 1671–1748.

An essay to silence the outcry that has been made in some places against regular singing. In a sermon preach'd at Framingham, by the Reverend Mr. Josiah Dwight . . . Boston, J. Eliot, 1725.

16 p. 17½ᶜᵐ.

Last leaf mutilated.

ML3001.D84

Earle, Jabez, 1676 ?–1768.

See PRACTICAL discourses, 1708.

Eastcott, Richard, 1740–1828.

Sketches of the origin, progress and effects of music, with an account of the ancient bards and minstrels. Illustrated with various historical facts, interesting anecdotes, & poetical quotations. By the Rev. Richard Eastcott . . . Bath, S. Hazard, 1793.

vii, [3], viii, iv p., 1 l., 277 p. 22½ᶜᵐ.

ML60.E13

Ebner, Wolfgang, *d.* 1665.

See CHIODINO, G. B. Arte prattica, 1653.

Einige zum allgemeinen nutzen deutlicher gemachte musikalische erwegungs- und andere leichter eingerichtete uibungs-wahrheiten, hrsg. von einem freunde dieser wissenschafft. Leipzig, In commission zu haben bey M. Blochbergern [1750 ?]

viii, 90 (*i. e.* 76) p. 21 x 17ᶜᵐ.

No. 66–79 omitted in paging.
Attributed to Georg Friedrich Lingke.

ML3805.A2E4

[Eisel, Johann Philipp] 1698–1763.

Musicus ἀυτοδίδακτος, oder Der sich selbst informirende musicus, bestehend sowohl in vocal- als üblicher instrumental-musiqve, welcher über 24. sorten sowohl mit saiten bezogener als blasender und schlagender instrumente beschreibet, die ein jeder . . . nach denen principiis fundamentalibus erlernen kan . . . ans licht gestellet, und mit vielen darzu dienlichen figuren und handgriffen erläutert von einem der in praxi erfahren. Erfurt, J. M. Funck, 1738.

4 p. l., 108 p. 1 illus., 17 pl. on 16 l. 21 x 17½ᶜᵐ.

MT6.A2E44

—— Der sich selbst informirende musicus, oder: Gründliche anweisung zu der vocal- und instrumental-music, welcher über 24. sorten, sowohl mit saiten bezogener, als blasend- und schlagender instrumenten, zugleich auch achtzehen darzu dienliche figuren und handgriffe enthält . . . Augsburg, J. J. Lotter, 1762.

7 p. l., 90 p. illus. 17 x 21ᶜᵐ.

MT6.A2E46

Der **eitle** musicant und schenkwirth als zwey wunder in der christen-
heit, besonders in den itzigen betrûbten kriegslåuften, nebst ange-
wiesener allgemeinen heilsordnung und einer auf die itzige krieges-
zeit gerichteten vorrede . . . [Halle, Waisenhaus-b.] 1760.

8 p. l., 104 p. 16½ᶜᵐ.

By Carl Heinrich von Bogatzky?

HV5478.A3E4

Éloge de M. d'Acquin, musicien, organiste de la chapelle du roi.
[Paris, 1773 ?]

p. 191–203. 16ᶜᵐ.

Caption title.
From "Le Nécrologe des hommes célèbres de France," edited by Palissot de
Montenoy, Poinsinet de Sivry, and others.

ML416.A37

Éloge de Monsieur Duni. [Paris, 1776 ?]

1 p. l., p. [165]–169. 16½ᶜᵐ.

Caption title.
From the same source as the preceding.

ML410.D91

Eloge de M. Le Clair. [Paris, 1767 ?]

p. 119–131. 16ᶜᵐ.

Caption title.
From the same source as the preceding.

ML410.L41E5

Elsmann, Heinrich.

Compendivm mvsicæ latino-germanicum, cum brevi tractatu de
modis. Accesserunt hymni sacri intercalares pro horis scholasticis,
georgiani ut vocant, fvnebres: omnia in usum inventutis[!] conscripta & congesta à m. Henrico Elsmano . . . VVolferbyti, Autore
sumptum faciente imprimebatur per Eliam Holwein, 1619.

[128] p. 15ᶜᵐ.

MT860.A2E5

Elst, Joannes van der, 1594 ?–1670.

Notæ Avgvstinianæ, sive Mvsices figvræ sev notæ novæ concinendis
modvlis faciliores, tabvlatvris organicis exhibendis aptiores; qvas
firmamento ecclesiæ magno patriarchæ divo Avrelio Avgvstino mvsices
ecclesiasticæ protectori venerabvndvs dedicat F. Ioannes vander Elst
. . . Gandavi, typis Maximiliani Graet, 1657.

2 p. l., 16 p. 11 pl. 23 x 18ᶜᵐ.

In 2 parts. The second part, "Explicatio ad musices voces," p. 9–16, is dated
at end, 1659. Bound with "Den ouden . . . grondt vande musiicke."

MT6.A2E49

Den ouden ende nieuwen grondt vande musiicke . . . Inde welcke
met korte ende klare reghels ende redenen wt-gheleydt wordt het
mergh vande musijcke, soo kerckelicke, figuréle, als instrumentéle,
soo voor de theorie als voor de practijcke, door P. I. V. E. A. Ghendt,
M. Graet, 1662.

xii, 76 p. diagrs. 23 x 18ᶜᵐ.

Dedicatory letter signed: F. Ioannes vander Elst Augustinianus.
Plates, same as in the "Notæ Avgvstinianæ," wanting.

MT6.A2E49

Emmanuel a' Conceptione.

See MANUEL DA CONCEIÇÃO.

Engel, Johann Jakob, 1741–1802.

Ueber die musikalische malerey. An den königl. kapell-meister, herrn Reichardt. Von J. J. Engel. Berlin, C. F. Voss und sohn, 1780.

48 p. 15½ᶜᵐ.

ML3855.A2E5

Engramelle, Marie Dominique Joseph, 1727–1781.

La tonotechnie, ou l'art de noter les cylindres, et tout ce qui est susceptible de notage dans les instrumens de concerts méchaniques. Ouvrage nouveau, par le pere Engramelle ... Paris, P. M. Delaguette, 1775.

4 p. l., xxvij, [1], 236, [4] p. front., v fold. pl. 20ᶜᵐ.

Pages 43–50, "Table des caractères," are printed on leaves 27 x 20ᶜᵐ.

ML1051.A2E6

Entire new and compleat instructions for the fife.

See The COMPLEAT tutor for the fife.

[Erculeo, Marzio] 1623–1706.

Il canto ecclesiastico. All' Altezza serenissima del Sig. prencipe cardinal d'Este, D. D. D. Modana, Per gli eredi Cassiani stamp. episc., 1686.

15 p. l., 3–65, [7] p. illus. 25ᶜᵐ.

Title vignette: ecclesiastical coat of arms. Dedication signed: D. Marzio Erculeo.

A second title precedes the text: Lvmi primi del canto fermo, ecclesiastico, gregoriano, corale, ò piano, cioè stabile, et vniforme à tvtti gli ecclesiastici. Emendato, composto, & insegnato da S. Gregorio Magno ... Per M. E. ad vso de scolari chierici delle scuole pie della Congregazione della B. V., e S. Carlo, è per loro essercizio il Confiteor, Fratres, antifone della B. Vergine, Adorna talamum, Si quæris, e messa de' morti con li suoi cinque responsorij nelle essequie più solenni, &c. Modana, Nella stampa delli eredi Cassiani stamp. episcopali, 1686.

MT860.A2E65

Erste musikalische preisaustheilung für das jahr 1791. Nebst vierzig kupfertafeln die aus dem Magnificat beider preisträger ein stück und die umarbeitung beider stücke vom preisrichter liefern. Frankfurt am Main, Varrentrapp und Wenner, 1794.

2 v. in 1 (v. 1: 32 p. 19 x 11½ᶜᵐ; v. 2: 40 p. 32 x 25½ᶜᵐ)

Vol. [2] engraved throughout, has caption title: Notenbeyspiele zur Ersten musikalischen preisaustheilung für das jahr 1791.

Listed under Abt Vogler in Kayser's "Bücher-lexicon."

ML76.V25

Eschenburg, Johann Joachim, 1743–1820, *translator.*

See BROWN, J. Betrachtungen über die poesie, 1769.

BURNEY, C. Nachricht von Georg Friedrich Händel's lebensumständen, 1785.

Eschstruth, Hans Adolf, *freiherr* **von,** 1756–1792.

Musicalische bibliothek, hrsg. von H. A. fr. v. Eschstruth . . . 1. stück. Marburg und Giesen, Bei Krieger dem jüngern, 1784.

152 p. 18½^{cm}.

Imperfect, wanting port. and "zwei stücke des . . . herrn kapellmeisters C. P. E. Bach."

The "2. stück" appeared in 1785; a "3. stück" was announced but not published. *cf.* Freystätter, Die musikal. zeitschriften.

ML4.E74

Espic de Lirou, Jean François, 1740 *or* 41–1806.

Explication du système de l'harmonie, pour abréger l'étude de la composition, & accorder la pratique avec la théorie; par le chevalier de Lirou. A Londres, et se trouve à Paris, chez Merigot [etc.] 1785.

2 p. l., 239 p. 7 pl. (1 fold.) 21½^{cm}.

ML3815.A2L7

L'Esprit des journaux, français et étrangers, par une societe de gens de lettres. Paris [etc.] 1783–1805.

6 v. 17^{cm}. monthly.

Incomplete collection of the parts of "L'Esprit des journaux" devoted to theater and music, detached from their respective volumes and bound together. Binder's subtitle reads "Comptes-rendus de musique et theatre."

ML270.3.E56

Essai methodique pour apprendre aux enfans a lire aussi aisément la musique, qu'on leur apprend à lire l'ecriture ordinaire. Liege, F. J. Desoer [1763?]

58 p. 16½^{cm}.

MT35.A2E78

An **essay** on the church plain chant . . . London, J. P. Coghlan, 1782.

3 v. in 1. 18^{cm}.

Appended: Antiphons which are sung whilst the Blessed Sacrament is exposed in the church of the English dames of St. Clare, at Aire in Artois. London, Printed by J. P. Coghlan, 1783. 1 p. l., 6 p.

CONTENTS.—pt. 1. Instructions for learning the church plain song.—pt. 2. Several anthems, litanies, proses and hymns, as they are sung in the public chapels at London.—pt. 3. A supplement of several anthems, litanies, proses and hymns.

MT860.A2E8

Essex, John, *translator.*

See RAMEAU, P. The dancing-master, 1728.

Estève, Pierre.

Nouvelle découverte du principe de l'harmonie, avec un examen de ce que M. Rameau a publié sous le titre de Démonstration de ce principe. Par M. Estève . . . Paris, S. Jorry, 1752.

xvj, 54, [3] p. 21½^{cm}.

ML3815.A2E8

See also MORAND, P. DE. Justification de la musique françoise, 1754.

Estwick, Sampson, *d.* 1739.

The usefulness of church-musick. A sermon preach'd at Christ-church, Novemb. 27. 1696. upon occasion of the anniversary-meeting of the lovers of musick, on St. Cæcilia's day. By S. Estwick ... London, T. Bennett, 1696.

2 p. l., 22 p. 19½ x 15ᶜᵐ.

ML3001.E77

État actuel de la musique du roi et des trois spectacles de Paris. Paris, Vente, 1772.

1 p. l., iv, [12], 140, vj, [6] p. 5 pl. (incl. front.) 13½ᶜᵐ.

Engr. t.-p. with ornamental border and coat of arms; line borders. Lettered: Almana[ch] du theatr[e]

Issued annually 1759–60, and 1767–78. The volumes for 1759–60 have title "État actuel de la musique de la chambre du roi et des trois spectacles de Paris ..." In these two issues Vente's name does not appear on the t.-p., but is found in the privilege. *cf.* Grand-Carteret, Les almanachs français.
L. of C. has only the issue of 1772.

ML1727.8.P2S4

Ettmüller, Michael Ernst, 1673–1732, *praeses.*

Disputatio effectus musicæ in hominem ... Lipsiæ, litteris J. G. Bauchii [1714]

39 p. 18 x 14½ᶜᵐ.

Diss.—Leipzig (C. G. Jöcher, respondent and author)

ML3920.A2E7

Euclides.

Εὐκλείδου Εἰςαγωγὴ ἁρμονικὴ. Τοῦ αὐτοῦ Κατατομὴ κανόνος. Euclidis Rudimenta mvsices. Eiusdem Sectio regulæ harmonicæ. E Regia bibliotheca desumpta, ac nunc primùm græcè & latinè excusa, Ioanne Pena regio mathematico interprete ... Parisiis, apud A. Wechelum, 1557.

2 p. l., 5–16, 10 numb. l. 20ᶜᵐ.

Printer's mark on t.-p.
The Rudimenta musices is now attributed to Cleonides.

ML171.E9

See also DAVY, C. Letters, 1787.

MEIBOM, M., *translator.* Antiqvæ mvsicæ avctores, 1652.

Eugenius *junior, pseud.*

See OWEN, JAMES.

Euler, Leonhard, 1707–1783.

Tentamen novae theoriae mvsicae ex certissimis harmoniae principiis dilvcide expositae. Avctore Leonhardo Evlero. Petropoli, ex typographia Academiae scientiarvm, 1739.

263 p. plates (3 fold.) tables (2 fold.) 27½ᶜᵐ.

Title vignette.

ML3805.A2E8

See also UNGER, J. F. VON. Entwurf einer maschine, 1774.

Eximeno y Pujades, Antonio, 1729–1808.

Dell' origine e delle regole della musica, colla storia del suo progresso, decadenza, e rinnovazione. Opera di D. Antonio Eximeno fra i Pastori Arcadi Aristosseno Megareo . . . Roma, Stamperia di M. A. Barbiellini, 1774.

6 p. l., 466 p., 1 l. illus., 23 fold. pl. (music, tables) port. 27ᶜᵐ.

ML159.E9

—— Del origen y reglas de la musica, con la historia de su progreso, decadencia y restauracion. Obra escrita en italiano por el abate Don Antonio Eximeno. Y traducida al castellano por D. Francisco Antonio Gutierrez . . . Madrid, Imprenta real, 1796.

3 v. illus., 22 fold. pl. (music, tables) 20ᶜᵐ.

ML159.E93

Dubbio di D. Antonio Eximeno sopra il Saggio fondamentale pratico di contrappunto del reverendissimo padre maestro Giambattista Martini. Roma, M. Barbiellini, 1775.

viii, 120 p. 28½ᶜᵐ.

MT55.A2E9

Exmes, François Le Prévost d'.

See LE PRÉVOST D'EXMES, FRANÇOIS.

Exposition de quelques nouvelles vues mathematiques dans la theorie de la musique. A Amsterdam, et se trouve à Paris, chez Cailleau, 1760.

30 p. 18ᶜᵐ.

ML3809.A2E97

Fabbrizi, Pietro.

Regole generali di canto fermo raccolte da diuersi autori da D. Pietro Fabritii Fiorentino. In questa quarta impressione corrette, & ampliate. Roma, M. A., & O. Campana, 1689.

80 p. incl. pl. 15½ᶜᵐ.

MT860.A2F12

—— Regole generali di canto fermo raccolte da diuersi autori da D. Pietro Fabritii Fiorentino, in questa quarta impressione corrette, & ampliate. Roma, Il Mascardi, 1708.

80 p. incl. pl. 15ᶜᵐ.

MT860.A2F13

Faber, Gregorius.

Mvsices practicæ erotematum libri ii, avtore M. Gregorio Fabro Luczensi, in Academia tubingensi, musices professore ordinario. Basileæ [1553]

4 p. l., 230, [2] p. diagrs. 15½ᶜᵐ.

Colophon: Basileæ, per Henrichvm Petri, anno salvtis M.D.LIII. mense martio. Guidonian hand on t.-p.; initials; printer's mark at end. Original t.-p. wanting; replaced by a facsimile.
Contains musical examples taken from the works of Josquin de Près, Okeghem, Anton Brumel and others.

ML171.F14

Faber, Heinrich, *d.* 1552.

Compen- || diolvm mvsicæ || pro incipientibvs. || Per magistrvm || Henricvm Fabrvm conscri- || ptum, ac nunc denuo, cum additio || ne alterius Compendioli, || recognitum. || Noribergae, || In Officina Ioannis Montani, || & Vlrici Neuberi [15—]

[32] p. 15ᶜᵐ.

The 1st edition cited is of Brunswick, 1548. In that issue the title reads as in this one, indicating the existence of an earlier edition. *cf.* Eitner, "Magister Heinrich Faber" (Monatshefte für musikgeschichte, 2 jahrg., 1870, p. 26 ff.)

ML171.F11

See also GUMPELTZHAIMER, A. Compendivm mvsicæ, 1616.

Faber, Nicolaus.

Mvsicae rvdimenta admodvm brevia atqve vtilia ... Ioannes Auentinus Thurinomarus edidit. [*Colophon:* Excusa in officina Millerana Augustæ Vindelicorū XII. cal. iunias. Anno a natiuitate Domini. M.D.XVI.]

[34] p. illus. 21ᶜᵐ.

Title as above taken from first two lines and last line of leaf Aij recto.
Frontispiece: Illvstrissimo prin || cipi Arionisto vtrivsqve Boiari- || ae dvci dedicatvm || [*woodcut*] || Nicolaus Faber Vuolazanus illustrissimi principis Arioni- || sti vtriusque Boiariæ cantor & a sacris. Ad lectorē || [*musical canon:*] Crede mihi melius nihil est quā musica quæ te || Efficiet doctū magnificūq, virum.
Signatures: A–B in fours, C in six, D in three. Printer's mark at end.
L. of C. has also another issue, in which the inscription of poem on recto of last leaf is arranged in six lines instead of seven, as in this issue, and has uniform type, the first line here being in much larger type.

ML171.F13

Faber, Petrus, 1540 *or* 41–1600.

Agonisticon Petri Fabri ... sive, De re athletica lvdisqve vetervm gymnicis, mvsicis, atque circensibus spicilegiorum tractatus, tribus libris comprehensi. Opvs tessellatvm. Nunc primum in lucem editum. Cum indice rerum ac verborum memorabilium locupletissimo ... Lvgdvni, apud F. Fabrum, 1592.

12 p. l., 363, [17] p. 24ᶜᵐ.

Printer's mark on t.-p.; side-notes.

GV17.F2

Faber *Stapulensis,* **Jacobus.**

See LE FÈVRE, JACQUES, *d'Étaples.*

Fabricius, Werner, 1633–1679.

Werneri Fabricii ... Unterricht, wie man ein neu orgelwerk, obs gut und beståndig sey, nach allen stücken, in- und auswendig examiniren, und so viel möglich, probiren soll. Frankfurt und Leipzig, 1756 [*sic*]

86 p. 17½ᶜᵐ.

ML555.A2F12

Falck, Georg, *d.* 1688 ?

. . . Idea boni cantoris, das ist: Getreu und gründliche anleitung /
wie ein music-scholar / so wol im singen / als auch auf andern instrumentis musicalibus in kurtzer zeit so weit gebracht werden kan / dass
er ein stück mitzusingen oder zu spielen sich wird unterfangen
dörffen; aus verschiedenen berühmten musicis colligirt / und der
music-liebenden jugend zu sonderbahrer lust-erweck- und nutzlichen
begreiffung zusammen geschrieben / und heraus gegeben von Georg
Falcken dem aelteren . . .   Nürnberg / Gedruckt bey W. M. Endter /
1688.

> 16 p. l., 209, [3] p.   17 x 20½^{cm}.

> In two parts.   Caption title reads "Institutionis musicæ practicæ erster[– an-
> derer] theil."

> MT770.A2F27

Falconnet,

Extrait d'une lettre écrite aux auteurs du Mercure, suivie d'un.
memoire qui répond à la question proposée dans çelui du mois de juin
dernier, au sujet du plainchant &c.   [n. p. 1733 ?]

> 19 p.   16½^{cm}.

> Caption title.
> The memoir has caption "Memoire sur l'autorité des musiciens en matiere
> de plainchant," and is signed: Burette et Falconnet, fils.

> ML3082.A2B8

Fanzago, Francesco, 1749–1823.

Elogi di tre uomini illustri, Tartini, Vallotti, e Gozzi, con una orazione gratulatoria.   Padova, C. Conzatti, 1792.

> 212 p.   20^{cm}.

> "Nel solenne ingresso alla dignità di procurator di S. Marco di S. E. Sig.
> cavalier Andrea Memmo gratulatoria della magnifica città di Padova": p.
> [157]–205.

> ML390.A2F2

Orazione del Signor abate Francesco Fanzago Padovano delle lodi
di Giuseppe Tartini, recitata nella chiesa de' rr. pp. Serviti in Padova
li 31. di marzo l'anno 1770, con varie note illustrata, e con un breve
compendio della vita del medesimo.   Padova, Stamperia Conzatti,
1770.

> 48 p. incl. front. (port.) illus.   24 x 19^{cm}.

> Title vignette.

> ML410.T18F1

Fayser, Johann, *of Arnstein.*

Παιδεία ‖ Mvsicae. ‖ Kindtliche Anlaytung oder ‖ vnderweysung
der Edlen ‖ Kunst Musica. ‖ Authore M. Ioanne Fessero ‖ Arnstei-
nensi Franco. ‖ G. Fabricivs. ‖ Diuina res est Musica, ‖ Mulcet
Deum, mulcet uiros. ‖ Quicunq̱ Musicam colunt, ‖ Amat Deus,
colunt uiri. ‖ Cum gratia & Priuilegio Imperiali. ‖ Avgvstæ Vinde-
licorvm ‖ Philippus Vlhardus ‖ excudebat [1572]

> [56] p. 1 illus.   15½^{cm}.

> Signatures: A–C in eights, D in four.

> ML171.F27

Fébure, Louis François Henri le.

See LEFÉBURE, LOUIS FRANÇOIS HENRI.

Fedeli, Giuseppe.

. . . Principj di canto fermo dati alla luce da D. Givseppe Fedele . . .
Cremona, M. Antonio dal Rè intaglia e stampa apresso S. Catterina
in Borgheto, 1722.

25 numb. l. 29 x 22½ᶜᵐ.

Title within ornamental border; title vignette (port.) Engraved throughout.

MT860.A2F29

Feijóo y Montenegro, Benito Jerónimo, 1675–1764.

Three essays or discourses on the following subjects, a defence or
vindication of the women, church music, a comparison between
antient and modern music. Tr. from the Spanish of Feyjoo; by a
gentleman. London, T. Becket, 1778.

2 p. l., 187 p. 21ᶜᵐ.

Translated by John Brett.

ML60.F34

Feillée, François de la.

See LA FEILLÉE, FRANÇOIS DE.

Feind, Barthold, 1678–1721.

Barth. Feindes / lt. Deutsche gedichte / bestehend in musicalischen
schau-spielen / lob- glückwünschungs- verliebten und moralischen
gedichten / ernst- und schertzhafften sinn- und grabschrifften / saty-
ren / cantaten und allerhand gattungen. Sammt einer vorrede Von
dem temperament und gemühts-beschaffenheit eines poeten / und
Gedancken von der opera. Erster theil. Mit kupffern und einem
vollständigen register. Stade, H. Brummer, 1708.

7 p. l., 678, [18] p., 2 l., [10], 651–786 p. plates. 17ᶜᵐ.

Double engr. t.-p. added.
Appended is a translation of Jeremias de Decker's "Lof der geldsucht," with
special t.-p.: Hrn. lic. Feindes aus dem holländischen übersetzte ausbündige
satyre vom lobe der geldsucht / an einigen hundert oerthern verbessert und
vermehrt, ans licht gestellt von Ferdinand Gasto von Perlensee . . . Cölln /
Bey P. Marteau, auf kosten der Societåt; [etc., etc.] 1709.

ML49.F34

Feldtenstein, C. J. von.

Erweiterung der kunst nach der chorographie zu tanzen, tånze zu
erfinden, und aufzusetzen; wie auch anweisung zu verschiedenen
national-tånzen; als zu englischen, deutschen, schwåbischen, pohl-
nischen, hannak- masur- kosak- und hungarischen; mit kupfern;
nebst einer anzahl englischer tånze. Von C. J. von Feldtenstein.
Braunschweig, 1772.

109, [1] p. viii fold. pl. 17ᶜᵐ.

GV1601.F3

Fernandes, Antonio.

Arte de mvsica de canto dorgam, e canto cham, & proporçoēs de musica diuididas harmonicamente. Composta por Antonio Fernandez ... Lisboa, P. Craesbeeck, impressor, 1626.

6 p. l., 125 numb. l.   fold. pl., diagrs.   19½ᶜᵐ.

Title vignette (coat of arms)

MT860.A2F36

[Fernández de Rojas, Juan] *d.* 1817.

Crotalogía; ó, Ciencia de las castañuelas.   Instruccion científica del modo de tocar las castañuelas para baylar el bolero ... Parte primera ... Su autor el licenciado Francisco Agustin Florencio [*pseud.*]   Madrid, Imprenta real, 1792.

3 p. l., x, 92 p.   15ᶜᵐ.

"Este opúsculo, que pasa por ser un tratado de tocar las castañuelas, no es en realidad sino una finísima sátira contra el furor enciclopedista que á fines del siglo pasado se nos vino de Francia."—Salvá y Mallen, Catálogo de la biblioteca de Salvá, 1872.   (For history *see* Pedrell's Cat. de la Bibl. mus. de la Diputatió de Barcelona, 1908–09, v. 2, p. 331)

MT720.A2F3

Ferrari, Carlo Antonio Porta.

See PORTA FERRARI, CARLO ANTONIO.

Ferrari, Ottavio, 1607–1682.

Octavii Ferrarii De pantomimis et mimis, dissertatio, in Patavino lyceo publice olim, magnoque cum adplausu recitata, nunc vero primum in lucem edita.   Cum duabus epistolis vna Iacobi Facciolati, altera Io. Phil. Slevogtii, & Io. Fabricii ad non neminis dubia de orthographia latina responsionibvs.   Wolffenbvttelii, svmtibvs G. Freytagii [1714]

63 p.   16½ᶜᵐ.

Ch.34.3015

Ferté, Denis Pierre Jean Papillon de la.

See PAPILLON DE LA FERTÉ, DENIS PIERRE JEAN.

Feuillet, Raoul Auger.

Recüeil de dances contenant un tres grand nombres, des meillieures entrées de ballet de M.ʳ Pecour, tant pour homme que pour femmes, dont la plus grande partie ont été dancées à l'Opera.   Recüeillies et mises au jour par M.ʳ Feüillet ... Paris, Chez le sieur Feüillet, 1704.

1 p. l., 5 numb. l., 128 (*i. e.* 228), 16 p.   diagrs.   24½ᶜᵐ.

Engraved throughout.   "Airs des dances contenuës en ce recüeil, qui sert de table à ce volume": 16 p. at end.

MT950.A2F48

Fèvre, Jacques le.

See LE FÈVRE, JACQUES, *d'Étaples.*

Feytou, Jean Étienne, 1742–1816, *editor.*

See FRAMERY, N. É.   Musique, 1791–1818.

Flaminio, Giovanni Antonio, *d.* 1536, *translator.*
See AARON, P.   Libri tres . . . [1516]

Florencio, Francisco Agustín, *pseud.*
See FERNÁNDEZ DE ROJAS, JUAN.

Florido, Francesco, *editor.*
See SCALETTA, O.   Scala di mvsica, 1642.

[Fludd, Robert] 1574–1637.
. . . De templo mvsicæ . . .   [n. p., n. d.]

> p. 159–259.   illus., fold. pl., diagrs.   31ᶜᵐ.
>
> Full title reads: Tractatus secundi pars II. De templo musica; in quo musica universalis tanquam in speculo conspicitur: in libros septem divisa.
> Detached from v. 1, "De macrocosmi historia," of Fludd's "Utriusque cosmi . . . metaphysica, physica atque technica historia," probably of the edition of Oppenheim and Frankfurt, 1617–24.
> Signatures: 1 l. unsigned, X–Z, Aa–Ii in fours, Kk in two.   The greater part of the illustrations are printed from engraved plates.
>
> ML100.A2F4

Fogliani, Lodovico, *d. ca.* 1540.
Mvsica theorica Ludouici Foliani Mutinensis: docte simul ac dilucide pertractata: in qua quãplures de harmonicis interuallis: non prius tentatae: continentur speculationes.   [*Colophon:* ℂ Venetiis per Io. Antonium & fratres de Sabio.   Anno Domini MDXXIX.   Mense iulii]

> 2 p. l., xliii numb. l.   wdcts.   29½ x 20ᶜᵐ.
> Leaves xiv and xlii numbered xix and xli respectively.
>
> ML171.F65

Foglietti, Ignazio Domenico, *translator.*
See LA FEILLÉE, F. DE.   Il cantore ecclesiastico, 1786.

Foliot, *Madame, pseud.*
Ce que l'on doit dire.   Re'ponse de Madame Foliot, a la lettre de Monsieur * * *.   [n. p., 1752]

> 8 p.   19ᶜᵐ.
> Caption title.
> No. 5 in a volume of pamphlets lettered Quere[lle] des Bouffo[ns]
> A reply to F. L. C. Marin's "Ce qu'on a dit . . . Lettre a Madame Foliot."
>
> ML1727.33.A1

Fond, Jean François de la.
See LAFOND, JEAN FRANÇOIS DE.

[Fontana, Francesco Luigi] *cardinal,* 1750–1822.

Vita di Benedetto Marcello, patrizio veneto. Con l'aggiunta delle risposte alle censure del Signor Saverio Mattei. Con l'indice delle opere stampate, e manoscritte, e alquante testimonianze intorno all' insigne suo merito nella facultà musicale. Venezia, A. Zatta e figli, 1788.

2 p. l., 108 p.   20ᶜᵐ.

Note at foot of p.·1: Questa vita fu scritta in lingua latina dal p. d. Francesco Fontana . . . e trovasi inserita nel tomo IX. dell' aurea opera: Vitæ Italorum doctrina excellentium, qui sæculo XVII. & XVIII. floruerunt, auctore Angelo Fabronio . . .
Translated by Giovenale Sacchi.

ML410.M31F5

Fontego, Silvestro Ganassi dal.

See GANASSI, SILVESTRO, *dal Fontego.*

Ford, Thomas, 1598–1674.

Singing of psalmes the duty of Christians under the New Testament, or A vindication of that gospel-ordinance in v. sermons upon Ephesians 5. 19. wherein are asserted and cleared 1. that, 2. what, 3. how, 4. why, we must sing. By T. F. . . . London, Printed by A. M. for C. Meredith, 1653.

4 p. l., 175 (*i. e.* 159) p.   14ᶜᵐ.
Errors in paging.

ML3001.F67

—— Singing of psalmes the duty of Christians under the New Testament, or A vindication of that gospel-ordinance in v. sermons upon Ephesians 5. 19. wherein are asserted and cleared 1. that, 2. what, 3. how, 4. why, we must sing. The 2d ed., with many additions. By Tho. Ford . . . London, Printed by W. B. for F. Eaglesfield, 1659.

4 p. l., 164 p.   15 x 8½ᶜᵐ.

ML3001.F69

Forkel, Johann Nicolaus, 1749–1818.

Allgemeine geschichte der musik, von Johann Nicolaus Forkel . . . Leipzig, Schwickert, 1788–1801.

2 v. (v. 1: xxxvi, 504 p.; v. 2: xviii, 776 p.)   10 pl. (5 fold.)   24½ x 21ᶜᵐ.

Title vignette.
Closes with the first half of the sixteenth century. Further material for the work, left by Forkel, came into the hands of Schwickert, but no more was published.

ML159.F3

Allgemeine litteratur der musik; oder, Anleitung zur kenntniss musikalischer bücher, welche von den ältesten bis auf die neusten zeiten bey den Griechen, Römern und den meisten neuern europäischen nationen sind geschrieben worden. Systematisch geordnet, und nach veranlassung mit anmerkungen und urtheilen begleitet, von Johann Nicolaus Forkel. Leipzig, Schwickert, 1792.

xxiv, 540 p.   23½ᶜᵐ.

Forkel, Johann Nicolaus—*Continued.*

Contains a reprint of Joannes Tinctoris' "Terminorum musicae diffinitiorum" (p. 204–216)
"Verzeichniss musikalischer manuscripte, welche in verschiedenen europäischen, theils öffentlichen, theils privatbibliotheken aufbewahrt werden": p. 485–504.

ML105.F72

Musikalisch-kritische bibliothek, von Johann Nicolaus Forkel . . . Gotha, C. W. Ettinger, 1778–79.

3 v. 20½^{cm}.

ML4.M31

Ueber die theorie der musik, insofern sie liebhabern und kennern nothwendig und nützlich ist. Eine einladungsschrift zu musikalischen vorlesungen von Johann Nicolaus Forkel . . . Göttingen, Im verlag der wittwe Vandenhück, 1777.

38 p. 21 x 17^{cm}.

ML63.F72

Forkel, Johann Nicolaus, 1749–1818, *editor.*

See MUSIKALISCHER almanach für Deutschland [1782–89]

Forkel, Johann Nicolaus, 1749–1818, *translator.*

See ARTEAGA, S. Geschichte der italiänischen oper, 1789.

Fournier, Pierre Simon, 1712–1768.

Traité historique et critique sur l'origine et les progrès des caractéres de fonte pour l'impression de la musique, avec des épreuves de nouveaux caractères de musique, présentés aux imprimeurs de France. Par M. Fournier le jeune. A Berne, et se trouve a Paris, chez Barbou, 1765.

47, [2] p. 26 x 20^{cm}.

"Ariette, mise en musique par M. l'abbé Dugué. A Paris, Des nouveaux caractères, de Fournier le jeune. M.DCC.LXV": p. [39]–47.

ML112.A2F7

[Fraguier, Claude François] 1666–1728.

Examen d'un passage de Platon sur la musique.

(*In* Académie des inscriptions et belles-lettres, *Paris.* Histoire de l'Académie . . . Paris, 1746. 26^{cm}. [l. sér.] t. III, p. 111–122)

Separate.

ML168.P6F8

Framery, Nicolas Étienne, 1745–1810.

Avis aux poëtes lyriques, ou De la nécessité du rhythme et de la césure dans les hymnes ou odes destinés a la musique; par N. E. Framery . . . Imprimé par ordre du Comité d'instruction publique. Paris, Imprimerie de la république, brumaire, an IV [1795]

2 p. l., 36 p. 21.^{cm}.

ML3849.A2F8

Framery, Nicolas Étienne, 1745–1810, *editor.*

. . . Musique, pub. par MM. Framery et Ginguené . . .   Paris, Panckoucke, 1791–1818.

> 2 v. (v. 1: xij, 760 p.; v. 2: 2 p. l., 557, [3], 74, 114 p.) tables (1 fold.) 26½^{cm}.
>
> Forms part of the Encyclopédie méthodique (half-title reads: Encyclopédie méthodique . . . par une société de gens de lettres . . .)
> Vol. 2: "Pub. par MM. Framery, Guingené et de Momigny." (Vol. 1 ed. by Framery with the assistance of the Abbé Feytou and P. L. Guinguené; vol. 2, by J. J. Momigny)
> The "Dictionnaire de musique" of J. J. Rousseau is incorporated entire in this work, and such articles of the original "Encyclopédie" and its supplements as were judged to be of interest are preserved in this edition.
> Musical illustrations, engr., at end of v. 2 (74, 114 p.)
>
> > > ML100.A2F8

See also CALENDRIER musical universel [1788]

Framery, Nicolas Étienne, 1745–1810, *translator.*

See AZOPARDI, F.   Le musicien pratique, 1786.

France.

Mémoire, lettres patentes et arrêts.   Pour les organistes compositeurs de musique, faisans profession d'enseigner à toucher le clavecin, les instrumens d'harmonie, & servans à l'accompagnement des voix. Contre le roi & maître des ménestriers, & la Communauté des maîtres à danser, joueurs d'instrumens tant haut que bas & hautbois.   Paris, Impr. de Delaguette, 1751.

> 2 p. l., 60 p.   25 x 19^{cm}.
>
> Heraldic head-piece.
>
> > > ML271 1751

Recueil d'édit, arrêt du Conseil du roi, lettres-patentes, mémoires, et arrêts du Parlement, &c. en faveur des musiciens du royaume. [Paris] Impr. de P. R. C. Ballard, 1774.

> 2 p. l., ij, 227 p.   20^{cm}.
>
> "Le Corps de la musique de Sa Majesté . . . a fait rédiger ce recueïl, & . . . en a demandé l'impression."—Avertissement.
>
> > > ML271 1774

> LIBRARY OF CONGRESS HAS ALSO IN ML 271:
>
> **Arrest** du Conseil d'estat du roy.   Sur la requête du sieur de Lully, pour l'exécution du privilege à lui accordé, pour établir une Académie royale de musique à Paris.   Donné . . . le 14 avril 1672.   [2] p.
> **Permission** povr tenir Academie royale de musique, en faveur du sieur de Lully.   [Le vingt-septiéme iuin mil six cens soixante-douze]   [5] p.
> **Arrest** du Conseil d'etat du roy, qui ordonne que les comediens, farceurs, operateurs, & autres personnes de cette qualité, ne pourront s'établir dans la ville de Grenoble, & ne pourront y representer aucuns jeux . . . sans avoir obtenu la permission des officiers de police . . .   Du 29. aoust 1702.   4 p.
> **Lettres** patentes du roi, extraites des registres du Parlement.   [Les maîtres à danser ne pourront prendre d'áutres qualités que celle de maîtres à danser, joueurs d'instrumens, tant hauts que bas, & hautbois.   Impr. de la veuve Ballard, 1773]   4 p.
> **Édit** du roy, portant création d'offices de greffiers alternatifs & triennaux dans les villes de Paris & Lyon, & dans tous les hôtels-de-ville du royaume: et de sergens, archers . . . trompettes, tambours, fifres, portiers & gardes dans lesdits hôtels-de-ville.   Donné à Versailles au mois de mars 1709 . . .   [Paris, Prault pere]   8 p.

France—*Continued*.

Ordonnance de Sa Majesté pour la tranquillité des spectacles. Du 16 novembre 1720. [J. de La Caille] 3 p.

Arrest de la Cour de Parlement, portant condamnation de mort contre Loüis-Dominique Cartouche; Jean-Baptiste Madelaine, dit Beaulieu . . . Jean Blanchard, dit Gaillard ou Champagne, ou le Chanteur de chanson . . . Jean-Baptiste Messié, & le nommé le Camus . . . [Paris, L. D. Delatour & P. Simon, 1721] 4 p.

Arrest de la Cour de Parlement, portant condamnation d'estre rompu vif . . . contre Charles Le Clerc, dit Picard La Vallée, joüeur de violons aux guinguettes, convaincu de vols sur les grands chemins . . . Paris, L.-D. Delatour & P. Simon, 1722. 4 p.

Ordonnance du roy, concernant les spectacles des Comédies françoise & ita-.lienne. Du 25 avril 1751 . . . [Paris, Imprimerie royale, 1751] 2 p.

Arrest du Conseil d'état du roi, et lettres patentes sur icelui, du 11 fevrier 1764. Concernant la reconstruction de la salle de spectacle, à l'usage de l'Académie royale de musique . . . [Impr. de la veuve d'Houry] 16 p.

Lettres patentes du roi, en faveur de l'Académie royale de musique. Données à Versailles au mois de juin 1769 . . . [Paris, Imprimerie royale, 1769] 6 p.

Ordonnance du roi, portant augmentation de hautbois dans les compagnies de mousquetaires de la garde du roi. Du 16 février 1772 . . . [Paris, Imprimerie royale, 1772] [2] p.

Édit du roi, portant suppression de l'office de roi & maître des ménestriers. Donné à Versailles au mois de mars 1773 . . . [Paris, P. G. Simon, 1773] 3 p.

Lettres patentes du roi, qui annullent les concessions des charges de lieutenans généraux & particuliers du roi des violons. Données . . . le trois avril 1773 . . . [Paris, P. G. Simon, 1773] 4 p.

Ordonnance du roi, portant règlement sur les entrées aux représentations . . . de l'Opéra . . . & sur la police intérieure pendant la durée du spectacle. Du 29 mars 1776 . . . [Paris, Imprimerie royale, 1776] 6 p.

Arrest du Conseil d'état du roi, portant nouveau règlement pour l'Académie royale de musique. Du 30 mars 1776 . . . [Paris, Imprimerie royale, 1776] 12 p.

Arrêt du Conseil d'état du roi, contenant règlement pour l'Académie royale de musique. Du 27 février 1778 . . . [Paris, Imprimerie royale, 1778] 12 p.

Arrêt du Conseil d'état du roi, concernant les honoraires des auteurs qui travaillent pour l'Académie royale de musique. Du 10 avril 1778 . . . [Paris, Imprimerie royale, 1778] 3 p.

Arrêt du Conseil d'état du roi, concernant les loges louées à l'année à l'Opéra. Du 10 avril 1778 . . . [Paris, Imprimerie royale, 1778] 3 p.

Arrêt du Conseil d'état du roi, qui ordonne l'exécution des réglemens, & notamment de l'arrêt du Conseil du 10 avril 1778, concernant les honoraires des auteurs de poëmes & de musique pour l'Académie royale de musique. Du 16 octobre 1779 . . . [Impr. de Lottin l'aîné, 1779] 4 p.

Arrêt du Conseil d'état du roi, concernant l'Opéra. Du 17 mars 1780 . . . [Paris, Imprimerie royale, 1780] 6 p.

Ordonnance du roi, concernant les spectacles. Du 2 avril 1780 . . . [Paris, Imprimerie royale, 1780] 4 p.

Lettres-patentes du roi, pour l'établissement de l'Académie royale de danse en la ville de Paris, données au mois de mars mil six cent soixante-un . . . Impr. de P. R. C. Ballard, 1781. 15 p.

Déclaration du roi, portant réglement pour les spectacles établis à la suite de la cour. Du vingt-huit février mil sept cent quatre-vingt-deux . . . [Paris, P. G. Simon, 1782] 8 p.

Édit du roi, concernant le corps de la musique du roi. Donné . . . au mois de mai 1782 . . . [Paris, Imprimerie royale, 1782] 20 p.

Arrest du Conseil d'état du roi, concernant l'Opéra. Du trois janvier 1784 . . . [Paris, P. G. Simon, & N. H. Nyon, 1784] 8 p.

Arrêt du Conseil d'état du roi, contenant règlement pour l'Académie royale de musique. Du 13 mars 1784. Paris, Imprimerie royale, 1784. 1 p. l., 33 p.

Réglement pour l'Académie royale de musique. Du 13 janvier 1787 . . . [Paris, N. H. Nyon, 1787] 3 p.

France—*Continued.*

Proclamation du roi, sur un décret de l'Assemblée nationale, portant que toutes les anciennes ordonnances sur la nature & les formes du service, notamment sur la police des spectacles, doivent être exécutées provisoirement. Du 17 juin 1790 . . . [Chaumont, Impr. de Bouchard] 2 p.

[Franceschi, Francesco]

Apologia delle opere drammatiche di Metastasio . . .   Lucca, D. Marescandoli [17—]

vi, 300 p. 21½^{cm}.

The author's name is given in caption of dedicatory poem, p. iii.

ML3858.F81

Franck de Franckenau, Georg, 1643–1704, *praeses.*

. . . Dispvtatio medica ordinaria de musica . . .   Heidelbergæ, typis J. C. Walteri [1672]

[4] p. 18½ x 15^{cm}.

Diss.—Heidelberg (Benedictus Herrmannus, respondent)

ML3920.A2F81

Franco, Cirillo.

See João iv, *king of Portugal.*   Difesa della mvsica moderna [16—]

Franqueville, *Mme.* **de Latour de.**

See Latour de Franqueville, *Mme.* de.

Freigius, Johann Thomas, 1543–1583.

See Beurhusius, F.   Erotematum mvsicæ, 1580.

[Fréron, Élie Catherine] 1719–1776.

Lettres sur la musique françoise. En réponse à celle de Jean-Jacques Rousseau. A Géneve [*i. e.* Paris] 1754.

64 p. 20^{cm}.

A reprint of two letters previously published in Fréron's "Lettres sur quelques écrits de ce temps," London and Paris, 1752–54.

ML1727.33.R72F7

See also Hertel, J. W. Sammlung musikalischer schriften, 1757–58.

Freudenberg, *Fräulein* **von.**

See Kurtze anführung zum general-bass, 1733.

Kurtze und gründliche anleitung zum generalbasse,1744.

Freytag, Friedrich Gotthilf, 1723–1776, *translator.*

See Bollioud-Mermet, L. Abhandlung, 1750.

Frezza, Giuseppe, *dalle Grotte.*

Il cantore ecclesiastico; breve, facile, ed essatta notizia del canto fermo per istruzzione de' Religiosi minori conventuali, e beneficio commune di tutti gl' ecclesiastici, raccommandato alla protezzione del reverendissimo padre maestro Felice Rotondo da Monte Leone . . . ministro generale dell' istess' ordine de' Minori conventuali. Da f. Gioseppe Frezza dalle Grotte . . . Padova, Stamperia del Seminario, opera di G. Manetti, 1698.

166 (*i. e.* 164), [6] p. pl. 22^{cm}.

Title vignette: heraldic device. Added t.-p., illustrated. No. 161–162 omitted in paging.

MT860.A2F89

Frick, Christoph, 1577–1640.

Music-bůchlein, oder Nůtzlicher bericht von dem uhrsprunge / gebrauche vnd erhaltung christlicher music vnd also von dem lobe Gottes / welches die Christē . . . verrichten sollen . . . Mit vorher gesetztem summarischem inhalt / vnd zu ende hinzu-gethanem register . . . Durch m. Christophorum Friccium . . . Lůneburg / Gedruckt bey J. vnd H. Sternen / 1631.

12 p. l., 347, [13] p. 14½^{cm}.

Title within ornamental border. In 2 parts, part 2 with special t.-p.

1st edition, Leipzig, 1615, has title: Musica christiana, oder Predigt über die worte Psalm 98: Lobet den Herrn mit harfen und psalmen. In this (2d) edition another sermon is added.

ML3001.F73

Frick, Philipp Joseph, 1740–1798.

The art of musical modulation rendered easy and familiar, digested in twelve tables; shewing the shortest method of modulating thro' all the keys, in three and four parts. To which is perfixed [!] an explanatory preface, by P: I: Frike. [London] Printed by W. Napier [1786]

1 p. l., iv, 33 p. 24 x 33^{cm}.

Engraved with the exception of p. i–iv.

MT52.A2F7

A guide in harmony, containing the various manners in which every chord in four parts can be prepared, resolved, or otherwise freely used . . . composed by Joseph Frike . . . London, Printed for and sold by the author, 1793.

1 p. l., viii, 93 p. 24 x 33^{cm}.

Engraved with the exception of p. i–vi ("Introduction"?)

MT50.A2F8

A treatise on thorough bass, containing a plain and easy method for the performer by the help of many examples and several new essential rules, the pure manner of figuring and a repertory of every chord in harmony worthy the attention of young composers . . . by Joseph Frike . . . London, Printed for and sold by the author [1786]

1 p. l., 109 p. 23 x 30^{cm}.

Engraved throughout.

MT49.A2F7

Frischmuth, Marcus Hilarius, *pseud.*

See FUHRMANN, MARTIN HEINRICH.

Fritz, Barthold, 1697–1766.

Anweisung, wie man claviere, clavecins, und orgeln, nach einer mechanischen art, in allen zwölf tönen gleich rein stimmen könne, dass aus solchen allen sowol dur als moll wohlklingend zu spielen sey. Aufgesetzet von Barthold Fritzen ... 2. verm. und verb. aufl. Leipzig, J. G. I. Breitkopf, 1757.

6 p. l., 24 p.   22 x 18ᶜᵐ.

MT165.A2F5

—— Anweisung, wie man klaviere, clavecins, und orgeln nach einer mechanischen art in allen zwölf tönen gleich rein stimmen könne, dass aus solchen allen so wohl dur- als moll-klingend zu spielen sey. Nebst beygefügtem unterrichte, wie man klaviere gehörig behandeln soll und gut erhalten kann.   Von Barthold Fritzen ...   Wien, Binzische buchhandlung, 1799.

2 p. l., 19 p.   21½ x 17ᶜᵐ.

MT165.A2F7

Frosch, Johann, *d.* 1533.

Rervm ‖ mvsicarvm ‖ opvscvlvm rarvm ac in- ‖ signe, totius eius negotii rationem mira in- ‖ dustria & breuitate complectens, iam ‖ recens publicatum.   Ioan. ‖ Froschio, ‖ autore.   [*Colophon:* Argentorati apvd Petrvm ‖ Schœffer & Mathiam Apiarium.   Anno Salutis ‖ M.D.XXXV]

[78] p. incl. 2 tab.   fold. diagr.   28½ᶜᵐ.

Printer's mark on t.-p.; side-notes.   Signatures: 1 l. unsigned, 3 l. signed 2, 3 and 4 respectively, 2 l. unsigned, A–D in sixes, E in four, F in five.   Dedication has date 1532.
"Exempla": l. E v°–l. [Fv] r°.

ML171.F93

Frustabirbe, *avvocato, pseud.?*

Lettera dell' avvocato Frustabirbe, indirizzata al Signor Antonio Sacchini, maestro di cappella.   *Tormi l'onor cercasti ed il danaro Solo per odio, e senza tuo profitto: Perchè non m'hai o pezzo di somaro Col coltel di Baretti il cor trafitto?—Badini.*   In Roma, Alla bocca della Verità, 1774.

94, [1] p.   23ᶜᵐ.

"Elogj de' congiurati contro il Badini:" p. [79]–88.

ML410.S13F8

[Fuhrmann, Martin Heinrich] *b.* 1669.

Die an der kirchen Gottes gebauete satans-capelle; darin dem Jehova Zebaoth zu leid und verdruss, und dem Baal-Zebub zur freud und genuss, (1.) Die operisten und comœdianten mancher orten ihren zuschauern eine theologiam gentilium aus den griechischen und lateinischen fabel-mätzen, und eine moral aus des verlohrnen sohns catechismo vorbringen; und (2.) Die menschliche welsche wallachen

[Fuhrmann, Martin Heinrich]—*Continued.*

und Amadis-sirenen aus dem hohen lied Ovidii De arte amandi, lieb-liche Venus-lieder dabey singen; und (3.) Die Jubalisten mit geigen und pfeiffen nach des alten Adams lust und wust darzu klingen; und (4.) Sylvester mit seiner Herodias-schwester, und Arlequin in einem frantzösischen kälber-tantz herum springen; in einem wald-discours uber des autoris zwey letzte tractätlein wider die hamburgischen operisten und herrn d. Mayern betrachtet, von Caspar, Baltzer, Mel-cher. Und allen christlichen seelen zur anschau und abscheu vorge-stellet, von Marco Hilario Frischmuth [*pseud.*] Gedruckt zu Cölln am Rhein, und verlegt von der heil. drey könige erben. [Berlin, 1729]

96 p. 15½^{cm}.

ML63.F78

Das in unsern opern-theatris und comœdien-bühnen siechende christenthum und siegende heidenthum, auf veranlassung zweyer wider den Musicalischen patrioten sich empörenden hamburgischen theatral-malcontenten, Musandri und Harmonii, betrachtet, und . . . in einem gespräch vorgestellet von Liebhold und Leuthold . . . Ge-druckt zu Canterbury [*i. e.* Berlin, 1728]

32 p. 15½^{cm}.

"Zuschrift" signed: N. N. N. Dated: Ascher-mittwoch, 1728. Canterbury, in dem musicalischen haupt-quartir, 36. meilen von Hamburg.
Written in reply to an anonymous work pub. the same year under title: Ein paar derbe musikalisch-patriotische ohrfeigen dem . . . herrn Mattheson . . . zu wiederherstellung seines verlornen gehörs und verstandes . . . ertheilt von . . . Musandern und Harmonio.

ML63.F821

Musica vocalis in nuce, das ist: Richtige und völlige unterweisung zur singe-kunst / in wenig blättern / nach welcher ein informator seinen informandis die gantze vocal-music nach heutiger manier bald und leicht beybringen kan / ausgefertigt von Martin Henrich Fuhrmann . . . Berlin / Gedruckt bey J. Lorentz [1715]

64 p. 17½^{cm}.

MT6.A2F91

M. H. F. G. F. C. Musicalische strigel / womit (1.) Diejenige super-lativ-virtuosen aus der singenden und klingenden gesellschafft / so nicht chor-mässig als künstler die gräntzen des Apollinis seines musi-calischen reichs; sondern thor-mässig als hümpler die plätze des Apollyonis seiner music-kahlen barbarey vermehren; (2.) Diejenige super-kluge quacksalber aus der musical. gülde, so in des autoris Musical. trichter / sine fronte & fonte herüm stöhren, säuberlich geputzet werden. Denen canonicis zur nachricht / denen apocryphis zum unterricht / und dem neid zu leid herausgegeben, uñ in diese form gedruckt, damit dis tractätchen auf verlangen an dessen auch ange-fochtenen Musica in nuce könne beygebunden werden. Athen an der Pleisse [*i. e.* Leipzig, 17—]

36 p. 16 x 9½^{cm}.

MT6.A2F8

[Fuhrmann, Martin Heinrich]—*Continued.*

Musicalischer-trichter / dadurch ein geschickter informator seinen informandis die edle singe-kunst nach heutiger manier bald und leicht einbringen kan / darinn vitiosa ausgemustert: obscura erläutert: deficienta[!] aber erstattet / mit einer vorrede / von der heutigen music vollkommenheit / krafft / nutz und nothwendigkeit / hrsg. durch ein mitglied der singenden und klingenden gesellschafft . . . In verlegung des autoris. Franckfurt / an der Spree [*i. e.* Berlin] gedruckt 1706.

96p. 15½ x 18½cm.

Preface signed: Meines hertzens freude.

MT6.A2F9

Funk, Christlieb Benedict, 1736–1786.

De sono et tono . . . Lipsiae, litteris Langenhemiorvm haered. et Klavberthiis [1779]

16 p. 20½ x 16cm.

Programm (Ad capessendos summos in philosophia honores invitat procancellarius C. B. Funccius)—Univ. Leipzig.

ML3809.A2F9

—— Disquisitionem in doctrinam de sono et tono continvat . . . Christlib Benedictvs Fvnk . . . Lipsiae, ex officina Klavbarthia [1782]

8 p. 20½ x 16cm.

Programm (Ad celebrandam memoriam Henricianam, Ridelianam et Seyfertianam)—Univ. Leipzig.

ML3809.A2F9

Fusée de Voisenon, Claude Henri de.

See VOISENON, CLAUDE HENRI DE FUSÉE, *abbé* DE.

Fux, Johann Joseph, 1660–1741.

Gradus ad Parnassum, sive Manuductio ad compositionem musicæ regularem, methodo novâ ac certâ, nondum antè tam exacto ordine in lucem edita: elaborata à Joanne Josepho Fux . . . Viennæ Austriæ, typis Joannis Petri van Ghelen, 1725.

5 p. l., 280 p. 1 illus. 32cm.

Added t.-p., engr.

MT40.A2F99

—— Practical rules for learning composition, translated from a work intitled Gradus ad Parnassum, written originally in Latin by John Joseph Feux . . . London, J. Preston [1791 ?]

1 p. l., 49 p. 35½cm.

Engraved throughout.

MT40.A2F998

Fux, Johann Joseph—*Continued*.

—— Traité de composition musicale, fait par le célébre Fux. On peut en étudiant ce traité avec attention parvenir à bien composer en très peu de tems ... Tr. en français par le S^r. Pietro Denis ... Paris, M. Boyer [etc., 17—]

1 p. l., 272 p. 24^cm.

Engraved throughout. Only a partial translation of the "Gradus."
1st edition, Paris, 1773.

MT40.A2F996

—— Gradvs ad Parnassvm, oder Anführung zur regelmåssigen musikalischen composition ... ausgearb. von Johann Joseph Fux ... Aus dem lateinischen ins teutsche übersetzt, mit ... anmerckungen versehen und heraus gegeben von Lorenz Mizlern ... Mit sieben und funfzig kupfertafeln in quart. Leipzig, Mizler, 1742.

4 p. l., 197, [3] p. LVII pl. on 29 fold. l. (music) 21½ x 16½^cm.

Title vignette

MT40.A2F993

Gabler, Matthias, 1736–1805.

Der instrumentalton; eine physikalische abhandlung verfasset von Matthias Gabler ... als Joseph Hubbauer ... für den grad des magisteriums aus der weltweisheit geprüfet wurde. Im monate august 1775. [Ingolstadt] Gedruckt bey J. F. Lutzenberger [1776]

1 p. l., 42 p. 20 x 16^cm.

ML3807.G12

Gabriel da Annunciação, *b*. 1681.

Arte de cantocham resumida, para o uso dos Religiosos Franciscanos observantes da Santa Provincia de Portugal. Composta pelo padre Fr. Gabriel da Annunciaçam ... Lisboa Occidental, Officina da musica, 1735.

6 p. l., 83 p. 1 illus. 21^cm.

MT860.A2A61

Gaffurio, Franchino, 1451–1522.

Angelicum ac diuinum opus musice ‖ Franchini Gafurii laudensis Re ‖ gii musici: ecclesieq̄ Me ‖ diolanensis phonasci: ‖ materna lingua ‖ scriptum. [*Colophon:* Impressum Mediolani per Gotardum de põte Anno Salutis Millesimo quin ‖ gētesimo octauo die sextadecima septembris . . .]

[96] p. illus., diagrs. 28½^cm.

Signatures: A in four, B–F in sixes, G–H in fours, I in six. 1st ed. Milan, 1496.
ML171.G10

℃ Apologia Franchini Gafurii musici aduersus Ioannem ‖ Spatarium & complices musicos bononienses. [*Colophon:* ℃ Impressum Taurini per magistrum Augustinum de Vi ‖ comercato. Anno domini. M.D.XX. die XX. Aprilis]

[19] p. diagrs. 28^cm.

Caption title. Signature: A of ten leaves.
Ends with: Cum opera nostra sana sint si sane intelligantur / & sententiæ nostræ rectæ nisi peruertantur. Quo fit: ut & si incõcessa rabie torquearis: harmonia Gafurii & Ioannes Grolierius patronus æternum uiuant (followed by the arms of Jean Grolier)

ML171.G105

Gaffurio, Franchino—*Continued.*

℃ Franchini Gafurii Laudensis Regii Musici publice ‖ profitentis: Delubriq, Mediolanensis Phona ‖ sci: de Harmonia Musicorum In ‖ strumentorum Opus. ‖ Io. Iacobi Lomatii Epygrāma. ‖ Vt quondam e Phrygia matrem Nasica Deorum ‖ Aduectam meruit solus ut exciperet, ‖ Sic fieri solus noster Grolierius hospes ‖ Cœlestis meruit cultor & Harmoniæ ‖ Et merito: nam cum foueat pascatq, sorores: ‖ Quæ poterat Diuæ gratior esse domus? [*Colophon:* ℃ Impressum Mediolani per ‖ Gotardum Pontanum Calco ‖ graphum die. xxvii. Nouem ‖ bris. 1518. Authoris præfectu ‖ ræ Anno trigesimoquinto. Leo ‖ ne Decimo Põtifice Maximo: ‖ ac Christianissimo Francorum ‖ Rege Francisco Duce Medio ‖ lani. Fœlici Auspicio Regnan ‖ tibus]

4 p. l., c numb. l., [4] p. illus., diagrs. 28ᶜᵐ.

Woodcut on t.-p.; initials; on verso of 4th prelim. leaf the arms of Jean Grolier; printer's mark at end. LXI omitted in numbering leaves; LXIII repeated.

ML171.G11

Practica musicae. [Mediolani, Guillermus Le Signerre, 1496]

28½ᶜᵐ.

Hain 7407, Proctor 6067, Panzer, v. 2, p. 83, Copinger.

ML171.G12

—— Practica Musicae vtriusq, ‖ cantus excellentis fran ‖ chini gaffori Lau- ‖ dēsis. quatuor ‖ libris mo ‖ dulatis ‖ sima.‖ [*Colophon:* Impressa Brixie opera & impensa Angeli Britannici: anno salutis. M.D.VIII. ‖ die ultimo maii]

[222] p. 31½ᶜᵐ.

Signatures: 4 l. unsigned, a–b in eights, c in six, A–K in eights, L in five.

ML171.G121

—— Practica musicae vtriusq, cātus excellētis Frāchini Gaffori Laudēsis. Quattuor libris modulatissima: sūmaq, diligētia nouissime īpressa. [*Colophon:* Musicæ Franchini Laudensis: cantoris solemnissimi pratica quattuor libris compræhēsa explicit. Impressa nouissime Venetiis: multisq, erroribus expurgata per Augustinum de Zannis de Portesio bibliopolam accuratissimum. Anno dominicæ incarnationis. M.D.XII. die. XXVIII. iulii]

82 numb. l. illus. 30½ᶜᵐ.

Title-page has woodcut 21½ x 16½ᶜᵐ, signed "L." 4 large initials, 2 full page illustrations. The woodcut, initials and illustrations are in this copy roughly colored by hand.

ML171.G13

Galeazzi, Francesco, 1758–1819.

Elementi teorico-pratici di musica, con un saggio sopra l'arte di suonare il violino analizzata, ed a' dimostrabili principj ridotta. Opera utilissima a chiunque vuol applicar con profitto alla musica, e specialmente a' dilettanti, e professori di stromenti d'arco, di Francesco Galeazzi . . . Ascoli, F. Cardi, 1817, 1796.

2 v. (v. 1: xviii, [2], 286, [2] p.; v. 2: viii, xxvi, 327, [1] p.) 14 fold. pl., fold. tables. 21½ᶜᵐ.

Galeazzi, Francesco—*Continued.*

Vol. 1: Ed. 2., ricorretta, e considerabilmente dall' autore accresciuta col'-l'aggiunta di molte, e nuove tavole in rame, e specialmente di quattro gran pro-spetti concernenti l'arte dell' arco.

Vol. 2 has slightly varying title, with imprint: Roma, Stamperia di M. Puccinelli, 1796.

MT6.A2G15

Galeota, Onofrio, *pseud.*

See GALIANI, FERDINANDO.

Galiani, Ferdinando, 1728–1787.

See MATTEI, S. Se i maestri di cappella son . . . artigiani [1785 ?]

Galilei, Vincenzo, *d.* 1591.

Dialogo di Vincentio Galilei nobile fiorentino della mvsica antica, et della moderna. Fiorenza, G. Marescotti, 1581.

2 p. l., 149, [10] p. illus., diagrs. (1 fold.) 32^{cm}.

Title within ornamental design; printer's mark at end. The folding diagram is 7 x 31^{cm}. Between p. 40 and 41 in this copy is inserted a pen and ink illustra-tion, headed: Cithara nova et antiqua. Ms. notes throughout the book and the following note on t.-p.: Con le note e correttioni di . . . Don Barttolomeo Cara-sciolo.

ML171.G15

Fronimo, dialogo di Vincentio Galilei . . . sopra l'arte del bene inta-volare, et rettamente sonare la mvsica negli strumenti artificiali si di corde come di fiato, & in particulare nel liuto. Nuouamente ristam-pato, & dall' autore istesso arrichito, & ornato di nouità di concetti, & d'essempi. Vineggia, Appresso l'herede di G. Scotto, 1584.

4 p. l., 182 p. 32½^{cm}.

Title vignette (repeated on last page)

MT640.G25

Galle, Daniel.

See SCHURTZFLEISCH, C. S. De hymnis ecclesiæ veteris [1725]

Galle, Philippe, 1537–1612.

See STRAET, J. VAN DER. Enconivm mvsices [ca. 1600]

Galliard, John Ernest, 1687 ?–1749, *translator.*

See RAGUENET, F. A comparison between the French and Italian musick, 1709.

TOSI, P. F. Observations on the florid song, 1743.

Galliculus, Johannes.

Isagoge ‖ Ioannis ‖ Gallicv- ‖ li de ‖ compo- ‖ sicione ‖ cantvs. ‖ Lipsiæ, apud Valenti- ‖ num Schumannū An. ‖ Christi. M.D.XX.

[46] p. 16½^{cm}. (*In* Rhaw, Georg. Enchiridion vtriusq̃ musicę practicę. [Lipsiæ, 1520] [pt. 3])

ML171.R42

Galliculus, Johannes—*Continued*.

—— Libellvs de ‖ compositione ‖ cantvs. ‖ Ioannis Gallicvli. ‖ Vitebergae ‖ apud Georgium ‖ Rhau. ‖ Anno M.D.XLVI.

[19] p. 15ᶜᵐ.

Title within ornamental border, colored by hand. Signatures: a–B in eights, c in four.
"Exemplvm omnivm regvlarvm": [2] p. at end.

ML171.G17

Gallini, Giovanni Andrea Battista, 1728–1805.

A treatise on the art of dancing. By Giovanni Andrea Gallini. London, Printed for the author and sold by R. Dodsley [etc.] 1772.

2 p. l., [ix]–xvi, [17]–292 p. fold. front. 20½ᶜᵐ.

—— —— Copy 2.

GV1601.G17

Ganassi, Silvestro, *dal Fontego*.

Opera Intitulata Fontegara ‖ Laquale īsegna a sonare di flauto chō tutta l'arte opportuna a esso īstrumento ‖ massime il diminuire ilquale sara utile ad ogni īstrumento di fiato et chorde: et āchora a ‖ chi si dileta di canto, cōposta per syluestro di ganassi dal fōtego sonator đ la Illᵐᵃ. Sᵃ. D. Vᵃ. [*Colophon :* ℂ Impressum Venetiis per Syluestro di ganassi ‖ dal fontego sonator della illustrissima si ‖ gnoria di Venetia hautor ₚprio. ‖ MDXXXV]

[158] p. 15½ x 21ᶜᵐ.

Title and accompanying woodcut within heavy black border. Signatures: 4 l. unsigned, ▩, A–S in fours (last l. blank)

MT342.A2F55

[Garcin, Laurent] *d.* 1788.

Traité du mélo-drame, ou Réflexions sur la musique dramatique ... Paris, Vallat-la-Chapelle, 1772.

xxxij, 380, [3] p. 19½ᶜᵐ.

ML1727.35.G2

Gaspar, Michael, *pseud.*

See MICHELL, HENRY.

Gasparini, Francesco, 1668–1727.

L'armonico pratico al cimbalo. Regole, osservazioni, ed avvertimenti per ben suonare il basso, e accompagnare sopra il cimbalo, spinetta, ed organo. Di Francesco Gasparini ... Venezia, A. Bortoli, 1708.

118, [2] p. 22 x 17½ᶜᵐ.

MT68.A2G17

—— L'armonico pratico al cimbalo, regole, osservazioni, ed avvertimenti per ben suonare il basso, e accompagnare sopra il cimbalo, spinetta, ed organo. Di Francesco Gasparini ... 4. impressione. Venezia, A. Bortoli, 1745.

4 p. l., 86 p., 1 l. 24½ᶜᵐ.

Title vignette.

MT68.A2G175

Gatta, Marco della.

Breve ra'gguaglio delle principali regole del canto fermo gregoriano parte prima divisa in nove dialoghi con breve appendice del canto fratto, opera del rev. sacerdote D. Marco della Gatta ... per uso, e studio de' convittori del seminario diocesano ... Napoli, V. Orsini, 1793–94.

2 v. in 1 (v. 1: xxvi, [2], 132 p.; v. 2: viii, 85, [2], 137, [2] p.) 1 illus. 26ᶜᵐ.

Vol. 2 has title: Esempj e cantilene di canto fermo gregoriano con appendice di messe, ed officiatura de' morti. Parte seconda ...

MT860.A2G26

Gaudentius.

See MEIBOM, M., *translator.* Antiqvæ mvsicæ avctores, 1652.

Gaultier, Aloïsius Édouard Camille, 1746?–1818.

Méthode pour apprendre a lire la musique, et a battre la mesure en très-peu de temps, faisant partie du cours d'études élémentaires de M. l'abbé Gaultier, destiné à instruire les enfans en les amusant, par le moyen de plusieurs jeux ... Paris, Au Cours des jeux instructifs pour la jeunesse, 1789.

24 p. 3 fold pl. 18½ᶜᵐ.

Appended: Cours de jeux instructifs pour la jeunesse, sous la protection du gouvernement ... Par M. l'abbé Gaultier. 14 p., 1 l.

MT35.A2G18

[Gauthier, François Louis] 1696–1780.

Traité contre les danses et les mauvaises chansons, dans lequel le danger & le mal qui y sont renfermés sont démontrés par les témoignages multipliés des Saintes Ecritures, des ss. pp. des conciles, de plusieurs evêques du siécle passé & du nôtre, d'un nombre de théologiens moraux & de casuistes, de jurisconsultes, de plusieurs ministres protestans, & enfin des payens même. Paris, Froullé, 1785.

36, 347 p. 17ᶜᵐ.

"Revu par L.-E. Rondet."—Barbier, Dict. des ouvrages anonymes.
First edition, 1765.

ML3920.A2G19

[Gauthier de Montdorge, Antoine] 1700–1768.

Reflexions d'un peintre sur l'opera. La Haye, P. Gosse, 1743.

41 p. 16½ᶜᵐ.

ML3858.G27

Gaviniés, Pierre, 1726–1800.

See LATOUR DE FRANQUEVILLE, *Mme.* DE. Mon dernier mot [1781]

Gebst, Volckmarus Leisringius.

Corona musices, qvam ex lectissimis & svavissimis, ac ex musarū charitumᐦ viridario decerptis flosculis, cùm antiquitatis dignitate, et multiplici utilitate; tum concinna jucunditate, e perpetua durabilitate, æstimandis, collegit, & sub orationis jugum coëgit ac revocavit: et deniᐦ publicè exhibuit Volckmarus Leisringius Gebst ... Jenæ, typis VVeidnerianis, 1611.

[16] p. 19½ x 15½ᶜᵐ.

Title within ornamental border. Signatures: A–B in fours.

ML64.G3

Gedanken über die welschen tonkünstler. Zur beantwortung des im sieben und dreissigsten stücke der hamburgischen Freyen urtheile befindlichen Schreibens an den herrn verfasser des Kritischen musikus an der Spree. Halberstadt, C. E. I. Weldige, 1751.

23 p. 21½ x 17ᶜᵐ.

ML275.3.G26

Gehot, Jean, *b. ca.* 1756.

The art of bowing on the violin, calculated for the practice & improvement of juvenile performers, by Joseph Gehot. London, G. Goulding [179–?]

9 p. 25 x 31ᶜᵐ.

MT267.A2G31

Geminiani, Francesco, 1680?–1762.

The art of accompaniament, or A new and well digested method to learn to perform the thorough bass on the harpsichord, with propriety and elegance, by F. Geminiani. Opera 11ᵗʰ . . . London, Preston and son [1753?]

2 v. (v. 1: 1 p. l., 4, 33 p.; v. 2: 1 p. l., 4, 36 p.) 36½ᶜᵐ.

Engraved, with exception of preliminary matter (p. 1–4) in each vol.
Vol. 2: Opera 11ᵗʰ. Part the 2ᵈ. Treating of position and motion of harmony, and the preparation and resolution of discords.

MT49.A2G4

The art of playing on the violin; containing all the rules necessary to attain to a perfection on that instrument, with great variety of compositions, which will also be very useful to those who study the violoncello, harpsichord &c. Composed by F. Geminiani . . . Opera IX. London, Printed for the author by J: Johnson, 1751.

1 p. l., 9, 51 p. 34 x 25½ᶜᵐ. (*With his* Rules for playing in a true taste. [London, 1745?])

Not identical with pt. v of Prelleur's "Modern musick-master." The first edition, according to the Oxford history of music, can not have been issued before 1734.

MT262.A2G32

——— L'art de jouer le violon, contenant les regles necessaires a la perfection de cet instrument, avec une grande varieté de compositions très-utiles a ceux qui jouent le violoncelle ou le clavessin, &c. Par F. Geminiani. Opera IX. Gravé par Madame de Lusse . . . Paris, De la Chevardiere; [etc., etc., 17—]

2 p. l., 55 p. 34ᶜᵐ.

Added t.-p., illustrated.

MT262.A2G31

The art of playing the guitar or cittra, containing several compositions with a bass for the violoncello or harpsichord . . . by F: Geminiani . . . Edinburgh, Printed for the author by R: Bremner, 1760.

1 p. l., 2–51 p. 35½ᶜᵐ.

Engraved throughout.

MT582.A2G2

Geminiani, Francesco—*Continued.*

Compleat instructions for the violin, containing the easiest and best methods for learners to obtain a proficiency, with some useful directions, lessons, graces, &c. by Geminiani. To which is added a favorite collection of airs, marches, minuets, &c. with several excellent peices [!] for two violins . . . [London] G. Goulding [*ca.* 1790 ?]

1 p. l., 28, [2] p. front., pl. 17 x 24ᶜᵐ. (*With* Entire new . . . instructions for the fife. London [17—])

Caption title: New instructions for the violin. Engraved throughout.

MT356.A2E62

Guida armonica, o Dizionario armonico. Being a sure guide to harmony and modulation, in which are exhibited, the various combinations of sounds, consonant, and dissonant, progressions of harmony, ligatures and cadences, real and deceptive. By F. Geminiani. Opera x . . . London, Printed for the author, by J. Johnson [1742]

3 p. l., 34 p. front. 33½ᶜᵐ.

Engr. t.-p.

MT52.A2G3

—— A supplement to the Guida armonica, with examples shewing it's use in composition: by F. Geminiani. London, Printed for the author, by J. Johnson [17—]

4 p. l., 10 p. 33½ᶜᵐ. (*With his* Guida armonica. London [1742])

MT52.A2G3

—— Dictionaire harmonique, ou Guide sur pour la vraie modulaison. Par F. Geminiani. Dictionarium harmonicum, of Zeekere wegwyzer tot de waare modulatie . . . Amsterdam, Aux depens de l'auteur, 1756.

4 p. l., 34 p. 34½ᶜᵐ.

Title-page, verso blank.—Privilegie. p. l. [2]—Au lecteur (French and Dutch in parallel columns) p. l. [3]—Methode de composer suivant ce dictionaire (French and Dutch) p. l. [4]—[Modulations] 34 p., engr.

MT52.A2G32

Rules for playing in a true taste on the violin, German flute, violoncello and harpsicord, particularly the thorough bass; exemplify'd in a variety of compositions on the subjcts [!] of English, Scotch and Irish tunes; by F. Geminiani. Opera VIII. [London, 1745 ?]

2 p. l., 2–19 p. 34 x 25½ᶜᵐ.

MT262.A2G32

A treatise of good taste in the art of musick . . . by F. Geminiani. London, 1749.

1 p. l., 4, [2], 30 p. front. 37½ᶜᵐ.

Engraved, with the exception of 4 pages following t.-p.

MT80.A2G32

Gerber, Ernst Ludwig, 1746–1819.

Historisch-biographisches lexicon der tonkûnstler, welches nachrichten von dem leben und werken musikalischer schriftsteller,
berûhmter componisten, sânger, meister auf instrumenten, dilet-
tanten, orgel- und instrumentenmacher . . . enthâlt; zusammengetragen von Ernst Ludwig Gerber . . . Leipzig, J. G. I. Breitkopf,
1790–92.

2 v. (v. 1: xiv, [2] p., 992 col.; v. 2: 1 p. l., 860 col., xvi, 86 p.) 22½ᶜᵐ.

"Verzeichniss derjenigen musikalischen werke, welche bey dem sammeln
dieser nachrichten am meisten zu rathe gezogen worden sind:" v. 1, 2 p. following p. xiv.
"Anhang, welcher nachrichten von bildnissen, bûsten und statûen berûhmter
tonlehrer und tonkûnstler . . . desgleichen von berûhmten orgelwerken und
ein instrumenten-register enthâlt": v. 2, xvi, 86 p. at end.

ML105.A2G36

Gerbert, Martin, *freiherr von Hornau,* 1720–1793.

De cantv et mvsica sacra a prima ecclesiae aetate vsqve ad praesens
tempus.　Avctore Martino Gerberto . . .　Typis San-Blasianis, 1774.

2 v. (v. 1: 10 p. l., 590 p.; v. 2: 6 p. l., 409, [29], 112 p.)　illus., xxxv pl. (partly
fold., incl. facsims.)　26 x 20ᶜᵐ.

Title vignette; head-pieces; initials.
"Missa in coena Domini": 112 p. at end of v. 2.

ML3002.A2G3

Martini Gerberti . . . Iter alemannicum, accedit italicum et galli-
cum.　Sequuntur Glossaria theotisca ex codicibus manuscriptis a
sæculo ix. usque xiii.　Typis San-Blasianis, 1765.

4 p. l., 519, [15], 144 p.　18ᶜᵐ.

Z1001.G44

Gerbert, Martin, *freiherr von Hornau,* 1720–1793, *editor.*

Scriptores ecclesiastici de musica sacra potissimum.　Ex variis
Italiæ, Galliæ & Germaniæ codicibus manuscriptis collecti et nunc
primum publica luce donati a Martino Gerberto monasterii et congreg.
S. Blasii in Silva Nigra abbate, s. Q. R. I. P. . . .　Typis San-Blasianis
1784.

3 v.　fronts., fold. tables.　26 x 20½ᶜᵐ.

ML170.G3

Gervasio, Giovanni Battista.

Methode très facile pour apprendre à jouer de la mandoline à
quatre cordes, instrument fait pour les dames.　Avec les regles les
plus éxactes pour la façon de se servir de la plume . . .　Par Mͬ. J. B.
Gervasio . . .　Œuvre 1ͬ.　Paris, Boüin; [etc., etc., 17—]

1 p. l., 15 p.　34½ᶜᵐ.

Engraved throughout.

MT602.A2G3

Gesius, Bartholomäus, *d.* 1613.

Synopsis mvsicæ practicæ, variis exemplis illustrata, et exercitiis
ad 12. modos in utroque cantu, regulari scilicet ac transposito ampli-
ficata.　In usum scholasticæ juventutis francofurtensis cis Viadrum
conscripta a Bartholomæo Gesio . . .　Francofurti Marchionum, typis
& impensis Johannis Eichorn, 1609.

[240] p.　14ᶜᵐ.

Signatures: A–P in eights.

MT6.A2G39

Gestrinius, Sueno.

See LUNDIUS, D. Dissertatio gradualis [1707]

Gianotti, Pietro, *d.* 1765.

Le guide du compositeur, contenant des regles sures pour trouver d'abord, par les consonnances, ensuite par les dissonnances, la basse fondamentale de tous les chants possibles, & dans tous les genres de musique; avec les moyens les plus sûrs pour réussir dans la recherche & la connoissance du ton dans le sujet . . . Par M. Gianotti. Paris, Durand [etc.] 1759.

xxiv, 310, [6], 39 p. (engr.) 20ᶜᵐ.

"Exemples": 39 p. at end.

MT68.A2G43

Gibel, Otto, 1612–1682.

Ottonis Gibelii . . . Introductio musicæ theoreticæ didacticæ, in quâ præcipua ejus principia, cum primis vero mathematica . . . summâ pariter perspicuitate ac brevitate proponuntur; nec tantùm ad monochordum, sed alia quoq̆ hodie usitatiora & nobiliora instrumenta, tùm secundùm veterem tùm novam musices rationem, accuratè applicantur. Pars generalis . . . Bremæ, typis & sumptibus J. Köhleri, 1660.

6 p. l., 128 p. diagrs. on fold. l. 19 x 14½ᶜᵐ. (*With his* Propositiones mathematico-musicæ. Minden an der Weser, 1666)

The second and concluding part mentioned in the preface was not published.

ML3809.A2G4

Propositiones mathematico-musicæ, das ist: Etliche fûrnehme und gar nûtzliche musicalische auffgaben / auss der mathesi demonstriret, und nach beschaffenheit in beygefûgten kupfferstûcken kûnstlich repræsentiret und fûr augen gestellet / allen wahren music-liebhabern zum besten auffgesetzet und an tag gegeben. Von Ottone Gibelio. Minden an der Weser, J. E. Heydorn, 1666.

2 p. l., 53 (*i. e.* 44) p. fold. pl., fold. tab. 19 x 14½ᶜᵐ.

Last four pages numbered 50–53 for 41–44.

ML3809.A2G4

Ginguené, Pierre Louis, 1748–1816, *editor.*

See FRAMERY, N. É. Musique, 1791–1818.

Glareanus *i. e.* **Heinrich Loriti,** *of Glarus,* 1488–1563.

Glareani Δωδεκάχορδον . . . Basileæ. [*Colophon:* Basileae per Henrichvm Petri mense septembri anno post Virginis partvm. M.D.XLVII]

10 p. l., 470, [6] p. illus., diagrs. 31½ᶜᵐ.

Printer's mark at end.
Glareanus' autograph presentation copy to Francisco Spinola. Inserted at end are 4 leaves containing in ms. (1) Presentation note: Anno a Jesu Christi natali MDLIII. Clarissimo viro P. Francisco Spinola Glareanus a Friburgo Brisgoa. D. M. (2) Ode: Ad ornatissimum virum P. Franciscum Spinolam Glareani Trimetri. (3) Codex Glareani manu emendatus in his maximè, quæ necessitas postulabat, cætera, quæ innumera quidem sunt, et à mediocris ingenij cantoribus videri faciliter poterunt, in genere duntaxat ac breuiter hic perstricta conspiciuntur. (4) Alia huius codicis errata quæ prima relectione minus animaduersa fuere denuo ipsius Glareani cura ac manu huc pernotata conspiciuntur.
At end, in a different hand: Decessit anno 1563, ætatis 75.
The third part contains examples from the works of Okeghem, Obrecht, Josquin de Près and others.

ML171.G54

Glareanus *i. e.* **Heinrich Loriti**—*Continued.*

Dvo elegiarvm libri || Henrici Glareani || Helvetii ad || Vlderĭ- ||
cvm. || Zinlivm || Doggivm. [*Colophon:* Basileae in aedibvs Ioannis ||
Frobenij Hammelburgensis diligen- || tissimi apud Alemannos || Chal-
cographi, || expensis || autē || Gertrudæ || Lachneræ uxoris || Frobenij.
Anno domini || M.D.XVI. Decimooctauo || Calendas Decembreis.]

[42] p. 21ᶜᵐ. (*With his* Isagoge in mvsicen. Basileæ, 1516)

Title within ornamental border; initials; printer's mark at end. Signatures
continuous with those of his Isagoge in mvsicen: F–I in fours, K in five.

ML171.G56

Isagoge in mvsicen || Henrici Glarea || ni Helvetii || poe. lav. || e
quibusq̇ bonis au || thorib⁹ latinis & græcis ad || studiosorū utilitatē ||
multo labore || elaborata. || Ad Falconem coss. || vrbis Aventicensis.
[Basileæ, 1516]

[39] p. diagrs. 21ᶜᵐ.

Title within woodcut border by Hans Holbein the younger; initials; printer's
mark of J. Frobenius on t.-p. Signatures: A–E in fours. Preface dated: Basileæ,
1516.

ML171.G56

Musicæ epitome ex Gla- || reani Dodecachordo || Vnà cum || qvinqve
vocvm melodiis svper || eivsdem Glareani Panegyrico de Helve || tica-
rum XIII urbium laudibus, per Manfredum || Barbarinum Coregien-
sem. || Basileæ [1559]

8 p. l., 150, [2] p. 1 illus., fold. tab., diagrs. 15 x 11½ᶜᵐ.

Colophon on p. 103 and on recto of last leaf: Basileæ, || ex officina Hieronymi ||
Cvrionis, impensis Hen || rici Petri, anno || M.D.LIX. men- || se martio.
Guidonian hand on t.-p. (repeated on p. 5) Preliminary leaves 7–8 blank.
Printer's mark on p. [104] and on last page.
Caption of preface: Ioannes Litauicus Vuonnegger lectori S.
"Mensuralis Musices || ex Glareani Dode- || cachordo Compendium ": p. 105–
150.

ML171.G55

See also BOETHIUS, A. M. S.   Opera omnia [1570]

Glaser, Johann Adam.

See WEIDLING, C.   Exercitatio philologica [1686]

Godin d'Abguerbe, Quentin.

See PARFAICT, F.   Dictionnaire des théatres, 1756.

Goetting, Valentin.

Compendium || mvsicæ mo- || dulativæ, quale brevitate ordinis ||
commoditate & facilitate nun- || quam visum, || Observatum & in
usum puero- || rum jam primúm ad Musicam adhiben- || dorum Col-
lectum á || Valentino Gœttingi VVitzen- || husano Musicæ studioso, ||
Anno salutis 1587. editum secundó in gratiam || tám docentium quám
discentium, || Accessit Exercitiū Musicum, ad || duodecim Dode-
cachordi modos & puerorum inci- || pientium captum accommodatum,
|| Cum Præfatione Henningi Dedekindi || Cantoris Salzensis. || . . .
[*Colophon:* Erphordiæ Georgius Bauman excudebat]

[64] p. 16ᶜᵐ.

Goetting, Valentin—*Continued.*

Signatures: A–D in eights. Ms. note on fly-leaf: "Deux exemplaires connus: à la Bibl. Fétis (n° 5465) et celui-ci. A[lfred] W[otquenne]"
Title, with dedicatory verse "Ad Fridericum Beurhusium" at foot of page.—Insignia nobilium de Sachsa. t.-p. verso.—Poem "In insignia nobilium de Sachsa" signed H. D. N. F. l. [2] r°.—Aeqvo lectori, bonis viris, et iuvenibus musicæ studiosis salutem dicit Henningus Dedekindus Neostadianus. (Running title "Præfatio") l. [2] v°–l. [11] r°.—Epistola nobilibvs ingenvis et honestis adolescentibvs, stemmatis sui nobilitatem liberalium artium studio illustrantibus: Sigismvndo de Sachsa [et al.] ingeniis musicæ amantibus, salutem & plenum liberalium studiorum amorem optat Valentinus Gœttingi VVitzenhus. (dated 1586) l. [11] v°–l. [13] r°.—Instrvctio ad docentes initia musicæ. l. [13] v°–l. [14] v°.—Methodus hujus Compendii. l. [15] r°.—Compendivm mvsicæ modulativæ. l. [15] v°–l. [19] v°.—Ad lectorem. l. [20] r°.—Henricvs Gottingi ludi Gebeseni moderator suo fratri s. d. p. (poem) l. [20] v°.—Exercitivm musicum pro incipientibus. l. [21] r°–l. [32] v°.—Fragmentum ex Henningi Dedekindi literis ad autorem missis. [Colophon] l. [32] v°.

ML171.G63

Goeze, Johann Melchior, *d.* 1727.

Der weit-berühmte musicus und organista wurde bey trauriger leich-bestellung des weyland edlen und kunst-hoch-erfahrnen herrn Andreæ Werckmeisters, treu-verdient-gewesenen organistens bey unserer St. Martini-kirche, und kônigl. preuss. wohl-bestallt-gewesenen inspectoris über alle orgel-wercke im fürstenthumb Halberstadt, welcher am abgewichenen 26. octobr. des 1706ten jahres in Jesu seelig verstorben, in einer stand-rede dargestellet von Iohann Melchior Gôtzen . . . [Quedlinburg?] Gedruckt 1707.

[16] p. 19½ x 16ᶜᵐ. (*With* Werckmeister, Andreas. Musicalische paradoxal-discourse. Qvedlinburg, 1707)

ML3800.A2W4

Gogava, Antonius Hermannus, 1529–1569, *translator.*

Aristoxeni mvsici antiqviss. Harmonicorvm elementorvm libri III. Cl. Ptolemæi Harmonicorum, seu de musica lib. III. Aristotelis de obiecto auditus fragmentum ex Porphyrij commentarijs. Omnia nunc primum latine conscripta & edita ab Ant. Gogauino . . . Venetijs, apud V. Valgrisium, 1562.

165, [1] p. diagrs. 22½ᶜᵐ.

Printer's mark on t.-p. and on last page.

ML171.G65

Goldschad, Gotthelf Conrad, *b.* 1719.

Chorvm mvsicvm gloriam Christi celebrantem ex Ps. LXVIII. v. 26. sistit . . . M. Gotthelff Conrad Goldschad. Dresdae, literis Harpeterianis [1751]

[12] p. 19½ᶜᵐ.

Programm—St. Annaschule, Dresden.

ML3001.G62

Gomes da Silva, Alberto José, *d.* 1795.

Regras de acompanhar para cravo, ou orgaõ, e ainda tambem para qualquer outro instrumento de vozes, reduzidas a breve methodo, e facil percepçaõ . . . por Alberto Joseph Gomes da Silva . . . Lisboa, F. L. Ameno, 1758.

4 p. l., 39 (*i. e.* 47), [2] p. tab., diagr. 20½ x 16ᶜᵐ.

Pages 45–47 wrongly numbered 37–39. Pages [21–24] and [35–42] contain "exemplos."

MT68.A2G63

Gonzaga, Silvio Valenti-, *cardinal.*

See VALENTI-GONZAGA, SILVIO, *cardinal.*

Gori, Antonio Francesco, 1691–1757, *editor.*

See BANDINI, A. M.   Commentariorvm de vita . . . Ioannis Bapt. Doni, 1755.
DONI, G. B.   Lyra Barberina, 1763.

Gori Pannilini, Francesco de'.

Lettera dell' abate Francesco de' Gori Pannilini . . . sopra l'opera dell' abate Giuseppe Pizzati che ha per titolo *La scienza de' suoni e dell' armonia, diretta specialmente a render ragione de' fenomeni, e a conoscer la natura e le leggi della medesima, ed a giovare alla pratica del contrappunto. Opera dell' ab. Giuseppe Pizzati divisa in cinque parti. In Venezia 1782. appresso Gio. Gatti.*   Pisa, J. Grazioli, 1782.

39 p.   15 x 8½cm.

MT50.A2P692

Gorton, William.

Catechetical questions in musick, containing a hundred and seventy questions, fairly answered and made plain to the meanest capacity. By William Gorton . . .   London, Printed by W. Pearson for the author, 1704.

3 p. l., 41 p.   14cm.

MT7.A2G7

Gottsched, Luise Adelgunde Viktoria (Kulmus) 1713–1762.

See GRIMM, F. M., *freiherr* VON.   Ici sont ecrits les vingt-un chapitres [17—]

[Goudar, Ange] 1720–1791.

Le brigandage de la musique italienne . . .   [n. p.] 1777.

2 p. l., viij, 156 p.   19½cm.

The dedication, "Épitre aux amateurs de la musique italienne du parterre de l'Opéra de Paris," is signed: Jean-Jacques Sonnette [pseud. of Ange Goudar]

ML1727.35.G6

Goudar, *Mme.* **Sara,** *d. ca.* 1800.

De Venise.   Rémarques sur la musique & la danse, ou Lettres de M.r G . . . à Milord Pembroke.   Venise, C. Palese, 1773.

3 p. l., 3–136 p.   19½cm.

ML3845.A2G68

—— Supplement aux Remarques sur la musique, & la danse, ou Lettres de M.r G . . . a Milord Pembroke.   Venise, C. Palese, 1773.

95 p.   16½cm.

ML3845.A2G69

Œuvres mêlées de Madame Sara Goudar . . .   Amsterdam, 1777.

2 v. in 1 (v. 1: xij, 203 p.; v. 2: 2 p. l., 198 p.)   17cm.

CONTENTS.—t. 1. Lettres sur les divertissements du carnaval de Naples & de Florence.—t. 2. Remarques sur la musique italienne & sur la danse, a Milord Pembroke.

DG447.G6

Gournay, B. C., *d. ca.* 1794.

Lettre a M. l'abbé Roussier, sur une nouvelle règle de l'octave que propose M. le marquis de Culant; par M. Gournay . . . Paris, Royez [etc.] 1785.

36, [2] p. 21½^{cm}.

MT50.A2G6

Graaf, Christiaan Ernst, *b. ca.* 1726.

Proeve over de natuur der harmonie in de generaal bas, benevens een onderricht eener korte en regelmaatige becyffering, door C. E. Graaf . . . 's Graavenhaage, B. Wittelaer, 1782.

46 p. xɪ fold. pl. 20½^{cm}.

MT49.A2G8

Grassineau, James, *d.* 1769.

A musical dictionary; being a collection of terms and characters, as well ancient as modern; including the historical, theoretical, and practical parts of music . . . The whole carefully abstracted from the best authors in the Greek, Latin, Italian, French, and English languages. By James Grassineau . . . London, J. Wilcox, 1740.

xii, 347 p. 4 pl. (3 fold.) 20^{cm}.

Paging irregular.
Translated, with additions, from the French of Sébastien de Brossard, probably under the supervision of Dr. Pepusch.

ML108.A2B7

Gratus, Veridicus, *pseud.*

See PRINTZ, W. C. Phrynis Mitilenæus, 1696.

[Gresset, Jean Baptiste Louis] 1709–1777.

Discours sur l'harmonie. Paris, J.-N. Le Clerc, 1737.

2 p. l., 89, [1] p. 20½^{cm}.

Title vignette.
"Le manuscrit que je publie aujourd'hui est secret depuis mil sept cens trente-trois. Ce discours fut alors composé en latin, pour être prononcé dans un pays éloigné de Paris. L'auteur le traduisit en même temps pour une dame, & tel qu'on le trouve ici."—Preface.

ML3815.A2A5

Grétry, André Ernest Modeste, 1741–1813.

Mémoires, ou essai sur la musique, par M. Grétry . . . Paris, Chez l'auteur; [etc., etc.] 1789.

2 p. l., 565, [3] p. 20½^{cm}.

ML410.G83A

—— Mémoires, ou essais sur la musique; par le c.^{en} Grétry . . . Paris, Imprimerie de la république, pluviôse, an v [1797]

3 v. 21^{cm}.

A reprint of the first edition, 1789, with two additional volumes.
"Liste des ouvrages dramatiques mis en musique par l'auteur de ces essais": v. 3, p. [465]–[473]

ML410.G83A1

[Grimaldi, Francesco Antonio] 1741–1783.

Lettera sopra la musica all' eccellentissimo Signore Agostino Lomellini gia' doge della serenissima repubblica di Genova. [Napoli, 1766] lxiv p. 22^{cm}.

Title vignette.
Signed: Francesco Antonio Grimaldi.

ML3800.A2G7

[Grimm, Friedrich Melchior, *freiherr* **von]** 1723–1807.

Le petit prophète de Boehmischbroda. [n. p., 1753]

56 p. front. 19½^{cm}.

Caption title: Ici sont ecrits les vingt-un chapitres de la prophétie de Gabriel Joannes Nepomucenus Franciscus de Paula Waldstorc, dit Wasdstoerchel . . .
"Réponse du coin du roi au coin de la reine [par l'abbé de Voisenon] Seconde edition corrigée & augmentée": p. 49–56.

ML1727.33.G8

—— Ici sont ecrits les vingt-un chapitres de la prophétie de Gabriel Joannes Nepomucenus Franciscus de Paula Waldstorch, dit Waldstoerchel, natif de Boehmischbroda en Bohême . . . il les a écrits de sa main, & il les appelle sa vision. Lat. canticum Cygni bohemici. [n. p., 17—]

58 p. 19^{cm}.

Caption title.
No. 11 in a volume of pamphlets lettered Quere[lle] des Bouffo[ns]
In part an imitation and in part a translation by Frau Gottsched of Le petit prophète de Boehmischbroda. *cf.* Fétis, Biog. univ. des musiciens.

ML1727.33.A1

—— Les vingt-un chapitres de la prophétie de Gabriel-Joannes-Nepomucenus-Franciscus de Paula Waldstorch, dit Waldstoerchel, qu'il appelle sa vision. Lat. canticum Cygni bohemici. Imprimé à Prague en Bohême [*i. e.* Paris, 17—]

1 p. l., 43 p. 16½ x 9½^{cm}.

ML3925.G86

Grosvenor, Benjamin, 1676–1758.

See PRACTICAL discourses, 1708.

Grube, Hermann, 1637–1698.

Hermanni Grube . . . De ictu tarantulæ, & vi musices in ejus curatione, conjecturæ physico-medicæ. Francofurti, ex bibliopolio Hafniensi, D. Paulli, 1679.

7 p. l., 76, [10] p. 18^{cm}.

RC426.G88

Gruber, Johann Sigmund, 1759–1805.

Beyträge zur litteratur der musik, hrsg. von Johann Sigmund Gruber . . . Nürnberg, In commission bey G. W. Gruber; [etc., etc.] 1785.

116, [4] p. 16^{cm}.

Based upon an unpublished list by C. S. Zeidler. *cf.* Preface.

ML116.G88

Gruber, Johann Sigmund—*Continued.*

—— Beyträge zur litteratur der musik, hrsg. von Johann Sigmund Gruber . . . Frankfurt und Leipzig, 1790.

2 v. in 1 (v. 1: 116 p.; v. 2: 74 p.)   17ᶜᵐ.

Part 2, forming a supplement to part 1 and also .to the author's "Litteratur der musik," is here published for the first time.

ML116.G89

Litteratur der musik, oder Anleitung zur kentnis der vorzüglichen musikalischen bûcher, fûr liebhaber der musikalischen litteratur bestimmt. Hrsg. von einem liebhaber der musik. Nûrnberg, Auf kosten des verfassers, 1783.

56 p.   16ᶜᵐ.

ML111.A2G8

Gruner, Caspar.

. . . Ein ratschlag wider die gotlosen tentz . . . Caspar Gruner. [n. p.] 1525.

[11] p.   18ᶜᵐ.

At head of title: "Euangelion Marci. vj." Title within ornamental border. Signatures: A in four, B in two.

GV1740.G8

Gualterotti, Francesco Maria.

La mvsica, idilio di Francescomaria Gvalterotti. Al m. illustre, e m. reuer. Sig. il Sig. Fabbrizio Alba Bocca. Firenze, Z. Pignoni, 1626.

25, [1] p.   18ᶜᵐ.

In verse.
Coat of arms on t.-p.; printer's mark (?) at end.

ML64.G9

[Guerson, Guillaume]

UTilissime musicales regule neces ‖ sarie plani cantus / simplicis contra ‖ pûcti / rerû factarû / tonorû vsuali ‖ um: necnō artis accē- tuandi ‖ tam speculatiue ꝙ pra ‖ ctice: acriori lima ‖ mundate. [Parisiis, F. Regnault, 1518]

[63] p.   1 illus.   20ᶜᵐ.

Colophon: ℭ Utilissime musicales regule ne ‖ cessarie plani cantus / simplicis cõ- ‖ trapuncti: rerum factaruꝫ: tonorū ‖ vsualium: necnon artis accētuan- ‖ di epistolas et euãgelia: que antea mendose erant: nunc vero correcte ‖ Impresse Anno salutifere passio- ‖ nis Millesimo quingentesimo de- ‖ cimo octauo Penultima Mensis ‖ Augusti.
Signatures: A–D in sixes, E in eight. Diii and Diiii transposed in binding.
Rubricated; gothic type. Printer's mark on t.-p; illustration, Guidonian hand, on recto of l. [4]

ML171.G82

Gugl, Matthaeus.

Fundamenta partituræ in compendio data. Das ist: Kurtzer und gründlicher unterricht, den general-bass, oder partitur, nach denen reglen recht und wohl schlagen zu lernen. In den druck gegeben von Matthæo Gugl . . . Augspurg und Insprugg, J. Wolff, 1757.

1 p. l., 50 p.   16½ x 20½ᶜᵐ.

First edition, Salzburg, 1719.

MT49.A2G9

Guidetti, Giovanni, 1532–1592.

Directorivm chori ad vsvm omnivm ecclesiarum cathedralium, & collegiatarum a Ioanne Gvidetto olim editum, et nvper ad novam Romani breuiarij correctionem ex pręcepto Clementis VIII. impressam restitutum, & plurimis in locis auctum, & emendatum. Accesserunt huic postremæ editioni quamplures hymnorum, & antiphonarum toni, qui in præcedentibus desiderabantur. Romæ, apud A. Phęum, 1615.

4 p. l., 619, [3] p. 16½ᶜᵐ.

Rubricated.

M2150.A2G92

—— Directorivm chori. Ad vsvm omnivm ecclesiarum cathedralium, & collegiatarum. A Ioanne Gvidetto olim editum. Et nvper ad novam Romani breuiarij correctionem ex præcepto Clementis VIII. impressam restitutum, & plurimis in locis auctum, & emendatum. Huic postremæ editioni præter errorum correctionem nouissimè accesserunt Officium angeli custodis, & Missa pro defunctis, cum antiphonis integris, ac responsorijs, quæ in defunctorum officio desiderabantur. Monachii, apud N. Henricum, 1618.

4 p. l., 649, [3] p. 17ᶜᵐ.

Rubricated.

M2150.G94

[Guilford, Francis North, *1st baron*] 1637–1685.

A philosophical essay of musick, directed to a friend . . . London, J. Martyn, 1677.

25 (*i. e.* 35) p., 1 l. fold. tab. 20ᶜᵐ.

Page 35 wrongly numbered 25.

ML3805.A2G9

Guisbarchi, Annio.

L'ecclesiastico in coro ammonito dal suo prelato a salmeggiare nella forma, che deve, con tre' raggionamenti messi sotto gli occhi di tutti quelli, che tengono l'obligo del servizio corale, cioè canonici, beneficiati, cappellani, e musici. Dal conte Annio Guisbarchi . . . 2. ed. ricorretta, ed in più luoghi ampliata, e specialmente con un' aggiunta in fine di Ricordi di S. Carlo Borromeo, e d'un avvertimento circa la maniera di portarsi nelle publiche processioni. Roma, Stamperia di G. Zempel, 1745.

111 p. 16½ᶜᵐ.

MT860.A2G96

Gumpeltzhaimer, Adam, 1559–1625.

Compendivm mvsicæ latino-germanicvm. Studio & operâ Adami Gumpelzhaimeri . . . Nvnc editione hac sexta nonnvsqvam correctum, & auctum. Avgvstæ, typis et impensis I. V. Schoenigij, 1616.

45 numb: l., 47–78, 47–78, 79–82 p. illus. 20 x 16½ᶜᵐ.

Title within historiated border. Pages 47–78 numbered in duplicate.
Title-page mutilated; title in part from Becker's Systemat.-chron. darstellung d. musikalischen lit., Nachtrag, 1839. With this copy is bound a collection of canons for from two to six voices, [30] p., without title.
Based upon Heinrich Faber's 'Compendiolum musicae." Title of 1st edition, Augsburg, 1591, reads "Compendium musicae, pro illius artis tironibus. A m. Heinrico Fabro latinè conscriptum, & à m. Christophoro Rid in vernaculum sermonem conversum, nunc praeceptis & exemplis auctum studio & operâ Adami Gumpelzhaimeri."

MT6.A2G9

Gunn, John, *ca.* 1765–*ca.* 1824.

The theory and practice of fingering the violoncello, containing rules & progressive lessons for attaining the knowledge & command of the whole compass of the instrument, by John Gunn . . . London, Printed for & sold by the author [1793]

3 p. l., 96 p. pl. 33½^{cm}.

Engr. t.-p.
"Dissertation on the origin of the violoncello": p. [1]–32.

MT302.A2G97

Gutiérrez, Francisco Antonio, *d.* 1828, *translator.*

See EXIMENO Y PUJADES, A. Del origen . . . de la musica, 1796.

Guzmán, Jorge de.

Cvriosidades del cantollano, sacadas de las obras del reverendo Don Pedro Cerone de Bergamo, y de otros autores, dadas à luz a costa de Jorge de Guzman . . . Madrid, Imprenta de musica, 1709.

8 p. l., 272, [28] p. 21^{cm}.

MT860.A2G97

H., D. v.

See DE ZANGKUNST, 1788.

H., M. H.

See SCHREIBEN an die herren verfasser der Freyen urteile [1752]

Hahn, Georg Joachim Joseph.

Der nach der neuern art wohl unterwiesene general-bass-schüler, oder Gespräch zwischen einem lehrmeister und scholaren von dem general-bass . . . von Georg Joachim Joseph Hahn . . . 2. verb. und verm. aufl. Augsburg, J. J. Lotter, 1768.

4 p. l., 95 p. 18 x 21^{cm}.

. MT49.A2H2

Halle, Johann Samuel, 1727–1810.

Die kunst des orgelbaues, theoretisch und praktisch beschrieben von Johann Samuel Hallen . . . Nebst VIII. kupfertafeln. Brandenburg, J. W. Halle und J. S. Halle, 1779.

1 p. l., [215]–411 p. VIII (*i. e.* 6) pl. (2 fold.) 20½ x 17^{cm}.

Illustrated t.-p. Running title: Nachtrag zum Orgelbauer.
Issued also as part of the 6th volume of Halle's "Werkstätte der künste."

ML552.A2H18

Haltmeier, Carl Johann Friedrich.

Weiland herrn Carl Johann Friedrich Haltmeiers . . . Anleitung: wie man einen general-bass, oder auch handstücke, in alle tone transponiren könne; zum druck befördert von Georg Philip Telemann . . . Hamburg, Gedruckt bey J. G. Piscator, 1737.

16 p. 10 pl. (music) 20½ x 17½^{cm}.

Published also in Mizler's Neu eröffnete musikalische bibliothek, 2. bd., 2. th., p. 256–268.

MT42.A2H19

Hammett, John, 1678 *or* 9–1773.

Promiscuous singing no divine institution; having neither president nor precept to support it, either from the musical institution of David, or from the gospel dispensation. Therefore it ought to be exploded, as being a humane invention, tending rather to gratify the carnal ears of men, than to be acceptable and pleasing worship to God. By John Hammett . . . [n. p.] Printed in the year 1739.

1 p. l., iii, 29 p. 17cm.

"Newport? Printed by the Widow Franklin?"—Evans, American bibliography, v. 2, p. 140.

ML3001.H22

The **harpsichord** illustrated and improv'd; wherein is shewn the Italian manner of fingering, with suits of lessons for beginners & those who are already proficients on that instrument and the organ, with Rules for attaining to play a thorough bass, also with Rules for tuning the harpsichord or spinnet. London, W. Dicey [etc., 174–]

2 p. l., 48, 4 p. front. 24½cm.

Engraved throughout.
Published also as part 6 of Peter Prelleur's "Modern musick-master" (*cf.* The compleat tutor for the harpsichord)
"A dictionary explaining such Greek, Latin, Italian & French words as generally occur in musick": 4 p. at end.

MT252.A2H28

The **harpsichord** preceptor. Being a new & complete introduction to playing the harpsichord, organ, or pianoforte. Containing i. A familiar elucidation of the first principles of music, with the most modern . . . method of playing the above instruments. ii. Thirty easy & pleasing lessons . . . progressively arranged, with preludes, canzonetts, & a duett for 2 performers . . . London, S., A. & P. Thompson [178–?]

2 p. l., 2–28 p. 23½ x 32½cm.

Engraved throughout.

MT252.A2H3

Harris, William, *d.* 1740.

See PRACTICAL discourses, 1708.

Harrison, John, 1693–1776.

A description concerning such mechanism as will afford a nice, or true mensuration of time; together with some account of the attempts for the discovery of the longitude by the moon: as also an account of the discovery of the scale of musick. By John Harrison . . . London, Printed for the author, 1775.

108 p. 21cm.

QB107.H26

[Hartong,]

Musicus theoretico-practicus, bey welchem anzutreffen i. Die demonstrativische theoria musica auf ihre wahre principia gebauet, von vielen arithmetischen subtilitæten befreyet, dahingegen die

[Hartong]—*Continued.*

abwechslung derer harmonien, die daher entstehende scalæ, und die
aus der harmonie entspringende melodie . . . vestgestellet werden.
II. Die methodische clavier-anweisung mit regeln und exemplen.
Wozu noch kommet eine anführung zu fugirenden fantasien, zu rechter executirung dess chorals, zu rechtem gebrauch eines neu-inven-
tirten circuli. Ausgefertigt von P. C. Humano [*pseud.*] Nürnberg,
Gedruckt bey A. J. Felsseckers seel. erben, 1749.

2 p. l., 88, [2], 15 p., 2 l., 33 p. 21½ x 16½ᶜᵐ.

Part 2 has special t.-p. and separate paging.
Musical examples: 33 p. at end.

MT6.A2H19

Hase, Wolfgang, *b. ca.* 1600.

Gründliche einführung in die edle music oder singe kunst / anfangs
der gemeinen jugend zum besten / und insonderheit für die schule der
stadt Osteroda gestellet / jetzo aber vermehret und verbessert / und
zum andern mal dem druck übergeben durch Wolfgangum Hasen . . .
Gosslar, Gedruckt bey N. Dunckern, in verlegung des autoris, 1657.

87 p. 15ᶜᵐ.

MT935.A2H2

Hasse, Johann Adolph, 1699–1783.

Beyträge zu wahrer kirchenmusik, von Johann Adolf Hasse, und
Johann Adam Hiller. 2. verm. aufl. Leipzig, A. F. Böhme, 1791.

35 p. 16ᶜᵐ.

Hiller here proposes to translate into German the words of some of Hasse's compositions and to publish the translations together with the music. Pages 14–35
contain extracts from the proposed work.

ML410.H35H3

Hawkins, *Sir* **John,** 1719–1789.

An account of the institution and progress of the Academy of
ancient music. With a comparative view of the music of the past and
present times. By a member . . . London, Printed in the year 1770.

24 p. 21½ᶜᵐ.

ML28.L8A54

A general history of the science and practice of music, by Sir John
Hawkins . . . London, T. Payne and son, 1776.

5 v. front., illus. (incl. ports., facsims., music), v pl., diagrs. 28 x 22ᶜᵐ.

ML160.H39

[Hayes, William] 1706–1777.

The art of composing music by a method entirely new, suited to the
meanest capacity. Whereby all difficulties are removed, and a person who has made never so little progress before, may, with some
small application, be enabled to excel. London, J. Lion, 1751.

vi, [7]–32 p. 21½ᶜᵐ.

An attack upon Barnabas Gunn, composer and at one time organist of Gloucester
cathedral.

ML410.G933H2

[Hayes, William]—*Continued.*

Remarks on Mr. Avison's Essay on musical expression. Wherein the characters of several great masters, both ancient and modern, are rescued from the misrepresentations of the above author; and their real merit asserted and vindicated. In a letter from a gentleman in London to his friend in the country . . . London, J. Robinson, 1753.

1 p. l., 133 p.   2 fold. pl. (music)   17½ᶜᵐ.

ML3847.A96

Heck, Johann Caspar, *b.* 1740.

The art of fingering. Or, The easiest and surest method how to learn to play on the harpsicord . . . exemplified by a gradation of fine lessons . . . each lesson being mark'd with the most proper manner of fingering. To which is added a table of all the different keys, shewing the different manner of fingering the same. As also an explanation of all graces, shakes, &c. . . . By John Casper Heck. London, W. Randall & I. Abell [177–?]

1 p. l., 35 p.   24 x 32ᶜᵐ.

Engraved throughout.

MT222.A2H32

The art of playing thorough bass with correctness according to the true principles of composition, fully explained by a great variety of examples in various stiles; to which is added by way of supplement six lessons of accompaniment . . . the whole being designed for the use of such young composers & performers in general as are desirous of being well grounded in the science of harmony. By John Casper Heck.   London, I. Welcker [177–]

1 p. l., 99 p.   diagr.   39ᶜᵐ.

Engraved throughout.   On p. 94–99 Lesson I–VI by Corelli, Quantz and Graun.

MT49.A2H4

A complete system of harmony; or, A regular and easy method to attain a fundamental knowledge and practise of thorough bass; with the nature and various use of concords and discords explained, conformable to the modern composition. Illustrated by a variety of examples. By John Casper Heck . . . [London] Printed for, and sold by the author [1768?]

iv, 26, 19 p.   27 x 21½ᶜᵐ.   (*With* Bemetzrieder, Anton. Music made easy to every capacity. London, 1785)

Manuscript note on t.-p.: Printed for Messʳ Thompsons . . . London.

MT224.A2B45

Heinichen, Johann David, 1683–1729.

Neu erfundene und gründliche anweisung / wie ein music-liebender . . . könne zu vollkommener erlernung des general-basses, entweder durch eigenen fleiss selbst gelangen / oder durch andere . . . dahin angeführet werden / dergestalt / dass er so wohl die kirchen als theatralischen sachen / insonderheit auch das accompagnement des recitativs-styli wohl verstehe / und geschickt zu tractiren wisse. Wobey zugleich auch andere schöne vortheil in der music an die hand gegeben / und alles mit vielfachen exempeln, und . . . nützlichen composition-regeln erläutert worden. Nebst einer ausführlichen vorrede. Heraus gegeben von Johann David Heinchen. Hamburg, B. Schiller, 1711.

2 p. l., 284 p.   20 x 15½ᶜᵐ.

MT49.A2H46

Heinichen, Johann David—*Continued.*

—— Der general-bass in der composition, oder: Neue und gründliche anweisung, wie ein music-liebender mit besonderm vortheil, durch die principia der composition, nicht allein den general-bass im kirchen- cammer- und theatralischen stylô vollkommen, & in altiori gradu erlernen; sondern auch zu gleicher zeit in der composition selbst, wichtige profectus machen kônne. Nebst einer einleitung oder musikalischen raisonnement von der music überhaupt, und vielen besondern materien der heutigen praxeos. Hrsg. von Johann David Heinichen ... Dressden, Bey dem autore, 1728.

4 p. l., 960, [28] p. tab. 21 x 16½ᶜᵐ.

MT49.A2H47

Herbst, Johann Andreas, 1588–1666.

Mvsica moderna prattica, ouero Maniera del bvon canto. Das ist: Eine kurze anleitung / wie knaben und andere / so sonderbare lust und liebe zum singen tragen / auff jezige italienische manier ... kônnen unterrichtet werden. Alles aus den fürnemsten italienischen authoribus ... zu-sammen getragen / auch mit vielen clausulis und variationibus gezieret: sonderlich aber für die instrumentisten / auff violinen und cornetten zu gebrauchen / mit allerhand cadenzen vermehret / und zum drittenmahl in druck verfertiget / durch Johann-Andream Herbst ... Franckfurt, G. Müller [1658]

4 p. l., 76 p. 20 x 16ᶜᵐ.
Date of imprint trimmed off in binding.

MT915.A2H26

Musica poëtica, sive Compendium melopoëticum, das ist: eine kurtze anleitung / vnd gründliche vnterweisung / wie man eine schône harmoniam, oder lieblichen gesang ... componiren, vnd machen soll. So mehrentheils auss den fürnembsten / so wol alten als newen / lateinischen vnd italienischen authoribus vnd musicis ... zusammen getragen / vnd in dieses compendium kürtzlich verfasset / auch mit schônen clausulis vnd exemplis gezieret. Allen liebhabern dieser edlen kunst zum besten / vnd dienstlichem wolgefallen / in teutscher sprach ... an jetzo publiciret, vnd zum druck verfertiget: durch Johann Andream Herbst ... Gedruckt zu Nûrnberg / In verlegung J. Dûmlers / 1643.

4 p. l., 119 p. 19½ x 15½ᶜᵐ.

MT55.A2H53

Herbst, Johann Andreas, 1588–1666, *translator.*

See CHIODINO, G. B. Arte prattica, 1653.

Herold, Philipp.

Carmen heroicvm Philippi Heroldi Lipsici, De laudibus Mvsarum. [n. p.] 1558.

[14] p. pl. 21ᶜᵐ. (*With* Sebastiani, Claudius. Bellum musicale. Argent[orati] 1563)

ML171.S44

Hertel, Johann Wilhelm, 1727–1789.

Sammlung musikalischer schriften, grösstentheils aus den werken der Italiäner und Franzosen übersetzt, und mit anmerkungen versehen von Johann Wilhelm Hertel ... Leipzig, J. G. I. Breitkopf, 1757–58.

4 p. l., 136 p.; 1 p. l., [137]–254 p.   17½ᶜᵐ.

"Nachricht von neuen musikalischen schriften": p. 133–136, 250–254.

CONTENTS.—1. stück. Joh. Friedr. Löwens Anmerkungen über die odenpoesie. Des herrn von Voltaire gedanken von der oper. Eben desselben gedanken von den tragödien der Griechen. Der (!) herrn Remond von St. Mard Betrachtungen über die oper.—2. stück. Joh. Friedr. Löwens Anmerkungen über die geistliche cantatenpoesie. Von der dramatischen musik der alten; ein auszug aus ... Lives of the Roman poets, vol. ii. Anmerkungen über die musik überhaupt, aus des Patru et d'Ablancourt Dialogues sur les plaisirs. Brief des herrn Roy von der oper. Des herrn Frerons critik der Betrachtungen über die oper des herrn Remond von St. Mard. Schreiben an den herrn von L*s*r.: Woher es kömmt, dass einige tonarten in der musik anmuthig und sanfter, andere aber stark und rauschender klingen.

ML55.H37

Hess, Joachim, 1730–1810 *or* 11.

Dispositien der merkwaardigste kerk-orgelen, welken in de zeven Verëenigde Provincien als mede in Duytsland en elders aangetroffen worden. Benevens eene beschryving van het nieuw en uitmuntend orgel, in de St. Jans kerk te Gouda. Dienende tot een vervolg op de Luister van het orgel. Door Joachim Hess ... Gouda, By J. vander Klos, stads-drukker, 1774.

vi, 200 p.   21 x 16ᶜᵐ.

ML594.A2H2

Korte en eenvoudige handleyding tot het leeren van 't clavecimbel of orgel-spel, opgesteld ten dienste van leerlingen, door Joachim Hess ... 4. druk. Op nieuws overgezien, vermeerderd en verbeterd. Gouda, By J. van der Klos, stads-drukker, 1779.

4 p. l., 32 p.   fold. pl.   21 x 16½ᶜᵐ.

MT252.A2H58

Luister van het orgel, of Naauwkeurige aanwyzinge, hoe men, door eene gepaste registreering en geschikte bespeeling, de voortreffelyke hoedanigheden en verwonderenswaardige vermogens van een kerk- of huis-orgel in staat is te vertoonen. Tot onderrigting van alle liefhebbers van het orgel-spel, inzonderheid voor jonge organisten, leerlingen, en allen die zig eene bekwaame behandeling van het orgel tragten eigen te maaken. Opgesteld door Joachim Hess ... Gouda, By J. vander Klos, stads-drukker, 1772.

xii, 78 p.   21 x 16ᶜᵐ.

MT189.A2H3

Hesse, Johann Heinrich.

Kurze, doch hinlängliche anweisung zum general-basse, wie man denselben aufs allerleichteste, auch ohne lehrmeister, erlernen kann. Hrsg. von Johann Heinrich Hesse ... und bey eben demselben zu bekommen. Hamburg, Gedruckt von M. C. Bock [1776]

48 p.   20 x 18ᶜᵐ.

Title within ornamental border; head-pieces.

MT49.A2H53

Hewett, James.

An introduction to singing, or The rudiments of music; to which is added a compleat set of practical lessons, together with a collection of the best and most useful psalm tunes, in all their parts, and several anthems, by eminent masters. By James Hewett. [London] Sold by the author [etc.] 1765.

1 p. l., ii, [3]–23, iii, 4–104 p. 23½^{cm}.

Engraved in part.

M2136.A2H56

Heyden, Sebald, *d.* 1561.

De arte canendi, ac vero signorvm in cantibvs vsv, libri duo, autore Sebaldo Heyden. Ab ipso authore recogniti, mutati & aucti ... Norimbergæ, apud I. Petreium, 1540.

6 p. l., 163 p. 20 x 15½^{cm}.

1st edition, Nuremberg, 1537, has title: Musicae, id est, artis canendi libri duo.

ML171.H38

Hilaire, Cécile de Saint.

See SAINT HILAIRE, CÉCILE DE, *pseud.?*

Hiller, Johann Adam, 1728–1804.

Anweisung zum musikalisch-richtigen gesange, mit hinlänglichen exempeln erläutert, von Johann Adam Hiller. Leipzig, J. F. Junius, 1774.

11 p. l., [3]–224 p. 22 x 17½^{cm}.

Title vignette: "Canon quatuor vocum in unisono."

MT840.A2H65

—— Exempel-buch der Anweisung zum singen . . . hrsg. von Johann Adam Hiller. Leipzig, J. F. Junius, 1774.

64 p. 22 x 17½^{cm}. (*With his* Anweisung zum . . . gesange. Leipzig, 1774)

MT840.A2H65

—— Anweisung zum musikalisch-richtigen gesange, mit hinlänglichen exempeln erläutert, von Johann Adam Hiller. 2., verb. aufl. Leipzig, J. G. Feind, 1798.

7 p. l., [3]–220, [4] p. 22 x 17^{cm}.

Title vignette, same as in the edition of 1774.

MT840.A2H67

Anweisung zum musikalisch-zierlichen gesange, mit hinlänglichen exempeln erläutert, von Johann Adam Hiller. Leipzig, J. F. Junius, 1780.

4 p. l., xxx, [2] p., 1 l., 152 p. 21½ x 17½^{cm}.

Title vignette, same as in the foregoing. Signatures: "II. theil" (forms the second part of his "Anweisung zum musikalisch-richtigen gesange ")

MT840.A2H66

Hiller, Johann Adam—*Continued.*

Anweisung zum violinspielen, für schulen, und zum selbstunterrichte. Nebst einem kurzgefassten lexicon der fremden wörter und benennungen in der musik, entworfen von Johann Adam Hiller. Leipzig, Breitkopf [1792]

2 p. l., 86 p.   21 x 16½ᶜᵐ.

MT278.A2H46

—— Anweisung zum violinspielen, für schulen, und zum selbstunterrichte. Nebst einem kurzgefassten lexicon der fremden wörter und benennungen in der musik, entworfen von Johann Adam Hiller. Grätz, C. F. Trötscher, 1795.

2 p. l., 87 p.   20 x 16½ᶜᵐ.

MT278.A2H47

Beyträge zu wahrer kirchenmusik, von Johann Adolf Hasse, und Johann Adam Hiller. 2. verm. aufl. Leipzig, A. F. Böhme, 1791.

35 p.   16ᶜᵐ.

Hiller here proposes to translate into German the words of some of Hasse's compositions and to publish the translations together with the music. Pages 14–35 consist of extracts from the proposed work.

ML410.H35H3

Kurze und erleichterte anweisung zum singen, für schulen in städten und dörfern . . . von Johann Adam Hiller. Leipzig, J. F. Junius, 1792.

6 p. l., 99, [1] p.   21½ x 17½ᶜᵐ.

MT935.A2H57

Lebensbeschreibungen berühmter musikgelehrten und tonkünstler neuerer zeit, von Johann Adam Hiller. Erster theil. Leipzig, Dykische buchhandlung, 1784.

5 p. l., 320 p.   21ᶜᵐ.

In alphabetical arrangement, A–Ta, with Hiller's autobiography at end (p. 286–320) No more published.

ML390.A2H63

Nachricht von der aufführung des Händelschen Messias, in der domkirche zu Berlin, den 19. may 1786, von Johann Adam Hiller . . . Berlin, Gedruckt bey C. S. Spener [1786]

32 p.   35½ x 20½ᶜᵐ.

Title vignette.

ML410.H13H4

Hiller, Johann Adam, 1728–1804, *editor.*

See ADLUNG, J.   Anleitung zur musikalischen gelahrtheit, 1783.
LINGKE, G. F.   Kurze musiklehre, 1779.
WÖCHENTLICHE nachrichten, 1766–70.

Hiller, Johann Adam, 1728–1804, *translator.*

See CHABANON, M. P. G. DE.   Ueber die musik, 1781.

Hinrichs, Johann Christian, *b.* 1760.

Entstehung, fortgang und ietzige beschaffenheit der russischen iagdmusik. Von Iohann Christian Hinrichs ... S^t. Petersburg, Gedrukt bei I. K. Schnoor, auf kosten des verfassers, in commission bei I. D. Gerstenberg et c°, 1796.

3 p. l., xiv p., 1 l., 24, [3] p., 1 l.   7 pl. on 5 l.   27½ x 22½^{cm}.

Engr. t.-p.   On pl. 2–5 specimens of music.
"Lebenslauf des erfinders der jagdmusik Johann Anton Maresch ...": p. vii–xiv.

ML1337.A2H6

Hirsch, Andreas, *translator.*

See KIRCHER, A.   Kircherus Jesuita germanus Germaniæ redonatus, 1662.

Hoegi, Pierre.

A tabular system whereby the art of composing minuets is made so easy that any person, without the least knowledge of musick, may compose ten thousand, all different, and in the most pleasing and correct manner.   Invented by Sig.^{r} Piere Hoegi.   London, Printed at Welcker's musick shop [1770?]

2 p. l., 8 p.   24 x 33^{cm}.   (*With* Pasquali, Nicolo. The art of fingering, the harpsichord.   London [17—])

Engraved throughout.

MT252.A2P31

[Holbach, Paul Henri Thiry, *baron* d'] 1723–1789.

Arrêt rendu a l'amphithe'atre de l'Opera, sur la plainte du milieu du parterre, intervenant dans la querelle des deux coins.   [n. p., 1752]

15 p.   19^{cm}.

Caption title.
No. 3 in a volume of pamphlets lettered Quere[lle] des Bouffo[ns]

ML1727.33.A1

Holden, John.

An essay towards a rational system of music.   By John Holden ... Glasgow, Printed for the author; London, Sold by R. Baldwin, 1770.

viii, 148 p.   XII pl.   17½ x 22^{cm}.

MT50.A2H726

Holder, William, 1616–1698.

A treatise of the natural grounds, and principles of harmony.   By William Holder ...   London, Printed by J. Heptinstall, for the author, and sold by J. Carr, 1694.

5 p. l., 204 p.   2 pl. (1 fold.) diagrs.   19^{cm}.

ML3815.A2H6

Holder, William—*Continued.*

—— A treatise of the natural grounds, and principles of harmony. By William Holder . . . To which is added, by way of appendix: Rules for playing a thorow-bass; with variety of proper lessons, fuges, and examples . . . Also directions for tuning an harpsichord or spinnet. By the late Mr. Godfrey Keller . . . The whole being revis'd, and corrected from many gross mistakes committed in the first publication of these rules. London, Printed by W. Pearson for J. Wilcox [etc.] 1731.

3 p. l., [202] p. fold. pl., diagrs. 20^{cm}.

Errors in paging.

ML3815.A2H7

Hollbusch, Johann Sebastian.

Tonsystem von Johann Sebastian Hollbusch; abgefasset in einem gespräche zweier freunde. Mainz, Gedruckt bey Häfners sel. erben, 1792.

4 p. l., 200 p. 17½^{cm}.

ML3815.A2H75

[Holler, Aegidius] *b.* 1751.

Solfeggio nuovo, facile e sicuro per tutti i tuoni del canto fermo, proposto agli studiosi di esso da D. Diego Orelli. Siena, Appresso V. Pazzini Carli, e figlj a spese dell' autore, 1797.

28 p. 28½^{cm}.

MT870.A2H73

Holtheuser, Johann.

Enconivm mvsicae, artis antiqviss: et divinae carmine elegiaco scriptum, et recitatum in celeberrima Academia vvittebergensi, in prælectione musicæ Henrici Fabri. anno, 1551. 26. april. a Ioanne A. Holthevsero Hilperhvsano. Adiecta svnt in fine Epigrammata in laudem mvsicae à uarijs scripta. Erphordiae, 1551.

[31] p. illus. 19 x 14½^{cm}.

Illustration on t.-p. ("Mvsica") repeated on p. [30]; arms of Hildburghausen on p. [31] Colophon: Excusum Erphordiae per Martinum de Dolgen. Signatures: A–D in fours.

ML171.H64

Hooch, Dirk van der.

See De ZANGKUNST, 1788.

L'Hopital, musicien. Paris, L. Cellot, & A. Jombert jeune, 1778.

22 p. 20^{cm}.

Proposes that the children in the Hôpital général be educated in music.

ML63.H71

Hotteterre, Jacques, *d.* 1760 *or* 61.

Methode pour la musette, contenant des principes, par le moyen desquels on peut apprendre à joüer de cet instrument, de soy-même au défaut de maître. Avec un nouveau plan pour la conduite du souflet, & plusieurs instructions pour le toucher, &c. Plus un recueil d'airs, & quelques préludes, dans les tons les plus convenables. Par M[r]. Hotteterre, ordinaire de la musique de la chambre du roy. Oeuvre x. Paris, Impr. de J-B-C. Ballard, 1738.

viij, 84, [2] p.; 1 p. l., 32 p. front., pl. 28[cm].

In two parts. The second part is engraved, with the exception of the title (Seconde partie de la Methode . . . Contenant plusieurs suittes, d'airs, vaude-villes, menuets, symphonies, &c. . . . Recueillis & ornez de leurs agréments par l'autheur. Ensemble des préludes dans différens modes, par le même) "Catalogue des oeuvres du s[r] Hotteterre": p. [85]

MT530.H78

Principes de la flute traversiere, ou flute d'Allemagne, de la flute a bec, ou flute douce, et du haut-bois, divisez par traitez. Par le sieur Hotteterre–le Romain . . . Amsterdam, Aux dépens d'E. Roger [1708]

2 p. l., 46, [1] p. 7 pl. (6 fold.) 20[cm].

MT342.A2H75

Hoyle, John, *d.* 1797 ?

Dictionarium musica [!], being a complete dictionary: or, treasury of music. Containing, a full explanation of all the words and terms made use of in music, both speculative, practical and historical. All the words and terms made use of by the Italians, are also inserted. The whole compiled from the best antient and modern authors who have wrote on the subject. By John Hoyle . . . London, Printed for the author, and sold by S. Crowder; [etc., etc.] 1770.

2 p. l., 112 p. 20½[cm].

For the most part a mere abridgment of Grassineau.

ML108.A2H78

—— A complete dictionary of music. Containing a full and clear explanation, divested of technical phrases, of all the words and terms, English, Italian, &c. made use of in that science . . . The whole compiled from the best ancient and modern authors . . . by John Hoyle . . . London, H. D. Symonds [etc.] 1791.

iv, 160 p. 21[cm].

ML108.A2H8

Huber, Johann Ludwig, 1723–1800.

Tamira, ein drama. Nebst einer abhandlung über das melodrama, von d. Huber . . . Tübingen, Cotta, 1791.

136 p. 16½[cm].

Title vignette.
Albert Schatz, in the ms. catalogue of his collection of librettos, gives the author as Ferdinand Ludwig, not Johann Ludwig, Huber.

ML48 S11295

Hughes, William, *d.* 1798.

The efficacy and importance of musick: A sermon preach'd in the cathedral-church of Worcester, at the annual meeting of the Three choirs, Worcester, Gloucester and Hereford, Wednesday, September 13, 1749 . . . By William Hughes . . . London, S. Mountfort [1749]

vii, 24 p. 20ᶜᵐ.

ML3920.A2H86

Remarks upon church musick. To which are added several observations upon some of Mr. Handel's oratorio's, and other parts of his works. By William Hughes . . . 2d ed. Worcester, R. Lewis, 1763.

ix, 46 p. 20ᶜᵐ.

ML3869.A2H86

Hugo *Reutlingensis.*

See SPECHTSHART, HUGO, *of Reutlingen.*

Humanus, P. C., *pseud.*

See HARTONG.

ₗ**Hunold, Christian Friedrich**₎ 1680–1721.

Theatralische / galante und geistliche gedichte / von Menantes [*pseud.*] Hamburg / G. Liebernickel, 1706.

7 p. l., 241 (*i. e.* 269), 80, [7] p. front. 16½ᶜᵐ.

No. 207–208 omitted in paging; p. 257–271 numbered 227–241.
The book is in form of a treatise on the technique of librettos.
"Der gestürtzte und wieder erhöhte Nebucadnezar, könig zu Babylon / unter dem grossen propheten Daniel, in einem singe-spiel auf dem grossen hamburgischen schau-platze vorgestellet im jahr 1704" : p. [137]–196.
"Der blutige und sterbende Jesus / wie selbiger in einem oratorio musicalisch gesetzt / und in der Stillen woche / montags und mittewochs zur vesper-zeit auffgeführet worden / durch Reinhard Keisern" : p. [3]–35.

ML49.A2H9

Huygens, Constantijn, *heer van Zuilichem,* 1596–1687.

Ghebruik, en onghebruik van 't orghel, in de kerken der Vereenighde Nederlanden. Beschreeven door Constantyn Huigens, ridder. heere van Zuylichem, Zeelhem, ende Monickeland . . . Verrijkt met eenighe zanghen. Amsterdam, A. G. vanden Heuvel, 1660.

6 p. l., 180 p. 15ᶜᵐ.

Added t.-p., engr.: Constantijn Huygens Orgel gebruyk, inde kerke der Vereenighe Neederlande. Verrykt met eenige zange . . .
Preceding the text are three poems laudatory of Huygens, the first by P. C. Hooft, the second and third by H. F. Waterloos. At end (p. 143–180) are six poems by Waterloos.
First edition published anonymously, Leyden, 1641.

ML3001.H98

Illuminato *da Torino.*

Canto ecclesiastico facile della Settimana santa del p. f. Illuminato da Torino . . . Per uso, e commodo di tutti gli ecclesiastici sì secolari, che regolari . . . Venezia, G. Tomasini, 1729.

4 p. l., 291, [1] p. coat of arms. 26½ᶜᵐ.

M2150.A2I29

Imbert,

Nouvelle méthode, ou principes raisonnés du plein-chant, dans sa perfection, tirés des élémens de la musique: contenant aussi une méthode de serpent . . . les maîtres trouveront dans ladite méthode, toutes sortes de pieces de chant choisies, comme: duo, trio, quatuor, messes, proses, hymnes . . . pour enseigner à leurs éleves. Par M. Imbert . . . Paris, Veuve Ballard & fils [etc.] 1780.

viii, 50 p., 2 l., [53]–268, [2] p. 5 pl. (1 fold.) 17ᶜᵐ.

MT860.A2 I32

Introductory lessons, practised by the Uranian society, held at Philadelphia for promoting the knowledge of vocal music. Jan. 1, 1785. [Philadelphia, 1785]

2 p. l., iv, 20 p. pl. 11½ x 25½ᶜᵐ.

Engraved throughout.
Probably compiled by Andrew Adgate, president of the society.

MT870.A2U72

Iriarte y Oropesa, Tomás de, 1750–1791.

La música, poema. Por D. Tomas de Yriarte . . . Madrid, Imprenta real de la Gazeta, 1779.

10 p. l., 126, xl p., 1 l. front., 5 pl. 23½ᶜᵐ.

ML3800.A2I 8

—— La música, poema, por D. Tomas de Yriarte . . . 2. ed. Madrid, Imprenta real, 1784.

10 p. l., 126, xl p. front., 5 pl. 23ᶜᵐ.

ML3800.A2I 82

Irol, Pablo Minguet é.

See MINGUET É IROL, PABLO.

Iso,

Memoire pour le sieur Iso, maître de musique, demandeur. Contre le sieur Lagarde, aussi maître de musique, défendeur. [Paris, Impr. de Knapen, 17—]

6 p. 24½ x 19ᶜᵐ.

Caption title. Signed: Mᵉ Richer, avocat. Amiot, procureur.
Iso identical with Yzo, author of "Lettre sur celle de M. J. J. Rousseau"?

ML423.Y97

Jackson, William.

A scheme demonstrating the perfection and harmony of sounds; wherein is discover'd the true coincidence of tones into diapasons and where all musical intervals unite and incorporate to the minutest part of their exact proportions agreeable to the proportions of numbers; likewise the exact difference betwixt greater and lesser intervals and how they are compounded together in musical concordance . . . To Edward Barker . . . this scheme is humbly inscribed by the author William Jackson. [London, 1726?]

chart. 65 x 34½ᶜᵐ fold. to 21 x 16ᶜᵐ.

Engraved chart, with vignette and ornamental border.

MT15.A2J14

Jacob,　　*d.* 1772.

Méthode de musique sur un nouveau plan.　Par M. Jacob . . .
Paris, Chez l'auteur [etc.] 1769.

2 p. l., 66, [2] p.　fold. pl.　20ᶜᵐ.

MT6.A2J14

Jamard,　　1734–1815.

Recherches sur la théorie de la musique, par M. Jamard . . .　Paris,
Jombert; [etc., etc.] 1769.

1 p. l., xxvii, [1], 296, [4] p.　fold. pl.　20½ᶜᵐ.

A development of the theory of Ballière.

ML3800.A2J2

Janovka, Tomáš Baltazar, *b.* 1660.

Clavis ad thesaurum magnæ artis musicæ, seu Elucidarium omnium
ferè rerum ac verborum, in musica figurali tam vocali, quàm·instru-
mentali obvenientium.　Consistens potissimùm in definitionibus &
divisionibus; quibusdam recentioribus de scala, tono, cantu, & genere
musicæ &c. sententijs, variísque exqvisitis observationibus . . . alpha-
betico ordine compositum à Thoma Balthasare Janovvka . . .　Impensis authoris, apud quem venalis invenitur.　Vetero-Pragæ, in
Magno collegio Carolino typis Georgij Labaun, 1701.

10 p. l., 324 p.　16ᶜᵐ.

ML108.A2J2

See also VOGT, M. J.　Conclave Thesauri magnæ artis musicæ,
1719.

Jesus Maria, Carlos de.

See CARLOS DE JESUS MARIA.

[João IV] *king of Portugal,* 1604–1656.

Difesa ‖ della ‖ mvsica ‖ moderna ‖ contro ‖ la falsa opinione ‖ del
vescovo ‖ Cirillo Franco ‖ tradotta ‖ di spagnvolo ‖ in ‖ italiano.
[Venetia, 16—]

74 p.　20½ᶜᵐ.

Dedication signed: Incerto autore D. B. (*i. e.* Duque de Bragança)

Engr. t.-p. with emblematic border and arms of the House of Bragança.　In
lower part of border: C. Dolcetta fece in Venetia.

"Lettera [del vescouo Cirillo Franco a] Hugolino Gualteruzzi, sopra l'impro-
prietà delli musici moderni nelle loro compositioni delle messe, e canto ec8le-
siastico.　Và impressa nella sua lingua toscana, nel terzo libro delle lettere
illustri stampate in Venetia per Aldo Manutio 1567 . . . Puntualmente stà
tradotta, ma non parola per parola, per il mal suono, che haurebbe fatto nella
lingua castigliana": p. 14–27.

"Alcvni essempi della più antica musica": p. 63–74.

ML3920.A2J8

Jöcher, Christian Gottlieb, 1694–1758.

See ETTMÜLLER, M. E.　Disputatio effectus musicæ [1714]

Jones, Edward, *Bardd y brenin,* 1752–1824.

Musical and poetical relicks of the Welsh bards: preserved, by tradition and authentic manuscripts, from very remote antiquity; never before published. To the bardic tunes are added variations for the harp, harpsichord, violin, or flute: with a select collection of the pennillion and englynion, or, epigrammatic stanzas, poetical blossoms, and pastoral songs, of Wales, with English translations. Likewise, a general history of the bards and druids ... To which is prefixed, a copious dissertation on the musical instruments of the aboriginal Britons ... by Edward Jones ... A new ed., doubly augm., and improved ... London, Printed for the author, 1794.

2 p. l., 183, viii p.   2 pl. (incl. front.)   34½ᶜᵐ.

A second volume was published in 1802 under title: The bardic museum. "Jones had prepared a third volume, a portion only of which was published at his death, the remainder being issued subsequently."—Grove, Dict. of music.

M1742.A2J77

[Jones, William] 1726–1800.

A treatise on the art of music; in which the elements of harmony and air are practically considered, and illustrated by an hundred and fifty examples in notes, many of them taken from the best authors: the whole being intended as a course of lectures, preparatory to the practice of thorough-bass and musical composition ... Colchester, Printed for the author, by W. Keymer, 1784.

1 p. l., iii, [2], xii, 61, 40 p.   33ᶜᵐ.

Ms. signature at end of dedication: W. Jones. The music, though paged consecutively (1–40), is inserted throughout text.

MT50.A2J79

[Jourdan, Jean Baptiste] 1711–1793.

Le correcteur des Bouffons a l'ecolier de Prague.   [n. p., 1753?]

20 p.   19ᶜᵐ.

No. 8 in a volume of pamphlets lettered Quere[lle] des Bouffo[ns]

ML1727.33.A1

Seconde lettre du correcteur des Bouffons a l'ecolier de Prague. Contenant quelques observations sur l'opera de Titon, Le jaloux corrigé, & Le devin du village.   [n. p., 1753?]

22 p.   18ᶜᵐ.

ML1727.33.J8

Journal der tonkunst. Hrsg. von Heinrich Christoph Koch ... 1.–2. stück. Erfurt, G. A. Keyser, 1795.

16, [2], [17]–142 p., 6 p. (music); viii, [143]–261, [1] p.   19ᶜᵐ.

Part 2: Erfurt, G. A. Keyser, und Braunschweig, In dem Musikalischen magazin auf der höhe, 1795.

ML4.J6

Journal des spectacles, représentés devant Leurs Majestés, sur les théâtres de Versailles & de Fontainebleau, pendant l'année 1765 ... [Paris] Impr. de P. R. C. Ballard, 1766.

2 v. 21ᶜᵐ.

The "Journal" proper (16 p.), a calendar of the spectacles, precedes the texts (each separately paged) of the following: (t. 1) Intermedes d'amour pour amour. Les Incas du Perou.   Prologue des Indes galantes.   Les sauvages, entrée ajoutée aux Indes galantes.   Fragments, composés du prologue des Amours des dieux, de l'acte de L'amour enjoué, et de celui de La danse.   Thétis et Pélée.   Renaud d'Ast.—(t. 2) Silvie.   Palmire.   La vengeance de l'amour, ou Diane et Endimion, pantomime héroïque.   La fée Urgele.   Programme du ballet d'Églé.   Le triomphe de Flore.   Zenis et Almasie.   Thesée.   Erosine.

ML48.J7

[Jumilhac, Pierre Benoît de] 1611–1682.

La science et la pratique du plain-chant, où tout ce qui appartient à la pratique est étably par les principes de la science, et confirmé par le témoignage des anciens philosophes, des peres de l'eglise, & des plus illustres musiciens ...   Par un religieux Benedictin de la congregation de S. Maur.   Paris, L. Bilaine, 1673.

1 p. l., xiv, 400 p. incl. 7 pl.   26½ᶜᵐ.

"Exemples": p. 314–397.

ML3082.A2J8

Junker, Carl Ludwig, d. 1797.

Einige der vornehmsten pflichten eines kapellmeisters oder musikdirektors.   Von Carl Ludwig Junker.   Winterthur, H. Steiner und comp., 1782.

48 p.   14ᶜᵐ.

MT85.A2J9

Portefeuille für musikliebhaber.   Charakteristik von 20 componisten; und Abhandlung über die tonkunst.   Leipziger ostermesse, 1792.

1 p. l., 109, 119 p.   19ᶜᵐ.

A reprint of his "Tonkunst" and "Zwanzig componisten."

ML60.J95

Tonkunst.   C. L. Junker.   Ψυχῆς ἰατρεῖον.   Bern, Typographische gesellschaft, 1777.

19 p. l., 119 p.   19ᶜᵐ.

Title vignette.

ML3845.A2J8

Ueber den werth der tonkunst, von C. L. Junker ...   Bayreuth und Leipzig, J. A. Lübecks sel. erben, 1786.

viii, 174 p.   17½ᶜᵐ.

Title vignette.

ML3920.A2J9

Zwanzig componisten, eine skizze, von Carl Ludwig Junker ... Bern, Typographische gesellschaft, 1776.

xvi, 109 p.   18 x 10ᵒᵐ.

Title vignette.

ML390.A2J9

Junker, Carl Ludwig—*Continued.*

See also MUSIKALISCHER almanach . . . 1782.
MUSIKALISCHER und kûnstler-almanach . . . 1783.

Jussow, Johann Andreas.

See SCHMID, J. A. De cantoribvs ecclesiae, 1708.

Justinus à Desponsatione B. M. V.

R. p. Justini Carm. Musicalische arbeith und kurtz-weil. Das ist:
Kurtze und gute regulen: der componier und schlag-kunst â 4.
Leichte und schwâre exempelen / und fragen. Voll- und lehr-griffige
schlag-stuck. Dem scholarn: zwey hand voll arbeith. Dem lieb-
haber: zwey hand voll kurtz-weil . . . Augspurg und Dillingen /
J. C. Bencards seel. wittib und erben, 1723.

8 p. l., 132 p., 1 l. 29ᶜᵐ.

MT6.A2J9

Kalkbrenner, Christian, 1755–1806.

Kurzer abriss der geschichte der tonkunst, zum vergnûgen der liebhaber der musik. Hrsg. von C. Kalkbrenner . . . Berlin, F. Maurer,
1792.

128 p. 17½ᶜᵐ.

ML159.K12

Theorie der tonkunst, mit dreyzehn tabellen, von C. Kalkbrenner
. . . Erster theil. Berlin, J. J. Hummel [1789]

3 p. l., vi, 40 p.; 1 l., 13 p. (engr.) 29 x 24ᶜᵐ.

No more published.

MT6.A2K2

Kausch, Johann Joseph, 1751–1825.

Johann Joseph Kausch's . . . Psychologische abhandlung ûber den
einfluss der tône und ins besondere der musik auf die seele; nebst
einem anhange ûber den unmittelbaren zwek der schônen kûnste.
Bresslau, Bei J. F. Korn, dem âlteren, 1782.

xvi, 200 p., 1 l. 20 x 11½ᶜᵐ.

ML3920.A2K2

Keeble, John, 1711–1786.

The theory of harmonics: or, An illustration of the Grecian harmonica. In two parts: I. As it is maintained by Euclid, Aristoxenus,
and Bacchius senior. II. As it is established on the doctrine of the
ratio: in which are explained the two diagrams of Gaudentius, and
the Pythagorean numbers in Nicomachus. With plates, an introduction to each part, and a general index. By John Keeble . . . London, Printed for the author, and sold by J. Walter [etc.] 1784.

3 p. l., 204, xxiii, [2] p. xxix pl. on 20 l. (incl. tables) 30 x 24ᶜᵐ.

ML3805.A2K26

Keinspeck, Michael.

Liliū musice plane ‖ Michaelis künspeck musici Alexā ‖ drini. nouis quibusdam additamē ‖ tis Per J. A. A. eius discipulum pri ‖ dem illustratum. ‖ Hexasticon In cōmendationem ‖ Fragrantis Lilij. ‖ Discite nūc iuuenes Musas celebrare canoras ‖ Atϙ animum corpus ϙ simul releuare periclis ‖ Candidulum florem spirantem germine leto ‖ Ingeniū curamϙ dico coniūge loquenti ‖ Hic etenim medicam possis haurire salutem ‖ Corporis ac anime melioris munera vite. [*Colophon:* ¶Explicit Lilium Musice plane Micha ‖ elis kunspeck musici Alexandrini bene ‖ meriti. Per Mathiam Hupfuff ciuem ‖ Argentinesi impressus. Anno salutis nr̄e ‖ Millesimo. Quingentesimo sexto]

[31] p.   20½ᶜᵐ.

ML171.K34

Keiser, Reinhard, 1674–1739.

See MATTHESON, J.   Das neu-eröffnete orchestre, 1713.

Keller, Gottfried, *d.* 1704.

A compleat method, for attaining to play a through bass upon either organ, harpsichord or theorbo lute, by the late famous Mʳ. Godfry Keller; with variety of proper lessons & fuges, explaining the several rules through-out the whole work; & a scale for tuning yᵉ harpsichord or spinet, all taken from his own copies which he design'd to print.   Note in this celebrated work for yᵉ ease of practitioners all yᵉ chords are correctly explain'd both with figures & notes.   London, R. Meares [*ca.* 1714]

1 p. l., 14 numb. l.   31¼ᶜᵐ.

Engraved throughout.

MT49.A2K29

—— Rules for playing a thorow-bass, by the late famous Mr. Godfrey Keller.

(*In* Holder, William.   A treatise of . . . harmony.   London, 1731.   20ᶜᵐ. p. 159–202)

ML3815.A2H7

Kellner, David, *d.* 1748.

Treulicher unterricht im general-bass . . . hrsg. von D. K.   2. und verm. aufl.   Nebst einer vorrede hn: G. P. Telemanns.   Hamburg, C. Herold, 1737.

3 p. l., 99, [9] p.   illus., tables.   22 x 18ᶜᵐ.

MT49.A2K3

—— Treulicher unterricht im general-bass, worinne . . . allerhand sothane neu-erfundene vortheile an die hand gegeben werden, vermöge welcher einer in kurtzer zeit alles, was zu dieser wissenschafft gehöret, sattsam begreiffen kan . . . hrsg. von David Kellner . . .   3. aufl.   Mit einer vorrede des herrn Daniel Solanders . . .   Hamburg, C. Herold, 1743.

3 p. l., 98, [6] p.   tables., diagrs.   21 x 17½ᶜᵐ.   (*With* Eisel, Johann P.   Musicus ἀυτοδίδακτος.   Erfurt, 1738)

MT6.A2E44

Kellner, David—*Continued.*

—— Treulicher unterricht im general-bass . . . hrsg. von David Kellner . . . 7., mit vierzehn melodien von C. P. E. Bach verm. aufl. Hamburg, J. G. Herold [1796]

1 p. l., 64, [2], 16 p. illus. 21¼ x 27½^{cm}.

The music has special t.-p.: Neue melodien zu einigen liedern des neuen hamburgischen gesangbuchs, nebst einigen berichtigungen von Carl Philipp Emanuel Bach . . . Im verlag der Heroldschen buchhandlung, 1787.

According to Gerber, Neues . . . lexikon der tonkünstler, the present edition is the 8th, the 7th edition having appeared in 1782.

MT49.A2K31

Kellner, Johann Christoph, 1736–1803.

Grundriss des generalbasses; eine theoretisch-praktische anleitung für die ersten anfänger entworfen, von J. C. Kellner. Op. XVI. Erster theil. Cassel, Gedruckt auf kosten des verfassers [17—]

47, [1] p. 17 x 20½^{cm}.

MT49.A2K35

Kessel, Johann Christian Bertram, *d.* 1823.

Unterricht im generalbasse zum gebrauche für lehrer und lernende, von Joh. Christian Bertram Kessel. Neue verb. und verm. aufl. Leipzig, C. G. Hertel, 1791.

8 p. l., 110, [2] p. 20^{cm}.

"Zusätze, von der fantasie": p. 67–106.

MT49.A2K42

Kircher, Athanasius, 1602–1680.

Athanasii Kircheri . . . Mvsvrgia vniversalis, sive Ars magna consoni et dissoni in x. libros digesta . . . Romæ, ex typographia hæredum F. Corbelletti, 1650.

2 v. (v. 1: 11 p. l., 690 p.; v. 2: 1 p. l., 462, [36] p.) front. (v. 2) illus., plates (2 fold.) port., tables, diagrs. 33¼^{cm}.

Title vignette; added t.-p., engr. in v. 1. Vol. 2 has title abbreviated, with imprint: Romae, typis Ludouicī Grignani, 1650.

ML100.A2K5

—— . . . Kircherus Jesuita germanus Germaniæ redonatus: sive Artis magnæ de consono & dissono ars minor; das ist / philosophischer extract und auszug / aus dess welt-berühmten teutschen Jesuiten Athanasii Kircheri . . . Musurgia universali . . . ausgezogen und verfertiget . . . von Andrea Hirschen . . . Schw. Hall, Gedruckt bei H. R. Laidigen, 1662.

[16], 375, [25] p. 15½^{cm}.

ML100.A2K55

Kircher, Athanasius—*Continued.*

Athanasii Kircheri . . . Phonurgia nova, sive Conjugium mechanico-physicum artis & natvræ paranympha phonosophia concinnatum; quâ universa sonorum natura, proprietas, vires effectuúmq̦ prodigiosorum causæ, novâ & multiplici experimentorum exhibitione enucleantur; instrumentorum acusticorum, machinarúmq̦ ad naturæ prototypon adaptandarum, tum ad sonos ad remotissima spatia propagandos, tum in abditis domorum recessibus per occultioris ingenii machinamenta clam palámve sermocinandi modus & ratio traditur, tum denique in bellorum tumultibus singularis hujusmodi organorum usus, & praxis per novam phonologiam describitur. Campidonæ, per Rudolphum Dreherr, 1673.

22 p. l., 229, [16] p.   illus., plates, port., diagrs.   34ᶜᵐ.

Title vignette; added t.-p., engr.

ML3805.A2K58

Kirchrath, Reiner.

Theatrum musicæ choralis, das ist: Kurze und gründlich erklärte verfassung der aretinischer und gregorianischer singkunst, zusammengetragen und in druck gegeben von Reinero Kirchrath . . . Köln am Rheine, Bey J. G. Langen, 1782.

4 p. l., iv, 88, [2] p.   23 x 19ᶜᵐ.

Title within ornamental border.

MT860.A2K58

Kirnberger, Johann Philipp, 1721–1783.

Allegro, für das clavier alleine, wie auch für die violin mit dem violoncell zu accompagniren, von Johann Philipp Kirnberger componirt und vertheidiget.   Berlin, Gedruckt bey G. L. Winter, 1759.

1 p. l., 13 p.   31½ᶜᵐ.

The defense of the "Allegro" was written in reply to a criticism by Marpurg in his "Kritische briefe," of July 28, November 24, and December 1, 1759.

MT59.A2K59

Der allezeit fertige polonoisen- und menüettencomponist, von Johann Philipp Kirnberger.   Berlin, G. L. Winter, 1757.

10, xxix p.   22 x 27½ᶜᵐ.

MT64.A2K3

—— L'art de composer des menuets et des polonoises sur le champ, par Mr. Jean-Phil. Kirnberger.   Berlin, G.-L. Winter, 1757.

10, xxix p.   21 x 28ᶜᵐ.

MT64.A2K4

Anleitung zur singekomposition, mit oden in verschiedenen sylbenmaassen begleitet, von Ioh. Phil. Kirnberger . . . Berlin, G. I. Decker, 1782.

1 p. l., 85, [1] p.   28½ x 32ᶜᵐ.

MT64.A2K5

Gedanken über die verschiedenen lehrarten in der komposition, als vorbereitung zur fugenkenntniss, von Johann Philipp Kirnberger . . . Berlin, G. J. Decker, 1782.

31 p.   22½ x 18ᶜᵐ.

MT55.A2K59

Kirnberger, Johann Philipp—*Continued.*

Grundsätze des generalbasses, als erste linien zur composition von Johan Philip Kirnberger . . . Berlin, J. J. Hummel [1781]

3 p. l., vi, 88 p.; 1 p. l. (blank), 45 pl. on 25 l. (musical examples) 24½ x 20^{cm}.

Another L. of C. copy of the examples has an engr. title, as above, with the words "nebst xxxxv kupfertafeln " added.

MT49.A2K6

Die kunst des reinen satzes in der musik aus sicheren grundsåtzen hergeleitet und mit deutlichen beyspielen erläutert von Joh. Phil. Kirnberger . . . Berlin, In commission bey C. F. Voss, 1771–79.

2 v. 20½ x 17^{cm}.

Title vignette. Vol. 2 is in 3 parts, each having special t.-p., with imprint: Berlin und Königsberg, G. J. Decker und G. L. Hartung, 1776 [–79]
Collation: v. 1: 5 p. l., 250, [5] p. fold. tab., 2 fold. l. (musical examples); v. 2: 2 p. l., 153, [1] p.; 2 p. l., [3]—232, [2] p.; 2 p. l.; [3]–188 p.

MT40.A2K6

Methode sonaten aus 'm ermel zu schüddeln, von Johann Philipp Kirnberger . . . Berlin, Gedruckt bey F. W. Birnstiel, 1783.

7 p. 37½ x 22^{cm}.

MT62.A2K47

Die wahren grundsåtze zum gebrauch der harmonie, darinn deutlich gezeiget wird, wie alle möglichen accorde aus dem dreyklang und dem wesentlichen septimenaccord, und deren dissonirenden vorhålten, herzuleiten und zu erklåren sind, als ein zusatz zu der Kunst des reines satzes in der musik, von Johann Philipp Kirnberger . . . Berlin und Königsberg, G. J. Decker und G. L. Hartung, 1773.

115 (*i. e.* 113) p. 20½ x 17^{cm}. (*With his* Kunst des reinen satzes in der musik. Berlin, 1771–79. v. 1)

Last page numbered 115 for 113.

MT40.A2K6

See also Sulzer, J. G. Allgemeine theorie der schönen künste, 1792–99.

Klein, Johann Joseph, 1740–1823.

Versuch eines lehrbuchs der praktischen musik in systematischer ordnung entworfen von Johann Joseph Klein . . . Mit kupfern. Gera, C. F. Bekmann, 1783.

12 p. l., 264 (*i. e.* 164), [12] p. diagrs. (1 fold.) 21½^{cm}.

Title vignette. No. 132-231 omitted in paging.

MT6.A2K5

Knecht, Justin Heinrich, 1752–1817.

Erklårung einiger von einem der r. g. b. in Erlangen angetasteten, aber missverstandenen grundsåtze aus der Voglerschen theorie . . . von Justin Heinrich Knecht . . . Nebst angehångten anmerkungen über herrn Löhleins einleitung in den zweyten theil seiner Clavierschule. Ulm, Gedruckt bey C. U. Wagner, 1785.

35 p. 22 x 18^{cm}.

Head and tail pieces.
Written in reply to Johann Michael Weissbeck's "Protestationsschrift, oder Exemplarische widerlegung einiger stellen . . . der kapellmeister Voglerischen Tonwissenschaft und tonsetzkunst."

MT40.A2K7

Knecht, Justin Heinrich—*Continued*.

Kleines alphabetisches wôrterbuch der vornehmsten und interessantesten artikel aus der musikalischen theorie. Verfasst von Justin Heinrich Knecht. Ulm, Wohlersche buchhandlung, 1795.

viii, 117 p., 1 l. 20ᶜᵐ.

ML108.A2K5

Vollstândige orgelschule fûr anfânger und geûbtere, hrsg. von Justin Heinrich Knecht . . . Leipzig, Breitkopfische musikhandlung [1795-98]

3 v. 31 x 24ᶜᵐ.

Vol. 3: In der Breitkopf- und Hârtelschen musikhandlung.
Of the six parts announced in the preface of vol. 3 only the first three were published.

CONTENTS.—1. abth. Die anfangsgrûnde der orgelspielkunst.—2. abth. Die kenntnis der vornehmsten orgelregister.—3. abth. Eine theoretisch-praktische abhandlung ûber das choralspiel auf der orgel.

MT182.A2K73

Kobrich, Johann Joseph Anton Bernhard, *b. ca.* 1720.

Johann Anton Kobrichs . . . Grûndliche clavierschule, durchgehends mit praktischen beyspielen erklâret. Augsburg, M. Riegers sel. sôhne, 1782.

2 p. l., 47 p. illus. 35ᶜᵐ.

Title within ornamental border; title vignette; head-piece.
"Kurze anzeige des general-basses": p. 23-32.

MT222.A2K75

Koch, Heinrich Christoph, 1749-1816.

Versuch einer anleitung zur composition, von Heinrich Christoph Koch . . . Leipzig, A. F. Bôhme, 1782-93.

3 v. 18ᶜᵐ.

MT40.A2K76

Koch, Heinrich Christoph, 1749-1816, *editor*.

See JOURNAL der tonkunst, 1795.

Koesfelt, Coenraad Zumbag de.

See ZUMBAG DE KOESFELT, COENRAAD.

Koesfelt, Lothar Zumbag de.

See ZUMBAG DE KOESFELT, COENRAAD. Institutiones musicæ, 1743.

Kollmann, August Friedrich Christoph, 1756-1829.

An essay on musical harmony, according to the nature of that science and the principles of the greatest musical authors. By Augustus Frederic Christopher Kollmann . . . London, J. Dale, 1796.

xviii, 128 p., 40 p. (music, engr.) 34ᶜᵐ.

MT50.A2K8

Kollmann, August Friedrich Christoph—*Continued.*

—— An essay on practical musical composition, according to the nature of that science and the principles of the greatest musical authors. By Augustus Frederic Christopher Kollmann . . . London, Printed for the author, 1799.

xx, 106 p., 1 l., 67 p. (music, engr.) 34^{cm}.

The 1 l. contains list of works published by the author.

MT40.A2K77

Kolof, Lorenz Christoph Mizler von.

See MIZLER VON KOLOF, LORENZ CHRISTOPH.

[Koswick, Michael]

Compendiaria Musice ‖ artis aeditio, cuncta q̃ ad practicam attinent ‖ mira quadam breuitate complectens. ‖ ℂ Cum quibusdam nouis additionibus. ‖ [wdct.] ‖ *Inuentum Samii modosq̃ vatis* ‖ *Si paucis cupias habere verbis* ‖ *Me paruum / facito / legas libellum* ‖ *Et paruo redimas / vale viator.* ‖ ℂ Lipsi impressit Uuolffgangus Monacen̄. 1517.

[30] p. 21½ x 16^{cm}.

Signatures: A in four, B–C in sixes (last leaf blank)
Koswick's name appears in the caption of the dedication.

ML171.K73

[Kraus, Joseph Martin] 1756–1792.

Wahrheiten die musik betreffend, gerade herausgesagt von einem teutschen biedermann. Frankfurt am Mayn, Eichenbergsche erben, 1779.

142 p. 19^{cm}.

In 3 parts: (1) Erstes stück (2) Erste fortsetzung (3) Zweyte fortsetzung.

ML60.K72

[Krause, Christian Gottfried] 1719–1770.

Von der musikalischen poesie . . . Berlin, J. F. Voss, 1752.

11 p. l., 484, [19] p. 18½ x 10½^{cm}.

ML3849.A2K91

Kriner, Joseph, *d.* 1807.

Klavier-meister oder Die durch die theorie aufgelöste practische abhandlung über den general bass mit beygesetzter finger ordnung vom Joseph Kriner, musick compositeur.

[67] p. 28¾^{cm}.

18th cent. ms., presumably the author's autograph.

MT49.A2K84

Kritische briefe über die tonkunst, mit kleinen clavierstücken und singoden begleitet, von einer musikalischen gesellschaft in Berlin . . . Berlin, F. W. Birnstiel, buchdrucker, 1760–64.

3 v. in 2. 22 x 17½^{cm}.

Published weekly June 23, 1759–Sept. 6, 1760; June 20, 1761–Feb. 6, 1762 (none for Dec. 26); June 12, 1762–Jan. 15, 1763; June 11–Sept. 17, 1763. Edited by Friedrich Wilhelm Marpurg, who is also author of the greater part of the letters.

ML4.K92

Kürzinger, Ignaz Franz Xaver.

Getreuer unterricht zum singen mit manieren, und die violin zu spielen. Zum gebrauch und nutzen der anfänger; zur erleichterung deren herren chorregenten, cantoren, thurnermeistern, und andern, die sich mit instruiren beschäftigen. Nebst einem alphabetischen anhang der mehrsten sachen, welche einem rechtschaffenen sänger, oder instrumentisten zu wissen nöthig sind. Zusammengetragen von Ignatz Franz Xaver Kürzinger . . . Augsburg, J. J. Lotter, 1763.

2 p. l., 95, [1] p.   illus.   21½ x 17^{cm}.

MT7.A2K9

Kuhnau, Johann, 1660–1722.

See MYLIUS, A.   Jura circa musicos ecclesiasticos [1688]
    PRINTZ, W. C.   Musicus curiosus, 1691.
                   Musicus magnanimus, 1691.
    WERCKMEISTER, A.   Cribrvm mvsicvm, 1700.

Kuntzen, Johann Paul, 1696–1757.

See MATTHESON, J.   Gültige zeugnisse, 1738.

Kunzen, Friedrich Ludwig Aemilius, 1761–1817, *editor*.

See MUSIKALISCHE monathsschrift [1792]
    MUSIKALISCHES wochenblatt [1791–92]
    STUDIEN für tonkünstler, 1793.

Kurtze anführung zum general-bass, darinnen die regeln, welche bey erlernung des general-basses zu wissen nöthig, kürtzlich und mit wenig worten enthalten. Allen anfängern des claviers zu nützlichen gebrauch zusammen gesetzet. 2. ed. Leipzig, A. Martini, 1733.

8 p. l., 80 p.   17 x 10^{cm}.   (*With* Mizler von Kolof, Lorenz C. Anfangsgründe des general basses. Leipzig [1739])

Dedicated to Mlle. Jeanne Eleonore Wolff; dedication signed "A." Has been attributed to a certain Fräulein von Freudenberg, a young girl, pupil of David Kellner in Stockholm, but the general tenor of the dedication would lead to the supposition that the author was of mature age and was the music teacher of Mlle. Wolff. In the British museum catalogue the work is ascribed to J. F. Andrien.

MT49.A2M68

—— Kurtze und gründliche anleitung zum generalbasse, worinne die zu dieser wissenschaft nöthige regeln kürtzlich und deutlich enthalten. Denen liebhabern des claviers, absonderlich aber den anfängern desselben zum nutzen aufgesetzt. 3. und verb. aufl. Leipzig, A. B. Martin, 1744.

4 p. l., 70 p.   17^{cm}.

MT49.A2K9

Kurtze anweisung zur sing-kunst. Vor die schule zur Neustadt an der Orla. Jena, Gedruckt bey C. L. Kempffen, 1651.

[14] p.   15 x 8½^{cm}.

MT7.A2K94

Kurtzgefasstes musicalisches lexicon, worinnen eine nützliche anleitung und gründlicher begriff von der music enthalten, die termini technici erkläret, die instrumente erläutert und die vornehmsten musici beschrieben sind, nebst einer historischen beschreibung von der music nahmen, eintheilung, ursprung, erfindung, vermehrung und verbesserung . . . Alles aus derer besten und berühmtesten musicorum ihren schrifften mit fleiss zusammen gesucht . . . Chemnitz, J. Christoph und J. D. Stössel, 1737.

8 p. l., 430 p. 17ᶜᵐ.

Taken largely from Walther's Musicalisches lexicon, 1732. Eitner gives as editor a certain Barnickel.

"Verzeichniss derer autorum und bücher, so zu diesem Musicalischen lexico gebraucht worden:" [2] p. preceding p. [1]

ML100.A2K9

—— **Kurtzgefasstes** musicalisches lexicon, worinnen eine nützliche anleitung und gründlicher begriff von der music enthalten, die termini technici erkläret, die instrumente erläutert und die vornehmsten musici beschrieben sind, nebst einer historischen beschreibung von der music nahmen, eintheilung, ursprung, erfindung, vermehrung und verbesserung . . . Alles aus derer besten und berühmtesten musicorum ihren schrifften mit fleiss zusammen gesucht . . . Neue aufl. Chemnitz, J. Christoph und J. D. Stössel, 1749.

431, [1] p. 17½ᶜᵐ.

"Verzeichniss derer autorum und bücher, so zu diesem Musicalischen lexico gebraucht worden": p. [432]

ML100.A2K91

Kurze anweisung das trommel-spielen auf die leichteste art zu erlernen, nebst sieben in noten gesetzte stücke und märsche mit anmerkungen von einem tonkünstler. Berlin, Gedruckt bey G. L. Winters wittwe, 1777.

xix p. 17 x 21ᶜᵐ.

MT662.A2K9

Laag, Heinrich, 1713–1797.

Anfangsgründe zum clavierspielen und generalbas, von Henrich Laag . . . Osnabrück, J. W. Schmid, 1774.

74, [2] p. 20 x 17ᶜᵐ.

MT49.A2L15

L'Abbé *le fils.*

See SAINT-SÉVIN, JOSEPH BARNABÉ.

Labbet, Antoine Jacques, *abbé de Morambert.*

See MORAMBERT, ANTOINE JACQUES LABBET, *abbé* DE.

La Borde, Jean Baptiste de, 1730–1777.

Le clavessin electrique; avec une nouvelle théorie du méchanisme et des phénomenes de l'électricité. Par le R. P. Delaborde . . . Paris, H. L. Guerin & L. F. Delatour, 1761.

xij, 164, [3] p. II fold. pl. 17½ x 10ᶜᵐ.

ML1055.A2L12

[La Borde, Jean Benjamin de] 1734–1794.

Essai sur la musique ancienne et moderne . . .   Paris, Impr. de P.-D. Pierres, et se vend chez E. Onfroy, 1780.

4 v. in 5.   illus., plates, fold. tables.   26 x 20^{cm}.

Vol. [5] has half-title only: Parties séparées des chansons à 4 parties.
"M. l'abbé Roussier a accompagné ce mémoire d'une grande quantité de notes, de quélques observations, & d'une table raisonnée des matieres."—v. 3, p. 678.
"Morceaux de musique du 16.e et 17.e siècle": v. 2, p. 75–108.   "Choix de chansons mises à quatre parties": v. 2, 178 p. at end.

ML100.A2L2

Mémoires historiques sur Raoul de Coucy.   On y a joint le recueil de ses chansons en vieux langage, avec la traduction & l'ancienne musique.   Paris, Impr. de P.-D. Pierres, 1781.

2 v. in 1 (v. 1: 3 p. l., 108 p.; v. 2: 106, 12 p.)   pl., 3 port.   13 x 6½^{cm}.

ML410.C85L1

Mémoires sur les proportions musicales, le genre énarmonique des Grecs et celui des modernes.   Par l'auteur de l'Essai sur la musique. Avec les observations de M. Vandermonde . . . & des remarques de M. l'abbé Roussier.   Supplément a l'Essai sur la musique.   Paris, Impr. de P.-D. Pierres, 1781.

1 p. l., xiv, 70 p.   25½ x 19¼^{cm}.

"Lettre de l'auteur de l'Essai sur la musique, à M. l'abbé Roussier" and "Réponse de M. l'abbé Roussier": p. [i]–xiv.

ML3809.A2L14

Lacassagne, Joseph, *b.* 1720?

Traité général des élémens du chant . . . par M. l'abbé Lacassagne . . . Paris, Chez l'auteur; [etc., etc.] 1766.

4 p. l., 188 p., 2 l.   22^{cm}.

Engraved throughout; ornamental borders.
"Cet ouvrage, imprimé dès 1742, ne fut publié qu'en 1766."—Fétis, Biog. univ. des musiciens.

MT835.A2L2

L'uni-cléfier musical, pour servir de supplément au Traité général des élémens du chant . . . par M. l'abbé Lacassagne, & pour servir de réponse à quelques objections.   [Paris, Impr. de G. Desprez, 1768]

16, xii p.   22^{cm}.   (*With his* Traité général des élémens du chant. Paris, 1766)

Caption title.   Line borders.

MT835.A2L2

Lacépède, Bernard Germain Étienne de La Ville sur Illon, *comte de,* 1756–1825.

La poëtique de la musique.   Par M. le comte de La Cepède . . . Paris, Imprimerie de Monsieur, 1785.

2 v. (v. 1: xij, 384 p.; v. 2: 2 p. l., 352 p.)   20½^{cm}.

ML3845.A2L3

La Croix, A. Phérotée de, *d. ca.* 1715.

L'art de la poësie françoise et latine, avec une idée de la musique sous une nouvelle methode, *Omnia in pondere, numero & mensura.* En trois parties. Par le sieur de La Croix. Lyon, T. Amaulry, 1694.

15 p. l., 662 p. front. 16ᶜᵐ.

PC2504.L2

La Cuisse, de.

Le répertoire des bals, ou Theorie pratique des contredanses, décrites d'une maniere aisée avec des figures démonstratives pour les pouvoir danser facilement, auxquelles on a ajouté les airs notés. Par le Sr de La Cuisse . . . Paris, Cailleau [etc.] 1762–65.

3 v. front. (v. 2) fold. plates, diagrs. 19½ᶜᵐ.

Engraved throughout; line borders. Imprint varies.
Vol. 1 is in 2 parts. The 2d part has special t.-p.: Suite du Répertoire des bals, ou Recueil de contredanses. Par le S. de La Cuisse. Paris, Mᵉˡˡᵉ Castagnery, 1762. The same title occurs in vol. 2 and 3, following the special title, which reads: Suite du Répertoire des bals, ou ii.ᵉᵐᵉ [–3ᵉ] volume du Recueil des airs et figures des meilleures et plus nouvelles contredanses . . .
The dances are in 18 "cahiers," 100 "feuilles," each dance constituting a "feuille" (with special t.-p., vol. 2–3) These parts were issued both separately and in volumes.
Vol. 4 wanting in L. of C. set.

GV1590.L3

La Feillée, François de.

Méthode nouvelle pour apprendre parfaitement les regles du plain-chant et de la psalmodie, avec des messes et autres ouvrages en plain-chant figuré et musical, à l'usage des paroisses et des communautés religieuses. Par Mr de La Feille'e . . . A Poitiers, & se vend a Paris, chez J. T. Herissant, 1748.

3 p. l., 384 p. 17½ᶜᵐ.

"Motets pour les principales fêtes de l'année & autres fêtes ordinaires, à l'élevation du très-saint sacrement": p. 248–300.

MT860.A2L14

—— Méthode nouvelle pour apprendre parfaitement les regles du plain-chant et de la psalmodie, avec des messes & autres ouvrages en plain-chant figuré & musical, à voix seule & en partie . . . 3. ed., augm., rev. & cor. par M. de La Feillée . . . Poitiers, J. Faulcon, l'aîné, 1775.

viii, 600 p. 17ᶜᵐ.

"Motets pour les principales fêtes de l'année, & autres fêtes ordinaires": p. 328–525.

MT860.A2L16

——Il cantore ecclesiastico, ossia Metodo facile per imparare il canto fermo secondo le regole francesi, ridotte in italiana favella, ed ampliate dal prete Ignazio Domenico Foglietti . . . Pinerolo, Dalle stampe di G. Peyras, e G. Scotto, 1786.

252 p. 16½ᶜᵐ.

"Aggiunta di alcune messe proprie de santi concesse da' sommi pontefici, le quali non sono notate in canto nel Graduale romano, ed alle quali si è aggiunto il canto": p. 151–208. "Quinque missæ pro majoribus festis, auctore D. D. Humont": p. 209–248.

MT860.A2F78

La Ferté, Denis Pierre Jean Papillon de.

See PAPILLON DE LA FERTÉ, DENIS PIERRE JEAN.

L'Affillard, Michel.

Principes tres-faciles pour bien apprendre la musique, qui conduiront promptement ceux qui ont du naturel pour le chnat [!], jusqu'au point de chanter toute sorte de musique proprement, et à livre ouvert; par le S^r L'Affillard ... Très-nouvelle ed., à l'usage du monde. [Paris] Impr. de J–B–C. Ballard, 1747.

185, [1] p.   2 fold. pl.   12½ x 19^{cm}.

MT870.A2L3

Lafond, Jean François de.

A new system of music, both theorical and practical, and yet not mathematical: written in a manner intirely new; that's to say, in a style plane and intelligible; and calculated to render the art more charming, the teaching not only less tedious, but more profitable, and the learning easier by three quarters ... By John Francis de La Fond ... London, Printed for the author, 1725.

4 p. l., lxxxiii, 180, [6] p.   20^{cm}.

Following the text are the words "The end of the first volume"; according to Barclay Squire, no more of the work has been published.

MT7.A2L16

Laisement, Charles Louis Denis Ballière de.

See BALLIÈRE DE LAISEMENT, CHARLES LOUIS DENIS.

Lambranzi, Gregorio.

Nuoua e curiosa scvola de' balli theatrali. Prima parte continente cinquanta balli di diverse nationi, e figure theatrali con i loro vestimenti, si che, come si deue contenera nelle positure di questi balli rapresentate da una leggiera, ma virtuosa maniera, e con le arie, e con pieno, e necessario auvertimento, come ogn' uno hà da contenersi in simili balli, si che questi ancor senza d'un ballarino si possono facilmente apprenderli, e senza aver conoscenza della chorographia ogn'uno da se solo con ogni facilita legendo i medemi e uedendo le positure potrà imprimerseli nella memoria, inuentati e dati alla luce, da Gregorio Lambranzi, maestro de' balli francesi, inglesi, ridiculi e serij in aria ed à terra, e compositore de' balli theatrali, disegnati, e intagliati da Giovanni Giorgio Puschner, intagliator di rame in Norimberga a: MDCCXVI.

2 v. in 1 (v. 1: 2 p. l., 4 p., 50 pl.; v. 2: 1 p. l., 51 pl.)   30^{cm}.

Italian title followed by title in German on t.-p. of v. 1. Added t.-p. "Deliciæ theatrales," with port. of the author.

Vol. 2 has illustrated title: Sig: Greg: Lambranzi, maestro di balli. Neue und curjevse theatrialische tantz-schul zweitter theil. Nürnberg, Verlegt von Ioh. Iacob Wolrab.

Preface and description of the dances in Italian, followed by same preface in German. Each plate has at head the tune for the dance represented and at foot the description in German.

MT950.A2L27

La Molette, Philippe du Contant de.

See DU CONTANT DE LA MOLETTE, PHILIPPE.

[Lamorlière, Jacques Rochette de] 1719–1785.

Lettre d'un sage a un homme très respectable, & dont il a besoin . . . [Paris, 1754]

1 p. l., 18 p. 17½^{cm}.

A reply to Jean Jacques Rousseau's "Lettre sur la musique françoise."
"Reponse de l'homme respectable": p. 18.

ML1727.33.L2

[La Mothe Le Vayer, François de] 1588–1672.

Discovrs sceptiqve svr la mvsiqve. [Paris, 1662 ?]

p. 535–552. 35½^{cm}.

Caption title.
Ms. note on fly-leaf: Taken from his Works, Paris, 1662, 2 vols. folio. This "Discours" was (first?) printed by Mersenne, to whom it was addressed, in his "Questions harmoniques," Paris, 1634, a fact which Fétis seems to have overlooked. (Signed "J. E. M.," i. e. James E. Matthew)

ML63.L16

Petit discovrs chrestien de l'immortalité de l'ame: auec le corollaire, & vn discours sceptique sur la musique. 3. ed. Paris, A. de Sommaville, 1647.

4 p. l., 251, [1] p., 1 l. 16^{cm}.

Ch.17.1781

Lampadius, Autor, *d.* 1559.

Compendivm mvsices, tam figurati quàm plani cantus ad formam dialogi, in usum ingenuæ pubis ex eruditis musicorum scriptis accurate cōgestum, quale ante hac nunquam uisum, & iam recens publicatum. Adiectis etiam regulis de concordantiarum & componendi cantus artificio, summatim omnia musices præcepta pulcherrimis exemplis illustrata, succincte & simpliciter complectens. Præterea additæ svnt formvlæ intonandi psalmos, & ratio accentus ecclesiastici, legendorum quoque euangeliorum & epistolarum. Ab Avctore Lampadio Luneburgensi elaborata. Bernæ in Helvetiis, per S. Apiarium, 1554.

[112] p. 15½^{cm}.

Signatures: A–G in eights. Printer's mark on last page.
Preface by Eberhard von Rümlang, dated 1546; dedication dated 1537. 1st edition Bern, 1537.

ML171.L16

Lampe, Friedrich Adolf, 1683–1729.

Friderici Adolfi Lampe De cymbalis vetervm libri tres, in quibus quaecunque ad eorum nomina, differentiam, originem, historiam, ministros, ritus pertinent, elucidantur . . . Trajecti ad Rhenum, ex [officina] bibliopolae Guilielmi a Poolsum, 1703.

15 p. l., 405, [43] p. 9 pl. 14 x 7½^{cm}.

Added t.-p., engr.
"Index authorum, qui hoc tractatu citantur": p. [430–440]

ML169.A2L23

Lampe, John Frederick, *d.* 1751.

The art of musick. By John Frederick Lampe . . . London, C. Corbett, 1740.

5 (*i. e.* 4), [4], 60 p.   9 pl.   20^{cm}.

ML3836.A2L3

A plain and compendious method of teaching thorough bass . . . With proper rules for practice. The examples and lessons curiously engraved on copper plates. By John Frederick Lampe . . . London, J. Wilcox, 1737.

1 p. l., viii, 9–45 p.   93 pl. (partly fold.)   28^{cm}.

MT49.A2L23

Lanfranco, Giovanni Maria.

Scintille di mvsica di ‖ Giovan Maria Lanfranco da Te- ‖ rentio Parmegiano, che mostrano a leggere il Canto Fermo, ‖ & Figurato, Gli accidēti delle Note Misurate, Le Pro- ‖ portioni, I Tuoni, Il Contrapunto, Et la diuisione ‖ del Monochordo, Cō la accordatura de ua- ‖ rii instrumenti, Dalla quale nasce un ‖ Modo, onde ciascū per se stesso ‖ imparare potra le uoci di ‖ La, Sol, Fa, Mi, Re, Vt . . . ‖ In Brescia per Lodouico Britannico 1533.

4 p. l., 143 p.   diagrs.   15½ x 21^{cm}.

ML171.L26

Langlé, Honoré François Marie, 1741–1807.

Traité d'harmonie et de modulation, par H. F. M. Langlé . . . Ce traité est divisé en deux parties, la 1re donne la connoissance de tous les ac.^{ds} praticables en harmonie, la seconde renferme toutes les modulations possibles . . . Paris, Vve Naderman [1797]

1 p. l., 96 p.   34^{cm}.

Engraved throughout. Label of Cochet, Paris, mounted over imprint.
An earlier edition was published by Boyer in 1793.

MT50.A2L27

Traité de la basse sous le chant, précédé de toutes les regles de la composition, par H. F. M. Langle . . . Paris, Naderman [1798]

1 p. l., 304 p.   33 x 25½^{cm}.

MT40.A2L27

[Laporte, Joseph de] 1713–1779.

Anecdotes dramatiques . . . Paris, Veuve Duchesne, 1775.

3 v.   17½^{cm}.

By J. M. B. Clément and the Abbé de Laporte.

CONTENTS.—v. 1. Pièces de théatre. A–M.—v. 2. N–Z. Supplément. Anecdotes.—v. 3. Auteurs et acteurs. A–Z. Additions. Arrêts et réglements, concernant la Comédie françoise. Réglements concernant la Comédie italienne. État des personnes qui composent l'Academie royale de musique, en janvier 1775. État des Comédiens ordinaires du roi, janvier 1775. État des comédiens italiens ordinaires du roi.

ML102.O6C6

[Larghi, Desiderio]

Il modo di solfeggiare all' uso francese-ricavato da due lettere familiari, scritte da uno ad un' altro amico in lingua toscana, introdotto nuovamente in Siena dal m. r. Signore Fausto Frittelli . . . Siena, Nella stamp. del pub., 1744.

26 p. 21cm.

The letters are signed: Desiderio Larghi.

MT44.A2L17

Lasalle,

Analyse du Rapport de M. Jean-Jacques Le Roue, administrateur des etablissemens publics, concernant l'Opéra; présenté à M. le procureur-général-syndic du département de Paris, par le sieur de La Salle, secrétaire perpétuel de l'Académie royale de musique, bréveté du roi. [Paris, Impr. de Mayer & compagnie, 1791?]

31 p. 20cm.

Caption title.

ML1727.8.P2L17

La Salle, Jean François Démotz de.

See DÉMOTZ DE LA SALLE, JEAN FRANÇOIS.

Lasser, Johann Baptist, 1751–1805.

Vollständige anleitung zur singkunst, sowohl für den sopran, als auch für den alt. Von Johann Baptist Lasser . . . München, Zu finden beym verfasser, und in der Falterschen musikhandlung, 1798.

176 p. incl. 4 pl. 20½ x 25½cm.

The 1st edition appeared under title: "Anleitung zur singkunst," Landshut, without date. *cf.* Wurzbach, Biog. lex. d. kaiserthums Oesterreich.

MT885.A2L16

[Latour de Franqueville, *Mme.* de] *d.* 1789.

Mon dernier mot [ou Réponse à la lettre que M. D. L. B. a adressée à M. l'abbé Roussier, en tête du supplément à l'Essai sur la musique, par l'auteur de l'Errata de l'Essai sur la musique: Paris? 1781]

1 p. l., 50 p. 22cm.

By some authorities attributed to Pierre Gaviniés.
"[Réimprimé] dans le 30e volume des Œuvres de J. J. Rousseau, édit. de Genève, 1782."—Quérard, La France littéraire.

ML100.A2L3

[Laugier, Marc Antoine] 1711–1769.

Apologie de la musique françoise, contre M. Rousseau. *Nostras qui despicit artes barbarus est.* [Paris] 1754.

2 p. l., 78 p. 19½cm. (*With* Rochemont, de. Reflexions d'un patriote. Lausanne, 1754)

ML1727.33.R67

Sentiment d'un harmoniphile, sur différens ouvrages de musique . . . A Amsterdam, et se trouve à Paris, chez Jombert [etc., 1756]

168 p. 12 fold. pl. (music) 18 x 10cm.

In two parts; part 1 dated at end: Mars, 1756.
Erroneously attributed to the Abbé Morambert and Antoine de Léris. *cf.* Freystätter, Die musikal. zeitschriften, and Fétis, Biog. univ. des musiciens.

ML195.L18

L'Aulnaye, François Henri Stanislas de, 1739–1830.

De la saltation théatrale, ou Recherches sur l'origine, les progrès, & les effets de la pantomime chez les anciens, avec neuf planches coloriées . . . par M. de L'Aulnaye . . .   Paris, Barrois l'aîné, 1790.

2 p. l., 100, civ p.   viii pl.   20½ᶜᵐ.

Ch. 34.3016

L'Aulnaye, François Henri Stanislas de, 1739–1830, *editor.*

See ROUSSIER, P. J.   Mémoire sur la nouvelle harpe, 1782.

Lauremberg, Peter, 1585–1639, *editor.*

See SARTORIUS, E.   Musomachia, 1642.

Lauriso Tragiense, *academic name.*

See BIANCHI, GIOVANNI ANTONIO.

[Laus de Boissy, M. A.] *b.* 1747.

Lettre critique sur les ballets de l'opéra, adressée à l'auteur du Spectateur français, par un homme de mauvaise humeur.   2. éd. . . .   [Paris, 17—]

vij, [3]–27 p.   19ᶜᵐ.

Reprint of his "Lettre critique sur notre danse théâtrale," Paris, 1771.   *cf.* Quérard, La France littéraire.

ML3460.A2L6

[La Vallière, Louis César de La Baume Le Blanc, *duc* de] 1708–1780.

Ballets, opera, et autres ouvrages lyriques, par ordre chronologique depuis leur origine; avec une table alphabetique des ouvrages et des auteurs.   Paris, C. J. B. Bauche, 1760.

4 p. l., 298, [2] p.   18½ᶜᵐ.

Title vignette.

ML102.O6L16

Lavington, George, *bp. of Exeter,* 1684–1762.

The influence of church-music.   A sermon preach'd in the cathedral-church of Worcester, at the anniversary meeting of the choirs of Worcester, Hereford, and Gloucester, September 8. 1725 . . .   By George Lavington . . .   2d ed.   London, J. & J. Knapton, 1726.

26 (*i. e.* 34) p.   19ᶜᵐ.

Pages 33–34 wrongly numbered 25–26.

ML64.L8

La Voye Mignot,   de.

Traité de mvsiqve, povr bien et facilement apprendre à chanter & composer, tant pour les voix que pour les instruments.   Divisé en trois parties.   Où se voyent tous les exemples des principales regles & obseruations pratiquées par les plus excellens autheurs.   Par le sieur de La Voye.   Paris, R. Ballard, imprimeur, se vendent chez R. de Ninville, 1656.

2 p. l., 107 (*i. e.* 115), [7] p.   22½ x 17ᶜᵐ.

Page 115 wrongly numbered 107.

MT6.A2L29

The **lawfulness**, excellency and advantage of instrumental music. A 2d ed. (with necessary improvements, which now render the sense entirely plain) of the Lawfulness, excellency and advantage of instrumental music in the public worship of God, but chiefly of organs. Philadelphia, A. Steuart, 1763.

16 p. 18°.

Title taken from the old L. of C. printed catalogue. The pamphlet itself is misplaced and could not be found for recataloguing.

Apparently this is not a *bona fide* second edition of the pamphlet "The lawfulness and advantage of instrumental musick in the public worship of God . . . By a Presbyterian" (Philadelphia, W. Dunlap, 1763. 38 p.) but a satirical reply. Compare Sonneck's "Francis Hopkinson and James Lyon," 1905, p. 131–132.

Lebeuf, Jean, 1687–1760.

Traité historique et pratique sur le chant ecclesiastique. Avec le directoire qui en contient les principes & les régles, suivant l'usage présent du diocèse de Paris, & autres. Précedé d'une nouvelle methode, pour l'enseigner, & l'apprendre facilement. Par M. l'abbé Lebeuf . . . Paris, C. J. B. Herissant [etc.] 1741.

4 p. l., 190, [6] p. 18^{cm}.

ML3082.A2L4

Le Blanc, Hubert.

Defense de la basse de viole contre les entréprises du violon et les prétentions du violoncel. Par Monsieur Hubert Le Blanc . . . Amsterdam, P. Mortier, 1740.

4 p. l., 148, [12] p. 13½^{cm}.

ML760.A2L4

Le Blanc, Louis César de La Baume, *duc de La Vallière.*

See LA VALLIÈRE, LOUIS CÉSAR DE LA BAUME LE BLANC, *duc* DE.

Leblond, Gaspar Michel, *called,* 1738–1809, *editor.*

See MÉMOIRES pour servir a l'histoire de la révolution opérée dans la musique, 1781.

[Le Cerf de La Viéville, Jean Laurent, *seigneur de Freneuse*] 1674–1707.

Comparaison de la musique italienne et de la musique françoise. Bruxelles, F. Foppens, 1704–06.

3 v. in 1. 17^{cm}.

Vol. 2 has title: Comparaison [etc.] Où, en examinant en détail les avantages des spectacles, & le mérite des compositeurs des deux nations, on montre quelles sont les vrayes beautez de la musique. 2. partie, qui contient, une nouvelle lettre. Un recueil de vers chantans. Et trois nouveaux dialogues. Dans lesquels sont renfermez, une histoire de la musique, & des opera. Une vie de Lulli. Une réfutation du traité de Mr Perraut, De la musique des anciens. Et un traité du bon goût en musique . . .

Vol. 3 has title: Comparaison [etc.] 3. partie, qui contient des fragmens d'un opera chrétien. Un discours sur la musique d'eglise. Une réponse à la Défense du Paralelle. Et un eclaircissement sur Buononcini.

Occasioned by Raguenet's "Parallèle des Italiens et des François en ce qui concerne la musique."

ML194.A2L3

See also BONNET, J. Histoire de la musique, 1726.

Leclerc, Jean Baptiste, 1756–1826.

Essai sur la propagation de la musique en France, sa conservation, et ses rapports avec le gouvernement, par J.-B. Leclerc . . . Paris, Imprimerie nationale, prairial, an ıv [1796]

66 p.   21ᶜᵐ.

ML270.3.L4

Ledwich, Edward, 1738–1823.

See WALKER, J. C.   Historical memoirs, 1786.

Lefébure, Louis François Henri, 1754–1839.

Bevues, erreurs et méprises de différents auteurs célèbres, en matières musicales.   Par M. Lefebure.   Paris, Knapen fils, 1789.

2 p. l., iv, [2], ij, 236, ij, [5] p., 1 l.   16ᶜᵐ.

ML3851.L4

Nouveau solfége, par L. Lefébure.   A Venise, et se trouve a Paris, chez Cailleau, 1780.

23 p.   pl.   20½ᶜᵐ.

MT44.A2L3

[Le Fèvre, Jacques] *d'Étaples, d.* 1537.

Musica libris quatuor demonstrata.   Parisiis, apud Gulielmum Cauellat, 1552.

44 numb. l.   diagrs.   20½ᶜᵐ.

Printer's mark on t.-p.
First edition, Paris, 1496.

ML171.L4

Leipziger allgemeine musikalische zeitung.

See ALLGEMEINE musikalische zeitung [1798]–1882.

Leite, Antonio da Silva.

See SILVA LEITE, ANTONIO DA.

Lenain,

Elemens de musique, ou Abrege' d'une theorie, dans laquelle on peut apprendre avec facilité l'art de raisonner & les principes de cette science: ouvrage utile aux commençans, & à ceux même qui ont des connoissances plus étendues.   Par M. Lenain . . .   Paris, Dessain junior [etc.] 1766.

1 p. l., xii, 156, [2] p.   17 x 9½ᶜᵐ.

MT7.A2L56

[Leopold, G.]

Gedanken eines liebhabers der tonkunst über herrn Nichelmanns tractat von der melodie.   [Nordhausen, 1755]

16 p.   21½ x 17½ᶜᵐ.   (*With* Baron, Ernst G.   . . . Abriss einer abhandlung von der melodie.   Berlin, 1756)

Caption title.
Signed: Caspar Dünkelfeind [pseud. of G. Leopold]

ML3851.B18

[Leopold, Georg August Julius] 1755–1827.

Gedanken und konjekturen zur geschichte der musik. Stendal, D. C. Franzen und J. C. Grosse, 1780.

39 p. 17ᶜᵐ.

ML3845.A2L4

Le Pileur d'Apligny,

Traité sur la musique, et sur les moyens d'en perfectionner l'expression. Par M. Le Pileur d'Apligny . . . Paris, Demonville [etc.] 1779.

viii, 174, [2] p. 19½ᶜᵐ.

ML3845.A2L5

[Le Prévost d'Exmes, François] 1729–1793.

Lully, musicien. [Paris, 1785?]

48 p. 19ᶜᵐ.
Caption title.
"Chiefly compiled by Le Prévost d'Exmes from various articles written by Sénecé, de Fresneuse, and Titon du Tillet."—Grove, Dict. of music.
Apparently issued as part of a series. Only a small portion of the paper cover remains, on the back, and on this is printed "Théâtre. 3." At end of text: "Fin de la vie de Lully."

———— ———— Copy 2.

To this copy are prefixed 3 prelim. leaves, a title-page (Portique ancien et moderne . . . 1. cahier. Paris, Cussac, 1785) and 2 leaves with "Approbation" and "Privilege du roi." The privilege is granted to "le sieur Joly," for "des ouvrages de sa composition, intitulés: Portique ancien et moderne." According to Barbier, the 1. cahier of the Portique is all that was published, and contains, not "Lully," but "Nanteuil."

ML410.L95L5

Léris, Antoine de, 1723–1795.

Dictionnaire portatif historique et littéraire des théatres, contenant l'origine des différens théatres de Paris; le nom de toutes les pieces qui y ont été représentées depuis leur établissement, & celui des pieces jouées en province, ou qui ont simplement paru par la voie de l'impression depuis plus de trois siecles; avec des anecdotes & des remarques sur la plûpart: le nom, & les particularités intéressantes de la vie des auteurs, musiciens & acteurs; avec le catalogue de leurs ouvrages, & l'exposé de leurs talens: une chronologie des auteurs, & des musiciens; avec une chronologie de tous les opéra, & des pieces qui ont paru depuis trente-trois ans. Par M. de Léris. 2. ed., rev., cor. & considérablement augm. Paris, C. A. Jombert, 1763.

xxxiv, 730 (*i. e.* 744) p. 17½ᶜᵐ.
Last 2 pages numbered 729–730 for 743–744.

Z2174.D7L4

See also LAUGIER, M. A. Sentiment d'un harmoniphile [1756]

Leroux, Jean Jacques, 1749–1832.

. . . Rapport sur l'Opéra, présenté au Corps municipal, le 17 août 1791, par J. J. Leroux, officier municipal, nommé administrateur au Département des établissemens publics, le 15 février dernier. Paris [Impr. de Le Becq] 1791.

2 p. l., 98 p., 1 l. 3 fold. tab. 21½ᶜᵐ.
At head of title: Municipalité de Paris. Administration des etablissemens publics.

ML1727.3.A2P2

Le Sueur, Jean François, 1760–1837.

Suite de l'Essai sur la musique sacrée et imitative, où l'on donne le plan d'une musique propre à la fête de Pâque. Par M. Le Sueur ... Paris, Veuve Herissant, 1787.

103 p. 21½^{cm}.

"Motet pour la veille de Pâque: La résurrection" (words only, Latin and French): p. [29]–39.

ML3869.A2L2

[Lesuire, Robert Martin] 1737–1815.

Lettre de M. Camille Trillo [*pseud.*] fausset de la cathédrale d'Ausch, sur la musique dramatique. Paris, Quillau l'aîné, 1777.

1 p. l., [5]–43 p. 16½^{cm}.

ML1727.35.L35

Lettera dell' autore del nvovo cembalo angelico inventato in Roma nell' anno MDCCLXXV. che serve d' istruzione per costruire lo stesso cembalo e ne significa i pregj. Roma, Stamperia di G. Zempel [1775]

38 p., 1 l. fold. pl. 20^{cm}.

ML655.A2L3

Lettre au sujet du spectacle des Avantures d'Ulisse a son retour du siége de Troye, jusqu'à son arrivée en Itaque. Tiré de l'Odissée d'Homere. Ouvert au palais des Thuilleries, dans la salle des machines, au mois de mars 1741. Inventé par le chevalier Servandoni ... Paris, Prault fils, 1741.

16 p. 19^{cm}.

No. 12 in a volume of pamphlets lettered Quere[lle] des Bouffo[ns]

ML1727.33.A1

Lettre d'un amateur de l'opera a M. de * * *, dont la tranquille habitude est d'attendre les évenemens pour juger du mérite des projets. A Amsterdam, et se vend a Paris, chez Couturier père, 1776.

1 p. l., 5–69 p. 19½^{cm}.

ML1727.3.A2L67

Lettre d'un Parisien, a son ami, en province, sur le nouveau spectacle des Eleves de l'Opéra, ouvert le 7 janvier ... Paris, Chez les marchands de nouveautés, & audit spectacle, 1779.

16 p. 19^{cm}.

"Les Eleves pour la danse de l'Opéra, ce théatre attendu depuis si long-tems ... s'est enfin ouvert le jeudi 7 janvier 1779, par la premiere représenta-tion de Jérusalem délivrée, ou Renaud & Armide, tragédie-pantomime en quatre actes [par M. Lebœuf]"

ML1727.8.P2L3

Lettre de M. de * * * à Madame de * * * sur les opera de Phæton, et Hyppolite et d'Aricie. [Paris, Impr. de C. F. Simon, fils, 1743]

15 p. 20½^{cm}.

ML1727.3.A2L65

Lettre de M. * * * négociant de Paris, a M. * * * son correspondant a D * * *. Au sujet de la messe solemnelle qui a été chantée en musique à grand-chœur & grand-orchestre, par MM. de l'Académie royale de musique, ou l'Opéra, dans l'eglise du prieuré royal des Bénédictins de S. Martin-des-Champs, au mois de décembre dernier, au profit des pauvres prisonniers détenus pour mois de nourrices. Le produit de la quête versé dans les mains de MM. de Boissy, trésoriers de la Société de charité de ces pauvres . . . [n. p.] 1786.

60 p. 16½cm.

ML3027.8.P2L2

Le Vayer, François de La Mothe.

See LA MOTHE LE VAYER, FRANÇOIS DE.

Levens,

Abregé des regles de l'harmonie, pour aprendre la composition, avec un nouveau projet sur un systéme de musique sans temperament, ni cordes mobiles . . . par Mr. Levens . . . Bordeaux, J. Chappuis, 1743.

viij, 92 p. 26 x 19½cm.

MT50.A2L38

[Lévesque, *Mme*. Louise (Cavelier)] 1703–1745.

Lettres et chansons, de Cephise et d'Uranie. Paris, Impr. de J. B. C. Ballard, 1731.

87, [4] p. 21½cm.

M1619.A2L65

Liberati, Antimo.

Lettera scritta dal Sig. Antimo Liberati in risposta ad vna del Sig. Ovidio Persapegi che gli fà istanza di voler vedere, ed' essaminare i componimenti di musica fatti dalli cinque concorrenti nel concorso per il posto di maestro di cappella della Metropolitana di Milano fatto sotto il dì 18. agosto 1684 . . . [Roma, Il Mascardi, 1685]

63, [1] p. 22 x 17cm.

Caption title.

MT55.A2L3

Light, Edward, 1747–1832.

The art of playing the guittar, by Edward Light; to which is added a variety of the most familiar lessons, airs, divertimentos, songs &c. properly adapted for that instrument. London, J. Preston [1795?]

1 p. l., 41 p. 23cm.

Engraved throughout.

MT580.A2L47

Lingke, Georg Friedrich, *d.* 1779?

George Friedrich Lingkens . . . Kurze musiklehre, in welcher nicht allein die verwandschaft aller tonleitern, sondern auch die jeder

Lingke, Georg Friedrich—*Continued.*

zukommenden harmonischen sätze gezeigt, und mit praktischen bey-spielen erläutert werden.   Leipzig, J. G. I. Breitkopf, 1779.

> viii, 86 p.   21½ x 17½^{cm}.
>
> Preface signed: Johann Adam Hiller.
>
> MT50.A2L4

Die sitze der musicalischen haupt-sätze in einer harten und weichen tonart und wie man damit fortschreitet und ausweichet in zwo tabellen entworffen, erklärt und mit exempeln erläutert von George Friedrich Lingken.   Leipzig, Gedruckt und in commission bey B. C. Breitkopf und sohn, 1766.

> 4 p. l., 60 p.   2 fold. tab.   22½ x 18½^{cm}.
>
> MT52.A2L42

> *See also* EINIGE . . . musikalische erwegungs- und andere . . . uibungs-wahrheiten [1750?]

Linguet,

Risposta di Linguet al Signor . . . .   Apologia della musica. [Napoli, 1786]

> 2 p. l., 3–163 p.   17½^{cm}
>
> Dedication signed: Nicola Pellegrini barone.
>
> ML63.M165

Linley, Francis, 1774–1800.

A new assistant for the piano-forte or harpsichord, containing the necessary rudiments for beginners, with twelve airs or short lessons, progressively arrang'd: to which is added, six sonatas . . . with pre-ludes, rules for thorough bass, a short dictionary of musical terms. &c. . . . compil'd, compos'd, and arrang'd, by F. Linley . . .   Balti-more printed & sold by I: Carr, and by B: Carr, Philadelphia & New York [179–]

> 3 p. l., [3]–32 p.   33^{cm}.
>
> Engraved throughout.
>
> MT222.A2L70

Lippius, Johann, 1585–1612.

Synopsis musicæ novæ omnino veræ atque methodicæ vniversæ, in omnis sophiæ prægustum παρέργως inventæ disputatæ & propositæ omnibus philomusis. Á M. Joanne Lippio . . .   Argentorati, im-pensis Pauli Ledertz, typis Caroli Kieffer, 1612.

> [160] p.   diagrs.   16½^{cm}.
>
> Signatures:):(, A–I in eights. Between leaves D8 and E is a folding leaf, "Nova scala syntona compendiosissima," 18 x 32^{cm}.
>
> MT6.A2L47

Lippius, Johann, 1585–1612, *præses.*

Disputatio musica prima[-tertia] . . .   Wittebergæ, typis I. Gor-mani, 1609–10.

> 3 v. in 1.   illus.   18 x 15½^{cm}.
>
> Diss.—Wittenberg (S. Carolus, respondent).
> Title within woodcut border. Subtitle varies.
>
> ML3809.A2L3

Lipsius, Justus, 1547–1606.

See PUTEANUS, E. Mvsathena, 1602.

Lirou, Jean François Espic de.

See ESPIC DE LIROU, JEAN FRANÇOIS.

Listenius, Nicolaus.

Mvsica Nicolai Listenii, ab avtore denuo recognita, multisq̱ nouis regulis & exemplis adaucta. Norimbergæ, apud Gabrielem Heyn, 1557.

[86] p.   16ᶜᵐ.

Signatures: a–e in eights, f in four (last leaf blank)
The 1st edition, Wittenberg, 1533, and several of the subsequent editions were published under title: Rudimenta musicæ.

MT6.A2L77

Liverziani, Giuseppe.

Grammatica della musica, o sia Nuovo, e facile metodo per istruirsi nell' intero corso della musica, non per anche posto in ordine da alcuno, ove premesse le notizie istoriche, e le proprietà della medesima, s'insegnano fin dai più remoti principj le regole per ben cantare, e suonare il cembalo, indi si procede allo studio del contrapunto, e composizione prattica. Di Giuseppe Liverziani . . . Parte prima. Roma, Stamperia P. Cracas, 1797.

xvi, 88 p. incl. front. (port.)   20ᶜᵐ.

No more published.

MT7.A2L78

Livre de galoubet.

36 unnumb. p.   12 x 20ᶜᵐ.

Anonymous 18th cent. ms. instruction book.

MT720.G3

Lobos, Mathias de Sousa Villa.

See SOUSA VILLA LOBOS, MATHIAS DE.

Locke, Matthew, 1630?–1677.

The present practice of musick vindicated against the exceptions and new way of attaining musick lately publish'd by Thomas Salmon, M. A. &c.; by Matthew Locke . . . To which is added Dvellvm mvsicvm by John Phillips, gent., together with a letter from John Playford to Mr. T. Salmon by way of confutation of his Essay, &c. . . . London, N. Brooke [etc.] 1673.

2 p. l., 96 p.   17ᶜᵐ.

ML432.A2S22

Löfgrön, Anton.

See BURMAN, E.   Dissertatio musica [1728]

Löhlein, Georg Simon, 1727–1781.

Anweisung zum violinspielen, mit pracktischen beyspielen und zur uebung mit vier und zwanzig kleinen duetten erläutert, von George Simon Löhlein. Leipzig und Züllichau, Waysenhaus- und Frommannische buchhandlung, 1774.

6 p. l., 136 p.   illus.   18 x 21½cm.

Title vignette.

MT262.A2L62

—— George Simon Löhlein's Anweisung zum violinspielen, mit praktischen beyspielen und zur uebung mit zwölf kleinen duetten erläutert, zum dritten mahl mit verbesserungen und zusätzen, auch mit zwölf balletstücken aus der oper Andromeda und der oper Brenno verm. hrsg. von Johann Friederich Reichardt. Leipzig und Züllichau, F. Frommann, 1797.

2 p. l., 123 p.   illus.   18½ x 22cm.

MT262.A2L63

Georg Simon Löhleins Clavier-schule, oder Kurze und gründliche anweisung zur melodie und harmonie, durchgehends mit practischen beyspielen erkläret. Leipzig und Züllichau, Waisenhaus- und Frommannische buchhandlung, 1765.

6 p. l., 188 p.   17½ x 22½cm.

Title vignette. In L. of C. copy the imprint date is partly erased.

MT224.A2L72

—— Georg Simon Löhleins Clavier-schule, oder Kurze und gründliche anweisung zur melodie und harmonie, durchgehends mit practischen beyspielen erkläret . . . Leipzig und Züllichau, Waisenhaus- und Frommannische buchhandlung, 1781–82.

2 v. in 1 (v. 1: 4 p. l., 190, [2] p.; v. 2: 4 p. l., 188 p.)   18 x 22½cm.

Title vignette. Vol. 1: 4. und verb. aufl., 1782.
Vol. 2 has title: Georg Simon Löhleins Clavier-schule, zweyter band. Worinnen eine vollständige anweisung zur begleitung der unbezifferten bässe / und andern im ersten bande fehlenden harmonien gegeben wird: durch sechs sonaten / mit begleitung einer violine erkläret. Nebst einem zusatze vom recitativ.

MT224.A2L73

Loescher, Caspar, 1636–1718, *praeses.*

. . . Dissertatio historico-theologica, de Saule per musicam curato . . . ex I. Sam. XVI, 14. seqq. . . . Wittenbergæ, typis C. Schrödteri [1688]

78, [2] p.   19cm.

Diss.—Wittenberg (Heinrich Pipping, respondent and author)

ML3920.A2L8

Löwen, Johann Friedrich, 1727–1771

See HERTEL, J. W.   Sammlung musikalischer schriften, 1757–58.

London. Academy of ancient music.

See ACADEMY of ancient music.

Loonsma, Stephanus Theodorus van.

Muzicaal A, B,-boek, of Den organist in zyn leerjaaren, zynde een kort begrip wegens de behandeling van het clauwier of clavicimbaal-spel. Opgesteld ten dienste voor de eerst beginnende jeugd . . . Door Step. Theod. van Loonsma . . . Amsterdam, A. Olofsen, 1741.

41, [1] p. incl. 6 pl. on 4 fold. l. 20 x 15½^{cm}.

Title vignette.

MT182.A2L86

López, Isidro, *editor.*

See PÉREZ CALDERÓN, M. Explicacion de solo el canto-llano, 1779.

López de Velasco, Sebastián, *editor.*

See MONTANOS, F. DE. Arte de canto llano, 1670.

López Remacha, Miguel, 1772–1827.

Arte de cantar, y compendio de documentos músicos respectivos al canto, por D. Miguel Lopez Remacha . . . Madrid, B. Cano, 1799.

8 p. l., 118 p. 2 fold. pl. 14½^{cm}.

MT820.A2L7

Lorente, Andrés, 1624–1703.

El porqve de la mvsica, en qve se contiene los qvatro artes de ella, canto llano, canto de organo, contrapvnto, y composicion, y en cada vno de ellos nvevas reglas, razon abreviada, en vtiles preceptos, aun en las cosas mas dificiles, tocantes à la harmonia musica, nvmerosos exemplos, con clara inteligencia, en estilo breve, que al maestro deleytan, y al discipulo enseñan, cuya direccion se verà sucintamente anotada antes del prologo . . . Por . . . el maestro Andres Lorente . . . Alcalà de Henares, Impr. de N. de Xamares, 1672.

14 p. l., 695 p. pl. 29½^{cm}.

MT40.A2L86

Lorenzoni, Antonio.

Saggio per ben sonare il flautotraverso; con alcune notizie generali ed utili per qualunque strumento, ed altre concernenti la storia della musica: opera del d.^{r} Antonio Lorenzoni. Vicenza, F. Modena, 1779.

91 p. illus. (coat of arms) IV fold. pl. 25^{cm}.

Title vignette; tail-piece.
According to Rockstro, this is an abridgment of Quantz's "Versuch."

MT340.A2L7

Loriti, Heinrich, *of Glarus.*

See GLAREANUS *i. e.* HEINRICH LORITI, *of Glarus.*

Lossius, Lucas, 1508–1582.

Erotemata ‖ mvsicæ ‖ practicæ, ex pro- ‖ batissimis qvibvsqve ‖ huius dulcissimæ artis scriptoribus accuratè ‖ & breuiter selecta, & exemplis puerili ‖ institutioni accōmodis illustrata, ‖ iam primvm ‖ ad

Lossius, Lucas—*Continued.*

usum scholæ Luneburgensis, ‖ & aliarum puerilium in ‖ lucem edita, à ‖ Lvca Lossio. ‖ Item. ‖ Melodiæ sex generum carminum vsitatiorum, in primis suaues, in gra- ‖ tiam puerorum selectæ ‖ & editæ. ‖ Noribergæ, M.D.LXIII. ‖ Cum Priuilegio ad decennium.

[223] p. 15ᶜᵐ.

In 2 parts, part 2 with special t.-p.: Melodiæ sex genervm carminvm . . .
Colophon: (1) Noribergæ, ‖ Excudebant Ioannes Montanus, & ‖ Vlricus Neuberus. (2) Noribergæ, Apud Iohannem Montanum, & ‖ Vlricum Neuberum. ‖ Anno 1563.
Signatures: A–L, A–C in eights (versos of [L viii] and [C viii], last page, blank)
Ms. notes.

ML171.L6

Lotti, Antonio, *d.* 1740.

See ACADEMY OF ANCIENT MUSIC. Letters, 1732.

Louet, Alexandre, 1753–1817.

Instructions théoriques et pratiques sur l'accord du piano-forte. Ouvrage qui apprend en très-peu de temps aux personnes les moins exercées, à accorder parfaitement cet instrument. Par Alexandre Loüet. Paris, Le Duc [etc.] an v (1797)

63, [1] p. 2 pl. 21½ᶜᵐ.

MT165.A2L6

Loulié, Étienne, *d. ca.* 1707.

Elements ou principes de musique mis dans un nouvel ordre . . . divisez en trois parties. La premiere pour les enfans. La seconde pour les personnes plus avancez en âge. La troisieme pour ceux qui sont capables de raisonner sur les principes de la musique. Avec l'estampe, la description & l'usage du chronometre . . . par le moyen duquel, les compositeurs de musique pourront desormais marquer le veritable mouvement de leurs compositions, & leurs ouvrages marquez par rapport à cet instrument, se pourront executer en leur absence comme s'ils en battoient eux-mesmes la mesure. Par M. Lovlie. Amsterdam, E. Roger, 1698.

110 p. fold. pl. 16½ᶜᵐ.

2d edition; 1st edition, Paris, 1696.

MT7.A2L91

[Lowe, Edward] *d.* 1682.

A revievv of some Short directions for performance of cathedral service, published for the information of such, as may be called to officiate in cathedrall or collegiate churches; or religiously desire to bear a part in that service. The 2d ed., with many usefull additions relating to the Common prayer-book as it is now established. By E. L. Oxford, Printed by W. Hall, for R. Davis, 1664.

4 p. l., 72 p. 15½ x 8½ᶜᵐ.

Dedication signed: Ed: Lowe.

MT88.A2L76

Ludwig, Johann Adam Jakob, 1730–1782.

Gedanken über die grossen orgeln, die aber deswegen keine wunderwerke sind. Bey gelegenheit der im jahre 1761 durch herrn Johann Nicolaus Rittern ... erbauten neuen orgel zu Nemmersdorf, von Johann Adam Jakob Ludwig ... Leipzig, Gedruckt bey J. G. I. Breitkopf, 1762.

15 p. 22 x 18^{cm}.

ML552.A2L9

Eine helle brille für die blöden augen eines albern haberechts zu Niemandsburg, welcher vor einiger zeit seine gedanken über die streitigkeit zwischen dem herrn hoforganisten Sorge zu Lobenstein und herrn secretair Marpurg in Berlin in druk ausgehen lassen, aufgesetzt von einem am Salstrome wohnenden Sorgianer. *Quasi me asinus calcitrasset.* [n. p., 1767]

[12] p. 23 x 19^{cm}.

Written in reply to an anonymous work (by J. L. Albrecht?) entitled "Gedanken eines thüringischen tonkünstlers über die streitigkeit, welche der herr ... George Andreas Sorge wider den herrn secret. Friedr. Wilh. Marpurg ... erreget hat." Ascribed also to Sorge.

ML63.L95

Lundius, Daniel, 1666–1747, *praeses.*

... Dissertatio gradualis de musica Hebræorum antiqua ... Upsaliæ, ex officina Werneriana [1707]

3 p. l., 65, [1] p. 15^{cm}.

Diss.—Upsala (S. Gestrinius, respondent and author)

ML166.A2L9

Luscinius, Ottmar, d. 1537.

Mvsicae institvtiones Othmari Nachtgall Argētini a nemine unquā prius pari facilitate tentatę, studiosis, qui ἀμούσοι esse nolint nō mediocriter conducibiles. . . Ioannes Knoblouch notis æreis excepit Argentoraci [1515]

[19] p. 19^{cm}.

Title in red and black within architectural border. Signatures: a in four, b in six.

On t.-p. following title: N. Gerbelij D. D. D. ad lecto ‖ rem hexastichon. ‖ Si tibi prædulces unquā placuere Camoenę ‖ Si lyra, si citharæ te rapuere soni, ‖ Si petis Amphiō fieri, uel Thraci' Orpheus ‖ Si te musarum non pudet esse ducem ‖ Non graue prædocti tibi sit legisse libellum ‖ Othmari, tenet has quas memoramus opes . . .

ML171.L93

Mvsvrgia ‖ seu praxis Mvsicæ. ‖ Illius primo quæ Instrumentis agitur certa ratio, ab Ottomaro ‖ Luscinio Argentino duobus Libris absoluta. ‖ Eiusdem Ottomari Luscinij, de Concentus polyphoni, id est, ‖ ex plurifarijs uocibus compositi, canonibus, Libri totidem. ‖ ℭ Argentorati apud Ioannem Schottum, ‖ Anno Christi. 1536. ‖ Cum gratia & priuilegio Imperiali, ‖ ad Quinquennium.

3 p. l., 102, [3] p. illus. 15½ x 19½^{cm}.

Mainly a translation of Sebastian Virdung's "Musica getutscht," Basel, 1511. The illustrations are reproductions of those in Virdung's work, and include a motet, p. 40–43, which appears in mensural notation and also in tablature for the clavichord and for the lute. Pages 58–59 contain tables showing the tablature for bass, tenor and discant flute.

ML171.L94

Lustig, Jacob Wilhelm, 1705–1796.

Inleiding tot de muzykkunde; uit klaare, onwedersprekeolyke gronden, de innerlyke geschapenheid, de oorzaaken van de zenderbaare uitwerkselen, de groote waarde, en 't regte gebruik der muzykkonst aanwyzende. Opgesteld door Jacob Wilhelm Lustig ... Groningen, Gedrukt voor den auteur, by H. Vechnerus, 1751.

8 p. l., 340, [20] p.　20½ᶜᵐ.

MT6.A2L97

Muzykaale spraakkonst; of, Duidelyke aanwyzing en verklaaring van allerhande weetenswaardige dingen, die in de geheele muzykaale practyk tot eenen grondslag konnen verstrekken. Opgesteld door Jacob Wilhelm Lustig ... Amsteldam, Gedrukt by A. Olofsen, 1754.

4 p. l., 206, [6] p.　xɪ fold pl.　21ᶜᵐ.

MT6.A2L98

Lustig, Jacob Wilhelm, 1706–1796, *translator.*

See SCHMIDT, J. M.　Musico-theologia [1756?]

[Mably, Gabriel Bonnot de] 1709–1785.

Lettres a Madame la marquise de P. ... sur l'opera. Paris, Didot, 1741.

xix, [5], 166 p.　16½ᶜᵐ.

Addressed to Madame de Pompadour.

ML1727.3.A2M11

Maccari, Orazio.

See WALKER, J. C.　Historical memoirs, 1786.

Mace, Thomas, 1613?–1709?

Musick's monument; or, A remembrancer of the best practical musick, both divine, and civil, that has ever been known, to have been in the world. Divided into three parts. The first part, shews a necessity of singing psalms well, in parochial churches, or not to sing at all; directing, how they may be well sung, certainly; by two several ways, or means; with an assurance of a perpetual national-quire; and also shewing, how cathedral musick, may be much improved, and refined. The second part, treats of the noble lute ... directing the most ample way, for the use of the theorboe ... Shewing a general way of procuring invention, and playing voluntarily, upon the lute, viol, or any other instrument; with two pritty devices; the one, shewing how to translate lessons, from one tuning, or instrument, to another; the other, an indubitable way, to know the best tuning, upon any instrument: both done by example. In the third part, the generous viol ... is treated upon; with some curious observations, never before handled, concerning it, and musick in general. By Tho. Mace ... London, Printed by T. Radcliffe, and N. Thompson, for the author, 1676.

10 p. l., 272 p.　front. (port.) illus.　31½ x 20ᶜᵐ.

MT640.M14

Magazin der musik. Hrsg. von Carl Friedrich Cramer . . . 1.–2. jahrg.; 1783–1786. Hamburg, In der Musicalischen niederlage [1783–86]

2 v. in 4. pl., fold. tables. 17½^{cm}.

2. jahrg., 1. hålfte, 1784; 2. hålfte, 1786.

ML4.M2

Le **Magazin** des modernes, almanach curieux, où l'on trouve autant d'esprit qu'il en faut pour se faire une réputation auprès des femmes. L'an de grace 1768. 2. éd., servant de seconde partie, rev., cor., & augm. de la musique complette de la petite comédie: musique exactement neuve & faite pour les paroles . . . A La Haye, chez Propice, imprimeur; et se trouve à Paris, chez la veuve Duchesne [1768]

2 p. l., 100, 67 p. 14 x 7^{cm}.

"Que ne peut pas l'amour? Comédie lyrique": p. [53]–67.

ML20.M14

Maggi, Girolamo, *d.* 1572.

Hieronymi Magii De tintinnabvlis liber postvmvs. Franciscvs Sweertivs F. Antuerp. notis illustrabat. Hanoviæ, typis Wechelianis, apud C. Marnium & heredes I. Aubrii, 1608.

98, [14] p. illus. 18^{cm}.

Printer's mark on t.-p.

CC200.M3 1608

—— Hieronymi Magii Anglarensis De tintinnabulis liber postumus. Franciscus Sweertius F. Antverp. notis illustrabat. Ed. novissima aucta, emendata, & figuris æneis exornata. Amstelodami, sumptibus A. Frisii, 1664.

16 p. l., 151, [26] p. illus., 2 fold. pl. 13½^{cm}.

Printer's mark on t.-p. Added t.-p., engr.

CC200.M3 1664

Magirus, Johann, *d.* 1631.

Artis mvsicae legibvs logicis methodicè informatæ libri dvo. Ad totum musicæ artificium, & comprimis solidum sonorum, modorumquè musicorum fundamentum, componendiᶐ rationem, rectè, & facilè agnoscendum valdè accommodi: revisi et recogniti, multisᶐ in locis emendati & correcti, ab auctore Iohanne Magiro . . . [Brunsvigæ] sumptibus avtoris, 1611.

8 p. l., 123, [1] p. 14½^{cm}.

MT6.A2M14

Mvsicae rudimenta verè fundamentalia ita ad[or]nata ut indè etiam, modi mvsici, cum notis & pausis, clavibus & vocibus, vel pveris, sine negotio insinuari, visibiles, & palpabiles fieri possint. In vsvm eorum, qui artem hanc divinissimam & breviter, & fundamentaliter, & docere, & discere volunt.· Pvblicata avctore Johanne Magiro, pastore. [Guelpherbyti] imprimebatur per Eliam Holwein, sumptibus auctoris, 1619.

[54] p. 15^{cm}.

Author's preface dated "Brunsvigæ, 1619."

MT7.A2M18

Magri, Gennaro.

Trattato teorico-prattico di ballo di Gennaro Magri . . .   Napoli, V. Orsino, 1779.

2 v. in 1 (v. 1: 11, 9–12, [3], [13]–143 p.; v. 2: 102 p.)   22 pl. (partly fold.)   22ᶜᵐ.

Title of v. 2 reads: Trattato di ballo teorico-prattico . . .

GV1590.M3

Mahault, Antoine.

Nieuwe manier om binnen korten tyd op de dwarsfluit te leeren speelen, tot gebruik van aanvangers en meer gevorderden opgesteld, door A. Mahaut.   2. druk, voorzien met 12 nooten tabula's.   Amsterdam, J. J. Hummel [17—]

1 p. l., 36 p. incl. plates. 1 illus. 18½ x 24ᶜᵐ.

Title and text in Dutch and French, in parallel columns.
First edition, 1759.

MT342.A2M22

[Mainwaring, John] *d.* 1807.

Memoirs of the life of the late George Frederic Handel.   To which is added, a catalogue of his works, and observations upon them . . . London, R. and J. Dodsley, 1760.

1 p. l., 208 p.   21ᶜᵐ.

ML410.H13M2

[Mairobert, Mathieu François Pidanzat de] 1727–1779.

Les prophéties du grand prophéte Monet.   [n. p.] 1753.

1 p. l., 16 p.   19ᶜᵐ.

No. 9 in a volume of pamphlets lettered Quere[lle] des Bouffo[ns]

ML1727.33.A1

Majer, Joseph Friedrich Bernhardt Caspar.

Joseph Friederich Bernhard Caspar Majers . . . Neu-eröffneter theoretisch- und pracktischer music-saal, das ist: Kurze / doch vollständige methode, so wohl die vocal- als instrumental-music gründlich zu erlernen / auch die . . . blasend- schlagend- und streichende instrumenten . . . durch die deutlichste exempla, in besondern tabellen, mit leichter mühe zu begreiffen.   Nebst einem . . . appendice und erklärung derer anjezo gebräuchlichsten griechisch- lateinisch- italiänisch- und französisch-musicalischen kunst-wörter.   2. und viel-vermehrte aufl.   Nürnberg, J. J. Cremer, 1741.

3 p. l., 117, [2] p.   front., illus., 4 pl.   17½ x 21ᶜᵐ.

First edition published Hall (Swabia) 1732 under title: Museum musicum theoretico-practicum.

MT6.A2M2

Malcior, *of Worms.*

See REISCH, G.   De principijs musice [n. d.]
WOLLICK, N.   Opus aureum, 1504.

Malcolm, Alexander, b. 1687.

A treatise of musick, speculative, practical, and historical. By Alexander Malcolm . . . Edinburgh, Printed for the author, 1721.

xxiv, 608 p. 6 fold. pl. 19½ᶜᵐ.

"An ode on the power of musick, inscrib'd to Mr. Malcolm . . . by Mr. Mitchell": p. [iii]-xii.

MT6.A2M23

—— A treatise of musick, speculative, practical, and historical. By Alexander Malcolm . . . London, J. Osborn [etc.] 1731.

xvi, 608 p. 19½ᶜᵐ.

"An ode on the power of musick, inscrib'd to Mr. Malcolm . . . by Mr. Mitchell": p. [iii]-xvi.

MT6.A2M24

[Mallio, Michele] 1756–1831.

Elogio storico della Signora Maria Rosa Coccia Romana, maestra pubblica di cappella, accademica filarmonica di Bologna, e tra i Forti di Roma Trevia, coll' aggiunta di varie lettere a lei scritte da uomini illustri, ed eruditi, e di varj componimenti poetici consecrati al di lei merito. Roma, Il Cannetti, 1780.

xcvi p. fold. port. 16½ᶜᵐ.

Caption title: Elogio storico . . . scritto dal Signor abbate Michele Mallio . . .
Pages lxxv–lxxvi canceled and replaced by a new leaf containing on recto the "Sonetto di Ulisse accademico Forte" in revised form, and on verso "Sonetto del r. p. Flaminio da Latera minore osservante" instead of "Sonetto di natale Maria Laschi accademico Forte."

ML410.C7M1

Malpied,

Traite sur l'art de la danse, dédié á Monsieur Gardel, l'ainé, maître des ballets de l'Academie royale de musique. Par M. Malpied . . . Paris, Boüin; [etc., etc., ca. 1780]

2 p. l., A–D, 122 p. diagrs. 21½ᶜᵐ.

Engraved throughout; title-page has ornamental border.

GV1590.M4

Mancini, Giovanni Battista, 1716–1800.

Pensieri, e riflessioni pratiche sopra il canto figurato. Di Giamba-tista Mancini . . . Vienna, Stamparia di Ghelen, 1774.

3 p. l., 188 p., 1 l. vign. 22 x 17ᶜᵐ.

Title vignette.

MT845.A2M3

Manfredini, Vincenzo, 1737–1799.

Difesa della musica moderna e de' suoi celebri esecutori, di Vin-cenzo Manfredini . . . Bologna, Stamperìa di C. Trenti, 1788.

207, [1] p. 19ᶜᵐ.

Upon the publication of the 2d volume of Stefano Arteaga's "Le rivoluzioni del teatro musicale italiano," Manfredini published a criticism (Giornale enci-clopedico, April, 1785) of ideas advanced in that volume. The present work contains the replies published by Arteaga in the 3d volume of his work and counter replies by Manfredini.

ML290.3.A2M27

Manfredini, Vincenzo—*Continued.*

Regole armoniche, o sieno Precetti ragionati per apprendere i principj della musica, il portamento della mano, e l'accompagnamento del basso sopra gli strumenti da tasto, come l'organo, il cembalo ec. Dedicate a Sua Altezza imperiale Paul Petrovicz ... da Vincenzo Manfredini ... Venezia, G. Zerletti, 1775.

xvi, 78 p., 1 l. incl. front. (port.)   20 fold. pl. (music)   26½ᶜᵐ.

Title vignette.

MT49.A2M27

—— Regole armoniche, o sieno Precetti ragionati per apprender la musica, di Vincenzo Manfredini.   2. ed. cor., ed accresciuta.   Venezia, A. Cesare, 1797.

2 p. l., 207, [1] p.   xx fold. pl. (music)   22ᶜᵐ.

MT40.A2M27

See also ARTEAGA, S.   Le rivoluzioni, 1783–88.

Manuductio ad cantum choralem gregoriano-moguntinum, quâ fundamenta hujus cantus; nec non modus canendi epistolas, evangelia, prophetias, collectas, versiculos, benedictiones, lectiones, capitula, aliaque ejuscemodi plura traduntur & exponuntur, jussu & authoritate ... d. Joannis Philippi, sanctæ sedis Moguntinæ archi-episcopi ... edita, ad usum clericorum ac ludirectorum archidiœcesis Moguntinæ & diœcesium Herbipolensis ac Wormatiensis. Moguntiae, typis C. Küchleri, 1672.

2 p. l., 143 p.   17 x 19ᶜᵐ.

MT860.A2M29

Manuel da Conceição, *d.* 1745.

Manuale seraphicum, et romanum, juxta usum Fratrum minorum denuo auctum cum variis processionibus, benedictionibus, & orationibus, aliisque multis; nec non cum ritibus ad sacramentum baptismi parvulorum, ac adultorum ministrandum ... Per fr. Emmanuelem a' Conceptione ... Ulyssipone Occidentali, ex Typographia musicæ, 1732.

2 v. (v. 1: 7 p. l., 317 p.; v. 2: 1 p. l., 332 p.)   20ᶜᵐ.

Title vignette.
Vol. 2 has title: Manuale seraphicum, et romanum, ad usum præcipuè Fratrum minorum, ac monialium ejusdem ordinis, in alma provincia Algarbiorum s. p. n. Francisci. Includens omnia pertinentia ad receptionem habitus noviciorum, tam fratrū, quam monialium, nec non ritus ad exequias defunctorum, &c. ...

MT860.A2M24

Marbach, Christian.

Evangelische singe-schule, darinnen diejenigen dinge deutlich gelehret und wiederholet werden / welche überhaupt allen evangelischen christen zur erbauung und beförderung der Gott wohlgefälligen singeandacht zu wissen nöthig und nützlich sind. Wohlmeynend eröffnet von m. Christian Marbach ... Bresslau und Leipzig, M. Rohrlach, 1726.

9 p. l., [3]–216, [8] p.   17ᶜᵐ.

Ch. 17. 1896

[Marcello, Benedetto] 1686–1739.

Il teatro alla moda, o sia Metodo sicuro, e facile per ben comporre, & esequire [!] l'opere italiane in musica all' uso moderno, nel quale si danno avvertimenti utili, e necessarij à poeti, compositori di musica, musici dell' uno, e dell' altro sesso, impresarj, suonatori, ingegneri, e pittori di scene, parti buffe, sarti, paggi, comparse, suggeritori, copisti, protettori, e madri di virtuose, & altre persone appartenenti al teatro. Dedicato dall' auttore del libro al compositore di esso. Stampato ne Borghi di Belisania per Aldiviva Licante, all' insegna dell' Orso in Peata. Si vende nella strada del Corallo alla porta del palazzo d'Orlando. E si ristamperà ogn' anno con nuova aggiunta. [Venezia, 17—]

72 p. 16½ᶜᵐ.

This edition is not described by Tessier, in the reprint of Venice, 1887, but corresponds to the one called by him the second (1733) except that the t.-p. shows no vignette.

ML3858.M28

Marcos y Navas, Francisco.

Arte, ó compendio general del canto-llano, figurado, y organo, en método facil, ilustrado con algunos documentos, ó capítulos muy precisos para el aprovechamiento, y enseñanza. Dividido en cinco tratados, de los que el primero manifiesta la teórica del canto-llano: el segundo su práctica, con el oficio de difuntos, sepultura, misa, y procesion: el tercero, y quarto la especulativa, y práctica del canto figurado, y de organo, segun el moderno estilo; y el quinto las nueve lamentaciones, y la bendicion del cirio, vestidas, ó adornadas de cláusulas sobre su mismo canto-llano. Su autor D. Francisco Marcos y Navas ... Madrid, J. Ibarra, impresor, 1777.

1 p. l., xx, 623 p. illus., diagr. 20ᶜᵐ.

MT860.A2M3

Mard, Toussaint Rémond de Saint-

See RÉMOND DE SAINT-MARD, TOUSSAINT.

Maret, Hugues, 1726–1786.

Eloge historique de Mʳ. Rameau, compositeur de la musique du cabinet du roi, associé de l'Académie des sciences, arts & belles-lettres de Dijon. Lu à la séance publique de l'Académie, le 25 août 1765, par M. Maret ... Dijon, Causse; [etc., etc.] 1766.

1 p. l., iv, [5]–78 p. 19½ᶜᵐ.

Pages [43]–78, "Notes."
Published also in Mémoires de l'Académie de Dijon, 1766.

ML410.R2M18

Maria, Carlos de Jesus.

See CARLOS DE JESUS MARIA.

Maria, Salvadore, da Vercelli.

See SALVADORE MARIA da Vercelli.

María, Tomás de Santa.

See TOMÁS DE SANTA MARÍA.

Marignan,   de.

Éclaircissemens donnés a l'auteur du Journal encyclopédique, sur la musique du Devin du village. Par le sieur de Marignan, comédien. A Bouillon, et se trouve a Paris, chez la veuve Duchesne, 1781.

30 p. 18ᶜᵐ.

ML410.R86M2

[Marin, François Louis Claude] 1721–1809.

Ce qu'on a dit, ce qu'on a voulu dire. Lettre a Madame Folio. [n. p., 1752?]

16 p. 19ᶜᵐ.

No. 4 in a volume of pamphlets lettered Quere[lle] des Bouffo[ns]

ML1727.33.A1

Marinelli, Giulio Cesare.

Via retta della voce corale, overo Osservationi intorno al retto esercitio del canto fermo divise in cinqve parti, oue si dà vn' esattissima, e facilissima instruttione di quest' arte, con vn nuouo modo di reggere, e mantenere il coro sempre in vna medesima voce, sì per la parte del corista, come anco dell' organista. Del p. f. Givlio Cesare Marinelli . . . Bologna, G. Monti, 1671.

4 p. l., 268 p. illus. 21ᶜᵐ.

MT860.A2M33

Marinoni, Giovanni Battista, *d.* 1647.

Fiori poetici raccolti nel funerale del . . . Signor Clavdio Monteverde, maestro di cappella della ducale di S. Marco. Consecrati da D. Gio: Battista Marinoni, detto Gioue . . . all' illvstrssimi [!] & ecceilentissimi [!] sig. procvratori di chiesa di S. Marco. Venetia, F. Miloco, 1644.

70 p., 1 l. 19½ᶜᵐ.

Engr. t.-p. with symbolical border and port. of Monteverdi.

ML410.M77M1

Marmontel, Jean François, 1723–1799.

Essai sur les revolutions de la musique en France. Par M. du Marmontel . . . [Paris, 1777]

1 p. l., 60 p. 21ᶜᵐ.

ML1704.A2M35

Marot, Clément, *pseud.*

See Sénecé, Antoine Bauderon de.

Marpurg, Friedrich Wilhelm, 1718–1795.

Abhandlung von der fuge, nach den grundsåtzen und exempeln der besten deutschen und auslåndischen meister entworfen von Friedrich Wilhelm Marpurg . . . Berlin, A. Haude, und J. C. Spener, 1753–54.

2 v. (v. 1: 4 p. l., xvi, 192, [4] p.; v. 2: 4 p. l., xxx, 147, [14] p.) 122 pl. 21½ x 18ᶜᵐ.

MT59.A2M35

Marpurg, Friedrich Wilhelm—*Continued.*

Anfangsgründe der theoretischen musik, von Friedrich Wilhelm Marpurg. Leipzig, J. G. I. Breitkopf, 1757.

4 p. l., 176 p. 21½ x 17½^{cm}.

ML3805.A2M3

Anleitung zum clavierspielen, der schönern ausübung der heutigen zeit gemäss entworfen von Friedr. Wilh. Marpurg. Nebst XVIII. kupfertafeln. Berlin, A. Haude und J. C. Spener, 1755.

6 p. l., 78, [6] p. XVIII pl. (partly music) 20½ x 17½^{cm}.

MT224.A2M35

—— Anleitung zum clavierspielen, der schönern ausübung der heutigen zeit gemäss entworfen von Friedrich Wilhelm Marpurg. Nebst XVIII. kupfertafeln. 2. verb. aufl. Berlin, Haude und Spener, 1765.

7 p. l., 3–78, [6] p. XX pl. on 10 l. (partly music) 20½ x 18^{cm}.

MT224.A2M354

—— Principes du clavecin, par Mr. Marpourg. Avec vingt planches. Berlin, Haude et Spener, 1756.

4 p. l., 92, [6] p. XX fold. pl. (partly music) 22 x 18^{cm}.

MT224.A2M36

Friedr. Wilh. Marpurgs Anleitung zur musik überhaupt und zur singkunst besonders, mit uebungsexempeln erläutert . . . Berlin, A. Wever, 1763.

7 p. l., [3]–171 p. 18^{cm}.

MT7.A2M2

Anleitung zur singcomposition, von Friedrich Wilhelm Marpurg. Berlin, G. A. Lange, 1758.

5 p. l., 206 p. front. (port.) 22 x 17½^{cm}.

Contains only the "1. hauptstück, Von dem prosodischen ausdruck eines textes, oder von der mechanik der singcomposition." Ledebur (Tonkünstler Berlin's) states that Marpurg had intended to complete the work with a second volume, but did not carry out his intention.

MT64.A2M35

Clavierstücke mit einem practischen unterricht für anfänger und geübtere, von Friedrich Wilhelm Marpurg. Berlin, Haude und Spener, 1762–63.

3 v. in 1. 19½ x 32^{cm}.

"Discurs des herrn Quanz über das clavieraccompagnement (. . . aus dessen Versuche &c. die flöte zu spielen . . .)": v. 3, p. [21]–27.

MT243.A2M23

Des Critischen musicus an der Spree erster band. Berlin, A. Haude und J. C. Spener, 1750.

4 p. l., 406 p. v fold. pl. (music) 21 x 17½^{cm}.

Issued weekly from March 4, 1749, to Feb. 17, 1750.

ML4.C93

Marpurg, Friedrich Wilhelm—*Continued.*

Handbuch bey dem generalbasse und der komposition mit zwo-drey- vier- fûnf- sechs- sieben- acht und mehrern stimmen, fûr an-fånger und geûbtere, von Friedrich Wilhelm Marpurg ... Nebst ... notentafeln ... Berlin, G. A. Lange, 1757–62.

341 p. 35 pl. 22 x 19ᶜᵐ.

In 4 parts, each with special t.-p. pt. [1]: 2. verm. und verb. aufl. 1762. pt. 2: 1757. pt. 3: Dritter und letzter theil, nebst einem hauptregister über alle drey theile. 1758. pt. 4: Anhang zum Handbuche [etc.] 1760.

MT49.A2M35

Herrn Georg Andreas Sorgens Anleitung zum generalbass und zur composition. Mit anmerkungen von Friedrich Wilhelm Marpurg. Nebst vier kupfertafeln ... Berlin, G. A. Lange, 1760.

6 p. l., 152 p. ɪᴠ pl. 21½ x 17ᶜᵐ.

A criticism by Marpurg of Sorge's "Compendium harmonicum."

MT50.A2M35

Historisch-kritische beytråge zur aufnahme der musik, von Fried-rich Wilhelm Marpurg ... Berlin, G. A. Lange, 1754–78.

5 v. fold. plates. 18ᶜᵐ.

Vol. 1 has imprint: Berlin, J. J. Schûtzens sel. wittwe, 1754. Errors in paging. Issued in 30 parts ("stücke") each with special t.-p.

ML4.H67

Kritische einleitung in die geschichte und lehrsåtze der alten und neuen musik, von Friedrich Wilhelm Marpurg. Nebst acht kupfer-tabellen. Berlin, G. A. Lange, 1759.

5 p. l., 246, [10] p. front. (port.) ᴠɪɪɪ pl. (partly music) 23 x 19½ᶜᵐ. Title vignette.

ML169.A2M35

Die kunst das clavier zu spielen, durch den verfasser des Critischen musicus an der Spree. Berlin, Haude und Spener, 1751.

27 p. ɪᴠ pl. 20½ x 17ᶜᵐ.

1st edition, Berlin, 1750.

MT220.A2M3

Legende einiger musikheiligen. Ein nachtrag zu den musikalischen almanachen und taschenbûchern jetziger zeit, von Simeon Meta-phrastes, dem jûngern [*pseud.*] Nebst 2. notentafeln [Canon ɪ–ɪɪ] Côlln am Rhein, Bey P. Hammern. [Breslau, Korn] 1786.

9 p. l., [3]–331, [1] p. fold. l. (music) 16½ᶜᵐ.

ML65.M58

Neue methode allerley arten von temperaturen dem claviere aufs bequemste mitzutheilen; auf veranlassung einer von dem herrn baron von Wiese zu Dresden vorgeschlagenen neuen stimmungsart entworfen von Friedrich Wilhelm Marpurg. Berlin, G. A. Lange, 1790.

6 p. l., 40 p. 23 x 20ᶜᵐ.

ML3809.A2M37

Marpurg, Friedrich Wilhelm—*Continued.*

Friedrich Wilhelm Marpurgs ... Versuch über die musikalische temperatur, nebst einem anhang über den Rameau- und Kirnberger-schen grundbass, und vier tabellen ... Breslau, J. F. Korn, 1776.

xiv p., 1 l., 319, [1] p. iv fold. pl. 19½^cm.

ML3809.A2M35

Marpurg, Friedrich Wilhelm, 1718–1795, *editor.*

See KRITISCHE briefe über die tonkunst, 1760–64.

Marpurg, Friedrich Wilhelm, 1718–1795, *translator.*

See ALEMBERT, J. L. R. D'. Systematische einleitung, 1757.

Marshall, William.

The propriety of singing the Psalms of David in New Testament worship. A sermon preached at Middle-Octoraro, April 13th, 1774. at the opening of the Associate Presbytery of Pensylvania. By William Marshall ... Perth, A. Sharp [etc.] 1776.

68 p. 17^cm.

ML3001.M28

Martianus Capella.

See MEIBOM, M., *translator.* Antiqvæ mvsicæ avctores, 1652.

Martín y Coll, Antonio, *b. ca.* 1680.

Arte de canto llano, y breve resvmen de svs principales reglas, para cantores de choro; dividido en dos libros; en el primero, se declara lo que pertenece à la theorica; y en el segundo, lo que se necessita para la practica, y las entonaciones de los psalmos con el organo. Dispvesto por Fr. Antonio Martin y Coll ... Madrid, Por la viuda de J. Garcia Infançon, 1714.

13 p. l., 144, [3] p. illus. 21 x 15½^cm.

Dedication engraved.

MT860.A2M35

—— Arte de canto llano, y breve resumen de sus principales reglas, para cantores de choro. Dividido en dos libros. En el primero se declara lo que pertenece à la theorica; y en el segundo lo que se necessita para la practica; y las entonaciones de los psalmos con el organo; y añadido en esta segunda impression con algunas adver-tencias, y el arte de canto de organo. Dispuesto por fray Antonio Martin y Coll ... Madrid, En la Imprenta de musica, por B. Peralta, 1719.

13 p. l., 340, [5] p. illus. 21^cm.

MT860.A2M36

Martínez Bravo, José de Torres.

See TORRES MARTÍNEZ BRAVO, JOSÉ DE.

Martini, Georg Heinrich, 1722–1794.

Beweis dass der neuern urtheile über die tonkunst der alten nie zulänglich und entscheidend seyn können. Womit die feyerliche rede . . . auf das amtsjubelfest herrn Christoph Stolzenbergs . . . ankündiget Georg Heinrich Martini . . . Regensburg, Gedruckt bey H. G. Zunkel [1764]

12 p. 21½ x 17cm.

ML169.A2M38

Martini, Giovanni Battista, 1706–1784.

Dissertatio de usu progressionis geometricæ in musica, auctore Joanne Baptista Martini . . . [n. p., 1766]

25 p. 28½cm.

"Questa dissertazione è inserita ne' Commentari dell' Istituto delle scienze di Bologna, tomo v. par ii. pag. 372–394 dell' edizione di Bologna per Lelio dalla Volpe."—Parisini, Della vita . . . del padre Gio. Battista Martini, 1887.

ML3809.A2M39

Esemplare, o sia saggio fondamentale pratico di contrappunto sopra il canto fermo dedicato all' eminentissimo . . . Sig. cardinale Vincenzo Malvezzi . . . da f. Giambattista Martini . . . Bologna, Lelio della Volpe, impressore [1774–76]

2 v. (v. 1: xxxii, 260 p.; v. 2: xxxxviii, 328 p.) fold. pl. 30cm.

Vol. 2 has title: Esemplare . . . di contrappunto fugato, dedicato all' illustrissimo . . . Monsignore Gennaro Adelelmo Pignatelli . . .
Consists of examples from celebrated composers with accompanying explanations; vol. 1 contains a prefatory outline of the elements and rules of counterpoint, vol. 2, of the fugue.

MT55.A2M38

Storia della musica . . . alla Sacra reale cattolica Maestà Maria Barbara . . . umiliato, e dedicato da fr. Giambatista Martini . . . Bologna, Lelio dalla Volpe, impressore, 1757–81.

3 v. fold. front., illus. (incl. ports.) 12 pl. (partly fold.) 2 fold. maps, 2 plans. 46cm.

Large paper edition. Title in red and black; initials; vignettes; ornamental borders. Bibliographical foot-notes. Numerous musical illustrations.
Vol. 2: All' Altezza serenissima elettorale di Carlo Teodoro . . . umiliato, e dedicato; v. 3: A Sua Altezza reale Don Ferdinando di Borbone . . .
The work was not completed. The 3 volumes published all deal with ancient music. The 1st vol., printed 1757, was not published until 1760 or after.

ML159.M2

—— Storia della musica . . . alla Sacra reale cattolica Maestà Maria Barbara . . . umiliato, e dedicato da fr. Giambatista Martini . . . Bologna, Lelio dalla Volpe, impressore, 1757–81.

3 v. illus. (incl. ports.) plates (partly fold.) fold. maps. 28 x 21½cm.

Title vignette. Bibliographical foot-notes. Same variations of title as in the large paper edition. Numerous musical illustrations.

ML159.M3

See also DONI, G. B. Lyra Barberina, 1763.
ZANOTTI, F. M. Lettere, 1782.

Martyres, Verissimo dos.

See VERISSIMO DOS MARTYRES.

Mason, William, 1724–1797.

Essays, historical and critical, on English church music. By William Mason . . . York, printed by W. Blanchard, and sold by J. Robson, London; [etc., etc.] 1795.

2 p. l., 264 p. 17ᶜᵐ.

"[The essay on cathedral music] originally prefixed to a collection of the words of anthems, &c. in the year 1782 . . . is hereby reprinted with some additions."

ML3001.M41

Masson, Charles.

Nouveau traite' des regles pour la composition de la musique, par lequel on apprend à faire facilement un chant sur des paroles; a composer à 2. à 3. & à 4. parties, &c. et à chiffrer la basse-continuë, suivant l'usage des meilleurs auteurs. Ouvrage tres-utile à ceux qui joüent de l'orgue, du clavecin, & du théorbe. Par C. Masson . . . 3. ed., rev. & cor. Paris, C. Ballard, 1705.

4 p. l., 127, [1] p. 19ᶜᵐ.

MT40.A2M42

Mather, Cotton, 1663–1728.

See WALTER, T. The grounds . . . of musick [17—]

Mather, Increase, 1639–1723.

See WALTER, T. The grounds . . . of musick [17—]

Mattei, Saverio, 1742–1795.

Memorie per servire alla vita del Metastasio, raccolte da Saverio Mattei. Ed. 1. Colle, Stamperia di A. M. Martini, e comp., 1785.

2 p. l., 3–136 p. 20½ᶜᵐ.

Half-title: Metastasio e Jommelli.
"Elogio del Jommelli, o sia Il progresso della poesia, e musica teatrale": p. 59–136.

ML410.J7M2

Se i maestri di cappella son compresi fra gli artigiani, probole di Saverio Mattei. Lettera al Signor Linguet. Guazzabuglio Filosarmonico, o sia Miscellaneo sulla Probole, Anti-probole, ed Aneddoto forense dell' abate Galiani. Sulla quistione se gli maestri di cappella son compresi fra gli artigiani, anti-probole di G. M. C. Per D. Lionardo Garofalo, risposta alla Probole. Ultima vera per gli probolisti a richiesta per gli antiprobolisti, o sia Spicilegio musico di Michelangelo Grisolia. Napoli, A spese di S. Palermo [17—]

38, [4], 3–16, 28, 43, 47, 47 p. 18ᶜᵐ.

First article has caption: All' illustre Signor cavaliere D. Luigi de' Medici de' principi di Ottajano, giudice della Gran corte e commessario della causa del maestro Cordella. Second article has half-title: Aneddoto forense, lettera al Signor Linguet, traduzione dal francese. Third article has special t.-p.: Guazzabuglio filosarmonico, o sia Miscellaneo verso-prosaico sulla Probole, Anti-probole, ed Aneddoto forense di D. Onofrio Galeota [pseud. of F. Galiani] . . . Fanta-

Mattei, Saverio—*Continued.*

sianopoli 22. luglio 1785.   Fourth article has special t.-p.: Sulla quistione [etc.]
anti-probole di G. M. C.   Napoli, S. Palermo, 1785.   Fifth article (signed: Luigi
Serio) and sixth article have each half-title as given on t.-p.

Appended: Spaventosissima descrizione dello spaventoso spavento che nci
spaventò a tutti quanti la seconda volta colla spaventevole eruzzione del Vesuvio
alli 15. giugno dell' anno 1794., che se ne fece la prima descrizione, che questa è la
seconda.   Fatta da D. Onofrio Galeota . . .   28 p.

ML63.M163

—— Se i maestri di cappella son compresi fra gli artigiani; probole
di Saverio Mattei, in occasione d'una tassa di fatiche domandata dal
maestro Cordella . . .   [3. ed.]   Napoli, G.-M. Porcelli, 1785.

48 p.   20½ᶜᵐ.

ML63.M16

Matthäi, Conrad, *b.* 1610.

Kurtzer / doch ausführlicher bericht / von den modis musicis,
welchen aus den besten / aeltesten / berühmtesten und bewerthesten
autoribus der music zusammen getragen / auff den unbeweglichen
grund der mess-kunst gesetzet und mit beliebung der löblichen Philo-
sophischen facultåt Churfl. br. pr. universität zu Königsberg / heraus
gegeben hat Conradus Matthæi, Brunsuicensis. [Königsberg] Gedruckt durch J. Reusnern / in verlegung des autoris, 1652.

12 p. l., 124 p. fold. tab.   19½ᶜᵐ x 15½ᶜᵐ.

MT45.A2M18

Mattheson, Johann, 1681–1764.

Behauptung der himmlischen musik aus den gründen der vernunft,
kirchen-lehre und Heiligen Schrift . . .   Hamburg, C. Herold, 1747.

4 p. l., 144, [8] p.   17ᶜᵐ.

Preface signed: Mattheson.

ML63.M17

Critica musica.   D. i. Grundrichtige untersuch- und beurtheilung /
vieler / theils vorgefassten / theils einfältigen meinungen / argumen-
ten und einwürffe / so in alten und neuen / gedruckten und unge-
druckten / musicalischen schrifften zu finden.   Zur müglichsten aus-
råutung aller groben irrthümer / und zur beförderung eines bessern
wachsthums der reinen harmonischen wissenschafft / in verschiedene
theile abgefasset / und stück-weise heraus gegeben von Mattheson . . .
[Pars I–VIII, 1.–24. stück]   Hamburg, Auf unkosten des autoris [etc.]
1722–25.

2 v. in 1 (v. 1: 368, [16] p.; v. 2: 8 p. l., 380, [21] p.) diagr.   21 x 17½ᶜᵐ.

Title varies.   Vol. 2: Gedruckt und zu bekommen bey seel. Thomas von
Wierings erben.

For full description and contents *see* Krome, Die anfänge des musikalischen
journalismus in Deutschland.

ML4.M42

De ervditione mvsica schediasma . . .

See his PHILOLOGISCHES tresespiel.

Exemplarische organisten-probe im artikel vom general-bass.
Welche mittelst 24. leichter / und eben so viel etwas schwerer exempel /

Mattheson, Johann—*Continued.*

aus allen tonen / des endes anzustellen ist / dass einer / der diese 48. prob-stücke rein trifft / und das darinn enthaltene wohl anbringt / sich ... rühmen möge: er sey ein meister im accompagniren ... Mit den nothwendigsten erläuterungen und anmerckungen / bey jedem exempel / und mit einer ausführlichen ... theoretischen vorbereitung / uber verschiedene musicalische merckwürdigkeiten / versehen von Mattheson ... Hamburg, Schiller- und Kissnerische buch-laden, 1719.

8 p. i., 128, 276 p. front. (port.) fold. pl. 21 x 18½ᶜᵐ.

MT49.A2M43

—— Johann Matthesons Grosse general-bass-schule. Oder: Der Exemplarischen organisten-probe 2. / verb. und verm. aufl. / bestehend in dreien classen / als: in einer gründlichen vorbereitung / in 24. leichten exempeln / in 24. schwerern prob-stücken: solcher gestalt eingerichtet / dass / wer die erste wol verstehet; und in den beiden andern classen alles rein trifft; so dann das darin enthaltene gut anzubringen weiss; derselbe ein meister im general-bass heissen könne. Hamburg, J. C. Kissners buchladen, 1731.

21 p. l., 484 p. pl. 21½ x 18½ᶜᵐ.

MT49.A2M44

—— A complete treatise of thorough bass, containing the true rules with a table of all the figures & their proper accompanyments, to which is added several examples of each figure, by John Matheson ... London, P: Hodgson [17—]

1 p. l., 32 p. 35ᶜᵐ.

Engraved throughout. The "true rules" occupy only p. 1, the rest of the work consisting of musical examples.

MT49.A2M442

Grundlage einer ehren-pforte, woran der tüchtigsten capellmeister, componisten, musikgelehrten, tonkünstler &c. leben, wercke, verdienste &c. erscheinen sollen. Zum fernern ausbau angegeben von Mattheson. Hamburg, In verlegung des verfassers, 1740.

2 p. l., xliv, 428, [16] p. 21 x 16½ᶜᵐ.

Engr. t.-p.

ML105.A2M42.

Gültige zeugnisse über die jüngste Matthesonisch-musicalische kernschrifft, als ein füglicher anhang derselben, zum druck befördert von Aristoxen, dem jüngern [*pseud.*] ... Hamburg, 1738.

15 p. 21½ x 18ᶜᵐ. (*With his* Kern melodischer wissenschafft. Hamburg, 1737)

Three letters, by C. H. P., J. P. Kuntzen and J. A. Scheibe respectively, with notes by Mattheson.

MT6.A2M44

Kern melodischer wissenschafft, bestehend in den auserlesensten haupt- und grund-lehren der musicalischen setz-kunst oder composition, als ein vorläuffer des Vollkommenen capellmeisters / ausgearbeitet von Mattheson. Hamburg, C. Herold, 1737.

9 p. l., 182, [8] p. illus. 21½ x 18ᶜᵐ.

MT6.A2M44

174

Mattheson, Johann—*Continued.*

Johann Mattheson's . . . Kleine general-bass-schule. Worin nicht nur lernende / sondern vornehmlich lehrende / aus den allerersten anfangs-gründen des clavier-spielens / überhaupt und besonders / durch verschiedene classen u. ordnungen der accorde stuffen-weise / mittelst gewisser lectionen oder stündlicher aufgaben / zu mehrer vollkommenheit in dieser wissenschafft / richtig / getreulich / und auf die deutlichste lehr-art / kürtzlich angeführet werden . . . Hamburg / J. C. Kissner / 1735.

8 p. l., 253, [13] p.   21 x 18^{cm}.

Added t.-p., engr., with date 1734.

Additions and corrections for his Grosse general-bass-schule, 2d ed., Heidelberg, 1731, on last page.

MT49.A2M45

Der Musicalische patriot / welcher seine gründliche betrachtungen / über geist- und weltl. harmonien / samt dem / was durchgehends davon abhänget / in angenehmer abwechselung zu solchem ende mittheilet / das Gottes ehre / das gemeine beste / und eines jeden lesers besondere erbauung dadurch befördert werde. Ans licht gestellet von Mattheson. Hamburg, 1728.

376 (*i. e.* 384) p.   19 x 15½^{cm}.

No. 73–80 repeated in paging.

Issued in weekly numbers as "Des Musikalischen patrioten erste [–drey und vierzigste] betrachtung."

ML4.M43

Die neuangelegte freuden-akademie, zum lehrreichen vorschmack unbeschreiblicher herrlichkeit in der veste göttlicher macht. Angepriesen von Johann Mattheson . . . Hamburg, J. A. Martini, 1751–53.

2 v. in 1 (v. 1: 2 p. l., 302, [22] p.; v. 2: 38 p. l., 322, [17] p.)   18^{cm}.

Vol. 2 has title: Johann Matthesons . . . Neuangelegter freuden-akademie zweyter band, mit vorgesetzter abhandlung betreffend alle freudenstörer und todwünscher.

Ch. 17. 1144

Das neu-eröffnete orchestre, oder Universelle und gründliche anleitung / wie ein galant homme einen vollkommnen begriff von der hoheit und würde der edlen music erlangen / seinen gout darnach formiren / die terminos technicos verstehen und geschicklich von dieser vortrefflichen wissenschafft raisonniren möge. Durch J. Mattheson, secr. Mit beygefügten anmerckungen herrn capell-meister Keisers. Hamburg, Auf unkosten des autoris, und zu finden in B. Schillers wittwe buchladen / 1713.

7 p. l., 338, [11] p.   front. (port.)   16^{cm}.

"9 seiten notenbeispiele" mentioned by Becker not in this copy.

MT6.A2M42

—— Das neu-eröffnete orchestre, oder Universelle und gründliche anleitung / wie ein galant homme einen vollkommnen begriff von der hoheit und würde der edlen music erlangen / seinen gout darnach formiren / die terminos technicos verstehen und geschicklich von dieser vortrefflichen wissenschafft raisonniren möge. Durch J. Mattheson,

Mattheson, Johann—*Continued.*

secr. Mit beygefügten anmerckungen herrn capell-meister Keisers. Hamburg, B. Schillers wittwe, 1713.

2 p. l., 338 p. 14½ᶜᵐ.

"9 seiten notenbeispiele" mentioned by Becker not in this copy.

MT6.A2M43

——Das beschützte orchestre,oder desselben zweyte eröffnung/worinn nicht nur einem würcklichen galant-homme, der eben kein professions-verwandter / sondern auch manchem musico selbst die alleraufrich-tigste und deutlichste vorstellung musicalischer wissenschafften / wie sich dieselbe . . . eigentlich und wahrhafftig verhalten / ertheilet; aller wiedrigen auslegung und gedungenen aufbürdung aber völliger . . . bescheid gegeben; so dann endlich des lange verbannet gewesenen ut re mi fa sol la, todte (nicht tota) musica, unter ansehnlicher begleitung der zwölff griechischen modorum . . . zu grabe gebracht und mit einem monument, zum ewigen andencken / beehret wird von Matthe-son. Hamburg, Schillerische buchladen, 1717.

11 p. l., 561, [1] p. 7 fold. pl. 14ᶜᵐ.

The greater part of the work was written in refutation of J. H. Buttstett's Ut, re, mi, fa, sol, la, tota musica.

MT6.A2M38

—— Das forschende orchestre, oder desselben dritte eröffnung. Darinn sensvs vindiciæ et qvartæ blanditiæ, d. i. der beschirmte sinnen-rang und der schmeichelnde quarten-klang / allen unpartheyischen syn-technitis zum nutzen und nachdenken; keinem menschen aber zum nachtheil / sana ratione & autoritate untersuchet / und vermuhtlich in ihr rechtes licht gestellet werden von Joanne Mattheson . . . Ham-burg / B. Schillers wittwe / und J. C. Kissner, 1721.

23 p. l., 789, [38] p. front. 15½ᶜᵐ.

MT6.A2M39

Die neueste untersuchung der singspiele, nebst beygefügter musi-kalischen geschmacksprobe, liefert hiemit Aristoxenus, der jüngere [*pseud.*] . . . Hamburg, C. Herold, 1744.

4 p. l., 168 p. 17ᶜᵐ.

ML3858.M41

Matthesons Philologisches tresespiel, als ein kleiner beytrag zur kritischen geschichte der deutschen sprache, vornehmlich aber, mit-telst gescheuter anwendung, in der tonwissenschaft nützlich zu gebrauchen. Subiuncta nouissima editione Schediasmatis de ervdi-tione mvsica . . . Hamburg, J. A. Martini, 1752.

16 p. l., 133, [9] p., 1 l., 29 p. 17ᶜᵐ.

"De ervditione mvsica" has special t.-p. and separate paging.

ML63.M18

Matthesonii Plvs vltra, ein stückwerk von neuer und mancherley art. Erster[-zweeter] vorrath . . . Hamburg, J. A. Martini, 1754-55.

382, [16] p. 2 fold. pl. (music) 17½ᶜᵐ.

Each part has special t.-p.
The third and fourth parts, published 1755-56, are wanting in L. of C. copy.

ML60.M432

Mattheson, Johann—*Continued.*

Der vollkommene capellmeister; das ist, Gründliche anzeige aller derjenigen sachen, die einer wissen, können, und vollkommen inne haben muss, der einer capelle mit ehren und nutzen vorstehen will: zum versuch entworffen von Mattheson.   Hamburg, C. Herold, 1739.

28, [4], 484, [20] p.   33½^{cm}.

Dedication signed: Johann Mattheson.
"Neues verzeichniss bisheriger Matthesonischer wercke": [1] p. at end.

MT85.A2M43

See also ABHANDLUNG von den pantomimen, 1749.

Mattheson, Johann, 1681–1764, *editor.*

See NIEDT, F. E.   Musicalische handleitung.
      RAUPACH, C.   Deutliche beweis-gründe, 1717.

[Maupoint,   ]

Biblioteque des theatres, contenant le catalogue alphabetique des piéces dramatiques, opera, parodies, & opera comiques; & le tems de leurs représentations.   Avec des anecdotes sur la plûpart des piéces contenuës en ce recüeil, & sur la vie des auteurs, musiciens & acteurs. Paris, L. F. Prault, 1733.

3 p. l., 369, [3] p.   20^{cm}.

Added t.-p., engr.

Z2174.D7M3

[Maxwell, Francis Kelly *called* **John]** *d.* 1782.

An essay upon tune.   Being an attempt to free the scale of music, and the tune of instruments, from imperfection.   Illustrated with plates . . .   Edinburgh, C. Elliot; [etc., etc.] 1781.

2 p. l., 290, [1] p.   xix fold. pl.   21^{cm}.

ML3809.A2M41

Mayeur de Saint Paul, François Marie, 1758–1818.

See DUMONT.   Le vol plus haut, 1784.

Meckenheuser,   *b. ca.* 1660.

Die so genannte: allerneueste, musicalische temperatur: oder, Die, von denen respectivè herren capellmeistern Bümlern, zu Onoltzbach, und hn. Mattheson zu Hamburg, gütigst communicirte, 12. rational-gleiche toni minores, oder semitonia in, und zwischen denen 13. clavi-bus, und denen 12. intervallis aller derselben octaven: des . . . herrn hof-rahts Hånflings, zu Onoltzbach.   Denen respectivè herren musicis practicis . . . zu beliebiger censur übergeben, von J. G. Mecken-heuser . . .   [Quedlinburg, 1727]

60 p., 1 l.   20½ x 17^{cm}.

Gerber, Eitner and others give the author's forenames as Jacob Georg; the dedication of the book is signed Johann Georg.

ML3809.A2M43

Mei, Girolamo.

Discorso sopra la mvsica antica, e moderna, di M. Girolamo Mei . . . Venetia, G. B. Ciotti, 1602.

[23] p. 19¼^{cm}.

Title vignette: printer's mark. Signatures: A–C in fours.
An abridged translation, by Pier del Nero, of the second book of an unpublished work by Mei, "De modis musicis veterum libri quatuor." The original ms. is in the Vatican library. *cf.* Gaspari, Catalogo della bibl. del Liceo mus. di Bologna, v. 1, p. 234.

ML171.M44

Meibom, Marcus, *d.* 1711, *editor.*

Antiqvæ mvsicæ avctores septem. Græce et latine. Marcvs Meibomivs restituit ac notis explicavit . . . Amstelodami, apud Ludovicum Elzevirium, 1652.

2 v. 5 fold. tab. 22½ x 16^{cm}.

Printer's mark: Minerva.
Vol. 2 has title: 'Αριστείδου Κοϊντιλιανοῦ Περὶ μουσικῆς βιβλία γ. Aristidis Qvintiliani De mvsica libri III. Marcvs Meibomivs restitvit, ac notis explicavit . . .

CONTENTS.—I. I. Aristoxeni Harmonicorvm elementorvm libri III. II. Evclidis [i. e. Cleonidæ?] Introdvctio harmonica. Euclidis Sectio canonis. III. Nicomachi Geraseni, Pythagorici, harmonices manvale. IV. Alypii Introdvctio mvsica. V. Gavdentii, philosophi, Introdvctio harmonica. VI. Bacchii senioris Introdvctio artis mvsicæ.—II. Aristidis Qvintiliani De mvsica libri III. & Martiani Capellæ De mvsica liber IX.

ML167.M49

Mellen, John, 1722–1807.

Religion productive of music. A discourse, delivered at Marlborough, March 24th, 1773, at a singing lecture . . . By John Mellen . . . Boston, I. Thomas, 1773.

34 p. 19^{cm}.

[Miscellaneous pamphlets, v. 319, no. 4]
Caption title: The service of God, a ground of gladness and singing. Psalm c. ver. 2 . . .

AC901.M5

Melody—the soul of music: an essay towards the improvement of the musical art: with an appendix, containing account of an invention . . . Glasgow, Printed in the Courier office, 1798.

82 p. 20½^{cm}.

The invention is a violin with double strings in octaves.

ML3920.A2M4

Memoire pour le sieur de Lanove, la demoiselle Gavssin, & consorts, opposans à la reception de la demoiselle Cleron [à la Comédie française] [n. p., ca. 1750]

20 p. 16^{cm}.

ML1727.3.A2M5

Mémoires pour servir a l'histoire de la révolution opérée dans la musique par M. le chevalier Gluck... A Naples et se trouve a Paris, chez Bailly, 1781.

2 p. l., 491 p.   front. (port.)   22^{cm}.

Edited by Gaspar Michel Leblond.

ML1727.35.M5

[Menestrier, Claude François] 1631-1705.

Des ballets anciens et modernes selon les regles du theatre.   Paris, R. Guignard, 1682.

28 p. l., 232 (*i. e.* 323), [5] p.   15^{cm}.

The privilege, dated 1679, is for Menestrier's "Philosophie des images", of which this forms a part. Errors in paging.

PN1991.M4

Des representations en musique anciennes et modernes.   Paris, R. Guignard, 1681.

12 p. l., 333, [3] p.   17^{cm}.

ML1700.A2M5

Mengoli, Pietro, 1625-1686.

Specvlationi di mvsica, dedicate all' eminentiss. ... Sig. card. Azzolini da Pietro Mengoli ... Bologna, Per l'herede del Benacci, 1670.

12 p. l., 295 p.   tables (2 fold.)   20½^{cm}.

ML3800.A2M3

Mercadier, Jean Baptiste, 1750-1816.

Nouveau systême de musique théorique et pratique, par M. Mercadier de Belesta ...   Paris, Valade, 1776.

lxxij, 304, [4] p.   viii fold. pl.   20½^{cm}.

ML3800.A2M4

Mermet, Louis Bollioud-

See BOLLIOUD-MERMET, LOUIS.

Mersenne, Marin, 1588-1648.

F. Marini Mersenni ... Harmonicorvm libri. In qvibvs agitvr de sonorvm natvra, cavsis, & effectibus: de consonantiis, dissonantiis, rationibus, generibus, modis, cantibus, compositione, orbisque totius harmonicis instrumentis ... Opus vtile grammaticis, oratoribus, philosophis, iurisconsultis, medicis, mathematicis, atque theologis ... Lvtetiæ Parisiorvm, sumptibus Gvillelmi Bavdry, 1635.

6 p. l., 184, 168 p.   illus., diagrs.   35½^{cm}.

Title vignette.

ML3805.A2M5

—— Harmonicorvm libri XII. In qvibvs agitvr de sonorvm natvra, cavsis, et effectibvs: de consonantiis, dissonantiis, rationibus, generibus, modis, cantibus, compositione, orbísque totius harmonicis

Mersenne, Marin—*Continued.*

instrumentis. Authore F. M; Merseno Minimo . . . Editio avcta.
Lvtetiæ Parisiorvm, sumptibus Gvillelmi Bavdry, 1648.

8 p. l., 184 (*i. e.* 172), 4, 168 p. illus., diagrs. 36ᶜᵐ.

Title in red and black; title vignette. No. 126–131, 154–159 omitted in paging
of part 1; other slight errors in paging.

ML3805.A2M6

Harmonie vniverselle . . . Par F. Marin Mersenne . . . Paris, S.
Cramoisy, 1636–37.

2 v. in 3. illus. (incl. port.) tables, diagrs. 37½ᶜᵐ.

Coat of arms of Antoine Barillon de Morangis, maître des requêtes ordinaires du
roi, in gilt, stamped on cover. Many irregularities in paging.
Collations of this work differ; the L. of C. copy is made up as follows:
Vol. [1] Title (in red and black): Harmonie vniverselle, contenant la theorie
et la pratique de la mvsiqve, où il est traité de la nature des sons, & des mouue-
ments, des consonances, des dissonances, des genres, des modes, de la composition, de la voix, des chants, & de toutes sortes d'instrumens harmoniques.
Par F. Marin Mersenne de l'ordre des Minimes. [vignette: printer's mark]
A Paris, chez Sebastien Cramoisy, imprimeur ordinaire du roy, ruë S. Jacques,
aux Cicognes. M.DC.XXXVI. Auec priuilege du roy, & approbation des docteurs.—Title-page, vᵒ: note, Les caracteres de mvsiqve sont de l'impression de
Pierre Ballard imprimeur de la musique du roy.— Title (Harmonie vniverselle)
with an engr. illustration, signed H. Le Roy; below, verse 22 of Psalm 70. Verso
blank.—p. l. [3]–p. l. [7]: Premiere preface generale av lectevr.—p. l. [7]
vᵒ: Extraict dv privilege dv roy. Approbation des theologiens de l'ordre des
Minimes.—p. 1–68: Livre de l'vtilité de l'harmonie, & des autres parties des
mathematiques.—Half-title: Traitez de la natvre des sons, et des movvemens
de toutes sortes de corps. Verso blank.—p. l. [2–3]: A tres-havt . . . prince Mon-
seignevr Lovis de Valois, conte d'Alais [etc.] (signed by the author)—p. l. [4]:
Preface au lecteur. Fautes suruenuës dans le second liure Des mouuemens.—
p. 1–84: Livre premier. De la natvre et des proprietez dv son.—p. 85–156:
Livre second. Des movvemens de tovtes sortes de corps.—p. 157–228: Livre
troisiesme. Dv movvement, de la tension, de la force, de la pesanteur, & des
autres proprietez des chordes harmoniques, & des autres corps.—p. 228: Fautes
de l'impression des trois liures precedens. Advertissement.—p. l. [1]: Leaf
with 4 diagrams on verso, recto blank.—p. l. [2] rᵒ: Aduertissement au lecteur.
Fautes suruenuës en l'impression. Verso blank.—p. 1–36: Traité de mechaniqve.
Des poids soustenvs par des puissances sur les plans inclinez à l'horizon. Des
puissances qui soustiennent vn poids suspendu à deux chordes. Par G. Pers.
de Roberual . . . —Vol. [2] Half-title: Traitez de la voix, et des chants. Verso
blank.—p. l. [2]–p. l. [3] rᵒ: A Monsievr Monsievr Hallé, seignevr de Bovcqveval
[etc.] (signed by the author)—p. l. [3] vᵒ–p. l. [4]: Preface au lecteur. Fautes
suruenuës en l'impression.—p. 1–88: Livre premier. De la voix, des parties
qvi servent à la former, de sa definition, de ses proprietez, & de l'oüye.—p. 89–
180: Livre second, Des chants (p. 117–128: Varietez des six notes de la sexte
mineure, ou maieure. Sept cens vingt chants de l'hexachorde mineur. p. 150–
151: Table des 256 varietez de quatre temps differens)—Half-title: Traitez des
consonances, des dissonances, des genres, des modes, & de la composition. Verso
blank.—p. l. [2–3]: A Monsievr, M. Nicolas Clavde Fabry, sieur de Peiresc et
de Callas [etc.] (signed by the author)—p. l. [4]–p. l. [6] rᵒ: Preface, & aduertissement au lecteur.—p. l. [6] vᵒ: Fautes suruenuës en l'impression.—p. 1–112:
Livre premier. Des consonances.—p. 113–140: Livre second. Des dissonances.—p. 141–196: Livre troisiesme. Des genres, des especes, des systemes, &
des modes de la musique (Plate bearing diagram between p. 164 and 165, duplicate between p. 166 and 167)—p. 197–282: Livre qvatriesme. De la composition
de mvsiqve.
Title: Seconde partie de l'Harmonie vniverselle: contenant la pratique des
consonances, & des dissonances dans le contrepoint figuré, la methode d'enseigner,
& d'apprendre à chanter. L'embellissement des airs. La musique accentuelle.
La rythmique, la prosodie, & la metrique françoise. La maniere de chanter les
odes de Pindar, & d'Horace. L'vtilité de l'harmonie, & plusieurs nouuelles
obseruations, tant physiques que mathematiques: auec deux tables, l'vne des

Mersenne, Marin--*Continued.*

propositions, & l'autre des matieres. *Cantate Domino canticum nouum, laus eius in ecclesia sanctorum.* Psal. 149. [vignette: printer's mark] A Paris, par Pierre Ballard, imprimeur de la musique du roy, demeurant ruë S. Iean de Beauuais, à l'enseigne du Mont Parnasse. M.DC.XXXVII. Auec priuilege du roy, & approbation des docteurs. Verso blank.—p. l. [2]: Av lectevr. Errata corrigez.—p. 283–330: Livre cinqviesme. De la composition de mvsiqve (p. 300–303: Fantaisie à quatre, composee par le sieur de Cousu)—p. 331–440: Livre sixiesme. De l'art de bien chanter.—p. 440–442: Fautes de l'impression du 5 & 6 liure, auec quelques auertissemens. Licence du general F. Franciscvs a Longobardis ordinis Minorum corrector generalis. Approbation des doctevrs.— Vol. [3] Half-title: Traité des instrumens a chordes. Verso blank.—p. l. [2]— p. l. [3] r°: A Monsievr Monsievr de Refvge, conseiller av Parlement (signed by the author)—p. l. [3] v°—p. l. [4]: Preface au lecteur. Fautes suruenuës en l'impression.—p. 1–40, numb. l. 41–46: Livre premier. Des instrumens (running title)—p. 45–92, 85–92, numb. l. 93–100: Livre second. Des instruments a chordes.—p. 101–176: Livre troisiesme. Des instrvmens a chordes.—p. 177–228: Livre qvatriesme. Des instrvmens a chordes (p. 186–189: Fantaisie a 5. composée par le sieur Henry le Ieune)—p. 225–308: Livre cinqviesme. Des instrvmens a vent.—p. l. [1]: A Monsievr Monsievr Pascal . . . (signed by the author)—p. l. [2]: Preface au lecteur. Fautes suruenuës en l'impression du traité de l'orgue.—p. 309–412: Livre sixiesme. Des orgves.—p. 1–72: Livre septiesme. Des instrvmens de percvssion (p. [66]–69: Requiem à cinq parties composé par Iacques Mauduit)—p. 73–79: Fautes de l'impression, & quelques aduis. Essay des moralitez tirees de la pure mathematique.—p. 1–28: Novvelles observations physiqves et mathematiqves.—p. [1–9]: Table des XIX. liures de musique.— p. [10]: Premiere observation.—p. [11–12]: Seconde observation.

ML100.A2M3

Les prelvdes de l'harmonie vniverselle, ov Qvestions cvrievses. Vtiles aux predicateurs, aux theologiens, aux astrologues, aux medecins & aux philosophes. Composees par le L. P. M. M. Paris, H. Gvenon, 1634.

    7 p. l., 224 p.   illus.   17½^{cm}.

ML3800.A2M5

Traité de l'harmonie vniverselle. Où est contenu la musique theorique & pratique des anciens & modernes, auec les causes de ses effets. Enrichie de raisons prises de la philosophie, & des mathematiques. Par le sieur de Sermes [*pseud.*] A Paris, pour Gvillavme Bavdry, 1627.

    2 pt. in 1 v.   illus., tables, diagrs.   18^{cm}.

    Title-page, with printer's mark (?) verso blank.—Epistre (A Monsievr Monsievr de Refvge, conseiller dv roy en sa cour de Parlement. Signed: F. de Sermes) [9] p.—Preface av lectevr, [7] p.—Sommaire des seize liures de la musique, [5] p.—Preface dv premier livre, [2] p.—Table des theoremes dv premier livre, [7] p.—Livre premier de la mvsiqve. Qui contient ce qu'enseignent Euclide, Ptolomée, Bacchius, Boëce, Guy Aretin, Faber, Glarean, Folian, Zarlin, Salinas, Galilée, l'Illuminato, Cerone, &c. & plusieurs autres choses qui n'ont point esté traitées iusques à present, p. 1–304, followed by Exemples des XII. modes, [4] p.— Title: Livre second de l'Harmonie vniverselle. Où l'harmonie de toutes les parties du monde est expliquée tant en general qu'en particulier. Par le sieur de Sermes. A Paris, povr Gvillavme Bavdry . . . M.DC.XXVII. Auec privilege du roy. Verso blank.—Epistre (A Monsievr Monsievr Covtel, conseiller dv roy en sa Covr des aydes. Signed: François de Sermes), [7] p.—Preface dv second livre, [8] p.—Table des theoremes dv second livre, [3] p.—Livre second des paralleles de la mvsiqve. Auquel on void le rapport qu'ont les sons, les consonances, & les autres interuales auec la rythmique [etc., etc.], p. 305–477 (p. 368 wrongly numbered 378, no. 369–370 omitted)—Fautes du premier liure. Fautes du second liure, [1] p.

ML3805.A2M68

Metaphrastes, Simeon, *der jüngere, pseud.*

See MARPURG, FRIEDRICH WILHELM. Legende einiger musik-heiligen, 1786.

Metodo per suonare il flauto con principj ristretti di musica.

[21] p. 30 x 21^{cm}.

18th cent. ms.
On p. [14] "Regole per aprendere la musica," which are extensively explained in the following "Spiegazione degl' antecedenti articoli."

ML96.M

Meude-Monpas, J. J. O. de.

Dictionnaire de musique, dans lequel on simplifie les expressions et les définitions mathématiques et physiques qui ont rapport à cet art; avec des remarques impartiales sur les poëtes lyriques, les vérificateurs, les compositeurs, acteurs, exécutants, ect, ect ... Par J. J. O. de Meude-Monpas, chevalier. Paris, Knapen et fils, 1787.

xvj, 232 p. 18½^{cm}.

ML108.A2M2

Meurs, Johannes van, 1579–1639, *editor.*

Aristoxenvs. Nicomachvs. Alypivs. Auctores musices antiquissimi, hactenus non editi. Ioannes Mevrsivs nunc primus vulgavit, & notas addidit. Lvgdvni Batavorvm, ex officinâ Lvdovici Elzeviri, typis G. Basson, 1616.

4 p. l., 160 (*i. e.* 196) p. 19½ x 13½^{cm}.

Printer's mark: open music book. Last page numbered 160 for 196.

CONTENTS.—'Αριστοξένου 'Αρμονικῶν στοιχείων βιβλία γ'.—Νικομάχου Γερασηνοῦ Πυθαγορικοῦ 'Αρμονικῆς ἐγχειρίδιον. Βιβλία δύο.—'Αλυπίου Εἰσαγωγὴ μουσική.

ML167.M57

See also PHILOSTRATUS. Epistolæ, 1616.

[Meusnier de Querlon, Anne Gabriel] 1702–1780.

Le code lyrique, ou reglement pour l'Opera de Paris. Avec des eclaircissemens historiques. A Utopie, chez Thomas Morus, à l'enseigne des Terres australes. [Paris] 1743.

1 p. l., 95 p. 15½ x 8½^{cm}.

ML1727.8.P2M59

[Meyer, Carl Gottfried] *compiler.*

Sammlung einiger nachrichten von berühmten orgel-wercken in Teutschland, mit vieler mühe aufgesetzt von einem liebhaber der musik. Breslau, C. G. Meyer, 1757.

2 p. l., 112 p. illus. 23 x 18^{cm}.

Appended is a description of organs in Dresden (Katholische kirche) Berlin (St. Nikolai) etc. 19 p. ms.

ML594.A2M3

[Meyer, Joachim] 1661–1732.

Unvorgreiffliche gedancken über die neulich eingerissene theatralische kirchen-music und denen darinnen bishero üblich gewordenen cantaten mit vergleichung der music voriger zeiten, zur verbesserung der unsrigen vorgestellet von J. M. D. [Lemgo] 1726.

70 p. 15½^{cm}.

ML3001.M61

Michaelis, Christian Friedrich, 1770–1834.

Ueber den geist der tonkunst, mit rücksicht auf Kants Kritik der ästhetischen urtheilskraft; ein ästhetischer versuch von Christian Friedrich Michaelis . . . Leipzig, Schäferische buchhandlung, 1795–1800.

2 v. (v. 1: 134, [2] p.; v. 2: 3 p. l., 160 p.) 18^{cm}.

Title vignette. Title of vol. 2 varies slightly.
"Verzeichniss einiger neuerer musikalisch-ästhetischer schriften und aufsätze": v. [1] p. 125–134.

ML3845.A2M62

Michel, Gaspar.

See LEBLOND, GASPAR MICHEL, *called.*

Michele, Antonio di, *d.* 1680.

La nvova chitarra di regole, dichiarationi, e figvre con la regola della scala. Composta da Don Antonino di Micheli . . . Con aggiunta d'arie siciliane, e sonate di varij auttori. Palermo, Per P. Coppula stamp. camer., 1698.

2 p. l., 70, [2] p. 1 illus., diagrs. 14½ x 21^{cm}.

Title vignette.
An earlier edition was published at Palermo in 1680.

MT582.A2M4

[Michell, Henry] 1714–1789.

De arte medendi apud priscos musices ope atque carminum epistola ad Antonium Relhan . . . Ed. altera & auctior . . . Londini, excudebat J. Nichols, 1783.

81, [1] p. 22^{cm}.

Caption of dedication: Viro summo comiti de Shelburne &c. s. p. d. Michael Gaspar [pseud. of Henry Michell]

ML3920.A2M5

Mignot,   de La Voye.

See LA VOYE MIGNOT,   DE.

Milbourne, Luke, 1649–1720.

Psalmody recommended in a sermon preach'd to the Company of parish-clerks, at St. Alban's Woodstreet, November 17. at St. Giles's in the Fields, November 22, 1712. and now publish'd at the desire of the hearers. By Luke Milbourne . . . London, J. Downing, 1713.

1 p. l., x, 35 p. 19^{cm}.

ML3001.M64

Milchmeyer, Johann Peter, 1750–1813.

Die wahre art das pianoforte zu spielen . . . von J. P. Milchmeyer . . . Zu haben in Dresden beym verfasser . . . Dresden, Gedruckt bei C. C. Meinhold, 1797.

4 p. l., 72 p. 23 x 32½^{cm}.

MT222.A2M64

Milioni, Pietro.

Vero e facil modo d'imparare a sonare, et accordare da se medesimo
la chitarra spagnuola, non solò con l'alfabetto, & accordatura ordinaria, mà anco con vn' altro alfabetto, & acordatura straordinaria,
nuouamente inuentati da Pietro Milioni, et Lodovico Monte compagni. Con vna regola per imparare il modo d'accordare sei chitarre,
per poterle sonare insieme in concerto, ciascuna per differente chiaue.
Venetia, G. Zim, 1684.

48 p. 1 illus. 9½ x 15½ᶜᵐ.

Illustrated t.-p.
Earlier editions were published in 1644, 1652, etc.

M127.M6

Miller, Edward, 1731–1807.

Elements of thorough bass and composition, in which the rules of
accompaniment for the harpsichord or piano-forte are rendered amusing by the introduction of eight Italian, eight French & twelve English songs collected from the works of eminent composers antient &
modern. With proper lessons for practise . . . by Edward Miller . . .
Opera quinta. London, Longman & Broderip [1787]

8, 88 p. 32ᶜᵐ.

Engraved, with the exception of p. [3]–8 (first group)

MT49.A2M5

—— A treatise on thorough bass and composition, in which the rules
of accompaniment are laid down and a variety of proper lessons are
given—the whole calculated for such performers as are unacquainted
with the principles of harmony, by Edwᵈ. Miller . . . Dublin, E. Lee
[1787]

1 p. l., 52 p. 33ᶜᵐ.

Engraved throughout.

MT49.A2M52

Mimnermus, *pseud.*

See PRINTZ, WOLFGANG CASPAR.

Mingotti, Regina (Valentini) 1728–1807.

An appeal to the publick, by Signora Mingotti. London, Printed
for the authoress [1756 ?]

1 p. l., 13 p. 20½ x 16ᶜᵐ.

Relating her contentions with the opera manager Vanneschi.

ML420.M46

[Minguet é Irol, Pablo] *d.* 1801?

Reglas, y advertencias generales que enseñan el modo de tañer
todos los instrumentos mejores, y mas usuales, como son la guitarra,
tiple, vandola, cythara, clavicordio, organo, harpa, psalterio, bandurria, violin, flauta travesera, flauta dulce, y la flautilla, con varios
tañidos, danzas, contradanzas, y otras cosas semejantes . . . [Madrid,
J. Ibarra, 1753–54]

[64] p. front., 17 pl. 14½ x 20ᶜᵐ.

In four parts, each with special t.-p. bearing the author's name. The approbation of part [1] is dated 1753, the t.-p. of part [4], 1754; the second and third
parts are not dated.

MT582.A2M3

[Mirabeau, Honoré Gabriel Riquetti, *comte* de] 1749–1791.

Le lecteur y mettra le titre. Londres, 1777.

95, [1] p. 21^{cm}.

An essay on music. Contains an analysis of a symphony by Raimondi, "Les aventures de Télémaque."

ML3845.A2M67

Mirus, Adam Erdmann, 1656–1727.

Kurtze fragen aus der musica sacra, worinnen denen liebhabern bey lesung der biblischen historien / eine sonderbahre nachricht gegeben wird / entworffen von M. Adam Erdmann Miro . . . Dresden, J. C. Zimmermann, 1715.

3 p. l., 180 p. front. 14^{cm}.

First edition, Görlitz, 1707.

ML166.A2M6

Missery, Antoine Suremain de.

See SUREMAIN DE MISSERY, ANTOINE.

Mizler von Kolof, Lorenz Christoph, 1711–1778.

Anfangs-gründe des general basses nach mathematischer lehr-art abgehandelt, und vermittelst einer hierzu erfundenen maschine auf das deutlichste vorgetragen von Lorenz Mizlern . . . Leipzig, Zu finden bey dem verfasser [1739]

4 p. l., 123 (*i. e.* 137), [1] p. v pl. 17½^{cm}.

Page 137 wrongly numbered 123.

MT49.A2M68

Dissertatio qvod mvsica scientia sit et pars ervditionis philosophicae . . . Ed. 2. avctior et longe emendatior cvm praefatione nova. Lipsiae et VVittebergae, recvsa in officina Hakiana, 1736.

4 p. l., 24 p. 19½ x 16^{cm}.

ML3800.A2M6

Musikalischer staarstecher in welchem rechtschaffener musikverständigen fehler bescheiden angemerket, eingebildeter und selbst gewachsener so genannten componisten thorheiten aber lächerlich gemachet werden. Als ein anhang ist des herrn Riva . . . Nachricht vor die componisten und sånger beygefüget, und aus dem italienischen ins deutsche übersetzet von Lorenz Mizlern, A. M. Leipzig, Auf kosten des verfassers [1740]

4 p. l., 118, [3] p. fold. pl. 16½^{cm}.

Issued monthly (1.–7. stück) 1739–40.
The appendix has title: Anhang zum Musikalischen staarstecher welcher bestehet in einer Nachricht vor die componisten und sånger, in italienischer sprache aufgesetzt vom herrn Riva, damaligen residenten des herzogs von Modena zu Londen, und daselbst hrsg. bey Tomaso-Edlin anno 1728 . . . Leipzig, 1740.
"Verzeichnis der schrifften und bücher, welche M. Lorenz Mizler . . . geschrieben": p. 117–118.

ML4.M89

Lorenz Mizlers . . . Neu eröffnete musikalische bibliothek, oder Gründliche nachricht nebst unpartheyischem urtheil von musikali-

Mizler von Kolof, Lorenz Christoph—*Continued.*

schen schriften und bůchern ... Leipzig, Im verlag des verfassers und bey Brauns erben in commission, 1739–54.

4 v. fold. plates, 3 port. (incl. front.) fold tables, fold. diagrs. $17\frac{1}{2}^{cm}$ (v. 4: 19^{cm})

Vol. 1 was issued in 6 parts, 1736–38; vol. 2 in 4 parts, 1740–43; vol. 3 in 4 parts, 1746–52. Of vol. 4 only the first part was published. Contains music.

Vol. 2 has title: Lorenz Mizlers Musikalische bibliothek ... worinn alles, was aus der mathematik, philosophie und den schönen wissenschafften zur erläuterung und verbesserung sowol der theoretischen als practischen musik gehöret ... beygebracht wird ... Leipzig, Im Mizlerischen bůcherverlag, 1743. Vol. 3 and vol. 4, part 1, have same title with slight variations.

ML4.M37

See also Voigt, C. Gespräch von der musik, 1742.

Mizler von Kolof, Lorenz Christoph, 1711–1778, *translator.*

See Fux, J. J. Gradvs ad Parnassvm, 1742.

Molette, Philippe du Contant de la.

See Du Contant de La Molette, Philippe.

Moline, Pierre Louis, 1739–1820.

See Riedel, F. J. Ueber die musik des ritters Christoph von Gluck, 1775.

Momigny, Jérôme Joseph, *b.* 1762, *editor.*

See Framery, N. É. Musique, 1791–1818.

Monnet, Jean, 1703–1785.

Supplément au Roman comique [de Scarron], ou Mémoires pour servir a la vie de Jean Monnet, ci-devant directeur de l'Opéra-Comique à Paris, de l'Opéra de Lyon, & d'une Comédie françoise à Londres, ecrits par lui-même ... Londres, 1773.

2 v. in 1 (v. 1: 4 p. l., 135, [3] p.; v. 2: 2 p. l., 192, [6] p.) $18\frac{1}{2}^{cm}$.

ML429.M67

Monpas, J. J. O. de Meude-

See Meude-Monpas, J. J. O. de.

Montanos, Francisco de.

Arte de canto llano. Con entonaciones comunes de coro y altar, y otras cosas diversas, como se verà en la tabla. En todo và acentuado el punto con la letra, y algunas cosas remitidas puestas ad longum. Compuesto por Francisco de Montanos, y aora nuevamente corregido, y enmendado por Sebastian Lopez de Velasco ... Añadida la Missa del angel custodio ... Zaragoça, I. de Ibar, 1670.

2 p. l., 164 p. 21 x $15\frac{1}{2}^{cm}$.

MT860.A2M76

Arte de musica theorica y pratica, de Francisco de Montanos ... Valladolid, Impresso en casa de D. Fernandez de Cordova, 1592.

6 pt. in 1 v. illus., diagrs. 20^{cm}.

Title-page wanting; title taken from Catalogue de la bibliothèque de F. J. Fétis, Brussels, 1877.

ML171.M76

Montdorge, Antoine Gauthier de.

See GAUTHIER DE MONTDORGE, ANTOINE.

Monte, Lodovico.

Vero e facil modo d'imparare a sonare, et accordare da se medesimo la chitarra spagnuola, non solo con l'alfabetto, & accordatura ordinaria, mà anco con vn' altro alfabetto, & acordatura straordinaria, nuouamente inuentati da Pietro Milioni, et Lodovico Monte compagni. Con vna regola per imparare il modo d'accordare sei chitarre, per poterle sonare insieme in concerto, ciascuna per differente chiaue. Venetia, G. Zim, 1684.

    48 p.   1 illus.   9½ x 15½^{cm}.

    Illustrated t.-p.
    Earlier editions were published in 1644, 1652, etc.

                                  M127.M6

Montéclair, Michel Pignolet de, 1667–1737.

Nouvelle methode pour apprendre la musique par des demonstrations faciles, suivies d'un grand nombre de leçons à une et à deux voix, avec des tables qui facilitent l'habitude des transpositions et la conoissance des differentes mesures ... Par M^r. Monteclair ... Paris, Chez l'auteur [etc.] 1709.

    4 p. l., 64 p.   diagrs.   28 x 21½^{cm}.

    Engraved throughout; line borders.

                                  MT6.A2M77

Principes de musique. Divisez en quatre parties. La premiere partie contient tout ce qui appartient à l'intonation. La iime partie tout ce qui regarde la mesure et le mouvement. La iiie partie la maniere de joindre les paroles aux nottes et de bien former les agréments du chant. La ive partie est l'abregé d'un nouveau systême de musique, par lequel l'auteur fait voir qu'en changeant peu de choses dans la maniere de notter la musique, on en rendroit l'étude et la pratique plus aisées. Composez ... par M^r. de Montéclair ... Se vend a Paris, rue St Honoré à la Regle d'or [veuve Boivin, 1736]

    3 p. l., 133 p.   diagrs.   31½^{cm}.

    Engraved throughout.

                               MT835.A2M68

Montenegro, Benito Jerónimo Feijóo y.

See FEIJÓO Y MONTENEGRO, BENITO JERÓNIMO.

Montenoy, Charles Palissot de.

See PALISSOT DE MONTENOY, CHARLES.

Montes, Diego de Roxas y.

See ROXAS Y MONTES, DIEGO DE.

Morabin, Jacques, 1687–1762.

See CHÂTEAUNEUF, F. DE CASTAGNÈRES, *abbé* DE. Dialogue sur la musique des anciens, 1725.

Moraes Pedroso, Manuel de.

Compendio musico, ou Arte abbreviada em que se contém as regras mais necessarias da cantoria, acompanhamento, e contraponto . . . Por Manoel de Moraes Pedroso . . . Porto, Na officina episcopal do capitaõ M. Pedroso Coimbra, 1751.

6 p. l., 47, [3] p. illus. 20^{cm}.

MT40.A2M82

Morambert, Antoine Jacques Labbet, *abbé* de, 1721–1756.

See LAUGIER, M. A. Sentiment d'un harmoniphile [1756]

[Morand, Pierre de] 1701–1757.

Justification de la musique françoise. Contre la querelle qui lui a été faite par un Allemand & un Allobroge. Adressée par elle-même au coin de la reine le jour qu'avec Titon & l'Aurore elle s'est remise en possession de son théâtre . . . La Haye [*i. e.* Paris] 1754

2 p. l., viij, 55 p. 21½^{cm}.

"La deuxième critique [qui a paru contre Rousseau de Genève] . . . est de Morand le poète et d'Estève, ce qu'il y a de plaisant, c'est que dans la partie que Morand a faite, il a cité avec éloge des bribes du *Livre des beaux arts* par Estève, et dans celle qu' Estève a faite, il a cité des vers lyriques de Morand."—Extract from Bibl. nat. ms. français 22158 in 4° (*cf.* note under Bâton)

ML1727.33.M82

Morato, João Vaz Barradas Muitopão e.

See VAZ BARRADAS MUITOPÃO E MORATO, JOÃO.

Moreau, Henri, 1728–1803.

L'harmonie mise en pratique. Avec un tableau de tous les accords, la méthode de s'en servir, & des regles utiles à ceux qui étudient la composition ou l'accompagnement. Cet ouvrage qui est recueilli de tous les meilleurs auteurs, contient des exemples sur toutes les consonnances & dissonnances à deux, à trois, & à quatre parties, &c. de même que fugues, points d'orgue, chromatique, &c. . . . Par H. Moreau . . . Liege, J. G. M. Loxhay, 1783.

4 p. l., 128 p. A–I, K–P fold. pl. 20^{cm}.

MT50.A2M83

Moreschi, Giovanni Battista Alessandro.

Orazione in lode del padre maestro Giambattista Martini, recitata da Giambattista Alessandro Moreschi nella solenne accademia de' Fervidi l'ultimo giorno dell' anno 1784. Bologna, Stamperia di S. Tommaso d'Aquino, 1786.

38 p., 1 l. incl. front. (port.) 23 x 16½^{cm}.

ML423.M29M5

Moretus, Théodore, 1602–1667, *praeses.*

Propositiones mathematicæ ex harmonica, de soni magnitudine . . . Vratislaviæ, typis Baumannianis, exprimebat J. C. Jacob [1664]

[20] p. illus., diagrs. 17½ x 14½^{cm}.

Diss.—Breslau (Gottfried Fibig, respondent)

ML3807.A2F4

Morley, Thomas, 1557–1603 ?

A plaine and easie introdvction to practicall mvsicke, set downe in forme of a dialogue: deuided into three partes, the first teacheth to sing with all things necessary for the knowledge of pricktsong.   The second treateth of descante and to sing two parts in one vpon a plainsong or ground, with other things necessary for a descanter.   The third and last part entreateth of composition of three, foure, fiue or more parts with many profitable rules to that effect.   With new songs of, 2. 3. 4. and .5 parts.   By Thomas Morley . . .   Imprinted at London by P. Short, 1597.

3 p. l., 183, [35] p.   diagrs.   27½^{cm}.

Illustrated t.-p.; initials; head and tail pieces.
"Authors whose authorities be either cited or vsed in this booke": [1] p. at end.

MT6.A2M84

—— A plaine and easie introdvction to practicall mvsicke, set downe in forme of a dialogue: diuided into three parts.   The first teacheth to sing, with all things necessarie for the knowledge of pricktsong.   The second treateth of descante, and to sing two parts in one vpon a plainsong or ground, with other things necessarie for a descanter.   The third and last part entreateth of composition of three, foure, fiue or more parts, with many profitable rules to that effect.   With new songs of, 2. 3. 4. and 5. parts.   By Thomas Morley . . .   London, Imprinted by H. Lownes, 1608.

3 p. l., 183, [35] p.   29^{cm}.

Illustrated t.-p.; initials; head and tail pieces.
"Authors whose authorities be either cited or vsed in this booke": [1] p. at end.

MT6.A2M86

—— A plain and easy introduction to practical music, set down in form of a dialogue, divided into three parts, the first teacheth to sing, the second treateth of descant, the third treateth of composition, by Thomas Morley . . .   As printed in the year 1597.   Now reprinted for W. Randall, London, 1771.

5 p. l., iv, 257, [1] p., 1 l., 29 p.   diagrs.   26½ x 21½^{cm}.

Engraved t.-p.
"Motetts, canzonets &c. . . . in score": 1 l., 29 p. at end.

MT6.A2M87

Morlière, Jacques Rochette de la.

See LAMORLIÈRE, JACQUES ROCHETTE DE.

Mothe Le Vayer, François de la.

See LA MOTHE LE VAYER, FRANÇOIS DE.

[Moyria, Gabriel, *vicomte* **de]** 1771–1839.

Lettre sur la musique moderne.   Par G * * * M * * * . . .   Bourg, Dufour et Josserand, 1797.

56 p.   20½^{cm}.

ML195.M69

Mozart, Johann Georg Leopold, 1719–1787.

Versuch einer gründlichen violinschule, entworfen und mit 4. kupfertafeln sammt einer tabelle versehen von Leopold Mozart ... Augspurg, Verlag des verfassers, 1756.

8 p. l., 264 p., 2 l., [8] p.   front. (port.) 4 pl. (1 fold.)   22½ x 17½ᶜᵐ.

MT262.A2M9

—— Leopold Mozarts ... Gründliche violinschule, mit vier kupfertafeln und einer tabelle.   2. verm. aufl.   Auf kosten des verfassers. Augsburg, Gedruckt bey J. J. Lotter, 1770.

8 p. l., 268, [8] p.   front. (port.) 4 pl. (1 fold.)   22 x 18ᶜᵐ.

MT262.A2M92

Müller, August Eberhard, 1767–1817.

Anweisung zum genauen vortrage der Mozartschen c'avierconcerte hauptsächlich in absicht richtiger applicatur, von A. E. Müller. Leipzig, Breitkopf & Härtel [1796]

1 p. l., [1], 24 p.   32 x 26ᶜᵐ.

Engraved throughout.

MT247.A2M9

Müller, Johann Christian, 1749–1796.

Anleitung zum selbstunterricht auf der harmonika, von Johann Christian Müller.   Leipzig, S. L. Crusius, 1788.

4 p. l., 48 p.   25½ x 22ᶜᵐ.

Title vignette: port.

MT670.M9

Münster, Joseph Joachim Benedict,

Musices instructio in brevissimo regulari compendio radicaliter data. Das ist: Kûrzist- doch wohl gründlicher weeg und wahrer unterricht die edle sing-kunst denen regeln gemäss recht aus dem fundament zu erlernen ... in druck gegeben von Josepho Joachimo Benedicto Münster ...   8. aufl.   Nicht allein mit denen sieben fundamentalregeln, welche nicht mit worten alleine, wie bey der 1. aufl., sondern in scala musica zu leichterer eindruckung der jugend in der andern aufl. ganz ausgesetzter zu finden gewesen, sondern auch in der 3. mit noch einem denen versiculanten wohlanstândigen anhang vermehret. Augsburg, J. J. Lotter, 1768.

32 p.   18½ x 21ᶜᵐ.

MT44.A2M9

Scala Jacob ascendendô, & descendendô.   Das ist: Kûrtzlich / doch wohlgegründete anleitung / und vollkommener unterricht / die edle choral-music denen reglen gemäss recht aus dem fundament zu erlernen ... in druck gegeben von Josepho Joachimo Benedicto Münster ...   2. aufl.   Augspurg, J. J. Lotters seel. erben, 1756.

38 p.   17 x 21ᶜᵐ.

MT860.A2M83

Muitopão e Morato, João Vaz Barradas.

See VAZ BARRADAS MUITOPÃO E MORATO, JOÃO.

Murschhauser, Franz Xaver Anton, 1663–1738.

Academia musico-poetica bipartita. Oder: Hohe schul der musi-calischen composition in zwey theil eingetheilt. Per definitiones, divisiones, regulas universales & particulares, explicationes, limita-tiones, & objectionum solutiones &c. Mit emsiger untersuchung aller zu dieser hohen wissenschafft dienlichen materien / und umstånden / auch vermeidung aller unnothwendigen weitlåufftigkeiten &c. nach des welt-berühmten herrn Johann Caspar Kerlls . . . und anderer approbirten classicorum tradition getreulich . . . beschrieben / und durchaus mit exemplis wohl erlåutert / in druck hervor gegeben / durch Franciscum Xaverium Murschhauser . . . Erster theil. Wel-cher handelt von denen intervallis; dann von denen con- und disso-nantibus; nachgehends von denen tonis, oder modis musicis, sowohl choralibus, als figuratis, mit angehångten transpositionibus. Nûrn-berg, W. M. Endter, 1721.

7 p. l., 186, [10] p.   31½ᶜᵐ.

No more published.

In the present edition the title does not contain the words "Um dem vortreff-lichen herrn Mattheson ein mehres licht zu geben . . ." as in the edition of same place and date quoted by Vogeleis (Kirchenmusikalisches jahrb., 1901, p. 11) and in the Augsburg edition of 1721 given by Eitner.

Mattheson's reply was published in his Critica musica, p. 1–88 ("Die melopo-etische lichtscheere")

MT40.A2M98

Fundamentalische kurz, und bequeme handleithūg so wohl zur figural- als choral-music, aus denen alt- und neÿen approbierten, uohrnembsten kunst-meisteren underschidlicher nationen herausge-zogen, denen liebhaberen der edlen music-kunst zum besten, denen instructoribus zwar zum vortheil, denē lehrnēdē aber, als eine zur perfectiō höchst-nothwendige wissēschafft zu nuzen uerfast, und heruorgegeben durch Franz Xaueriū Antonium Murschhauser. München, In verlegung des authoris, 1707.

[33] p.   19 x 28ᶜᵐ.

Engraved throughout.

MT44.A2M92

A **musical** directory for the year 1794. To be continued annually. Containing the names and address of the composers & professors of music, with a number of amateurs . . . Also the names and address of the principal music-sellers, and instrument-makers . . . &c. Lon-don, Printed for the editor, pub. by R. H. Westley [1794]

vii, 87 p.   19ᶜᵐ.

Dedication signed: J. Doane.

ML286.8.L5D5

Musices choralis medulla, sive Cantus gregoriani fundamentalis tra-ditio, una cum tonis communibus, hymnis, antiphonis, lectione mensali &c. Ad usum Fratrum minorum strictioris observantiæ, provinciæ Saxoniæ S. Crucis, ordinis seraphici patris S. Francisci. Paderbornæ, typis Joachimi F. Buch, 1714.

1 p. l., 146, 92, 4 p.   13½ x 7½ᶜᵐ.

MT860.A2M87

Musik. Von Carl Friedrich Cramer . . . Dec. 1788–Apr. 1789. Copenhagen, S. Sönnichsen, 1789.

346 p.   4 fold. l. (music)   16^{cm}.

ML4.M3

Der **Musikalische** dillettante; eine wochenschrift.   Wien, Gedruckt bey J. Kurtzböcken, 1770.

424, [1] p.   22½ x 18^{cm}.

A treatise on thorough-bass, issued in 53 numbers, each of which is accompanied by music.
The dedication and index announced on p. 4 do not appear in this copy.
Has been ascribed to J. F. Daube. The preface, however, is signed "Die verfasser," and this accords with the advertisement in the Augsburger kunstzeitung cited by Freystätter, which reads "Der musikalische dilettante. Wochenschrift herausgegeben von einer gesellschaft virtuosen . . ."

ML4.M40

Musikalische monathsschrift.   1.–6. stück; jul.–dec. 1792.   Berlin, Neue berlinische musikhandlung [1792]

cover-title, 172 p.   26^{cm}.

J. F. Reichardt, F. L. A. Kunzen, editors.
Preceded by Musikalisches wochenblatt.
Reissued, Berlin, 1793, together with the Musikalisches wochenblatt, under title: Studien für tonkünstler und musikfreunde.

ML4.M45

Musikalische nachrichten und anmerkungen, 1770.

See Wöchentliche nachrichten, 1766–70.

Musikalische real-zeitung . . .   2. julii 1788–30. junii 1790.   Speier, Expedition dieser zeitung; [etc., etc., 1788–90]

4 v. in 1.   21½ x 17½^{cm}.   weekly.

H. P. C. Bossler, J. F. Christmann; editors.
The musical supplements were issued separately as "Anthologie zur Realzeitung."
Continued as "Musikalische correspondenz der Deutschen filarmonischen gesellschaft."

ML4.M48

Musikalischer almanach auf das jahr 1782.   Alethinopel [1782?]

20 p. l., 116 p.   17½^{cm}.

Added t.-p., engr. Facing p. 106 is a second title not included in paging: Musikalisches handbuch auf das jahr 1782. Alethinopel.
Attributed by most authorities to Carl Ludwig Junker. Eitner ascribes to Johann Friedrich Reichardt (Monatshefte für musikgeschichte, 12, 144)
Forkel quotes as a supplement to this: Sichtbare und unsichtbare sonnen- und mondfinsternisse, die sich zwar im Musikalischen handbuch oder Musikalmanach für das jahr 1782. befinden, aber nicht angezeigt sind. Alethinopel (Berlin) 1782.

ML20.M60

—— **Musikalischer** und künstler-almanach auf das jahr 1783. Kosmopolis [1783?]

16 p. l., [25]–168 p.   front.   17½^{cm}.

Ascribed to Carl Ludwig Junker.
The third and last issue appeared as "Musikalischer almanach auf das jahr 1784. Freyburg."

ML20.M61

Musikalischer almanach fûr Deutschland auf das jahr 1782–84, 1789. Leipzig, Schwickert [1782–89]

4 v. 16½–17½^{cm}.

Edited by Johann Nicolaus Forkel.

ML20.M63

Musikalischer almanach, hrsg. von Johann Friedrich Reichardt. Mit 12 neuen in kupfer gestochenen liedern. Berlin, J. F. Unger, 1796.

[177] p. 12 pl. 11 x 8½^{cm}.

No more published.

ML20.R3

Musikalisches handwôrterbuch, oder Kurzgefasste anleitung, sâmmtliche im musikwesen vorkommende, vornehmlich auslåndische kunstwôrter richtig zu schreiben, auszusprechen und zu verstehn. Nebst einem anhange, welcher sehr wichtige musik-vortheile und eine neue erfindung beschreibt. Ein buch fûr jeden, der die musik treibt, lehrt oder lernt ... Weimar, C. L. Hoffmanns seel. wittwe und erben, 1786.

10 p. l., [5]–222 p. fold. pl. 18^{cm}.

Ascribed to J. G. L. von Wilke.

ML108.A2M9

Musikalisches kunstmagasin, von Johann Friederich Reichardt ...
1.–2. bd. (I.–VIII. stûck); 1781–91. Berlin, Im verlage des verfassers, 1782–91.

2 v. 29 x 26^{cm}. quarterly.

"Chronologisches verzeichnis der ôffentlich im druck und kupferstich erschienenen musikalischen werke von Johann Friederich Reichardt": v. 1, p. 207–209; v. 2, p. 124–125.

ML4.M52

Musikalisches wochenblatt. 1.–2. hft. (stûck 1–24); 1791–92. Berlin, In der Neuen berlinischen musikhandlung [1791–92]

cover-title, 191, [1] p. 26^{cm}.

J. F. Reichardt, F. L. A. Kunzen, editors.
Superseded by the Musikalische monathsschrift.
Reissued Berlin, 1793, together with the Musikalische monathsschrift, under title: Studien für tonkünstler und musikfreunde.

ML4.M8

La **musique** du diable, ou Le Mercure galant devalisé. A Paris, chez Robert le Turc, ruë d'Enfer, 1711.

11 p. l., 381 p. front. 13½^{cm}.

Supposed adventures of Mlle. Desmâtins of the Opéra, in the Inferno. Introduces Lully and other celebrities of the time.

ML1727.3.A2M9

Mylius, Andrèas, 1649–1702, *praeses.*

... Jura circa musicos ecclesiasticos ... Lipsiæ, literis C. Banckmanni [1688]

[40] p. 19 x 14½^{cm}.

Diss.—Leipzig (J. Kuhnau, respondent and author)

ML3795.A2K87

N., N.

See ABREU, A. Escuela para tocar . . . la guitarra, 1799.

Nachgedanken herrn m. Joh. Gottl. Biedermanns rect. der schule zu Freyberg über sein programma De vita musica in einem verweisschreiben an eine hochwürdige person zu Freyberg entworfen. Freyberg, Auf kosten des verfassers, 1750.

8 p. 21½ x 17ᶜᵐ.

This is in reality a sharp attack on Biedermann, who had published the year preceding a pamphlet "De vita musica," directed against J. F. Doles.

The letter ends with the following verse: Wer Biedermannen nennt, wird einen Midas nennen, und Wer Biedermannen kennt, wird leicht den W— — kennen. In L. of C. copy the name Wilisch has been inserted in the last line with pen and ink.

ML64.B42

Nachtigall, Othmar.

See LUSCINIUS, OTTMAR.

Narro, Manuel, *d.* 1776.

Adicion al Compendio del arte de canto llano. Su autor el R. P. F. Pedro Villasagra . . . La escribia Don Manuel Narro . . . Valencia, Impr. de la viuda de J. de Orga, 1766.

12 p. 21ᶜᵐ. (*With* Villasagra, Pedro de. Arte, y compendio del canto llano. Valencia, 1765)

MT860.A2V6

Nassarre, Pablo, *b.* 1664.

Escvela mvsica, segvn la practica moderna, dividida en primera, y segvnda parte. Esta primera contiene qvatro libros, el primero trata del sonido armonico, de svs divisiones, y de sus efectos. El segvndo, del canto llano, de sv vso en la iglesia, y del provecho espiritual que produce. El tercero, del canto de organo, y del fin, porqve se introduxo en la iglesia, con otras advertencias necessarias. El qvarto, de las proporciones qve se contraen de sonido à sonido; de las que ha de llevar cada instrumento musico; y las observancias, que han de tener los artifices de ellos. Sv avtor el padre Fr. Pablo Nassarre . . . Zaragoza, Herederos de Diego de Larvmbe, 1723–24.

2 v. (v. 1: 14 p. l., 501, [10] p.; v. 2: 6 p. l., 506 p.) 30½ᶜᵐ.

Vol. 2 has title: Segvnda parte de la Escvela mvsica, que contiene quatro libros. El primero, trata de todas las especies, consonantes, y disonantes; de sus qualidades, y como se deven usar en la musica. El segvndo, de variedad de contrapuntos, assi sobre canto llano, como de canto de organo, conciertos, sobre baxo, sobre tiple, à tres, à quatro, y à cinco. El tercero, de todo genero de composicion, à qualquier numero de vozes. El qvarto, trata de la glossa, y de otras advertencias necessarias à los compositores. Compuesto por fray Pablo Nassarre . . . Zaragoza, Herederos de M. Roman, impressor de la Vniversidad, 1723.

MT60.A2N6

Fragmentos mvsicos. Reglas generales, y muy necessarias para canto llano, canto de organo, contrapunto, y composicion. Compvestos por Fr. Pablo Nassarre . . . Zaragoça, T. G. Martinez, 1683.

8 p. l., 142 p. 15½ᶜᵐ.

MT40.A2N25

Nassarre, Pablo—*Continued.*

—— Fragmentos musicos, repartidos en quatro tratados. En que se hallan reglas generales, y muy necessarias para canto llano, canto de organo, contrapunto, y composicion. Compuestos por Fr. Pablo Nassarre . . . Y aora nuevamente añadido el vltimo tratado por el mismo autor; y juntamente exemplificados con los caractères musicos de que carecìa. Sacalos a luz . . . D. Joseph de Torres . . . Madrid, En su imprenta de musica, 1700.

8 p. l., 288 p.   21ᶜᵐ.

MT40.A2N26

Nauss, Johann Xaver.

Gründlicher unterricht den general-bass recht zu erlernen, worinnen denen anfängern zum vortheil, nebst denen nothwendigsten regeln und exempeln, zugleich auch der finger-zeig mit ziffern sowohl im bass als discant deutlich gewiesen wird.   Von Johann Xaveri Nauss . . . Augsburg, J. J. Lotter, 1769.

32 p.   17½ x 20ᶜᵐ.

An earlier edition was published at Augsburg in 1751.

MT49.A2N2

Navas, Francisco Marcos y.

See MARCOS Y NAVAS, FRANCISCO.

Negri, Cesare, *b.* 1546?

Nuove inventioni di balli, opera vaghissima di Cesare Negri Milanese detto il Trombone . . . nella quale si danno i giusti modi del ben portar la vita, e di accomodarsi con leggiadria di movimento alle creanze, e grazie d'amore, convenevoli a tutti i cavalieri e dame per ogni sorta di balletto, e brando d'Italia, di Spagna e di Francia.   Con figure in rame, regola di musica et intavolatura di suono et di canto.   Milano, G. Bordone, 1604.

5 p. l., 296 (*i. e.* 312) p.   front. (port.) illus.   29½ᶜᵐ.

The frontispiece is a portrait of the author at the age of 66.   Title vignette; full page illustrations, several of which are repeated on different pages; errors in paging.   Caption title (Le gratie d'amore di Cesare de Negri . . .) is the same as the title of the 1st edition, 1602.

In L. of C. copy the t.-p. is wanting, and is replaced by a facsimile.

MT950.A2N3

Neidhardt, Johann Georg, *d.* 1739.

Johann George Neidhardts . . . Beste und leichteste temperatur des monochordi, vermittelst welcher das heutiges tages bräuchliche genus *diatonico-chromaticum* also eingerichtet wird / dass alle intervalla, nach gehöriger proportion, einerley schwebung überkommen / und sich daher die modi regulares in alle und iede claves, in einer angenehmen gleichheit / transponiren lassen: worbey vorhero von dem ursprunge der musicalischen proportionum, den generibus musicis, deren fehlern / und unzulänglichkeit anderer verbesserungen gehandelt wird.   Alles aus mathematischen gründen . . . aufgesetzt. Nebst einem darzu gehörigen kupffer.   Jena, Bey J. Bielcken, 1706.

5 p. l., [3]–104 p., 1 l.   19 x 15ᶜᵐ.

Plate wanting in this copy.

ML3809.A2N26

Neidhardt, Johann Georg—*Continued.*

Compositio harmonica. Problematice tradita per Joh. Georg Neidhart, regiae Borussorum musica magistrum.

159 p. 32ᶜᵐ.

Author's autograph, undated.

MT40.A2N45

Gåntzlich erschôpfte, mathematische abtheilungen des diatonisch-chromatischen, temperirten canonis monochordi, alwo, in unwiedersprechlichen regeln und handgreiflichen exempeln, gezeiget wird, wie alle temperaturen zu erfinden, in linien und zahlen darzustellen, und aufzutragen seyn. Den liebhabern gründlicher stimmung mitgetheilet, von Johann George Neidhardt ... Kônigsberg, C. G. Eckart, 1732.

6 p. l., 52 p. fold. pl. 20½ x 17½ᶜᵐ.

ML3809.A2N3

Sectio canonis harmonici, zur vôlligen richtigkeit der genervm modvlandi, hrsg. von Johann George Neidhardt ... Kônigsberg, C. G. Eckart, 1724.

8 p. l., 36 p. fold. pl. 21 x 17ᶜᵐ.

The plate is 14½ x 68ᶜᵐ.

ML3809.A2N32

[Nemeitz, Joachim Christoph] 1679–1753.

Von den musicalischen schauspielen, die man opern nennet.

(*In his* ... Vernûnfftige gedancken uber allerhand historische / critische und moralische materien. Franckfurt am Mayn, 1739–45. 18ᶜᵐ. 6. t., p. 162–189)

AC33.N4

Nero, Pietro del.

See MEI, G. Discorso sopra la mvsica, 1602.

Neue und erleichterte art zu solmisiren, nebst andern vortheilen, die singkunst in kurzer zeit zu erlernen. Denen herren lehrmeistern zu grosser bequemlichkeit, der musikliebenden jugend aber zum sonderbaren nutzen ans licht gestellet von P. J. L. C. R. & B. W. U. Ulm, J. G. Groschopff, 1763.

4 p. l., 56 p. illus. 17 x 20½ᶜᵐ.

MT44.A2R4

[Neuss, Heinrich Georg] 1654–1716.

Musica parabolica, oder parabolische music, das ist, erörterung etlicher gleichnisse und figuren, die in der music, absonderlich an der trommete befindlich, dadurch die allerwichtigsten geheimnisse der Heiligen Schrift ... abgemahlet wird ... [Leipzig, Heinsius erben] 1754.

124 p. 17 x 10ᶜᵐ.

"Kurtzer entwurf von der music. Den geist der weissheit und offenbahrung zur erkenntniss Gottes und seiner geheimen wahrheit zuvor": p. 90–124.

ML3800.A2N2

New and complete instructions for the fife.

See The COMPLEAT tutor for the fife.

New and complete instructions for the harpsichord, piano forte or organ, wherein the fundamental principles are fully explain'd . . . & by which any one may without the assistance of a master learn to play with taste and judgment in a short time. To which is added a valuable selection of favorite lessons, marches, airs, songs &c., also the rules of thorough bass by an eminent master . . . London, Printed for G. Astor n°. 79 Cornhill [17— ?]

32 p. 18 x 25½ᶜᵐ.

Published between 1798 and 1801. *cf.* Kidson, British music publishers.
Engraved throughout. This copy imperfect, wanting p. 23–24.

MT252.A2N3

A **new** and easie method to learn to sing by book: whereby one (who hath a good voice and ear) may, without other help, learn to sing true by notes. Design'd chiefly for, and applied to, the promoting of psalmody; and furnished with variety of psalm tunes in parts, with directions for that kind of singing . . . London, W. Rogers, 1686.

7 p. l., 104 p. 18ᶜᵐ.

MT870.A2N4

New instructions for the German flute.

See COMPLEAT instructions for the German flute.

Newman, John, 1677?–1741.

See PRACTICAL discourses, 1708.

Nichelmann, Christoph, 1717–1762.

Die melodie nach ihrem wesen sowohl, als nach ihren eigenschaften, von Christoph Nichelmann . . . Nebst 22. kupfer-tafeln . . . Dantzig, J. C. Schuster, 1755.

8 p. l., 175 p. xxii pl. on 12 l. 24 x 19ᶜᵐ.

The plates, with the exception of the first and last, are printed on both sides.

ML3851.N52

Nicolai, Ernst Anton, 1722–1802.

Die verbindung der musik mit der artzneygelahrheit, entworfen von d. Ernst Anton Nicolai.• Halle im Magdeburgischen, C. H. Hemmerde, 1745.

12 p. l., 70 p. 19ᶜᵐ.

ML3920.A2N5

Nicomachus *Gerasenus.*

See MEIBOM, M., *translator.* Antiqvæ mvsicæ avctores, 1652.
MEURS, J. VAN, *editor.* Aristoxenvs, 1616.

Niedt, Friedrich Erhardt, 1674–1717.

Friedrich Erhard Niedtens Handleitung / zur variation, wie man den general-bass, und darûber gesetzte zahlen variiren / artige inventiones machen / und aus einen schlechten general-bass præludia, ciaconen, allemanden, couranten, sarabanden, menueten, giquen

Niedt, Friedrich Erhardt—*Continued.*

und dergleichen leichtlich verfertigen könne / samt andern nötigen instructionen. Hamburg, Auf kosten des autoris, und bey B. Schillern zu finden / 1706.

[166] p. 17 x 20½^{cm}.

Unpaged. Signatures: a-x in fours (last leaf blank)

MT49.A2N54

Friderich Erhard Niedtens / musici, Musicalische handleitung / oder Gründlicher unterricht. Vermittelst welchen ein liebhaber der edlen music in kurtzer zeit sich so weit perfectioniren kan / dass er nicht allein den general-bass ... fertig spielen / sondern ... allerley sachen selbst componiren ... könne. Erster theil. Handelt vom general-bass, denselben schlecht weg zu spielen. Hamburg, B. Schiller, 1710.

[64] p. 17 x 21^{cm}.

First edition, Hamburg, 1700.

MT40.A2N46

—— Friederich Erhard Niedtens Musicalischer handleitung anderer theil / von der variation des general-basses, samt einer anweisung / wie man aus einem schlechten general-bass allerley sachen / als præludia, ciaconen, allemanden, &c. erfinden könne. Die 2. aufl. / verb. / verm. / mit verschiedenen grund-richtigen anmerckungen / und einem anhang von mehr als 60. orgel-wercken versehen durch J. Mattheson ... Hamburg / B. Schillers wittwe und J. C. Kissner / 1721.

6 p. l., 204 p. 17 x 19½^{cm}.

MT40.A2N47

—— Friederich Erhardt Niedtens Musicalischer handleitung dritter und letzter theil / handlend vom contra-punct, canon, motteten, choral, recitativ-stylo und cavaten. Opus posthumum. Deme beygefüget Veritophili Deutliche beweis-gründe / worauf der rechte gebrauch der music / beydes in den kirchen und ausser denselben beruhet ... bessern nackdrucks [!] wegen mit einer vorrede zum druck befördert von Mattheson. Hamburg / Sel. B. Schillers erben / 1717.

2 v. in 1 (v. 1: 2 p. l., 68 p.; v. 2: 12 p. l., 56 p.) 17 x 21^{cm}.

"Veritophili Deutliche beweis-gründe," by Christoph Raupach, has special t.-p. and separate paging.
The work was not completed.

MT40.A2N48

Niemtschek, Franz Xaver.

Leben des k. k. kapellmeisters Wolfgang Gottlieb Mozart, nach originalquellen beschrieben vom Franz Niemtschek ... Prag, Herrlische buchhandlung, 1798.

2 p. l., 78 p. 19½ x 16^{cm}.

ML410.M9N3

Nierop, Dirk Rembrantsz. van, 1610–1682.

Mathematische calculatie, dat is, Wiskonstige rekening: leerende het vinden van verscheyden hemelloopsche voorstellen, en dat door de tafelen sinus tangents of logarithmus wiskonstelick uyt te rekenen:

Nierop, Dirk Rembrantsz. van—*Continued.*

als oock tuyghwerckelick op een liniael uyt te passen. Als mede 't
beschrijven en uytrekenen der zonwysers ... Noch is hier by
gevoeght de Wis-konstige musyka: waer in getoont wort de oorsake
van 't geluyt, de redens der zangh-toonen, en verscheyden dingen tot
de zangh en speel-konst behoorende. Door Dyrck Rembrantz van
Nierop ... Amsteldam, G. van Goedesbergen, 1659.

31, 167, 70 p.   tables (partly fold.) diagrs. (partly fold.)   19½ᶜᵐ.

Black-letter. Title vignette: portrait of the author. "Wis-konstige musyka"
has special t.-p. and separate paging.

ML3809.A2N37

Nivers, Guillaume Gabriel, *b.* 1617.

Dissertation sur le chant gregorien, dediée au roy. Par le Sʳ
Nivers ... Paris, Aux dépens de l'autheur, 1683.

8 p. l., 215, [1] p.   18½ᶜᵐ.

"Tabula tonorum": p. 175–188.   "Cantus ecclesiastici": p. 189–[216]

ML3082.A2N7

Methode certaine pour apprendre le plain-chant de l'eglise, dressée
par le Sʳ Nivers ... Nouv. ed. Paris, Impr. de J. B. C. Ballard
1745.

47, [1] p.   19ᶜᵐ.

"Exemples de quelques antiennes et respons": p. 27–47.

MT860.A2N58

Traité de la composition de mvsqve [!] Par le Sʳ Nivers ...
Paris, Chez l'autheur [etc.] 1667.

61 p.   17ᶜᵐ.

MT40.A2N73

Noble, Oliver, 1734–1792.

Regular and skilful music in the worship of God, founded in the
law of nature, and introduced into his worship, by his own institution,
under both the Jewish and Christian dispensations; shewn in a sermon, preached at the North meeting-house, Newbury-Port, at the
desire of the church and congregation, February 8th, 1774. by Oliver
Noble, A. M., pastor of a church in Newbury. Printed at the desire
of the Musical society, in Newbury-Port. And of a number of gentlemen and ladies who heard it ... Boston, Printed by Mills and Hicks,
for Daniel Bayley, in Newbury-Port, 1774.

46 p.   20ᶜᵐ.

ML3001.N75

Noinville, Jacques Bernard Durey de.

See DUREY DE NOINVILLE, JACQUES BERNARD.

Nopitsch, Christoph Friedrich Wilhelm, 1758–1824.

Versuch eines elementarbuchs der singkunst; vor trivial und nor-
malschulen sistematisch entworfen von Christoph Friedrich Wilhelm
Nopitsch ... Mit sechs erklärungstabellen. Nördlingen, Verlag des
verfassers, 1784.

2 p. l., [3]–35, [1] p.   vɪ fold. pl.   20 x 16ᶜᵐ.

MT935.A2N7

[Nougaret, Pierre Jean Baptiste] 1742–1823.

De l'art du théâtre en général, où il est parlé des spectacles de l'Europe, de ce qui concerne la comédie ancienne & nouvelle, la tragédie, la pastorale-dramatique, la parodie, l'opéra-sérieux, l'opéra-bouffon & la comédie-mêlée-d'ariettes, &c. Avec l'histoire philosophique de la musique, & des observations sur ses différens genres reçus au théâtre . . . Paris, Cailleau, 1769.

2 v. (v. 1: xxiv, 382 p.; v. 2: 3 p. l., [v]–viij, [5]–368, [2] p.) fronts. 17¼ᶜᵐ.

Added t.-p., engr.: De l'art du théâtre; où il est parlé des differens gens de spectacles, et de la musique adaptée au théâtre . . .

ML3858.N92

Le nouveau théâtre italien, ou Recueil general des comédies représentées par les Comédiens italiens ordinaires du roi. Nouv. éd., cor. & très-augm., & à laquelle on a joint les airs gravês des vaudevilles à la fin de chaque volume . . . Paris; Briasson, 1753.

10 v. 19½ᶜᵐ.

Added t.-p., engr. Each comedy has special t.-p. and separate paging.
"Mémoire pour servir l'histoire de la comédie italienne, depuis le rétablissement des comédiens italiens à Paris en 1716. jusqu'à la présente année 1752": v. 1, p. viij–xxxij.

PQ1231.I5N6

Nouvelle méthode pour aprendre le plain-chant parfaitement et en peu de tems, composée spécialement pour le diocèse de Rouen, conforme aux nouveaux livres de chant, dans laquelle se trouvent notées les proses & hymnes nouvelles. Rouen, Jore, pere & fils [1730 ?]

1 p. l., 90, [2] p. 17½ᶜᵐ.

MT860.A2R88

Noverre, Jean George, 1727–1810.

Lettres sur la danse, et sur les ballets, par M. Noverre . . . A Stutgard, et se vend a Lyon, chez A. Delaroche 1760.

2 p. l., 484 p. illus. (coat of arms) 17ᶜᵐ.

L3460.A2N94

—— Lettres sur la danse et sur les ballets. Par M. Noverre . . . 2. éd. A Londres, et se trouve a Paris, chez la veuve Dessain junior, 1783.

viij, 368 p. 20ᶜᵐ.

ML3460.A2N95

Nugent, Thomas, 1700 ?–1772, *translator.*

See Dubos, J. B. Critical reflections on poetry, 1748.

Nunes da Silva, Manuel, *b.* 1678.

Arte minima, que com semibreve prolaçam tratta em tempo breve, os modos da maxima, & longa sciencia da musica . . . seu author o P. Manoel Nunes da Sylva . . . Lisboa, Na officina de M. Manescal, impressor, à custa de A. Pereyra, & A. Manescal, 1704.

6 p. l., 44, 52, 136 p. pl., diagrs. 20¼ᶜᵐ.

First published Lisbon, 1685; reissued 1704 and 1725 with new t.-p.

MT6.A2N97

Observations pour les sujets retirés de l'Opéra; et pour les auteurs de ce théâtre. [Paris, Impr. de Prault, ca. 1790?]

24 p.   21^{cm}.

ML1727.3.P2O14

Observations sur la musique a grand orchestre, introduite dans plusieurs eglises & en dernier lieu à Notre-Dame de Paris; & sur l'admission des musiciens de l'Opéra dans ces eglises. [n. p., 1786?]

100 p.   16½^{cm}.

Caption title.   Dated at end: 9 décembre 1786.

ML3027.8.P2O2

Odier, Louis, 1748-1817.

Epistola physiologica inauguralis de elementariis musicæ sensationibus . . .   Edinburgi, apud Balfour, Auld, et Smellie, 1770.

49 p.   20^{cm}.

Thesis (M. D.)—Edinburgh.

ML3805.A2O21

Oelrichs, Johann Carl Conrad, 1722-1798.

Johann Carl Conrad Oelrichs . . . Historische nachricht von den akademischen würden in der musik und öffentlichen musikalischen akademien und geselschaften.   Berlin, C. F. Voss, 1752.

6 p. l., 52 p.   17^{cm}.

ML63.O28

Officium hebdomadæ sanctæ jvxta formam Missalis & Breviarii romani sub Urbano VIII. correcti: adjunctis, italico sermone declarationibus multarum rerum, quæ fiunt, & dicuntur in ejus recitatione.   Venetiis, ex typogr. J. Antonii Pezzana, 1777.

416 p.   16^{cm}.

Title vignette; rubricated.   In case.

Ch.17.1854

[Olio, Giovanni Battista dall'] 1739-1823.

La musica, poemetto.   Modena, La Società tipografica, 1794.

78 p., 1 l.   21^{cm}.

Prefatory letter signed: Giambatista dall' Olio.
The poem is accompanied by historical and explanatory notes.

ML64.O5

Olivier, Gabriel Raimond Jean de Dieu François, 1753-1823.

L'esprit d'Orphée, ou De l'influence respective de la musique, de la morale et de la législation . . .   Par le citoyen Olivier.   Paris, C. Pougens, an VI (1798)

2 p. l., 92 p.   21½^{cm}.

Caption title: Première étude, ou dissertation touchant l'influence de la musique sur les mœurs et le bonheur d'une nation . . .
L. of C. has also a title edition of this first "étude," published by Pougens in 1800, and a second and third "étude," issued by the same publisher in 1802 and 1804 respectively.

ML3920.A2O4

[Orazi, Giovanni Battista]

Saggio per costruire, e suonare un flauto traverso enarmonico che ha i tuoni bassi del violino, con due trii di genere enarmonico misti. Roma, Stamperia di M. Puccinelli, 1797.

18 p. 3 pl. (1 fold.) 34½cm.

Text and plates followed by 8 l. with the parts of the "Due trii . . . per tre traversi di nuova costruzione. In Roma nella calcografia Franzetti."

ML936.A2O8

Orelli, Diego, *originally* Aegidius Holler.

See HOLLER, AEGIDIUS.

The **organs** fvnerall, or The quiristers lamentation for the abolishment of superstition and superstitious ceremonies. In a dialogicall discourse between a quirister and an organist, an. Dom. 1642. London, G. Kirby [1642 ?]

[8] p. 18 x 13½cm.

Has been attributed to Joseph Brookbank.

ML3001.O72

Ornithoparcus, Andreas.

Musice Actiue ‖ Microlog[9] Andree Orni- ‖ toparchi Ostrofranci Meyningensis, Artiū ‖ Mgr̄i, Libris Quattuor digest[9]. Oīb[9] Mu- ‖ sicæ studiosis nō tā vtilis q̄ necessarius.‖ . . . [*Colophon:* ℭ Excussum est hoc opus, ab ipso authore denuo castigatum, ‖ recognitumq̄: Lipsie in edibus Valentini Schumanni, calco- ‖ graphi solertissimi: Mense Nouēbri: Anni virginei partus de- ‖ cimi septimi supra sesquimillesimū. Leone decimo Pont. Max. ‖ ac Maximiliano inuictissimo impatore orbi terrar[um] p̄sidētibus]

[107] p. diagrs. 21cm.

Title in red and black within ornamental border. Printer's mark at end. Signatures: A–M in fours, except A, C, F, which are in sixes.
On t.-p., following the title: Laurentius Thurschenreutinus Ad studio- ‖ sum Musices Lectorem. ‖ Musica: quam rursus mēdis purgauerit author: ‖ Iam redit ante oculos: lector amice: tuos. ‖ Iā redit ante oculos, Lypsick excussa Schumāni ‖ Arte Valentini: qui bene pressit eam. ‖ Arte Valentini facta est nitidissima tota: ‖ Et tibi Arionios afferet illa sonos.

MT6.A2O7

—— Andreas Ornithoparcvs his Micrologvs, or Introdvction: containing the art of singing. Digested into foure bookes. Not onely profitable, bvt also necessary for all that are studious of musicke. Also the dimension and perfect vse of the monochord, according to Guido Aretinus. By Iohn Dovland . . . London, T. Adams, 1609.

4 p. l., 80 (*i. e.* 90), [2] p. illus. 28½cm.

Title within ornamental border; title vignette; initials. Page 90 wrongly numbered 80.

MT6.A2O72

See also SEBASTIANI, C. Bellvm mvsicale [1563]

Oropesa, Tomás de Iriarte y.

See IRIARTE Y OROPESA, TOMÁS DE.

Orsolini, Giuseppe.

See BERARDI, A. Ragionamenti mvsicali, 1681.

Orville, André Guillaume Contant d'.

See CONTANT D'ORVILLE, ANDRÉ GUILLAUME.

Osio, Teodato.

L'armonia del nvdo parlare con ragione di nvmeri Pitagorici, discoperta da Teodato Osio, all' ecc.ᵐᵒ S.ʳ Don Fran.ᶜᵒ di Melo. Milano, C. Ferrandi [1637]

8 p. l., 35, [1], 191 p.　illus.　17ᶜᵐ.

Engr. t.-p.
Half-title: L'armonia del nvdo parlare, overo La mvsica ragione della voce continva, nella qvale a forza di aritmetiche et di mvsiche specvlationi si pongono alla prova le regole sino al presente stabilite da gl' osservatori del nvmero della prosa et del verso.

ML3849.A2O8

Oudoux, *abbé.*

Méthode nouvelle pour apprendre facilement le plain-chant, avec quelques exemples d'hymnes & de proses ... Par M. Oudoux ... 2. éd., rev., cor. & augm.　Paris, A. M. Lottin l'aîné, 1776.

2 p. l., 72, xcvi p.　fold. l. (music)　16½ᶜᵐ.

CONTENTS.—I. ptie. Méthode nouvelle.—II. ptie. Leçons propres à former la voix.

MT860.A2O93

Overend, Marmaduke, *d.* 1790.

A brief account of, and an introduction to, eight lectures, in the science of music ... in which are proposed, to be demonstrated and to be explained the radical sources of melody and harmony ... By Marmaduke Overend ... London, Printed for the author, and sold by Mess. Payne and son [etc.] 1781.

1 p. l., 20 p.　26 x 21½ᶜᵐ.

ML3809.A2O9

[Owen, James] 1654–1706.

Church-pageantry display'd: or, Organ-worship, arraign'd and condemn'd, as inconsistent with the revelation and worship of the gospel, the sentiments of the ancient fathers, the Church of England, and several eminent divines, both Protestants and Papists ... By Eugenius Junior [*pseud.*]—in answer to a letter about organs ... London, A. Baldwin, 1700.

1 p. l., 25 p.　20 x 16ᶜᵐ.

ML3001.O83

P., C. H.

See MATTHESON, J.　Gültige zeugnisse, 1738.

Paduani, Giovanni, *b. ca.* 1512.

Ioannis Padvanii Veronensis Institvtiones ad diuersas ex plurium uocum harmonia cantilenas, siue modulationes ex uarijs instrumentis fingendas, formulas penè omnes ac regulas, mira & perquam lucida breuitate complectentes.　Veronae, apud Sebastianum, & Ioannem fratres à Donnis, 1578.

4 p. l., 99, [1] p.　20½ᶜᵐ.

Title vignette: ecclesiastical coat of arms.　Errors in paging.

ML171.P22

Pagani, Pietro Antonio.

Breve trattato sopra il canto fermo, et sopra gli otto tuoni: con alcuni auisi intorno al corista, & cantore. Composto per il reuerendo p. f. Pietr' Antonio Pagani ... Venetia, G. A. Rampazetto, 1604.

31 numb. l., [2] p. 22ᶜᵐ.

Title within ornamental border; title vignette; rubricated.

MT860.A2P37

Paisley, James Hamilton, baron.

See ABERCORN, JAMES HAMILTON, 7th earl of.

Paixão Ribeiro, Manuel da.

Nova arte de viola, que ensina a tocalla com fundamento sem mestre ... com estampas das posturas, ou pontos naturaes, e accidentaes; e com alguns minuettes, e modinhas por musica, e por cifra ... por Manoel da Paixão Ribeiro ... Coimbra, Real officina da Universidade, 1789.

1 p. l., v, 51 p. 8 fold. pl. 22ᶜᵐ.

MT338.A2P2

[Palissot de Montenoy, Charles] 1730–1814.

Éloge de Jean-Philippe Rameau, compositeur de musique du cabinet du roi. [Paris, 1765?]

p. 39–67. 16½ᶜᵐ.

Caption title. Signature title, p. 57: "Nécrologe 1765." Taken from "Le Nécrologe des hommes célèbres de France."
"Catalogue des ouvrages de M. Rameau": p. 65–67.

ML410.R2P15

Panerai, Vincenzio.

Principj di musica teorico-pratici dell' ab: Vincenzio Paneraj ... Firenze, G. Volpini [n. d.]

[1], 13 p. 28 x 21½ᶜᵐ

Engraved throughout.
Another edition was published at Florence in 1750.

MT7.A2P26

Pannilini, Francesco de' Gori.

See GORI PANNILINI, FRANCESCO DE'.

Paolucci, Giuseppe, 1726–1776.

Arte pratica di contrappunto dimostrata con esempj di varj autori e con osservazioni di fr. Giuseppe Paolucci ... Venezia, A. de Castro, 1765–72.

3 v. in 1. 10 fold. l. (music) 22½ x 18ᶜᵐ.

Title vignette.

MT55.A2P3

Papillon de La Ferté, Denis Pierre Jean, 1727–1794.

See PARIS. ACADÉMIE ROYALE DE MUSIQUE. Précis sur l'Opéra [1789]

Papius, Andreas, 1542–1581.

And. Papii Gandensis De consonantiis, sev pro diatessaron libri dvo. Antverpiæ, ex officina Christophori Plantini, architypographi regij, 1581.

208, [22] p., 1 l. diagrs. 18¼^{cm}.

Printer's mark on t.-p.; initials. The 22 pages at end contain "Pater peccaui tribvs vocibvs" and "Als unverhoetz [Susan' vn iour] met ij. stimmen."
A revised edition of his "De consonantiis, sive harmoniis musicis contra vulgarem opinionem," Antwerp, 1568.

ML171.P27

Parfaict, Claude, 1701 ?–1777.

See PARFAICT, FRANÇOIS.

[Parfaict, François] 1698–1753.

Dictionnaire des théatres de Paris, contenant toutes les piéces qui ont été représentées jusqu'à présent sur les différens théâtres françois, & sur celui de l'Académie royale de musique: les extraits de celles qui ont été jouées par les comédiens italiens, depuis leur rétablissement en 1716, ainsi que des opéra comiques, & principaux spectacles des foires Saint Germain & Saint Laurent. Des faits anecdotes sur les auteurs qui ont travaillé pour ces théâtres, & sur les principaux acteurs, actrices, danseurs, danseuses, compositeurs de ballets, dessinateurs, peintres de ces spectacles, &c. . . . Paris, Lambert, 1756.

7 v. 17 x 9¾^{cm}.

By François and Claude Parfaict (completed and published by Quentin Godin d'Abguerbe)

ML102.O6P2

Memoires pour servir a l'histoire des spectacles de la foire. Par un acteur forain . . . Paris, Briasson, 1743.

2 v. in 1 (v. 1: 2 p. l., lxxxiv, 240 p.; v. 2: 2 p. l., 162 p.) 16½^{cm}.

By François and Claude Parfaict.

PN2633.P3

Paris. Académie royale de musique.

Mémoire justificatif des sujets de l'Académie royale de musique, en réponse à la lettre anonyme qui leur a été adressée le 4 septembre 1789, avec l'épigraphe: Tu dors, Brutus, et Rome est dans les fers. [Paris] 1789.

18 p. 20^{cm}.

ML1727.8.P2P23

. . . Petition, pour l'Académie royale de musique, a l'Assemblée nationale. [Paris, Impr. de Laillet & Garnéry, 1790]

8 p. 19½^{cm}.

Caption title.
At head of first page: Supplément à la Chronique de Paris, n° 246, année 1790.

ML1727.8.P2P3

Précis sur l'Opéra et son administration, et réponses à différentes objections. [Paris, 1789]

3 p. l., [3]–92 p. fold. tab. 25 x 20^{cm}.

By Papillon de La Ferté (*cf.* Pierre, Le Conservatoire national, 1900, p. 40)

ML1727.8.P2P4

Paris. Académie royale de musique—*Continued.*

Reglemens pour l'Académie royale de musique. Du 1er. avril 1792. Paris, Impr. de l'Opéra, 1792.

2 p. l., 44 p. fold. tab. 24 x 18½^{cm}.

ML1727.8.P2R24

See also FRANCE.

Paris. Conservatoire national de musique et de déclamation.

Organisation du Conservatoire de musique. [Paris, Impr. de la république, brumaire an v, 1796]

2 p. l., 58 p. 21¼^{cm}.

MT3.P2C3

Parran, Antoine, 1582–1650.

Traité de la mvsiqve theoriqve et pratiqve. Contenant les preceptes de la composition. Par le R. P. Antoine Parran . . . Paris, Par R. Ballard, seul imprimeur du roy pour la musique, 1646.

4 p. l., 143, [1] p. fold. pl., diagr. 24^{cm}.

Title vignette.
1st edition Paris, 1639.

MT40.A2P18

Parrilli, Felice.

Lettera villereccia di Felice Parrilli ad uno avvocato napoletano indiritta, in cui si propone un mezzano sistema per la quistione se i maestri di cappella son compresi fra gli artigiani . . . [Napoli? 1785?]

xii, 72 p. 20^{cm}.

The letter is dated: Mauro il dì 10. luglio 1785; the dedication, Napoli addì 28. agosto 1785.

ML63.P27

Pasquali, Nicolo, *d.* 1757.

The art of fingering the harpsichord; illustrated with examples in notes; to which is added, An approved method of tuning this instrument: by Nicolo Pasquali. Edinburgh, R. Bremner [1760?]

vii, 28 p. xv pl. on 8 l. 24½ x 33½^{cm}.

Text, except the first 4 pages, printed on leaves 24½ x 16^{cm}. Plates printed on both sides.

MT252.A2P3

——— The art of fingering, the harpsichord. Illustrated with examples in notes. To which is added, an approved method of tuning that instrument. By Nicolo Pasquali. London, R. Bremner [17—]

v, 28 p. xv pl. on 8 l. 24 x 33^{cm}.

Text printed on leaves 23½ x 18½^{cm}. Plates printed on both sides.

MT252.A2P31

Thorough-bass made easy: or, Practical rules for finding & applying its various chords with little trouble; together with variety of examples in notes, shewing the manner of accompanying concertos, solos,

Pasquali, Nicolo—*Continued.*

songs, and recitatives: by Nicolo Pasquali.   Edinburgh, R. Bremner [1757]

3 p. l., [3]–48 p. xxix pl. on 15 l.   24½ x 33½ᶜᵐ.   (*With his* Art of fingering the harpsichord. Edinburgh [1760?])

Text printed on leaves 24½ x 16ᶜᵐ. Plates printed on both sides.

MT252.A2P3

—— Thorough-bass made easy: or, Practical rules for finding & applying its various chords with little trouble; together with variety of examples in notes, shewing the manner of accompanying concertos, solos, songs, and recitatives: by Nicolo Pasquali.   London, R. Bremner [17—]

2 p. l., [3]–48 p. xxix pl. on 15 l.   24 x 33ᶜᵐ.   (*With his* Art of fingering, the harpsichord. London [17—])

MT252.A2P31

Passeri, Giovanni Battista, 1694–1780, *editor.*

See Doni, G. B.   Lyra Barberina, 1763.

Patru, Olivier, 1604–1681.

See Hertel, J. W.   Sammlung musikalischer schriften, 1757–58.

Pécourt, Guillaume Louis, 1653–1729.

See Feuillet, R. A.   Recüeil de dances, 1704.
   Rameau, P.   Abregé de la nouvelle methode [1725 ?]

Pedroso, Manuel de Moraes.

See Moraes Pedroso, Manuel de.

Peletier, Jacques, 1517–1582.

See Discours non plus melancoliqves qve divers, 1557.

Pemberton, E.

An essay for the further improvement of dancing; being a collection of figure dances, of several numbers, compos'd by the most eminent masters; describ'd in characters after the newest manner of Monsieur Feuillet. By E. Pemberton. To which is added, three single dances, viz. a chacone by Mr. Isaac, a passacaille by Mr. L'Abbe, and a jig by Mr. Pecour . . .   London, J. Walsh [etc.] 1711.

5 p. l., 54 pl. (partly fold.) 26 x 19ᶜᵐ.

MT950.A2P45

Péna, Jean, *d.* 1558? *translator.*

See Euclides.   Εὐκλείδου Εἰςαγωγὴ ἁρμονική, 1557.

Penna, Lorenzo, 1613–1693.

Direttorio del canto fermo, dal quale con breuità si apprende il modo di cantare in coro ciò s'appartiene à coristi, con la maniera di comporre il canto fermo, ad vno, due, è trè cori; dato in lvce da f. Lorenzo Penna . . .   Modana, Per gli eredi Cassiani stampatori episc., 1689.

96 p. 24ᶜᵐ.

MT860.A2P41

Penna, Lorenzo—*Continued.*

Li primi albori mvsicali per li principianti della musica figurata; distinti in tre' libri: dal primo spuntano li principij del canto figvrato; dal secondo spiccano le regole del contrapvnto; dal terzo appariscono li fondamenti per suonare l'organo ò clavicembalo sopra la parte; del padre frà Lorenzo Penna . . . 5. impresione. Bologna, P. M. Monti, 1696.

199 p. incl. illus., port. 22½ x 17ᶜᵐ.

"Terzo choro," etc., of example on p. 138 is on separate leaf attached to page.

MT6.A2P41

[Pepusch, John Christopher] 1667–1752.

A short treatise on harmony, containing the chief rules for composing in two, three, and four parts. Dedicated to all lovers of musick, by an admirer of this noble and agreeable science . . . London, Printed by J. Watts, 1730.

2 p. l., 84 p. 4 pl. 12 x 18½ᶜᵐ.

MT50.A2P2

——— A treatise on harmony: containing the chief rules for composing in two, three, and four parts. Dedicated to all lovers of musick, by an admirer of this agreeable science. The 2d ed., alter'd, enlarg'd, and illustrated by examples in notes . London, Printed by W. Pearson, 1731.

2 p. l., 227, [1] p., 1 l. incl. 4 pl. 11½ x 20½ᶜᵐ.

"In 1730 there was published anonymously 'A [short] treatise on narmony . . .' As the rules contained in the book were those Pepusch was in the habit of imparting to his pupils, and as they were published without the necessary musical examples, he felt compelled to adopt the work, and accordingly in 1731 published a 'Second edition' . . . It was conjectured that the first edition was put forth by Viscount Paisley, afterwards Earl of Abercorn."—Grove.

MT50.A2P22

See also GRASSINEAU, J. A musical dictionary, 1740.

Perego, Camillo, *d. ca.* 1574.

La regola del canto fermo ambrosiano, composta già d'ordine di S. Carlo dal reuer. p. Camillo Perego . . . Ed hora data alla stampa per commessione di Monsignor' illustrissimo, e reverendissimo Federico cardinale Borromeo arciuescouo . . . Milano, Per l'her. di P. Pontio, & G. B. Piccaglia, stampatori archiepiscopali, 1622.

2 p. l., 161, [5] p. illus. 23 x 17½ᶜᵐ.

Title vignette. Errors in paging.

MT860.A2P45

Pérez Calderón, Manuel.

Explicacion de solo el canto-llano, que para instruccion de los novicios de la provincia de Castilla del real y militar Orden de N. Señora de la Merced, redencion de cautivos, compuso el P. Fr. Manuel Perez Calderon . . . A que añade las cuerdas de Alamire, Gsolreut, Ffaut, y la que particularmente usa la santa iglesia de Toledo, llamada por eso cuerda toledana. Contiene asimismo todas las antífonas, lamentaciones. y responsorios de los tres dias de Tinieblas. Todo lo

Pérez Calderón, Manuel—*Continued.*

que para utilidad comun ha dispuesto, y da á luz el P. Fr. Isidro
Lopez ...   Madrid, Por D. J. Ibarra, impresor, 1779.

1 p. l., v, [1], 189 p. 1 illus. 21½^{cm}.

—— —— Copy 2.   MT860.A2P49

Le **petit** Rameau, ou Principes courts et faciles, pour apprendre
soi-même, & en peu de tems, la musique; avec tablettes de papier
nouveau, pour écrire ou noter tout ce que l'on desirera.   Paris,
Desnos [1772 ?]

48, 24, 48 p.   12 x 6^{cm}.

Approbation dated "11 juin 1772."

                 MT7.A2P44

Petri, Johann Samuel, 1738–1808.

Anleitung zur practischen musik, vor neuangehende sånger und
instrumentspieler, von Johann Samuel Petri ...   Lauban, J. C.
Wirthgen, 1767.

164 p., 1 l.   17½^{cm}.

                 MT6.A2P47

—— Anleitung zur praktischen musik, von Johann Samuel Petri.
[2. umgearb., verb. und verm. aufl.]   Leipzig, J. G. I. Breitkopf, 1782.

10 p. l., 484, [1] p.   22 x 17½^{cm}.

                 MT6.A2P49

Pfeiffer, August Friedrich, 1748–1817.

Ueber die musik der alten Hebråer, von August Friedrich Pfeiffer
...   Erlangen, W. Walther, 1779.

lix p.   fold. pl.   24½ x 19½^{cm}.

                 ML166.A2P52

Phillips, John, 1631–1706.

See Locke, M.   The present practice of musick vindicated, 1673.

Phillips, John.

Familiar dialogues on dancing, between a minister and a dancer,
taken from matter of fact, with an appendix containing some extracts
from the writings of pious and eminent men against the entertainments of the stage, and other vain amusements ...   By John Phillips ...   New-York, Printed by T. Kirk, 1798.

39 p.   21^{cm}.

                 GV1740.P5

Philodemus, *of Gadara.*

Philodemi De musica IV.   [Neapoli, ex Regia typographia, 1793]

3 p. l., 23 p., 1 l., 180 p. facsim.   40^{cm}.   (R. Accademia ercolanese di arche-
ologia, Naples.   Hercvlanensivm volvminvm qvæ svpersvnt tomvs I)

Title given above appears as half-title preceding the text.

A facsimile of the papyrus, with transcription and Latin translation on opposite pages.   Edited by Carlo Maria Rosini.

                 ML168.P45

Philodemus—*Continued.*

... In Philodemi *Περὶ μουσικῆς* librum IV. nuper ab academicis herculanensibus editum animadversionum particula I. [auctore C. G. Schuetz] [Jenae] ex officina Goepferdtii [1795]

[4] p. 35½ x 19½^{cm}.

Programm—Univ. Jena (Novi prorectoratvs avspicia ... indicit Acad. ienensis)

ML169.A2P5

Philomela franciscana, clarâ & brevi methodo decantans has ac certas regulas ad benè, perfectéque cantum ecclesiasticum addiscendum & docendum. Una cum tonis communibus, hymnis, antiphonis, lectione mensali, &c. ad usum FF. minorum recollectorum ordinis seraphici patris S. Francisci ... Augustæ Vindelicorum, typis Joannis Michaëlis Labhart, 1731.

2 p. l., 274 (*i. e.* 272) p. illus. 13½^{cm}.

No. 134–135 omitted in paging.

MT860.A2P55

Philostratus.

Philostrati Lemnii sophistæ Epistolæ quædam, partim nunquam, partim auctiores editæ. Ioannes Mevrsivs primus vulgavit, & adjunxit, De Philostratis dissertatiunculam. Lvgdvni Batavorvm, ex officinâ Lvdovici Elzevirii, typis Godefridi Basson, 1616.

24 p. 19¼ x 13½^{cm}. (*With* Meurs, Johannes van, *editor.* Aristoxenvs. Lvgdvni Batavorvm, 1616)

Printer's mark: open music book.

ML167.M57

Picerli, Silverio.

Specchio primo di mvsica, nel quale si vede chiaro non sol' il ... modo d'imparar di cantare di canto figurato, e fermo; ma vi si vedon' anco dichiarate ... tutte le principali materie, che iui si trattano, sciolte le maggiori difficoltà, che ... in essa occorrono, e scoperti nuoui segreti nella medesima circa il cantare, comporre, e sonar di tasti, nascosti ... Composto dal m. r. p. f. Silverio Picerli ... Napoli, O. Beltrano, 1630.

81, [9] p., 1 l. 20¼^{cm}.

The preface announces 3 parts but the third part apparently not published.

MT6.A2P59

—— Specchio secondo di mvsica, nel qvale si vede chiaro il ... modo di comporre di canto figurato, e fermo, di fare con nuoue regole ogni sorte di contrapnnti [!], e canoni, di fomar [!] li toni di tutt' i generi di musica reale, e finta ... e di porre in prattica quanto si vuole, e può desiderare di detti canto figurato, e fermo. Composto dal m. r. p. f. Silverio Picerli ... Napoli, M. Nucci, 1631.

7 p. l., 196 p. 20¼^{cm}. (*With his* Specchio primo di mvsica. Napoli, 1630)

MT6.A2P59

Picitono, Angelo da.

See ANGELO *da Picitono.*

Pidanzat de Mairobert, Mathieu François.

See MAIROBERT, MATHIEU FRANÇOIS PIDANZAT DE.

Pignolet de Montéclair, Michel.

See MONTÉCLAIR, MICHEL PIGNOLET DE.

Pileur d'Apligny,   le.

See LE PILEUR D'APLIGNY.

Pintado, Giuseppe.

Vera idea della musica e del contrappunto, di D. Giuseppe Pintado.
Roma, Stamperia di G. Puccinelli, 1794.

159 p.   20½^{cm}.

MT55.A2P65

Pipegrop, Heinrich.

See BARYPHONUS, HEINRICH.

Pipping, Heinrich, 1670–1722.

See LOESCHER, C.   Dissertatio historico-theologica [1688]

Pizzati, Giuseppe, 1732–1803.

La scienza de' suoni, e dell' armonia, diretta specialmente a render
ragione de' fenomeni, ed a conoscer la natura e le leggi della medesima,
ed a giovare alla pratica del contrappunto.   Opera dell' ab: Giuseppe
Pizzati, divisa in cinque parti.   Venezia, G. Gatti, 1782.

2 v. (v. 1: viii, 358 p., 1 l.; v. 2: 1 p. l., xlix pl. on 26 l.)   31^{cm} (v. 2: 34½^{cm})

Vol. [2], engraved throughout, has title: Tavole degli esempj appartenenti
alla Scienza de' suoni e dell' armonia . . .

MT50.A2P69

Planelli, Antonio, 1747–1803.

Dell' opera in musica, trattato del cavaliere Antonio Planelli . . .
Napoli, Stamperia di D. Campo, 1772.

272 p.   20½^{cm}.

ML3858.P7

Playford, Henry, *b.* 1657.

See The DANCING-MASTER, 1698.

Playford, John, 1623–1686?

An introduction to the skill of musick.   In two books.   The first:
the grounds and rules of mvsick, according to the gam-vt, and other
principles thereof.   The second: instructions & lessons for the bass-
viol: and instruments & lessons for the treble-violin.   By John Playford.   To which is added, The art of descant, or composing musick
in parts.   By Dr. Tho. Campion.   With annotations thereon, by Mr.
Chr. Simpson.   The 7th ed., cor. and enl.   London, Printed by W.
Godbid, for J. Playford, 1674.

7 p. l., 121, [3], 42, 10 p.   illus.   17^{cm}.

Playford, John—*Continued.*

The "Art of descant" has special t.-p. and separate paging.
The first edition was published in 1654 as "Breefe introduction to the skill of musick, for song and viall."
"Rules and directions for singing the Psalms": p. 71–89.
"The order of performing the divine service in cathedrals and collegiate chappels:" 10 p. at end.

MT7.A2P72

—— An introduction to the skill of musick, in two books. The first contains the grounds and rules of musick, according to the gam-ut, and other principles thereof. The second, instructions and lessons both for the basse-viol and treble-violin. By John Playford. To which is added, The art of descant, or composing of musick in parts, by Dr. Tho. Campion; with annotations thereon by Mr. Chr. Simpson. Also The order of singing divine service in cathedrals. The 8th ed. carefully cor. London, Printed by A. C. and J. P. for J. Playford, 1679.

7 p. l., 119, [3], 34, 7 p.   front. (port.) illus.   16^{cm}.

The "Art of descant" has special t.-p. and separate paging.

MT7.A2P73

—— An introduction to the skill of musick, in three books. The first contains the grounds and rules of musick, according to the gam-ut, and other principles thereof. The second, instructions and lessons both for the bass-viol and treble-violin. The third, the art of descant, or composing musick in parts: in a more plain and easie method than any heretofore published. By John Playford. The 12th ed. Corrected and amended by Mr. Henry Purcell. [London] Printed by E. Jones, for H. Playford, 1694.

9 p. l., 144 p.   front. (port.) illus.   17$\frac{1}{2}$^{cm}.

"A brief discourse of the Italian manner of singing . . . written some years since by an English gentleman who had lived long in Italy, and being returned, taught the same here": p. 31–46.

MT7.A2P75

—— An introduction to the skill of musick: in three books. By John Playford. Containing i. The grounds and principles of musick according to the gamut . . . ii. Instructions and lessons for the treble, tenor, and bass-viols; and also for the treble-violin. iii. The art of descant, or composing musick in parts; made very plain and easie by the late Mr. Henry Purcell. The 13th ed. [London] Printed by E. Jones, for H. Playford [etc.] 1697.

2 p. l., ix, [1], 134 p.   front. (port.) illus.   17 x 10^{cm}.

Parts 2 and 3 have each special t.-p.

MT7.A2P76

—— An introduction to the skill of musick: in three books: by John Playford. Containing i. The grounds and principles of musick, according to the gamut . . . ii. Instructions and lessons for the treble, tenor and bass-viols; and also for the treble-violin. iii. The art of descant, or composing musick in parts: made very plain and

Playford, John—*Continued.*

easie by the late Mr. Henry Purcell. The 15th ed. Corrected, and done on the new ty'd-note. London, Printed by W. Pearson, for H. Playford [etc.] 1703.

9 p. l., 180 (*i. e.* 170) p.   front. (port.) illus.   17ᶜᵐ.

Parts 2 and 3 have each special t.-p., dated 1700. No. 81–90 omitted in paging; no. 108 and 109 transposed.
"The order of performing the divine service in cathedrals, & collegiate chapels": p. 53–60.

MT7.A2P78

—— An introduction to the skill of musick: in three books: by John Playford. Containing I. The grounds and principles of musick, according to the gamut ... II. Instructions and lessons for the treble, tenor, and bass-viols; and also for the treble violin. III. The art of descant, or composing musick in parts; made very plain and easie by the late Mr. Henry Purcell. The 16th ed. Corrected, and done on the new ty'd note. London, Printed by W. Pearson, for J. Sprint, 1713.

9 p. l., 170 p.   illus.   16ᶜᵐ.

"The order of performing the divine service in cathedrals, & collegiate chapels": p. 53–60.

MT7.A2P79

—— An introduction to the skill of musick: in three books: by John Playford. Containing I. The grounds and principles of musick, according to the gamut ... II. Instructions and lessons for the treble, tenor, and bass-viols; and also for the treble-violin. III. The art of descant, or composing musick in parts: made very plain and easy by the late Mr. Henry Purcell. The 19th ed. Cor., and done on the new-ty'd note. London, Printed by W. Pearson, for B. Sprint, 1730.

9 p. l., 170 p.   front. (port.) illus.   17ᶜᵐ.

"The order of performing the divine service in cathedrals, and collegiate chapels": p. 53–60.

MT7.A2P793

See also The DANCING-MASTER, 1698.
LOCKE, M. The present practice of musick vindicated, 1673.

The **playhouse** pocket-companion, or Theatrical vademecum: containing, I. A catalogue of all the dramatic authors who have written for the English stage, with a list of their works, shewing the dates of representation or publication. II. A catalogue of anonymous pieces. III. An index of plays and authors. In a method entirely new, whereby the author of any dramatic performance, and the time of its appearance, may be readily discovered on inspection. To which is prefixed, a critical history of the English stage from its origin to the present time; with an enquiry into the causes of the decline of dramatic poetry in England ... London, Richardson and Urquhart [etc.] 1779.

2 p. l., [13]–179 p.   18ᶜᵐ.

Z2014.D7P7

Plutarchus.

Πλουτάρχου διάλογος Περὶ μουσικῆς. Dialogue de Plutarque sur la musique, tr. en françois. Avec des remarques. Par M. Burette. Paris, Imprimerie royale, 1735.

442, 31–126 p. 3 fold. pl. 26½ᶜᵐ.

One of 12 copies separately issued. Printed also in "Mémoires de littérature tirez des registres de l'Académie royale des inscriptions et belles lettres," vol. 10, 13, 15, 17, 1736–51.

The last instalment ("Suite des remarques [etc.]", §§ccxlv–cclxxi, and a "Dissertation," p. 61–126) has paging and signature of the "Mémoires."

"Dissertation servant d'épilogue & de conclusion aux remarques sur le traité de Plutarque touchant la musique; dans laquelle on compare la théorie de l'ancienne musique avec celle de la musique moderne. Par M. Burette": p. 61–126 at end.

ML168.P7B6

La poësie et la musique. Satire. A Monsievr Despreavx. Paris, D. Mariette, 1695.

3 p. l., 14, 8 p. 25ᶜᵐ.

"Cantiques spirituels [composez pour l'illustre maison de Saint Cyr, & mis en chant par Monsieur Moreau]": 8 p. at end.

ML270.2.A2P7

[Poisson, Léonard] 1695–1753.

Nouvelle methode, ou Traité théorique et pratique du plain-chant, dans lequel on explique les vrais principes de cette science, suivant les auteurs anciens & modernes; on donne des regles pour la composition du plain-chant, avec des observations critiques sur les nouveaux livres de chant . . . Paris, Lottin, le jeune, 1745.

4 p. l., 419, [5] p. 20ᶜᵐ.

MT860.A2P6

—— Traité théorique et pratique du plain-chant, appellé grégorien, dans lequel on explique les vrais principes de cette science, suivant les auteurs anciens & modernes; on donne des regles pour la composition du plain-chant, avec des observations critiques sur les nouveaux livres de chant . . . Paris, P. N. Lottin, & J. H. Butard, 1750.

4 p. l., 419, [5] p. 20ᶜᵐ.

MT860.A2P7

Polandus, Nicolaus, d. 1612.

Musica instrumentalis, von christlichem brauch der orgelwerck vnnd seytenspiel / bey dem heiligen gottesdienst / eine predigt / gehalten in der domkirchen zu Meissen / als die newe orgel / so das ehrwürdige domcapitul &c. von newem erbawen lassen / allda zu erst gebrauchet ward / Mit einer vorrede / darinnen etwas von bischoffs Bennonis wundern / wider die baierische papisten / berühret worden / Von Nicolao Polanto . . . Gedruckt zu Leipzig / durch Jacobum Popporeich / in verlegung Johann: Borners / des ältern / 1605.

45, [1] p. 18½ x 15½ᶜᵐ.

Line borders.

ML3001.P65

Ponzio, Pietro, 1532–1596.

Dialogo del r. m. Don Pietro Pontio Parmigiano, oue si tratta della theorica, e prattica di musica. Et anco si mostra la diuersità de' contraponti, & canoni. Parma, E. Viothi, 1595.

4 p. l., 152 p.   19½^{cm}.

Title vignette.

MT55.A2P7

Ragionamento di mvsica, del reuerendo m. Don Pietro Pontio Parmegiano. Ove si tratta de' passaggi delle consonantie, & dissonantie, buoni, & non buoni; & del modo di far motetti, messe, salmi, & altre compositioni; et d'alcvni avertimenti per il contrapuntista, & compositore, & altre cose pertinenti alla musica. Parma, E. Viotto, 1588.

2 p. l., 161, [3] p. incl. diagr.   20½^{cm}.

Title vignette.

MT55.A2P81

Porphyrius.

See GOGAVA, A. H., *translator.*   Aristoxeni . . . Harmonicorvm elementorvm libri III, 1562.

Porta, Persio della.

L'Arianna musicale del Signor Don Persio della Porta . . .   Napoli, D. A. Parrino, e M. L. Mutio, 1696.

6 p. l., 88, [4] p.   1 illus.   22½^{cm}.

Rubricated.

MT860.A2P8

Porta Ferrari, Carlo Antonio.

Il canto fermo ecclesiastico, spiegato a' seminaristi di Ferrara . . . da D. Carlo Antonio Porta Ferrari . . .   Modena, B. Soliani, stampator ducale, 1732.

viii, 77 p.   pl.   27 x 20^{cm}.

MT860.A2P83

Portique ancien et moderne, 1785.

See LE PRÉVOST D'EXMES, F.   Lully, musicien [1785 ?]

Portmann, Johann Gottlieb, 1739–1798.

Leichtes lehrbuch der harmonie, composition und des generalbasses, zum gebrauch für liebhaber der musik, angehende und fortschreitende musici und componisten, hrsg. von Johann Gottlieb Portmann . . . Darmstadt, Gedruckt durch J. J. Will, 1789.

2 p. l., 70 p., 1 l., 64 p. (engr.)   illus.   21½ x 17½^{cm}.

Musical examples: 64 p. at end.

MT6.A2P85

Die neuesten und wichtigsten entdeckungen in der harmonie, melodie und dem doppelten contrapuncte. Eine beilage zu jeder musicalischen theorie, von J. G. Portmann. Darmstadt, 1798.

8 p. l., 270, 19 p. (engr.)   17½^{cm}.

Musical examples: 19 p. at end.

MT50.A2P76

Potter, John.

Observations on the present state of music and musicians. With general rules for studying music . . . in order to promote the further cultivation and improvement of this difficult science. The whole illustrated with . . . remarks, intended for the service of its practitioners in general. With the characters of some of the most eminent masters of music. To which is added, A scheme for erecting and supporting a musical academy in this kingdom. By John Potter. London, C. Henderson, 1762.

4 p. l., 108 p. 20½^{cm}.

"Interspers'd in my lectures read at Gresham-college last Easter and Trinity terms."—Advertisement.

ML195.P82

Practical discourses of singing in the worship of God; preach'd at the Friday lecture in Eastcheap. By several ministers . . . London, Printed by J. Darby for N. Cliff [etc.] 1708.

x, 226 p. 17^{cm}.

CONTENTS.—Of the nature of the duty of singing, by Mr. Earle.—Arguments to prove the obligation of the duty, by Mr. Bradbury.—Of the excellence of singing, by Mr. Harris.—Objections against singing consider'd, by Mr. Reynolds.—Directions for the right performance of the duty of singing, by Mr. Newman.—Exhortation to singing, by Mr. Gravener.

ML3001.P89

Praetorius, Michael, 1571-1621.

Syntagma musicum; ex veterum et recentiorum, ecclesiasticorum autorum lectione, polyhistorûm consignatione, variarum linguarum notatione, hodierni seculi usurpatione, ipsius denique musicæ artis observatione: in cantorum, organistarum, organopœorum, cæterorumq́ue musicam scientiam amantium & tractantium gratiam collectum; et secundùm generalem indicem toti operi præfixum, in quatuor tomos distributum, à Michaële Prætorio . . . [n. p., 1615-20]

3 v. in 1. XLII pl. on 21 l., fold. tab. 22 x 17^{cm}.

Each vol. has special t.-p. (v. 1) Syntagmatis musici tomus primus complectens duas partes: quarum prima agit de musica sacra vel ecclesiastica . . . Wittebergæ, e typographéo J. Richteri, 1615 (Part 2 has half-title: Syntagmatis musici tomo primo. Conjuncta pars altera: videlicet, Historia de musica extra ecclesiam . . .) (v. 2) Syntagmatis musici . . . tomus secundus De organographia . . . Wolffenbûttel, Gedruckt bey E. Holwein, in verlegung des autoris, 1619. (v. 3) Syntagmatis musici . . . tomus tertius. Darinnen 1. Die bedeutung / wie auch abtheil- vnnd beschreibung fast aller nahmen / der italianischen / frantzösischen / englischen vnd jetziger zeit in Teutschland gebräuchlichen gesånge . . . 2. Was im singen / bey den noten vnd tactu, modis vnd transpositione, partibus seu vocibus vnd vnterschiedenen choris, auch bey den unisonis vnnd octavis zu observiren: 3. Wie die italianische vnd andere termini musici . . . zu verstehen vnd zu gebrauchen [etc., etc.] . . . Wolffenbûttel, Gedruckt bey E. Holwein, in verlegung des autoris, 1619.

The plates form the last part of vol. 2, with special t.-p.: Theatrum instrumentorum, seu Sciagraphia Michaëlis Prætorii C. Darinnen eigentliche abriss vnd abconterfeyung / fast aller derer musicalischen instrumenten, so jtziger zeit in Welschland / Engeland / Teutschland vnd andern ortern vblich vnd vorhanden seyn . . . Wolffenbûttel, 1620.

Part 1 in Latin, parts 2 and 3 in German. In the general table of contents, at the beginning of vol. 1, a fourth part is given in outline, which has never appeared.

ML100.A2P8

[Prelleur, Peter]

An introduction to singing after so easy a method, that persons of the meanest capacities may (in a short time) learn to sing (in tune) any song that is set to musick, with a choice collection of songs for one, two or three voices, with a thorough bass to each, by ỹ most eminent masters of ỹ age. London, D. Rutherford [17—]

32 p. 22ᶜᵐ.

Engraved throughout.

MT870.A2P63

The modern musick-master; or, The universal musician, containing, I. An introduction to singing . . . II. Directions for playing on the flute . . . III. The newest method for learners on the German flute . . . IV. Instructions upon the hautboy . . . V. The art of playing on the violin . . . VI. The harpsichord illustrated and improv'd . . . in which is included a large collection of airs, and lessons, adapted to the several instruments . . . With A brief history of musick . . . To which is added, a musical dictionary . . . Curiously adorn'd with cuts . . . 4th ed., finely engrav'd . . . London, At the Printing-office in Bow Church Yard, 1738.

8 v. in 1. fronts., plates (partly fold.) 23ᶜᵐ.

Vol. 1–[7] have each special t.-p.

MT6.A2P93

See also The COMPLEAT tutor for the German flute.
The COMPLEAT tutor for the harpsichord [175–]
The HARPSICHORD illustrated and improv'd ·[174–]

Preus, Georg.

Grund-regeln von der structur und den requisitis einer untadelhaften orgel, worinnen hauptsåchlich gezeiget wird, was bey erbauung einer neuen und renovirung einer alten orgel zu beobachten sey, auch wie eine orgel bey der ueberlieferung mûsse probiret und examiniret werden; in einem gespråch entworffen von Georg Preus, organisten an der Heil. Geist-kirche in Hamburg. Hamburg, C. W. Brandt, 1729.

7 p. l., 104 p. front. 16ᶜᵐ.

ML555.A2P9

Preus, Georg.

Observationes musicæ, oder Musicalische anmerckungen / welche bestehen in eintheilung der thonen / deren eigenschafft und wirckung / den music-liebenden zum besten heraus gegeben von Georg Preus, organist der stadt Greiffswald. Greiffswald/ Gedruckt bey D. B. Starcken [1706]

[24] p. fold. diagr. 20 x 15½ᶜᵐ.

"Musicalische exempel": 7 p. at end.

ML3809.A2P37

Prévost d'Exmes, François le.

See LE PRÉVOST D'EXMES, FRANÇOIS.

Prieto, Víctor, *editor.*

See ABREU, A. Escuela para tocar . . . la guitarra, 1799.

Primcock, A., *pseud.*

See RALPH, JAMES.

Primi elementi di musica prattica per gli studenti principianti di tal professione. A' quali si sono aggiunti alquanti solfeggi a due voci in partitura, d'eccellente autore. Venezia, A. Bortoli [170– ?]

68 p.   22 x 16½ᶜᵐ.

Published 1708 or earlier, as it is advertised in Gasparini's "L'armonico pratico," Venice, Bortoli, 1708.

MT870.A2P68

Principes abrégés de musique, en forme de dialogue, a l'usage des commençans. Metz, Behmer, an VI [1798 ?]

2 p. l., 18 p.   2 pl.   21ᶜᵐ.

MT7.A2P84

Principj di musica. Nei quali oltre le antiche, e solite regole vi sono aggiunte altre figure di note, schiarimento di chiavi, scale dei tuoni, lettura alla francese, scale semplici delle prime regole del cimbalo, violino, viola, violoncello, contrabasso, oboè, e flauto. Firenze, G. Chiari [1750 ?]

[1], 9 p.   25ᶜᵐ.

Illustrated t.-p.; line borders; engraved throughout.

MT7.A2P96

—— **Principj** di musica nei quali oltre le antiche, e solite regole vi sono aggiunte altre figure di note, schiarimento di chiavi, scale dei tuoni, lettura alla francese, scale semplici delle prime regole del cimbalo, violino, viola, violoncello, contrabbasso, oboè, e flauto. Venezia, A. Zatta, e figli [17—]

[1], 10 p.   28ᶜᵐ.

Title within ornamental border; line borders; engraved throughout.

MT7.A2P8

Prinner, Johann Jacob.

Musicalischer schlissl welcher aufspäret dass schreibkhästlein dess verstands, darinnen vnterschiedliche lädlein alss capitl begriffen, darvon jedes nach der ordnung seinen schaz zeiget. Sowoll dass instrument vnd clauir zuuerstehen, alss auch singen, geigen der violin, viola da gamba, violon vnd andrer geigen zuerlehrnen, wie auch die composition von grund auss zuergreiffen, die partitur oder den general bass zum accompagniren zuuerstehen. Welchen schlissl ich der lieben jugendt zum besten auf dass fleissigste an die handt reiche vnd mittheille dise edle khunst auf das leichteste vnd beste zu fassen, vnd khünfftig das erlehrnete widerumb vergessener massen zuerhollen auch verfasset anno 1677. Joannes Jacobus Prinner.

[174] p.   20½ x 15½ ᶜᵐ.

Author's autograph. Contains the "Musicalischer schlissl" (13 chapters, 100 p.), teaching the rudiments of music, use and notation of stringed instruments; the "Organische instruction" (21 p.), treating of organ and "clavier"; the "Fuga" (53 p.), treating of fugue and canon.

Eitner, in his Quellen-lexikon, gives Prinner's name as Prumer.

ML95.P7

Printz, Wolfgang Caspar, *of Waldthurn*, 1641–1717.

Exercitationes musicæ theoretico-practicæ curiosæ de concordantiis singulis, das ist Musicalische wissenschafft und kunst-ubungen von jedweden concordantien, in welchen jeglicher concordantz natur und wesen / composition, eigentlicher sitz, production, continuation und progressus aus gewissen gründen erkläret / und beschrieben werden . . . von Wolfgang Caspar Printzen / von Waldthurn . . . Dresden, J. C. Mieth, 1689.

9 v. in 1. 19½ x 16½cm.

Added t.-p., engr.: Wolfgang Caspar Printzens Musicalische wissenschafft [etc.]

Contains a "Prodromus" and eight dissertations, each with special t.-p. bearing imprint: Franckfurt und Leipzig, J. C. Mieth, 1687[–89]

MT55.A2P96

Historische beschreibung der edelen sing- und kling-kunst, in welcher deroselben ursprung und erfindung, fortgang, verbesserung, unterschiedlicher gebrauch, wunderbare würckungen, mancherley feinde, und zugleich berühmteste ausüber von anfang der welt biss auff unsere zeit in möglichster kürtze erzehlet und vorgestellet werden, aus denen vornehmsten autoribus abgefasset und in ordnung gebracht von Wolfgang Caspar Printzen, von Waldthurn . . . Dresden, J. C. Mieth, 1690.

3 p. l., 240 p. v pl. 19½ x 17cm.

ML159.P9

Musica modulatoria vocalis, oder Manierliche und zierliche singkunst / in welcher alles / was von einem guten sänger erfordert wird / gründlich und auf das deutlichste gelehret und vor augen gestellet wird . . . von Wolfgang Caspar Printzen / von Waldthurn . . . Schweidnitz / C. Okel / 1678.

4 p. l., 79, [1] p. pl. 19½ x 15cm. (*With his* Phrynis. Quedlinburg [etc.] 1676–77)

MT40.A2P95

Musicus curiosus, oder Battalus, der vorwitzige musicant, in einer sehr lustigen / anmuthigen / unertichteten / und mit schönen moralien durchspickten geschichte vorgestellet von Mimnermo, des Battali guten freunde. Freyburg / Verlegt von J. C. Miethen / 1691.

333 (*i. e.* 331) p. 15½cm x 9cm.

No. 319–320 omitted in paging. Frontispiece (added t.-p., engr.?) wanting.
Ascribed also to Johann Kuhnau.

ML410.K97A1

Musicus magnanimus, oder Pancalus, der grossmüthige musicant / in einer überaus lustigen / anmuthigen / und mit schönen moralien gezierten geschicht vorgestellet von Mimnermo, des Pancali guten freunde. Freyburg / Zu finden bey J. C. Miethen, 1691.

1 p. l., 262 p. 15½ x 9cm. (*With his* Musicus curiosus. Freyburg, 1691)

Added t.-p., engr.
Ascribed also to Johann Kuhnau.

ML410.K97A1

Wolffgang Caspar Printzens / von Waldthurn . . . Phrynis oder Satyrischer componist / welcher vermittelst einer satyrischen ge-

Printz, Wolfgang Caspar—*Continued.*

schicht alle und iede fehler / der ungelehrten / selbgewachsenen / unge-
schickten und unverständigen componisten höfflich darstellet / und
darneben lehret / wie ein musicalisches stück rein / ohne fehler und
nach dem rechten grunde zu componiren und zu setzen sey . . . Quedlinburg / C. Okel / 1676–77.

> 2 v. in 1. front. (v. 2) fold. pl. 19½ x 15ᶜᵐ.
>
> Added t.-p., engr. Unpaged (pagination trimmed off in binding?)
> Vol. 2 has title: Wolffgang Caspar Printzens/ von Waldthurn . . . Phrynis
> Mytilenæus, oder ander theil/ des Satyrischen componistens . . . Sagan, C.
> Okel, 1677.
>
> MT40.A2P95

—— Wolffgang Caspar Printzens von Waldthurn Phrynis Mitilenæus, oder Satyrischer componist, welcher, vermittelst einer satyrischen geschicht, die fehler der ungelehrten, selbgewachsenen, unge-
schickten, und unverständigen componisten höflich darstellet, und
zugleich lehret, wie ein musicalisches stück rein, ohne fehler, und
nach dem rechten grunde zu componiren und zu setzen sey, worbey
mancherley musicalische discurse . . . wie auch eine beschreibung
eines labyrinthi musici, nebst eingemengten lustigen erzehlungen
gefunden werden. Dressden und Leipzig, J. C. Mieth und J. C.
Zimmermann, 1696.

> 3 v. in 1. 4 fold. l. (music), fold. diagr. 20½ x 16½ᶜᵐ.
>
> Title varies. Added t.-p., engr. "Wunderbahrliche echo . . . in einer dop-
> pelten fugâ ligatâ . . . von Ismenia Stratonico :" 2d l.
> Vol. 3, although ready for publication in 1679, first appeared in this, the second,
> edition. A fourth part to the work was written, but was destroyed by fire.
> In the "prodromus" to vol. 1 of the present edition are included: (1) "Refu-
> tation des Satyrischen componisten . . . von . . . Matz Tapinsmus . . . und Charis
> Läusimpeltz" written by Printz himself (*cf.* p. 23 et seq.) and first pub. sepa-
> rately in 1678; (2) a pretended reply by Printz, "Declaration oder weitere erklä-
> rung der Refutation . . . von Philomuso Polyandro," 1679; (3) a colloquy by
> one of Printz's pupils, "Der aberwitzige pickelhering Jean Rebhu, in einem
> kurtzen gespräch entworffen von Veridico Grato," being a satirical reply to an
> attack on Printz, which appeared in a contemporary almanac, containing also
> "Lebensbeschreibung des abenteuerlichen Jean Rebhu."
>
> MT40.A2P96

[Prixner, Sebastian] 1744–1799.

Kann man nicht in zwey, oder drey monaten die orgel gut, und
regelmässig schlagen lernen? Mit ja beantwortet, und dargethan
vermittelst einer einleitung zum generalbasse. Verfasst für die
Pflanzschule des fürstlichen reichsstiftes St. Emmeram. Landshut,
Mit Hagenschen schriften, 1789.

> 223, [5] p., 1 l. incl. 2 fold. pl. 17 x 21ᶜᵐ.
>
> The plates are each counted as one page in numbering.
>
> MT182.A2P7

Provedi, Francesco.

Paragone della musica antica, e della moderna: ragionamenti ɪᴠ.
di Francesco Provedi coltellinajo sanese. [n. p., 17—]

> [107] p. 17 x 9ᶜᵐ.
>
> Dedication dated: Siena, 22 novembre 1752. Signatures: A5–[A12], B–D in
> twelves, E in ten.
>
> ML169.A2P7

Provedi, Francesco—*Continued.*

—— Paragone della musica antica, e della moderna: ragionamenti
IV. di Francesco Provedi coltellinajo sanese. [n. p., 17—]

4 p. l., p. 353–451.   16 x 9ᶜᵐ.

Dedication dated as in the foregoing.   Signature title: Opusc. tom. L.
Originally formed part of volume 50 of Calogera's " Raccolta d'opuscoli scientifici e filologici," Venice, 1754.   *cf.* Lichtenthal, Dizionario e bibl. della musica,
1826.
         ML169.A2P6

Psellus, Michael.

See ALARD, L.   De veterum musica, 1636.

Ptolemaeus, Claudius.

Κλαυδίου Πτολεμαίου 'Αρμονικῶν βιβλία γ'.   Claudii Ptolemæi Harmonicorum libri tres.   Ex. cod. mss. vndecim, nunc primum græce
editus.   Johannes Wallis . . . recensuit, edidit, versione & notis
illustravit, & auctarium adjecit.   Oxonii, e Theatro Sheldoniano,
1682.

10 p. l., 328 p.   front., tables, diagrs.   24ᶜᵐ.

Title vignette.
Appendix, " De veterum harmonica ad hodiernam comparata:" p. 281–328.
         ML168.P97

See also GOGAVA, A. H., *translator.*   Aristoxeni . . . Harmonicorvm
elementorvm libri III, 1562.

Puig, Bernardo Comes y de.

See COMES Y DE PUIG, BERNARDO.

Pujades, Antonio Eximeno y.

See EXIMENO Y PUJADES, ANTONIO.

Purcell, Henry, 1658 *or* 9–1695, *editor.*

See PLAYFORD, J.   An introduction to the skill of musick.

Purmann, Johann Georg, 1733–1813.

Antiquitates musicae . . . [Specimen I]   Francofurti ad Moenum,
excudebat I. P. Bayrhoffer [1776]

24 p.   23 x 18ᶜᵐ.

Programm—Gymnasium, Frankfurt a. M.
         ML64.P9

Puteanus, Erycius, 1574–1646.

Errici Pvteani . . . Modvlata Pallas, siue Septem discrimina vocvm,
ad harmonicæ lectionis nouum & compendiarium vsum aptata & con-
texta, philologo quodam filo.   Mediolani, apud Pontianos, 1599.

122, [5] p.   illus.   17½ᶜᵐ.
         ML171.P9

Puteanus, Erycius—*Continued.*

—— Eryci Pvteani Mvsathena, sive Notarvm heptas, ad harmonicæ lectionis nouum & facilem vsum. Eiusdem Iter nonianvm. Dialogus, qui epitomen Musathenæ comprehendit. Eiusdem De distinctionibvs syntagma, cum epistolâ Iusti Lipsii de eádem materiâ. Hanoviæ, typis Wechelianis, apud C. Marnium & heredes I. Aubrii, 1602.

103, [1] p. 17^{cm}.

2d edition of the Modulata Pallas.

MT44.A2P92

Quantz, Johann Joachim, 1697–1773.

Johann Joachim Quantzens . . . Versuch einer anweisung die flôte traversiere zu spielen; mit verschiedenen, zur befôrderung des guten geschmackes in der praktischen musik dienlichen anmerkungen begleitet, und mit exempeln erlâutert. Nebst xxiv. kupfertafeln. Berlin, J. F. Voss, 1752.

7 p. l., 334, [20] p., 1 l.   illus., xxiv pl. on 12 fold. l.   24 x 19^{cm}.

The plates contain the "exempel" and are printed on both sides.

MT342.A2Q2

See also LORENZONI, A.   Saggio per ben sonare il flautotraverso, 1779.

Quatremère de Quincy, Antoine Chrysostome, 1755–1849.

De la nature des opéras bouffons italiens, et de l'union de la comédie & de la musique dans ces poëmes; par M. Quatremere de Quincy.

(*In* L'Esprit des journaux . . . Paris [1789] 16½^{cm}. 18. année, t. IX, p. 281–308)

Separate.
Reprinted from the Journal encyclopédique.

ML3858.A2Q4

Querlon, Anne Gabriel Meusnier de.

See MEUSNIER DE QUERLON, ANNE GABRIEL.

Quétant, Antoine François, 1733–1823.

Essai sur l'opera-comique.

(*In his* Le serrurier, opera bouffon. Paris, 1765. 21^{cm}. p. [43]–47)

ML48 S5205

Quincy, Antoine Chrysostome Quatremère de.

See QUATREMÈRE DE QUINCY, ANTOINE CHRYSOSTOME.

Quintanilla, Giacinto.

Annotationi, regole e documenti necessarii per direttione del canto fermo estratti da diuerse auttori da Giacinto Quintanilla ad instanza di Suor Clara Maria Donati Monaca professa In S. Huomobono l'anno MDCLVII.

2 p. l., [16] p.   26×20½^{cm}.

Unpublished manuscript, probably in author's own hand.

MT860.A2Q4

Quintilianus, Aristides.

See ARISTIDES QUINTILIANUS.

Quirsfeld, Johann, 1642–1686.

Breviarium musicum, oder Kurtzer begriff wie ein knabe leicht und bald zur singe-kunst gelangen und die nöthigsten dinge darzu kúrtzlich begreiffen und erlernen kan. Nebenst einem anhange unterschiedener deductionen und fugen, nach den zwölff tonis musicis. Zusammen gebracht und aufs neue vermehret von M. Johanne Qvirsfelden . . . Dresden, M. G. Húbner, 1688.

6 p. l., 112 p. 16ᶜᵐ.

3d edition. 1st edition, Pirna, 1675.

MT870.A2Q8

R., P. J. L. C.

See NEUE . . . art zu solmisiren, 1763.

Rafaele, Benvenuto, *conte* **di San.**

See SAN RAFAELE, BENVENUTO, *conte* DI.

[Raguenet, François] 1660 ?–1722.

Paralele des Italiens et des François, en ce qui regarde la musique et les opéra. Paris, J. Moreau, 1602 [*i. e.* 1702]

4 p. l., 124, [12] p. 15ᶜᵐ.

ML1733.2.A2R1

—— La paix de l'opera, ou Parallele impartial de la musique françoise et de la musique italienne. Amsterdam, 1753.

40 p. 19½ᶜᵐ.

A much altered edition of the "Paralele," with notes by the editor.

ML1727.33.R2

—— A comparison between the French and Italian musick and opera's. Translated from the French; with some remarks. To which is added A critical discourse upon opera's in England, and a means proposed for their improvement. London, Printed for W. Lewis, and sold by J. Morphew, 1709.

3 p. l., 86 p. 21½ᶜᵐ.

"Sir John Hawkins conjectured, from internal evidence, that Galliard made the translation of the Abbé Raguenet's Parallèle, published in 1709 . . . and was the author of A critical discourse upon operas in England . . . printed at the end of that translation; whilst Dr. Burney . . . was of a contrary opinion."—Grove, Dict. of music.

ML1733.2.A2R12

[Ralph, James] *d.* 1762.

The touch-stone: or, Historical, critical, political, philosophical, and theological essays on the reigning diversions of the town . . . In which everything antique, or modern, relating to musick, poetry, dancing, pantomimes, chorusses, cat-calls . . . circus bear-garden, gladiators, prize-fighters . . . is occasionally handled. By a person

[Ralph, James]—*Continued.*

of some taste and some quality. With a preface, giving an account of the author and the work . . . London, 1728.

2 p. l., iii–xxviii, 237 p. 17ᶜᵐ.

Dedication signed: A. Primcock [pseud. of James Ralph]

PN2021.R29

—— The taste of the town: or, A guide to all publick diversions. Viz. I. Of musick, operas and plays . . . II. Of poetry, sacred and profane . . . III. Of dancing, religious and dramatical . . . IV. Of the mimes, pantomimes and choruses of the antients . . . v. Of audiences, at our theatrical representations . . . VI. Of masquerades, ecclesiastical, political, civil and military . . . VII. Of the athletic sports of the antients . . . London, Printed, and sold by the booksellers of London and Westminster, 1731.

xxviii, 237 p. illus. 16ᶜᵐ.

Epistle dedicatory signed: A. Primcock.
Reissue of "The touchstone."

PN2021.R3

[Rameau, Jean François] *b.* 1716.

La Rameïde, poeme . . . Inter ramos [*vignette*] lilia fulgent. Prix. 1. 3. 6. 12. 24. 48. 96. A Petersbourg, aux Rameaux couronnés. M.DCC.LXVI. [Paris, 1766]

28 p., 1 l. 19½ᶜᵐ.

ML410.R2R2

See also CAZOTTE, J. La nouvelle Raméide, 1766.

Rameau, Jean Philippe, 1683–1764.

Code de musique pratique, ou Méthodes pour apprendre la musique, même à des aveugles, pour former la voix & l'oreille, pour la position de la main avec une méchanique des doigts sur le clavecin & l'orgue, pour l'accompagnement sur tous les instrumens qui en sont susceptibles, & pour le prélude: avec de nouvelles réflexions sur le principe sonore. Par M. Rameau. Paris, Imprimerie royale, 1760.

1 p. l., xx, 237, 33 p. front. 26 x 19½ᶜᵐ.

Title vignette.
"Exemples du Code de musique pratique": 33 p. at end.

MT50.A2R16

Démonstration du principe de l'harmonie, servant de base à tout l'art musical théorique & pratique. Approuvée par messieurs de l'Académie royale des sciences . . . Par Monsieur Rameau. Paris, Durand [etc.] 1750.

xxiii, xlvij, 112 p. 5 fold. tab. 19½ᶜᵐ.

L. of C. has also another copy, with 4 unnumbered pages containing the privilege and errata, which are not in this copy. The two issues show slight typographical differences, *e. g.* in the second copy the signature letter on first page of each signature is preceded by an asterisk which does not appear in the first copy.
"Extrait des registres de l'Académie royale des sciences (rapport des commissaires nommés par l'Académie sur le mémoire de M. Rameau)": xlvij p.

ML3815.A2R17

Rameau, Jean Philippe—*Continued.*

Erreurs sur la musique dans l'Encyclopedie.   Paris, S. Jorry, 1755.

124 (*i. e.* 128) p.   19^{cm}.

No. 109–112 repeated in paging.

ML3805.A2R2

Extrait d'une reponse de M. Rameau a M. Euler, Sur l'identité des octaves, d'où résultent des vérités d'autant plus curieuses qu'elles n'ont pas encore été soupçonnées.   Paris, Durand, 1753.

2 p. l., 41 p.   19½^{cm}.   (*With his* Démonstration du principe de l'harmonie. Paris, 1750)

ML3815.A2R17

Generation harmonique, ou Traité de musique theorique et pratique. Par M. Rameau.   Paris, Prault fils, 1737.

8 p. l., 201 (*i. e.* 227), [13], xlvij, [4] p.   12 pl.   20¼ x 12^{cm}.

Title vignette.   Pages 226 and 227 numbered 208 and 201 respectively.

ML3815.A2R19

Nouveau systême de musique theorique, où l'on découvre le principe de toutes les regles necessaires à la pratique, pour servir d'introduction au Traité de l'harmonie; par Monsieur Rameau . . .   Paris, Impr. de J. B. C. Ballard, 1726.

viij, 114, [6] p.   2 fold. tab.   25 x 19½^{cm}.   (*With his* Traité de l'harmonie. Paris, 1722)

MT50.A2R17

Nouvelles réflections de M. Rameau.   Sur sa Démonstration du principe de l'harmonie . . .   Paris, Durand [etc.] 1752.

2 p. l., 85, [1] p., 1 l.   19½^{cm}.   (*With his* Démonstration du principe de l'harmonie.   Paris, 1750)

ML3815.A2R17

Observations sur notre instinct pour la musique, et sur son principe; où les moyens de reconnoître l'un par l'autre, conduisent à pouvoir se rendre raison avec certitude des différens effets de cet art.   Par Monsieur Rameau.   Paris, Prault fils [etc.] 1754.

xvj, 125, [1] p.   7 fold. pl.   19^{cm}.

ML3845.A2R2

Traité de l'harmonie reduite à ses principes naturels; divisé en quatre livres . . .   Par Monsieur Rameau . . .   Paris, Impr. de J. B. C. Ballard, 1722.

4 p. l., xxiv, 432, 17, [1] p.   25 x 19½^{cm}.

MT50.A2R17

—— A treatise of musick, containing the principles of composition. Wherein the several parts thereof are fully explained, and made useful both to the professors and students of that science.   By Mr. Rameau . . .   Tr. into English from the original in the French language . . . London, Printed by R. Brown, for the proprietor, and sold by J. Walsh, 1752.

4 p. l., 176, [2] p.   25½ x 20½^{cm}.

A translation of the third part of the Traité de l'harmonie.   1st edition, 1737.

MT50.A2R173

Rameau, Pierre.

Abregé de la nouvelle methode, dans l'art d'écrire ou de traçer toutes sortes de danses de ville ... mise au jour par le S^r. Rameau ... Ouvrage très utile pour toutes personnes qui ont sçu ou qui apprennent à danser, puis que par le secour de ce livre, on peut se remettre facilement dans toutes les danses que l'on à appris ... Paris, Chez l'auteur [etc., 1725 ?]

2 pt. in 1 v. (5 p. l., 111 (*i. e.* 109), [2] p.; 1 p. l., 83 p.) diagrs. 20^cm.

Running title: Abregé de la nouv. choregraphie.
No. 29–30 omitted in paging of part 1. Page 73 (probably "planche du bal") wanting in this copy.
Part 2, engraved throughout, has title: Seconde partie contenant douze des plus belles danses de Monsieur Pecour ... remis en choregraphie suivant la nouvelle correction et augmentation du S^r. Rameau ... (The tune for each dance is given)

GV1590.R33

Le maître a danser. Qui enseigne la maniere de faire tous les differens pas de danse dans toute la régularité de l'art, & de conduire les bras à chaque pas. Enrichi de figures en taille-douce, servant de démonstration pour tous les differens mouvemens qu'il convient faire dans cet exercice ... Par le sieur Rameau ... Paris, Rollin fils, 1748.

xxiv, 271, [1] p. 60 pl. (partly fold., incl. front.) 19½^cm.

Plates signed: P. Rameau, invenit et fecit.

GV1590.R3

—— The dancing-master: or, The art of dancing explained ... In two parts ... The whole containing sixty figures drawn from the life, and curiously engraved on copper plates. Done from the French of Monsieur Rameau, by J. Essex ... London, Printed and sold by him, and J. Brotherton, 1728.

xxxii, 160 p. 57 pl. (partly fold., incl. front.) 25^cm.

GV1590.R4

Ramoneda, Ignacio.

Arte de canto-llano en compendio breve, y methodo muy facil para que los particulares, que deben saberlo, adquieran con brevedad, y poco trabajo la inteligencia, y destreza conveniente. Su autor el P. Fr. Ignacio Ramoneda ... Madrid, Impr. de P. Marin, 1778.

8 p. l., 216 p. 21^cm.

MT860.A2R17

Rangoni, Giovanni Battista.

Essai sur le goût de la musique, avec le caractère des trois célèbres joueurs de violon, Messieurs Nardini, Lolli, & Pugnani, par Monsieur le marquis Jean-Baptiste de Rangoni ... Livourne, Impr. de T. Masi & comp., 1790.

vii, 2–91 p. 19½^cm.

Text in French and Italian on opposite pages. Added t.-p. in Italian.

ML3853.A2R19

Raparlier,

Principes de musique, les agréments du chant, et un Essai sur la prononciation, l'articulation et la prosodie de la langue françoise . . . Par M. Raparlier . . . Lille, P. S. Lalau, 1772.

4 p. l., 44 p. 1 illus. 26ᶜᵐ.

Title vignette; ornamental borders.

MT7.A2R17

Raselius, Andreas, *d.* 1602.

Hexachordvm, seu Qvæstiones mvsicæ practicæ, sex capitibus comprehensæ, quæ continent perspicua methodo ad praxin, ut hodie est, necessaria. Pro gymnasio poëtico s. p. q. ratisponensis, hoc ordine distinctæ, & idoneis exemplis, unà cum pulcherrima xii. modorum doctrina illustrata à M. Andrea Raselio . . . Noribergæ [in officina typographica Gerlachiana] 1589.

[175] p. 16ᶜᵐ.

Signatures: A–L in eights.

ML171.R28

Rauch, Christoph.

Theatrophania. Entgegen gesetzet der so genanten schrifft Theatromania. Zur verthâdigung der christlichen / vornemlich aber / deren musicalischen operen / und verwerffung aller heidnischen und von den alten kirchen-vâttern allein verdammeten schauspielen. In druck verfertiget durch Christophorum Rauch . . . Hannover, W. Schwendimann, 1682.

15 p. l., 15–150 p. 16½ x 9ᶜᵐ.

Against Anton Reiser's "Teatromania."

ML3858.R24

[Raupach, Christoph] *b.* 1686.

Veritophili Deutliche beweis-grûnde / worauf der rechte gebrauch der music, beydes in den kirchen / als ausser denselben / beruhet; aus der Heil. Schrifft / denen zeugnûssen der heil. vâter / und aus der theorie der music selbst / mit alt- und neuen / sowol geist -/ als weltlichen exempeln / nebst der mûglichen pflicht eines jeden christen im gebrauch dieser gôttl. gabe erôrtert / und mit ungemeinen bissher versteckt-gewesenen doch nôthigen erinnerungen / samt einer vorrede / heraus gegeben von Mattheson. Hamburg, Sel. B. Schillers erben / 1717.

12 p. l., 56 p. 17 x 21ᶜᵐ. (*In* Niedt, Friedrich E. . . . Musicalischer handleitung dritter und letzter theil. Hamburg, 1717)

"Veritophilus" is the pseudonym of Christoph Raupach.

MT40.A2N48

Ravn, Hans Mikkelsen, 1610–1663.

Heptachordum danicum, seu Nova solfisatio in qua musicæ practicæ usus tàm qvi ad canendum, qvàm qvi ad componendum cantum, sive choralem seu planum, sive mensuralem seu contrapunctum pertinet . . . ostenditur. Cui accessit Logistica harmonica musicæ theoricæ vera & firma præstruens fundamenta . . . studiô Johannis Michaelii Corvini. Hafniæ, typis Melchioris Martzan, 1646.

29 p. l., 209 p., 4 l., 56 p. 2 fold. tab. 19½ x 15½ᶜᵐ.

Added t.-p., engr.

MT6.AR219

Rawlins, John.

The power of musick, and the particular influence of church-musick: a sermon preached in the cathedral-church of Worcester, at the anniversary meeting of the choirs of Worcester, Hereford, and Gloucester, September 8. 1773. By John Rawlins ... Oxford, Clarendon-press, 1773.

2 p. l., 29 p. 20^{cm}.

ML3920.A2R18

Raymundo da Converção, 1601-1661.

Manval de tvdo o qve se canta fora do choro, conforme ao uzo dos religiosos, & religiosas da sagrada ordem de penitencia de nosso seraphico padre Saõ Francisco do reyno de Portugal. Pello p. fr. Raymvndo da Converçam ... contem as ceremonias do altar, & choro, em todos os actos solemnes que occorrem em o descurso do anno: conforme o breviario, missal mais correctos. Coimbra, Officina de R. de Carvalho Coutinho, 1675.

4 p. l., 485, [5] p. 20 x 15½^{cm}.

According to Vieira, this is a translation and revision cf an unpublished work of Luiz das Chagas, "Manual para todo lo que se canta fuera del coro [etc.]"

MT860.A2R19

Reading, John, 1588-1667.

A sermon lately delivered in the cathedral church of Canterbury, concerning church-musick. By John Reading ... London, Printed by T. Newcomb, 1663.

2 p. l., 18 p. 21½^{cm}.

ML3001.R31

Réflexions sur la musique, ou recherches sur la cause des effets qu'elle produit. Par M. V * * * *. A Amsterdam, et se trouve a Paris, chez Nyon l'aîné, 1785.

2 p. l., iij-xiij, [15]-82 p. 18½^{cm}.
Title vignette.

ML3830.R3

Regole d'alcuni capi necessarj, e piu' frequenti per l'osservanza delle sacre cerimonie, e del canto fermo ambrosiano, stampate per ordine del card. Federico Borromeo. Milano, Stamperia Pulini, 1795.

76 p. 15^{cm}:
Half-title: Liturgia Ambrosiana.

Ch.17.1854

Regole musicali per li principianti di cembalo. Nuova ed. accresciuta. Napoli, D. Sangiacomo, 1795.

60 p. 15½^{cm}.

MT224.A2R4

Reichardt, Johann Friedrich, 1752-1814.

Briefe eines aufmerksamen reisenden die musik betreffend. An seine freunde geschrieben von Johann Friederich Reichardt ... Frankfurt und Leipzig, 1774-76.

2 v. in 1 (v. 1: 4 p. l., 184 p.; v. 2: 134 p.) 16½^{cm}.
Vol. 2 published Frankfurt and Breslau.

ML275.3.R34

Reichardt, Johann Friedrich—*Continued.*

Geist des Musikalischen kunstmagazins von Johann Friederich Reichardt. Hrsg. von I. A[lberti] Berlin, Gedruckt und in commission bey J. F. Unger, 1791.

xii, 195, [1] p. 16½ᶜᵐ.

"Aufsätze und urtheile aus dem Musikalischen kunstmagazin."—Pref.

ML3845.A2R3

Johann Friedrich Reichardt an das musikalische publikum seine französischen opern Tamerlan und Panthée betreffend. Hamburg, In commission bey B. G. Hofmann [1787]

55 p. 15½ᶜᵐ.

ML410.R3A12

Joh. Friedrich Reichardt über die deutsche comische oper, nebst einem anhange eines freundschaftlichen briefes über die musikalische poesie. Hamburg, C. E. Bohn, 1774.

124 p. 27½ᶜᵐ.

"Zergliederung der comischen oper: Die jagd": p. 24–96.

ML410.H67R3

Leben des berühmten tonkünstlers Heinrich Wilhelm Gulden nachher genannt Guglielmo Enrico Fiorino. Erster theil. Berlin, A. Mylius, 1779.

1 p. l., 258 p. 16ᶜᵐ.

A romance, supposed by many to be partly autobiographical, although Reichardt himself denied this. Only the first part was published.

ML3925.A2R3

Schreiben über die berlinische musik an den herrn L. v. Sch. in M., von Johann Friedrich Reichardt. Hamburg, C. E. Bohn, 1775.

32 p. 16ᶜᵐ.

"Eine beylage zu dem ersten theile der Briefe eines aufmerksamen reisenden."

ML279.8.B2R3

Ueber die pflichten des ripien-violinisten, von Johann Friederich Reichardt . . . Berlin und Leipzig, G. J. Decker, 1776.

92 p. 16½ᶜᵐ.

MT68.A2R35

Reichardt, Johann Friedrich, 1752–1814, *editor.*

See LÖHLEIN, G. S. Anweisung zum violinspielen, 1797.
MUSIKALISCHE monathsschrift [1792]
MUSIKALISCHER almanach auf das jahr 1782.
MUSIKALISCHES kunstmagasin, 1782–91.
MUSIKALISCHES wochenblatt [1791–92]
STUDIEN für tonkünstler, 1793.

Reichenberger, Johann Nepomuk, 1737–1805.

Die ganze musikkunst, so, wie sie die weltweisheit und die mathematik leichtlich jeden lehrt, der auch zur musik am mindesten taug-

Reichenberger, Johann Nepomuk—*Continued.*

lich zu seyn scheinen dårfte, an das licht gegeben durch p. Johann Nepomuk Reichenberger . . . [Regensburg] 1777–80.

212 p. incl. tab. fold. tab. 18½ᶜᵐ.

In 3 parts, each with special t.-p. At end of part 3: Die fortsetzung folgt.

MT6.A2R3

Reinhard, Andreas.

Monochordum Andreæ Reinhardi Nivimontami [!] Lipsiæ,Valentin am Ende imprimeb., typis hæredum Beyeri, 1604.

64 p. diagrs. 15½ᶜᵐ.

Title within ornamental border, text within line borders; printer's mark on t.-p. At end: Lipsiæ, sumtibus Iohan. Rosii. bibliop.

ML171.R35

Reinhard, Leonhard, *b.* 1710.

Kurzer und deutlicher unterricht von dem general-bass, in welchem durch deutliche regeln und leichte exempel nach dem neuesten musicalischen stylo gezeiget wird, wie die anfånger in dieser hôchstnûtzlichen wissenschaft zu einer grûndlichen fertigkeit auf die leichteste art gelangen kônnen, verfertiget von Leonhard Reinhard . . . Augspurg, J. J. Lotters seel. erben, 1750.

60 p. 16½ x 21ᶜᵐ.

An earlier edition is cited by Heinsius, published at Augsburg in 1744.

MT49.A2R2

Reisch, Gregor, *d.* 1525.

. . . De principijs musice tractatus ɪ [–ɪɪ] . . . [n. p., n. d.]

[50] p. illus., fold. diagr. 22ᶜᵐ.

From Reisch's Margarita philosophica; the signatures and illustrations correspond to those of the 3d edition, Strassburg, 1508, as described by W. Eames in his "List of editions of the Margarita philosophica," 1886. The signatures are as follows: 3 l. unsigned, U in eight, X in six, Y in eight.

Leaf [1] recto: Illustration, inscribed Typvs Mvsices.—l. [1] vᵒ–l. [6] vᵒ: Liber quintus de principijs musice. Tractatus I . . . (Running title: Libri v tractatus I. Musice speculatiue)—l. [6] vᵒ–l. 13 rᵒ: Libri quinti tractacus [!] secûdus de praxi musicę (Running title, beginning with recto of l. [6]: Libri V tract. II. Musice practice)—l. 13 vᵒ: Illustration.—l. [14]–l. [25] rᵒ: Musica figurata (By Malcior of Worms)—l. [25] vᵒ: Illustration, inscribed Typvs Geometrie.

The folding leaf (part of which has been torn off) bears a diagr. on recto and another on verso, and is inserted between U and Uij.

ML171.R37

Rellstab, Johann Carl Friedrich, 1759–1813.

Versuch über die vereinigung der musikalischen und oratorischen declamation, hauptsåchlich fûr musiker und componisten mit erlåuternden beyspielen, von Johann Carl Friedrich Rellstab . . . Berlin, Im verlage der musikhandlung und musikdruckerey des verfassers [1786]

4 p. l., [3]–49, [1] p. 28 x 21½ᶜᵐ.

MT67.A2R37

Remacha, Miguel López.

See López Remacha, Miguel.

[Rémond de Saint-Mard, Toussaint] 1682–1757.

Reflexions sur l'opera.   La Haye, J. Neaulme, 1741.

1 p. l., v–x, 104 p.   16^{cm}.

ML1727.3.A2R26

See also HERTEL, J. W.   Sammlung musikalischer schriften, 1757–58.

Requeno y Vives, Vincenzo, 1743–1811.

Saggi sul ristabilimento dell' arte armonica de' greci e romani cantori del Signor abate D. Vincenzo Requeno . . .   Parma, Fratelli Gozzi, 1798.

2 v. (v. 1: 4 p. l., xxxix, 347, [4] p.; v. 2: 453, [6] p.)   pl.   20½^{cm}.

ML169.A2R4

Reynolds, Thomas, 1667 ?–1727.

See PRACTICAL discourses, 1708.

Reynvaan, Joos Verschuere-

See VERSCHUERE-REYNVAAN, JOOS.

Rhaw, Georg, 1488–1548.

Enchi- ‖ ridion vtri- ‖ usq̄ Musicę Practicę ‖ a Georgio Rhau- ‖ uo congestum. ‖ ℂ Isagoge Io- ‖ annis Galliculi De cã ‖ tus Compositione.   [Lipsiæ, 1520]

3 v. in 1.   illus.   16½^{cm}.

Title in red and black within woodcut border.   At end of part [1]: Explicit mvsica cho- ‖ ralis.   Nvnc ad ‖ mvsices men- ‖ svralis ‖ enchi- ‖ ridi- ‖ on ‖ pergamvs, ‖ Valentinvs Shv- ‖ man Lypsiæ ‖ impres- ‖ sit.
Part [2] has special t.-p. (with woodcut border): Enchiri ‖ dion mvsi ‖ cæ mensv- ‖ ralis ‖ . . . (Colophon, followed by printer's mark: ℂ Lipsiæ ex ædibus Valentini Schumañ ‖ Anno domini Millesimo quin- ‖ gentesimo vigesimo)
Part [3] has special t.-p. (with woodcut border): Isagoge ‖ Ioannis ‖ Gallicv- ‖ li de ‖ compo- ‖ sicione ‖ cantvs. ‖ Lipsiæ, apud Valenti- ‖ num Schumannū An. ‖ Christi. M.D.XX. (Colophon, preceded by printer's mark: ℂ Lipsiæ ex ædibvs ‖ Valentini Schv- ‖ man mense ma- ‖ io anno ‖ M.D.XX)
Signatures: a in eight, b–l in fours, m in three; A in eight, B–M in fours, N in three; A in eight, B–D in fours, E in three.
According to Fétis, Eitner, and others this is the 2d edition of Rhaw's "Enchiridion musices ex variis musicorum libris," Leipzig, 1518.

ML171.R42

Ribeiro, Manuel da Paixão.

See PAIXÃO RIBEIRO, MANUEL DA.

Ribeiro de Almeida Campos, João.

Elementos de musica . . .   Por . . . Joaõ Ribeiro de Almeida . . . Coimbra, Real imprensa da Universidade, 1786.

4 p. l., 92 p.   fold. pl.   14^{cm}.

MT7.A2R48

Riccati, Giordano, *conte,* 1709–1790.

Saggio sopra le leggi del contrappunto del conte Giordano Riccati . . .   Castel-Franco, G. Trento, 1762.

2 p. l., 155 p.   18^{cm}.

MT55.A2R49

Ricci, Pasquale, *b.* 1733.

Methode ou recueil de connoissances elementaires pour le forte-piano ou clavecin; œuvre melé de theorie et de pratique, divisé en deux parties, composé pour le Conservatoire de Naple par J. C. Bach et F. P. Ricci ... Paris, Le Duc [17—]

1 p. l., 12, 45 p.; 1 p. l., 48–75 p. 25½ x 32½^{cm}.

Title-page and musical examples engraved.

MT222.A2B12

Richer,

See Iso. Memoire [17—]

Riedel, Friedrich Justus, 1742–1785, *editor.*

Ueber die musik des ritters Christoph von Gluck verschiedene schriften, gesammelt und hrsg. von Friedrich Just. Riedel. Wien, Gedruckt bei Joh. Thom. edl. v. Trattnern, 1775.

xvi, 96 p. 17^{cm}.

Title vignette; head-pieces.

CONTENTS.—Brief des herrn von * * an die frau gräfin von * * über die neue oper. [By the Abbé Arnaud]—Brief an die frau von * * *, über die oper Iphigenie en Aulide. Paris vom 26. april 1774.—Gespräch zwischen Lulli, Rameau und Orpheus in den Elisäischen Feldern. Von herrn M * * * [P. L. Moline]—Auszug, aus dem Encyklopädischen journal [May 1774]

ML410.G5R42

Riederer, Johann Bartholomäus, 1720–1771.

D. Joh. Bartholomäus Riederers ... Abhandlung von einführung des teutschen gesangs in die Evangelisch lutherische kirche über-haupts und in die nürnbergische besonders. Wobey auch von den ältesten gesangbüchern und liedern so bis zum tode Lutheri heraus-gegeben und verfertigt worden gehandelt wird. Nürnberg, J. A. Endter, 1759.

8 p. l., 326 p. 17^{cm}.

"Nachträge dazu in seinen Nachrichten zur kirchen-geschichte."—Eitner, Biog.-bibl. quellen-lexikon.

"Abdruck eines seltenen büchleins ... Von der Evangelischen mess, wie sie zu Nürmberg im Newen spital, durch Andream Döber, gehalten würdt, caplan doselbst. 1525": p. 313–326.

ML3129.A2R5

Riedt, Friedrich Wilhelm, 1710 *or* 12–1784.

Versuch über die musikalische intervallen, in ansehung ihrer wahren anzahl, ihres eigentlichen sitzes, und natürlichen vorzugs in der composition, von Friedrich Wilhelm Riedt ... Berlin, A. Haude und J. C. Spener, 1753.

4 p. l., 32 p. diagr. 21½ x 18^{cm}.

ML3809.A2R5

Riepel, Joseph, 1707 *or* 8–1782.

Anfangsgründe zur musicalischen setzkunst: nicht zwar nach alt-mathematischer einbildungsart der zirkel-harmonisten, sondern durch-gehends mit sichtbaren exempeln abgefasset. De rhythmopoeïa,

Riepel, Joseph—*Continued.*

oder Von der tactordnung. Zu etwa beliebigem nutzen hrsg. von
Joseph Riepel . . . Frankfurt [etc., Gedruckt bey J. J. Lotter, Augs-
purg] 1752–68.

5 v. in 2. 34ᶜᵐ.

Each vol. has special t.-p. (v. 2) Grundregeln zur tonordnung insgemein.
Abermal durchgehends mit musicalischen exempeln abgefasst und gespräch-
weise vorgetragen von Joseph Riepel . . . Frankfurt [etc., Gedruckt bey C. U.
Wagner, Ulm] 1755.   (v. 3) Gründliche erklärung der tonordnung insbesondere,
zugleich aber für die mehresten organisten insgemein. Wieder durchaus mit
musikalischen exempeln abgefasst und gespräch-weise vorgetragen von Joseph
Riepel . . . Frankfurt [etc.] 1757.   (v. 4) Erläuterung der betrüglichen
tonordnung, nämlich das versprochene vierte capitel. Abermal durchaus mit
musicalischen exempeln abgefasst und gespräch-weise vorgetragen von Joseph
Riepel . . . Augsburg, J. J. Lotter, 1765. (v. 5) Fünftes capitel. Unent-
behrliche anmerkungen zum contrapunct . . . mit musikalischen exempeln
abgefasst, und wieder gesprächweise vorgetragen von Joseph Riepel . . . Regensburg, In commission bey herrn J. C. Krippner, 1768.

MT47.A2R55

Bassschlüssel, das ist, Anleitung für anfänger und liebhaber der setz-
kunst, die schöne gedanken haben und zu papier bringen, aber nur
klagen, dass sie keinen bass recht dazu zu setzen wissen, von Joseph
Riepel . . . hrsg. von Johann Kaspar Schubarth . . . Regensburg,
J. L. Montags erben, 1786.

5 p. l., 83, [1] p. 34ᶜᵐ.

MT49.R55

Harmonisches syllbenmass, dichtern melodischer werke gewiedmet,
und angehenden singcomponisten zur einsicht mit platten beyspielen
gesprächweise abgefasst . . . Durch Joseph ˙ Riepel . . . Regensburg, J. L. Perile, 1776.

2 p. l., 51, [6], 54–93, [1] p. 35ᶜᵐ.

Head and tail piece.

MT64.A2R3

Rigler, Franz Paul.

Anleitung zum gesange, und dem klaviere, oder die orgel zu spielen;
nebst den ersten gründen zur komposizion; als nöthige vorkenntnisse
der freyen und gebundenen fantasie; mit 2 anhängen: der 33 kir-
chenlieder; und 31 charakteristischen tonstücken verschiedener
meister dieses jahrhunderts . . . Verfasset: von Franz Paul Rigler . . . Ofen, Im verlage der Königl. hungar. universitätsbuch-
druckerey, 1798.

4 p. l., 510 p. 19 x 22½ᶜᵐ.

"Verzeichniss der besten musikalischen bücher; und der berühmtesten kom-
ponisten": p. 278–281.

MT40.A2R4

Riley, William.

Parochial music corrected. Containing remarks on the performance of psalmody in country churches, and on the ridiculous and profane manner of singing practised by the Methodists; reflections on the
bad performance of psalmody in London, Westminster, &c., with
some hints for the improvement of it in public worship; observations

Riley, William—*Continued.*

on the choice and qualifications of parish-clerks; the utility of teaching charity-children psalmody and hymns; the use of organs, and the performance of organists. By William Riley . . . To which are added, a scarce and valuable collection of psalm tunes . . . London, Printed for the author, 1762.

xix, 34 p. 22ᶜᵐ.

The psalm tunes are wanting in this copy.

ML3001.R45

Río, Antonio Ventura Roel del.

See ROEL DEL RÍO, ANTONIO VENTURA.

Riquetti, Honoré Gabriel, *comte de Mirabeau.*

See MIRABEAU, HONORÉ GABRIEL RIQUETTI, *comte* DE.

Risposta di un' anonimo al celebre Sig. Rousseau circa al suo sentimento in proposito d'alcune proposizioni del Sig. Giuseppe Tartini. Venezia, A. de Castro, 1769.

15 p. diagr. 20½ᶜᵐ.

Neither dedicated to Della Torre Tassis nor written by him, as internal evidence proves. Possibly written by the mathematician "padre Colombo," whom Burney mentions in connection with Tartini. Certainly not by Tartini himself, and is not to be confused with his "Risposta di Giuseppe Tartini . . ."

ML3805.A2T3

[Ritson, Joseph] 1752–1803, *editor.*

Ancient songs, from the time of King Henry the Third, to the revolution . . . London, J. Johnson, 1790.

2 p. l., lxxx, 332 p. illus. 18ᶜᵐ.

Title vignette.
"Observations on the ancient English minstrels," and " Dissertation on the songs, music, and vocal and instrumental performance of the ancient English:" p. i–lxxvi.

PR1187.R5

Riva, Giuseppe, *b. ca.* 1696.

See MIZLER VON KOLOF, L. C. Musikalischer staarstecher [1740]

[Robbé de Beauveset, Pierre Honoré] 1714–1792.

Satire a Monsieur le marquis D . . . [n. p., 17—]

22 p., 1 l. 19ᶜᵐ.

In verse. No. 6 in a volume of pamphlets lettered Quere[lle] des Bouffo[ns] Attributed to "M. Robbé" in the ms. table of contents prefixed to the collection.

ML1727.33.A1

Rocca, Angelo, 1545–1620.

De campanis commentarivs a fr. Angelo Roccha . . . ad Sanctam ecclesiam catholicam directvs, in quo multa non minus admiratione, ac scitu digna, quam lectu iucunda, in ecclesia Dei reperiri narratur . . . Romæ, apud G. Facciottum, 1612.

viii, 166, [26] p. plates (partly fold.) 22ᶜᵐ.

Illus. t.-p.; initials; text within line borders.

CC200.R7

Rocchi, Antonio, 1724–1780.

Istituzioni di musica teorico-pratica di D. Antonio Rocchi . . . Della teoria matematica, libro primo. Del genere diatonico . . . Venezia, Stamperia Albrizziana, 1777.

60 p. 26^{cm}.

ML3809.A2R6

[Rochemont,   de] *b. ca.* 1715.

Reflexions d'un patriote sur l'opera françois, et sur l'opera italien, qui présentent le parallele du goût des deux nations dans les beaux arts. Lausanne, 1754.

xij, 137, [1] p. 19^{cm}.

ML1727.33.R67

Rochette de Lamorlière, Jacques.

See LAMORLIÈRE, JACQUES ROCHETTE DE.

Rochlitz, Johann Friedrich, 1769–1842, *editor.*

See ALLGEMEINE musikalische zeitung [1798]–1882.

Roel del Río, Antonio Ventura.

Institucion harmonica, ò Doctrina musical, theorica, y practica, que trata del canto llano, y de organo; exactamente, y segun el moderno estilo explicada, de suerte que escusa casi de maestro . . . Escrita por Don Antonio Ventura Roel del Rio . . . Madrid, Herederos de la viuda de J. Garcia Infanzòn, 1748.

18 p. l., 279, 53 p. 21½^{cm}.

"Motetes y obras diferentes al Santissimo y à Nra Sra": 53 p. at end.

MT860.A2R6

Röllig, Karl Leopold, *d.* 1804.

. . . Die orphica, ein neues musikalisches instrument, erfunden von hr. E.[!] L. Röllig . . .

(*In* Journal des luxus und der moden. Weimar, 1796. 19½^{cm}. 11. jahrg., februar, p. 87–98. fold. pl.)

Detached copy.

ML1015.A2R63

Roger, Joseph Louis, *d.* 1761.

Tentamen de vi soni et musices in corpus humanum. Authore Josepho, Ludovico Roger . . . Avenione, apud Jacobum Garrigan, 1758.

117, [3] p. pl. 19½^{cm}.

ML3920.A2R72

Rojas, Juan Fernández de.

See FERNÁNDEZ DE ROJAS, JUAN.

Rolle, Christian Carl, *b.* 1714.

Neue wahrnehmungen zur aufnahme und weitern ausbreitung der musik. Von Christian Carl Rolle . . . Berlin, A. Wever, 1784.

2 p. l., 106, [2] p. 16^{cm}.

"Ehren-gedächtniss Johann Friedrich Agricola, königlich-preussischen hof-compositors (hof-componisten) nach Grauns tode capelldirektors": p. 92–95. "Ehren-gedächtniss Carl Heinrich Graun": p. 96–106.

ML60.R74

Rollet,

Méthode pour apprendre la musique sans transposition, avec quatre vingt leçons à deux parties, sur toutes les clefs, toutes les mesures, et tous les tons qui sont usités dans la musique . . . composée par M^r. Rollet . . . Paris, Chez M^r. Le Menu; [etc., etc., 1780]

1 p. l., 98 p. 32½ x 26½^{cm}.

Engraved throughout.

MT222.A2R7

[Romaine, William] 1714–1795.

An essay on psalmody . . . London, 1775.

iv, 5–368 p. 19^{cm}.

Preface signed: W. R.
"A collection out of the book of Psalms, suited to every Sunday in the year," p. [155]–368, has special t.-p.

ML3186.A2R7

Romero de Ávila, Gerónimo.

Arte de canto-llano, y organo, ò Promptuario musico, dividido en quatro partes. La primera trata de la especulativa del canto-llano. La segunda, de la práctica del mismo canto. La tercera, de la especulativa, y práctica de todo hymno, sequencia, ò prosa. Y la quarta, de la especulativa, y práctica del canto de organo, segun el moderno estilo. Su autor Don Geronymo Romero de Avila . . . Madrid, J. Ibarra, 1762.

8 p. l., 535 p. illus. 21 x 16^{cm}.

MT860.A2R76

Rondet, Laurent Étienne, 1717–1785, *editor.*

See GAUTHIER, F. L. Traité contre les danses, 1785.

Rosa, Onorato.

Regole del canto fermo detto gregoriano spogliate dell' antica loro oscurità, e registrate con brevità, e chiarezza dal r. p. f. Onorato Rosa da Cairano . . . Napoli, Stamperia degli eredi di Moro, 1788.

xii, 96 p. 23 x 18½^{cm}.

MT860.A2R78

Rosario, Domingos do.

See DOMINGOS DO ROSARIO.

Rosini, Carlo Maria, 1748–1836, *editor.*

See PHILODEMUS, *of Gadara.* De musica [1793]

Rosseto, Vincenzo, *translator.*

See VANNEO, S.   Recanetvm de mvsica avrea, 1533.

Rossetti, Biagio.

Blasii Ros- ‖ setti Veronensis li- ‖ bellus de rudimentis Musices. ‖ De triplici musices specie. ‖ De modo debite soluēdi divinū pensum. ‖ Et de auferendis nonnullis abusibus in dei ‖ templo. ‖ Quę omnia sub compendio candidus lector ‖ inueniet. ‖ ℂ Cum priuilegio prout in breue cont.   [*Colophon:* ℂ Veronę, per Stephanum, & fratres de Nicolinis ‖ de Sabio, sumptu & requisitione D. Blasii Roset- ‖ ti pręsbyteri, in Ecclesia maiori Organistæ. ‖ MDXXIX. mense Septembrio]

[104] p.   22½ᶜᵐ.

Title within woodcut border.   Signatures: a–n in fours.

ML171.R7

Rossi, Lemme, *d.* 1673.

Sistema mvsico, ouero Mvsica specvlativa doue si spiegano i più celebri sistemi di tutti i tre generi, di Lemme Rossi Perugino.   [*Colophon:* In Pervgia, Nella Stampa episcopale, per Angelo Laurenzi. Con licenza de' superiori. 1666]

6 p. l., 179, [1] p.   diagrs.   25ᶜᵐ.

Head and tail piece; initials.

ML3805.A2R8

Rossino, Francesco di.

Grammatica melodiale teorico-pratica esposta per dialoghi, nella quale ... insegnasi il modo d'imparare anche di per se il vero canto ecclesiastico, o sia canto fermo, trattine i primi rudimenti.   Divisa in tre parti.   Opera del p. f. Francesco di Rossino ...   Con in fine un appendice pratica, la quale servirà di direttorio al clero tanto secolare, che regolare, particolarmente ai religiosi francescani ...   Roma, I Lazzarini, 1793.

xxiv, 396 p.   29 x 22½ᶜᵐ.

MT860.A2R82

Roth, Georg Michael, 1769–1817.

Ueber die bisherige unmöglichkeit einer philosophie des bildes, der musik und sprache, von Georg Michael Roth.   Göttingen, J. C. Dieterich, 1796.

xxxii, 95 p.   19ᶜᵐ

Ch.26.2.5479

Roullet, François Louis Gaud Lebland, *marquis* du.

See Du ROULLET, FRANÇOIS LOUIS GAUD LEBLAND, *marquis.*

Rousseau, Jean.

Methode claire, certaine et facile, pour apprendre à chanter la musique, sur les tons transposez comme sur les naturels.   A battre la mesure à toutes sortes de mouvemens ordinaires & extraordinaires.

Rousseau, Jean—*Continued.*

A faire les ports de voix, & les cadances sur la musique avec regularité; et a connoître où il faut faire les tremblemens dans les livres où ils ne sont point marquez. Le tout expliqué & mis en ordre par Jean Rousseau . . . Paris, Chez l'autheur [etc.] 1683.

> 4 p. l., 64 p. 12 x 18½ᶜᵐ.
> The 1st edition was published by Ballard in 1678.
>
> > MT7.A2R8

Traité de la viole, qui contient une dissertation curieuse sur son origine. Une démonstration generale de son manche en quatre figures, avec leurs explications. L'explication de ses jeux differents, & particulierement des pieces par accords, & de l'accompagnement à fond. Des regles certaines, pour connoître tous les agrémens qui se peuvent pratiquer sur cét instrument dans toutes sortes de pieces de musique. La veritable maniere de gouverner l'archet, & des moyens faciles pour transposer sur toutes sortes de tons. Par Iean Rovsseav . . . Paris, C. Ballard, imprimeur, 1687.

> 8 p. l., 151 p. fold. tab. 18½ᶜᵐ.
> "Modelles povr la transposition . . .": p. 120–151.
>
> > MT338.A2R7

Rousseau, Jean Jacques, 1712–1778.

Dictionnaire de musique, par J. J. Rousseau . . . Paris, Veuve Duchesne, 1768.

> jx, [3], 548 (*i. e.* 556), [2] p. A–N fold. pl. (partly music) 26½ᶜᵐ.
> Title vignette. No. 473–480 repeated in paging.
>
> > ML108.A2R7

—— Dictionnaire de musique. Par J. J. Rousseau . . . Amsterdam, M. M. Rey, 1768.

> 2 v. (v. 1: xvi, 504 p.; v. 2: 2 p. l., 372 p.) A–N fold. pl. (partly music), fold. tab. 18ᶜᵐ.
>
> > ML108.A2R8

—— A complete dictionary of music. Consisting of a copious explanation of all words necessary to a true knowledge and understanding of music. Tr. from the original French of J. J. Rousseau. By William Waring. 2d ed. London, J. Murray; [etc., etc.] 1779.

> 1 p. l., 468 p. 24ᶜᵐ.
>
> > ML108.A2R86

Lettre sur la musique françoise. Par J. J. Rousseau. *Sunt verba & voces, prætereaque, nihil.* [n. p.] 1753.

> 2 p. l., 92 p. 17½ᶜᵐ.
>
> > ML1727.33.R7

—— Lettre sur la musique françoise, par J. J. Rousseau . . . 2. éd. [n. p.] 1753.

> 4 p. l., 92 p. 20½ᶜᵐ.
>
> > ML1727.33.R72

Rousseau, Jean Jacques—*Continued.*

Traités sur la musique.   [Geneve, 1781 ?]

437, [1] p.   24 fold. pl. on 19 l. (partly music)   20ᶜᵐ.

The general title is in the form of a half-title, without imprint; the first essay
has special t.-p. with imprint "Geneve, 1781." The plates include "Airs principaux du Devin du village" (pl. I–X)
   Half-title, title-page and a slight variation in paging excepted, this issue
corresponds to another of the same year: Œuvres posthumes de Jean-Jaques
Rousseau, ou Recueil de pieces manuscrites, pour servir de supplément aux
éditions publiées pendant sa vie.   Tome troisième.   Geneve, 1781.

   CONTENTS.—Projet concernant de nouveaux signes pour la musique.—Dissertation sur la musique moderne.—Essai sur l'origine des langues, où il est parlé
de la mélodie & de l'imitation musicale.—Lettre a Monsieur l'abbé Raynal, au
sujet d'un nouveau mode de musique, inventé par M. Blainville.—Examen de
deux principes avancés par M. Rameau, dans sa brochure intitulée: Erreurs
sur la musique, dans l'Encyclopédie.—Lettre a M. Burney sur la musique,
avec fragmens d'observations sur l'Alceste italien de M. le chevalier Gluck.
Extrait d'une reponse du petit faiseur a son prête-nom, sur un morceau de l'Orphée de M. le chevalier Gluck.

ML60.R86

   See also BÂTON, C.   Examen de la lettre de M. Rousseau, 1753.
      FRAMERY, N. É.   Musique, 1791–1818.

Rŏussier, Pierre Joseph, 1716–1790?

   L'harmonie pratique, ou Exemples pour le Traité des accords, par
M. Roussier . . .   Mis au jour par M. Bailleux.   Paris, Chez l'éditeur;
[etc., etc., 1775]

xvj, [2], 111 (*i. e.* 113) p., 1 l.   21ᶜᵐ.

   Engraved, with the exception of the 18 pages preceding the examples.

—— —— Copy 2.

   Title-page, half-title and preliminary matter (xvj p.) wanting.

MT49.A2R6

   Mémoire sur la musique des anciens, où l'on expose le principe des
proportions authentiques, dites de Pythagore, & de divers systêmes
de musique chez les Grecs, les Chinois & les Egyptiens.   Avec un
parallèle entre le systême des Egyptiens & celui des modernes.   Par
M. l'abbé Roussier . . .   Paris, Lacombe, 1770.

2 p. l., xxiv, 252 p.   illus., pl. (music), fold. tab.   26ᶜᵐ.

ML162.A2R7

   Mémoire sur la nouvelle harpe de M. Cousineau, luthier de la reine;
par M. l'abbé Roussier . . . mis au jour par M. F. Delaunay . . .
Paris, Lamy, 1782.

40 p.   18ᶜᵐ.

ML1006.A2R7

   Observations sur différens points d'harmonie, par M. l'abbé Roussier . . .   A Genève, et se trouvent à Paris, chez Bailleux, 1755.

4 p. l., 249 p.   fold. pl.   21ᶜᵐ.

MT50.A2R86

   Traité des accords, et de leur succession; selon le systéme de la
basse-fondamentale; pour servir de principes d'harmonie à ceux

Roussier, Pierre Joseph—*Continued.*

qui étudient la composition ou l'accompagnement du clavecin. Avec une methode d'accompagnement . . . Paris, Duchesne; [etc., etc.] 1764.

xxviij, [4], 192 p. 3 pl. (1 fold.) fold. tab. 20½ᶜᵐ.

Dedication signed: Roussier.

MT49.A2R4

—— Traité des accords, et de leur succession; selon le systéme de la basse-fondamentale; pour servir de principes d'harmonie à ceux qui étudient la composition ou l'accompagnement du clavecin; avec une méthode d'accompagnement . . . Paris, Bailleux, 1764.

xxxij, 192 p. 3 pl. (1 fold.) fold. tab. 21ᶜᵐ.

Dedication signed: Roussier.

MT49.A2R5

See also LA BORDE, J. B. DE. Essai sur la musique, 1780.
Mémoires sur les proportions musi-
cales, 1781.

Roussier, Pierre Joseph, 1716–1790? *editor.*

See AMIOT, J. M. Mémoire sur la musique des Chinois, 1779.

Roxas y Montes, Diego de.

Promptuario armonico, y conferencias theoricas, y practicas de canto-llano, con las entonaciones de choro, y altar, segun la costumbre de la santa iglesia cathedral de Cordoba, y de otras. Compuesto por D. Diego de Roxas, y Montes . . . Cordoba, Impresso por A. Serrano, y D. Rodriguez, 1760.

13 p. l., 482 p. v fold. pl. 20½ᶜᵐ.

MT860.A2R9

Roy, Pierre Charles, 1683–1764.

See HERTEL, J. W. Sammlung musikalischer schriften, 1757–58.

Rümlang, Eberhard von.

See LAMPADIUS, A. Compendivm mvsices, 1554.

Ruetz, Caspar, 1708–1755.

Widerlegte vorurtheile vom ursprunge der kirchenmusic, und klarer beweis, dass die gottesdienstliche music sich auf Gottes wort gründe, und also göttliches ursprungs sey, der gleichgültigkeit in ansehung dieser art des gottesdienstes entgegen gesetzet von Caspar Ruetz . . . Lübeck, J. Schmidt, 1750.

12 p. l., 114, [C] p. 19ᶜᵐ.

Title vignette: printer's mark.

ML3001.R92

Widerlegte vorurtheile von der beschaffenheit der heutigen kirchen-music und von der lebens-art einiger musicorum, ans licht gegeben von Caspar Rüetz . . . Lübeck, P. Böckmann, 1752.

8 p. l., 175, [9] p. 19ᶜᵐ.

ML3001.R93

Ruetz, Caspar—*Continued*.

Widerlegte vorurtheile von der wirkung der kirchenmusic, und von den darzu erfoderten unkosten, nebst einer vorrede von der musicalischen liebhaberey, ans licht gestellt von Caspar Ruetz ... Rostock und Wismar, J. A. Berger und J. Boedner, 1753.

23 p̆. l., 152, [15] p. 18½^{cm}.

ML3001.R94

Ruggero, Francesco Girolamo.

Dichiarazione della eccellente musica seguita in Novara coll' intervento de primi virtuosi d'Itaglia nell' occasione del famoso trasporto del sagro corpo di S. Gaudenzo, primo vescovo, e protettore di detta città, spiegata dal prete Francesco Girolamo Ruggero ... Vercelli, Nella stampa di P. A. Gilardone, 1711.

15, [1] p. 18^{cm}.

ML290.8.N6R9

Rules; or a short and compleat method for attaining to play a thorough bass upon the harpsicord or organ. By an eminent master. Also an explanation of figur'd time, with the several moods & characters made use of in musick. To which is added, a dictionary, or explication of such Italian words, or terms, as are made use of in vocal, or instrumental musick. London, Printed for & sold by I: Walsh [1715?]

42 p. 21^{cm}.

Engraved throughout.
The dictionary (pages 10–42) was published separately, London, 1724, as "A short explication of such foreign words, as are made use of in musick books."

MT49.A2R9

[Rulhière, Claude Carloman de] 1734–1791.

Jugement de l'orchestre de l'Opéra. [n. p., 175–]

8 p. 16½^{cm}.

Caption title.

ML1727.33.R95

Sabbatini, Luigi Antonio, 1739–1809.

Elementi teorici della musica colla pratica de' medesimi, in duetti, e terzetti a canone accompagnati dal basso, ed eseguibili sì a solo, che a più voci, di f. Luigi Antonio Sabbatini ... Roma, Stamperia P. Cracas, e G. Rotilj socio, 1789–95.

3 v. in 1. 23½ x 30^{cm}.

Vol. 2 has title: Elementi pratici della musica formati in duetti a canone accompagnati dal basso ... Parte seconda. Ed. 2. ... 1795.

MT55.A2S11

La vera idea delle musicali numeriche segnature diretta al giovane studioso dell' armonìa da f. Luigi Ant.° Sabbatini ... Venezia, S. Valle, 1799.

iv, clxxix, [1] p. 29½^{cm}.

MT50.A2S11

Sacchi, Giovenale, 1726–1789.

Del nvmero e delle misvre delle corde mvsiche e loro corrispon-
denze, dissertazione del p. D. Giovenale Sacchi Bernabita. Milano
[G. Mazzucchelli] 1761.

126 p. 20^{cm}.

ML60.S11

Della divisione del tempo nella musica, nel ballo e nella poesia.
Dissertazioni III del p. D. Giovenale Sacchi Bernabita. Milano [Per
G. Mazzucchelli nella stamperia Malatesta] 1770.

4 p. l., 248 p. diagr. 20^{cm}. (*With his* Del nvmero . . . delle corde mvsiche.
Milano, 1761)

ML60.S11

Della natura e perfezione della antica musica de' Greci e della
utilita che ci potremmo noi promettere dalla nostra applicandola
secondo il loro esempio alla educazione de' giovani; dissertazioni III
del p. D. Giovenale Sacchi Bernabita. Milano [Per A. Mogni nella
stamperìa Malatesta] 1778.

5 p. l., 207 p. 20^{cm}.

ML60.S12

Delle quinte successive nel contrappunto e delle regole degli accompagnamenti; lettera del p. D. Giovenale Sacchi al . . . Sig. Wincislao
Pichl . . . Milano, Per C. Orena, stampería Malatesta, 1780.

183 p. 20^{cm}. (*With his* Della natura . . . della antica musica de' Greci.
Milano, 1778)

ML60.S12

Don Placido, dialogo del p. Don Giovenale Sacchi . . . dove cercasi:
se lo studio della musica al religioso convenga o disconvenga. Pisa,
L. Raffaelli, 1786.

152 p. 20^{cm}.

ML63.S12

Vita del cavaliere Don Carlo Broschi, scritta da Giovenale Sacchi
. . . Vinegia, Stamperia Coleti, 1784.

48 p. 19½^{cm}.

ML420.B8S14

See also ZANOTTI, F. M. Lettere, 1782.

Sacchi, Giovenale, 1726–1789, *translator.*

See FONTANA, F. L. Vita di Benedetto Marcello, 1788.

Saché, Étienne, *d. ca.* 1724.

Traité des tons de l'eglise selon l'usage romain, dans lequel la
game ancienne et nouvelle est mise au commencement. Avec
plusieurs autres chants pour vespres, complies, matines, la haute
messe, &c. . . . Par E. Saché . . . Lisieux, R. Le Boullenger,
M. DC. LXCIV [*i. e.* 1676]

8 p. l., 47, [1], 136 p. illus. 14½^{cm}.

ML3082.A2S2

[Saint Hilaire, Cécile de] *pseud.?*

Lettre a l'auteur des Lettres sur les hommes célebres dans les sciences, la litterature & les beaux arts. Sous le regne de Louis xv. Amsterdam, P. Marteau. [Paris?] 1752.

32 p. 15^{cm}.

Signed: Cecile de Saint Hilaire.
Mainly a comparison of the art of Lully and Rameau.

ML410.L95S14

Saint-Mard, Toussaint Rémond de.

See RÉMOND DE SAINT-MARD, TOUSSAINT.

[Saint-Sévin, Joseph Barnabé] 1727–1803.

Principes du violon pour apprendre le doigté de cet instrument, et les différends agréments dont il est susceptible . . . par M^r. l'Abbé le fils. Ces principes sont suivis de deux suites d'airs d'opéra à deux violons . . . de plusieurs leçons dans le genre de sonates avec la basse chiffrée pour le clavecin, d'exemples analogues à ces leçons, de préludes . . . et d'une suite de jolis airs variés pour un violon seul . . . Paris, Des Lauriers [1761?]

2 p. l., 81 p. 35^{cm}.

Engraved throughout.

MT262.A2S24

Sala, Nicola, 1701–1800.

Regole del contrappunto pratico di Nicola Sala Napoletano, primo maestro nel Reale conservatorio della Pieta' de' Torchini, dedicate alla maestà di Ferdinando iv. re delle Due Sicilie &c. Napoli, Stamperia reale, 1794.

3 v. in 2. 52 x 36^{cm}.

Title vignette. The work consists almost entirely of contrapuntal examples and exercises, which are printed from engraved plates.

MT55.A2S2

Salinas, Francisco de, 1513–1590.

Francisci Salinæ . . . De musica libri septem, in quibus eius doctrinæ veritas tam quæ ad harmoniam, quàm quæ ad rhythmum pertinet, iuxta sensus ac rationis iudicium ostenditur, & demonstratur. Cvm duplici indice capitum & rerum . . . Salmanticæ, excudebat M. Gastius, 1577.

2 p. l., 438, [18] p. incl. fold. tab. diagrs. (1 fold.) 29½^{cm}.

Title vignette: coat of arms. Printer's mark at end.

ML171.S16

Salle,   la.

See LASALLE.

Salle, Jean François Démotz de la.

See DÉMOTZ DE LA SALLE, JEAN FRANÇOIS.

Salmon, Thomas, 1648–1706.

An essay to the advancement of musick, by casting away the perplexity of different cliffs. And uniting all sorts of musick: lute, viol, violin, organ, harpsechord, voice, &c. in one universal character. By Thomas Salmon . . . London, Printed by J. Macock, and are to be sold by J. Car, 1672.

8 p. l., 92 p. 5 fold. pl. (partly music) 17^{cm}.

Added t.-p., engr. Preface signed: John Birchensha.

ML432.A2S2

Salmon, Thomas—*Continued.*

A proposal to perform musick, in perfect and mathematical proportions. Containing, I. The state of musick in general. II. The principles of present practice; according to which are, III. The tables of proportions, calculated for the viol, and capable of being accommodated to all sorts of musick. By Thomas Salmon . . . Approved by both the mathematick professors of the Vniversity of Oxford. With large remarks upon this whole treatise, by the reverend and learned John Wallis . . . London, J. Lawrence, 1688.

6 p. l., 42 p. 4 pl. 23 x 18½ᶜᵐ.

ML3807.A2S17

A vindication of an Essay to the advancement of musick, from Mr. Matthew Lock's Observations. By enquiring into the real nature, and most convenient practise of that science. By Thomas Salmon . . . London, Printed by A. Maxwell, and are to be sold by J. Car, 1672.

2 p. l., 85, 20 p. fold. pl. 17½ᶜᵐ.

Written in the form of a letter to Dr. John Wallis. The 20 p. at end contain a letter to Salmon signed N. E., concerning his Essay and Locke's "Observations."

ML432.A2S3

Salvadore Maria *da Vercelli.*

Nelle funebri pompe del Signor arcimaestro in musica David Peres, maestro di camera di S. R. M. fedelissima felicemente regnante orazione. Tributo d'ossequio di frà Salvadore Maria da Vercelli . . . Lisbona, Stamperia reale, 1779.

15 p. 20½ᶜᵐ.

ML410.P27S15

Samber, Johann Baptist.

Manuductio ad organum, das ist: Gründlich- und sichere handleitung durch die höchst-nothwendige solmisation, zu der edlen schlagkunst . . . Sambt einer kurtz-verfassten information von denen kirchen- oder choral-tonen, wie solche geschwind zuerkennen, und auff denen in cornet-ton gestimmten orgl-wercken abzuschlagen seynd. Alles mit vilen in kupffer gestochenen figuren und exemplen gezieret / und mit sonderbahren fleiss zusam̄en getragen / auch das erste mahl in den druck gegeben durch M. Joannem Baptistam Samber . . . Zu finden bey dem authore. Saltzburg / Gedruckt durch J. B. Mayrs / seel. wittib / und erb., 1704.

8 p. l., 177, [6] p. 16½ x 22½ᶜᵐ.

MT182.A2S2

—— Continuatio ad Manuductionem organicam, das ist: Fortsetzung zu der Manuduction oder handleitung zum orgl-schlagen; worinnen . . . begriffen seynd . . . I. Was gestalten die in besagter Manuductione vorgezeigte intervalla und concenten in auf- und absteigend-haltend- und springenden noten auff dem clavier sollen genommen und geschlagen werden / sambt beygefügten nutzlichen exercitiis. II. Wird die natur und namen der registern in verschidenen orgl-wercken zu erkennen / solche zu verwechslen / und zu combiniren / demonstrirt: und zugleich / was in compositione der galantarien / als

Samber, Johann Baptist—*Continued.*

allemanden / couranten / sarabanden / menueten / &c. ... zu beobachten ... dem günstigen liebhaber solcher capriccien hiemit communicirt ... III. Auff was weise eine gute harmonia ... zu componiren und zu setzen seye ... IV. Wie man allerley fugen ... formiren solle / der rechte weeg gewisen ... auss vilen approbirten authoribus, auch eigner praxi zusammen getragen und verlegt durch M. Joannem Baptistam Samber ... Saltzburg, Gedruckt bey J. B. Mayrs seel. wittib und sohn, 1707.

4 p. l., 239, [4] p.   VIII pl.   18 x 23½ᶜᵐ.

MT182.A2S21

San Rafaele, Benvenuto, *conte* **di.**

Lettere due sopra l'arte del suono, del Signor co: Benvenuto di S. Rafaele, Torinese.   Vicenza, A. Veronese, 1778.

38 p.   15½ᶜᵐ.

ML63.S16

Sander, F. S., *d.* **1796.**

Kurze und gründliche anweisung zur fingersetzung für clavierspieler mit genau bestimmten regeln und beygefügten exempeln. Hrsg. von F. S. Sander.   Bresslau, F. E. C. Leuckart, 1791.

iv, 24 p.   20½ x 25ᶜᵐ.

MT220.A2S2

Santa María, Tomás de.

See TOMÁS DE SANTA MARÍA.

Santoro, Fabio Sebastiano, *b.* **1671.**

Scola di canto fermo, in cui s'insegnano facilissime, e chiare regole per ben cantare, e componere ...   Dal sacerdote D. Fabio Sebastiano Santoro ...   Con infine le considerazioni di novissimi, ed altre cose utili à chi spera il paradiso.   Napoli, Stamperia di Novello de Bonis, 1715.

8 p. l., 108, [1], 109–292, [16] p.   front. (port.) illus.   22 x 16½ᶜᵐ.

MT860.A2S23

Sanz y Celma, Gaspar Francisco Bartolomé, 1640–1710.

Instrvccion de mvsica sobre la gvitarra española; y metodo de svs primeros rvdimentos, hasta tañerla con destreza.   Con dos laberintos ingeniosos, variedad de sones, y dances de rasgueado, y punteado, al estilo español, italiano, francès, y inglès.   Con vn breve tratado para acompañar con perfeccion, sobre la parte muy essencial para la guitarra, arpa, y organo, resumido en doze reglas, y exemplos los mas principales de contrapunto, y composicion ...   Compvesto por el licenciado Gaspar Sanz ...   Zaragoça, Herederos de D. Dormer, 1674.

3 pt. in 1 v.   40 pl. (partly music), port.   21½ x 28½ᶜᵐ.

MT582.A2S2

Sartorius, Erasmus, 1578–1637.

Musomachia, id est Bellum musicale. Ante quinque lustra bellige-ratum in gratiam Er: Sar: nunc denuò institutum à primo ejus aucto-re Petro Laurembergio professore academico. [Rostochii] Richelianis arma suppeditantib.⁹ à Johanne Hallervordio toti orbi indictum, 1642.

1 p. l., 78 p. 15ᶜᵐ.

The 1st edition was published at Hamburg in 1622 as "Erasmi Sartori . . . Bel-ligerasmus, id est Historia belli exorti in regno musico."

ML63.S17

Saunier de Beaumont, *d. ca.* 1750.

Lettre sur la musique ancienne & moderne, a Madame la duchesse de * * *. Avec des anecdotes intéressantes. Par M. Saunier de Beaumont . . . Paris, Veuve Pissot, 1743.

1 p. l., 50 p. 15½ᶜᵐ.

ML1727.3.A2S2

Sauveur, Joseph, 1653–1716.

Système general des intervalles des sons, & son application à tous les systêmes & à tous les instrumens de musique. Par M. Sauveur.

(*In* Académie des sciences, Paris. Histoire de l'Académie . . . année 1701. Paris, 1704. 297–364, [2] p. 25½ᶜᵐ. III fold. tab.)

Detached copy.

ML3809.A2S2

Sayas, Juan Francisco de.

Musica canonica, motetica, y sagrada, su origen, y pureza con que la erigió Dios para sus alabanzas divinas . . . Escrita por Don Juan Francisco de Sayas . . . Pamplona, Por M. J. de Rada, impressor [1761 ?]

10 p. l., 411, 405–411 p. 20½ᶜᵐ.

ML3000.A2S27

Scaletta, Orazio, *d.* 1630.

Scala di mvsica molto necessaria per principianti. Di Horatio Scaletta . . . Dall' istesso ampliata di molti essempij, & auuertimenti molto vtili, per cantar polito, e bene. Et in questa vltima impres-sione da D. Florido . . . corretta. Roma, A. Fei, 1642.

1 p. l., 29, [1] p. 1 illus. 22 x 16½ᶜᵐ.

MT44.A2S28

Scheibe, Johann Adolph, 1708–1776.

Johann Adolph Scheibens . . . Abhandlung vom ursprunge und alter der musik, insonderheit der vokalmusik . . . Mit einer histo-rischen und critischen vorrede versehen, worinn vom inhalte dieser abhandlung, und von einigen andern musikalischen sachen gehandelt wird. Altona und Flensburg, Kortische buchhandlung, 1754.

lxxx, 107 p. 18½ᶜᵐ.

ML3800.A2S31

Scheibe, Johann Adolph—*Continued.*

Eine abhandlung von den musicalischen intervallen und geschlechten, abgefasset von Johann Adolph Scheibe. Hamburg, Auf kosten des verfassers, 1739.

8 p. l., 114 p., 1 l.   3 fold. l. (musical examples)   18^{cm}.

ML3809.A2S4

Johann Adolph Scheibens . . . Critischer musikus.   Neue verm. und verb. aufl.   Leipzig, B. C. Breitkopf, 1745.

24 p. l., 1059, [24] p.   20½^{cm}.

Appeared in weekly numbers (irregular) 1737-1740.

ML4.C82

Johann Adolph Scheibe . . . Ueber die musikalische composition. Erster theil.   Die theorie der melodie und harmonie.   Leipzig, Schwickert, 1773.

lx, 600 p.   fold. tables.   20½ x 17^{cm}.

No more published.

MT6.A2S31

See also MATTHESON, J.   Gültige zeugnisse, 1738.

Scheibel, Gottfried Ephraim, 1696–1759.

Zufällige gedancken von der kirchen-music, wie sie heutiges tages beschaffen ist, allen rechtschaffnen liebhabern der music zur nachlese und zum ergötzen wohlmeinende ans licht gestellet von Gottfried Ephraim Scheibel.   Franckfurt und Leipzig, Zu finden beym authore, 1721.

2 p. l., 84 p.   16^{cm}.

ML3865.A2S3

Scheid, Johann Friedrich.

. . . Dissertatio inauguralis de jure in musicos singulari, germ. Dienste und obrigkeit der spielleuth / Rappolsteinensi comitatui annexo, quam solo Deo præside, auctoritate amplissimæ Facultatis juridicæ argentoratensis, pro licentia summos in utroque jure honores et privilegia doctoralia rite consequendi solenniter defendet Jo. Fridericus. Scheid, Francofurt. ad Mœn. d. xix. maji anno MDCCXIX. hor. & loc. consuet.   Argentorati, literis J. Pastorii [1719]

2 p. l., 52 p.   18½ x 15^{cm}.

This copy closely trimmed in binding.
"Documenta": p. 44–49.

ML63.S34

Scheyrer, Bernhard.

Mvsica choralis theoro-practica, das ist: Ein nutzliche underweisung / wie man das choral gesang . . . in kurtzer zeit ergreiffen möge. Aus vnderschidlichen / sowol lateinisch: als teutschen authoribus . . . zusammen getragen / auch in ein bequeme ordnung redigirt vnnd verfasset / vnnd . . . in truck verfertiget.   Durch p. f. Bernardvm Scheyrer . . .   München, Gedruckt durch J. Jäcklin, 1663.

4 p. l., 92 p.   19½ x 16^{cm}.

MT860.A2S32

Schlegel, Franz Anton.

Gründliche anleitung die flöte zu spielen, nach Quanzens Anweisung. Hrsg. von Franz Anton Schlegel. Graz, J. G. Weingand und F. Ferstl, 1788.

166, [2] p. viii pl. on 4 l. 20ᶜᵐ.

Engr. t.-p.   MT342.A2S13

[Schlichtegroll, Adolf Heinrich Friedrich von] 1765–1822.

Mozarts leben . . . Grätz, J. G. Hubeck, 1794.

32 p. front. (port.) 18ᶜᵐ.

Printed also in Schlichtegroll's "Nekrolog auf das jahr 1791," Gotha, 1792, 2. jahr, 2. bd., p. 82–112.

ML410.M9S34

[Schlick, Rudolph]

Exercitatio qua mvsices origo prima, cvltvs antiqvissimvs, dignitas maxima, & emolumenta, quæ tàm animo quàm corpori humano confert summa, breuiter ac dilucidè exponuntur . . . Spiræ, typis Bernardi Albini, 1588.

48 p. 14½ᶜᵐ.

Dedication signed: Rodolphvs Schlick Misnensis, medic. d.   The present copy has been closely trimmed in binding, and the author's name is supplied with pen and ink at head of title.

ML171.S34

Schmid, Christian Ernst, 1715–1786.

Cantandi ritvm per noctes festorvm apvd Ebraeos exponit et viris clarissimis doctissimisqve dn. Ioanni Friderico Wittichio . . . dn. Ioanni Lvdovico Gensekenio . . . [et al.] lavream magisterialem ipsis d. xxx. april. cɪɔɪɔccxxxviii. a Levcoride rite impositam sincere gratvlatvr Collegivm examinatorio-dispvtatorivm Deylingianvm, interprete Christiano Ernesto Schmidio . . . Lipsiae, ex officina Langenhemiana [1739]

xvi p. 18 x 15½ᶜᵐ.

ML166.A2S3

Schmid, Jo[hann] An[dreas] 1652–1726, *praeses.*

De cantoribvs ecclesiae V. et N. T. . . . Helmstadii, litteris Hammianis, 1708.

1 p. l., 44 p. 19 x 16ᶜᵐ.

Diss.—Helmstedt (J. A. Jussov, respondent and author)

Ch.16.1193

Schmidt, Johann Michael, 1728–1799.

Musico-theologia, oder Erbauliche anwendung musicalischer wahrheiten, entworfen von m. Johann Michael Schmidt, d. z. h.   Bayreuth und Hof, J. G. Vierling, 1754.

5 p. l., [3]–312, [14] p. 17ᶜᵐ.

Half-title: Musico-theologia. Oder, Anleitung zur erkånntniss Gottes und seines willens aus der music.

ML3800.A2S35

Schmidt, Johann Michael—*Continued*.

—— Musico-theologia, of Stigtelyke toepassing van muzikaale waarheden; ontworpen door Mr. Johann Michael Schmidt. Uit het Hoogduitsche vertaald door Jacob Wilhelm Lustig . . . Amsterdam, A. Olofsen [1756 ?]

xxiii, [1], 261, [25] p.   16½^{cm}.

The publisher's dedication is dated July, 1756.

ML3800.A2S36

[Schmith, Amand Wilhelm]

Philosophische fragmente über die praktische musik . . . Wien, Gedruckt in der K. K. Taubstummeninstitutsbuchdruck., 1787.

7 p. l., 164, [6] p.   17^{cm}.

Preface signed: Dr. A. W. S.

ML3800.A2S34

Schneegass, Cyriacus, 1546–1597.

Isagoges mvsicæ libri dvo.   Tam theoricæ quám practicæ studiosis inseruire iussi.   Annexo ad finem tractatulo, ex poetica desumto: paucisq̃, de canendi elegantia obseruationibus: nec non solmisandi exercitio.   Methodo facili & perspicua itâ conscripti, ut neq̃, necessaria artis præcepta, cum selectioribus exemplis omittantur, neq̃, superuacanea discentibus obtrudantur.   Autore m. Cyriaco Snegassio   Μουσικὴν ἔρως διδάσκει.   M.D. XCVI.   [*Colophon*: Erphordiae Georgius Bauman excudebat. anno salvtis.1596]

[189] p.   15½^{cm}.

Signatures: A–M⁸ (recto of [Mvj], verso of [Mvij] and last leaf blank)
2d edition; 1st edition Erfurt, 1591.
"Exercitivm δωδεκατονον discentium captui solerter attemperatum: quo singuli modi elegantibus fugis principales clausulas complexis, & conuenienti textui applicatis, egregiè illustrantur. Omnes sunt duarum vocum: in hypodiapason decantanda . . . Autore Philippo Avenario": l. Hiij–[Hvij]
"Fvgae viginti ex solmizandi exercitio Iohannis Steuerlini descriptæ, & ad calcem opusculi in tyronum gratiam & usum, (commostratis modis) annexæ": l. [Ivj]–Miij r°.   ML171.S36

Schreiben an die herren verfasser der Freyen urteile.   [n. p.] 1752.

11 p.   20½ x 16½^{cm}.

Signed: M. H. H.   Dated: Neustadt, den 26. februar, i. j. 1752.

ML275.3.S35

Schröter, Christoph Gottlieb, 1699–1782.

Christoph Gottlieb Schröters . . . letzte beschäftigung mit musicalischen dingen; nebst sechs temperatur-planen und einer noten-tafel [8 pt. Canon infinitus]   Nordhausen, 1782.

4 p. l., 52 p.   1 l. (music), diagrs.   20½ x 17^{cm}.

ML3809.A2S5

Deutliche anweisung zum general-bass, in beständiger veränderung des uns angebohrnen harmonischen dreyklanges, mit zulänglichen exempeln: wobey ein umständlicher vorbericht der vornehmsten vom general-basse handelnden schriften dieses jahrhunderts; von Christoph Gottlieb Schröter . . . Halberstadt, J. H. Gross, 1772.

xxiv, 202, [6] p.   23½ x 18½^{cm}.

MT49.A2S38

Schröter, Christoph Gottlieb—*Continued.*

Sendschreiben an hr. hoch-edlen, den herrn magister Lorenz Mizler, preisswürdigen stiffter der längst gewünschten Societät der musicalischen wissenschafften, in welchem i. der bevorstehenden reformation der music; ii. einer aufgabe wegen der temperatur; iii. einiger nüzlicher erfindungen gedacht; und etliche nöthige erinnerungen für die tonkünstler . . . eingeschaltet worden, von Christoph Gottlieb Schröter . . . Nordhausen, 1738.

16 p. 16^{cm}.

Published also in Mizler's Neu eröffnete musikalische bibliothek, 3. bd., 3. th., Leipzig, 1747.

ML3809.A2S46

Schröter, Johann Georg.

Churfürstl. mayntzisches gnädigstes privilegium, wie auch derer clöster und gemeinden attestata wegen derer verfertigten neuen orgelwercke / ertheilet Johann Georg Schrötern . . . [Erffurth?] Gedruckt anno 1723.

24 p. 21 x 17½^{cm}.

ML424.S37

[Schuback, Jacob] 1726–1784.

Von der musicalischen declamation. Göttingen, Vandenhoecks wittwe, 1775.

48 p. 18½^{cm}.

ML3849.A2S3

Schubart, Christian Friedrich Daniel, 1739–1791.

Schubart's leben und gesinnungen. Von ihm selbst, im kerker aufgesetzt . . . Stuttgart, Bei den gebrüdern Mäntler, 1791–93.

2 v. (v. 1: xviii, 292 p.; v. 2: 2 p. l., iii–vi p., 1 l., vii–xiv, 320 p.) fronts. (v. 1: port.) 4 pl. 17^{cm}.

Title vignette. Vol. 2: Hrsg. von seinem sohne, Ludwig Schubart.

PT2510.S5Z8

Schubart, Ludwig Albrecht, 1765–1811.

Schubart's karakter, von seinem sohne Ludwig Schubart . . . Erlangen, Auf kosten des verfassers, 1798.

viii, 168 p. 16½^{cm}.

PT2510.S5Z95

Schubart, Ludwig Albrecht, 1765–1811, *editor.*

See SCHUBART, C. F. D. Schubart's leben, 1791–93.

Schubarth, Johann Kaspar, 1756–1810, *editor.*

See RIEPEL, J. Bassschlüssel, 1786.

Schulz, Johann Abraham Peter, 1747–1800.

Entwurf einer neuen und leichtverständlichen musiktablatur, deren man sich, in ermangelung der notentypen, in kritischen und theoretischen schriften bedienen kann, und deren zeichen in allen buchdruckereyen vorräthig sind, nebst einem probeexempel, von J. A. P. Schulz . . . Berlin, Rellstab [1786]

1 p. l., 57, [1] p.   17 x 9½ᶜᵐ.

ML431.A2S39

See also SULZER, J. G.   Allgemeine theorie der schönen künste, 1792–99.

Schurtzfleisch, Conrad Samuel, 1641–1708, *praeses.*

. . . De hymnis ecclesiæ veteris . . . Wittenbergæ, imprimebat J. Wilcke [1725]

[16] p.   18 x 14ᶜᵐ.

Diss.—Wittenberg (Daniel Galle, respondent and author)

ML169.A2S3

Scorpione, Domenico, *b. ca.* 1645.

Riflessioni armoniche divise in due libri.   Nel primo de' qvali si tratta dello stato della musica in tutte l'età del mondo, e di materie spettanti al musico specolativo.   Nel secondo si dà il modo per ben comporre; si registrano con nuovo ordine sotto i loro generi tutte le varie specie de' contrapunti, delle fughe, delle imitationi, delle conseqvenze, e de' canoni: e si danno le regole per rivoltarli, e roversciarli con ogni faciltà per mezzo di numeri.   Composte dal padre fra Domenico Scorpione . . . Opera qvinta.   Napoli, De Bonis, 1701.

8 p. l., 219, [11] p., 1 l.   32½ᶜᵐ.

MT55.A2S32

Sebastiani, Claudius.

Bellvm. mvsicale, inter plani et mensvralis cantvs reges, de principatu in musicæ prouincia obtinendo, contendentes.   Clavdio Sebastiani Metensi, organista, authore . . .   [*Colophon:* Argent. in officina Pavli Machæropœi, anno M. D. LXIII.]

[174] p.   illus.   21 x 16ᶜᵐ.

Printer's mark on t.-p.   Signatures: ₓ, A–X in fours.
Chapters 31, 32, 34–36 are taken from the "Musice actiue micrologus" of Andreas Ornithoparcus.

ML171.S44

Secchi, Anacleto.

. . . De ecclesiastica hymnodia libri tres, in quibus de prestantia, effectibus, et modo rite psallendi in choro copiose agitur, avctore Anacleto Sicco . . . Bononiæ, apud C. Ferronū, 1629.

10 p. l., 381 (*i. e.* 371), [13] p.   21ᶜᵐ.

Engr. t.-p.   Numbers 329–338 omitted in paging.

Ch. 16.1193

—— Della hinnodia ecclesiastica libri tre, ne' quali della nobiltà, de gli effetti, e del modo, di bene e regolatamente cantare i salmi in choro, copiosamente si tratta: composti già dal r. p. d. Anacleto

Secchi, Anacleto—*Continued.*

Secchi ... et hora recati fedelmente di latino in volgare dal p. D. Donato Benzoni ... Milano, G. P. Cardi, 1643.

14 p. l., 511 p., 12 l. 17ᶜᵐ.

Added t.-p., engr. Printer's mark at end.

Ch. 16.1193

Seelen, Johann Heinrich von, 1688–1762.

... De patribvs edoctis mvsicam Eccles. XLIV. 5. collavdatis exercitatio philologico-historica, panegyri, qva d. XXVI. april. a. MDCCXXXVII. cantor solenni ritv inavgvrabitvr, praemissa a Io. Henr. a Seelen ... Gym. lvb. rect. Lvbecae, typis I. N. Greenii [1737]

16 p. 20½ x 17ᶜᵐ.

ML64.S33

... Principem mvsicvm ex sacra et profana historia exhibet et eximios ivvenes Olavm Mollervm, Flensburg. de ervditis mvsicis ac Petrvm Cramervm, Flensburg. de historia pvblice d. avgvst. dictvros patrvm reipvblicae, virorvm sacri ordinis ceterorvmqve stvdiis nostris faventivm splendida corona cingi decenter rogat Io. Henr. von Seelen, conrector. Flensbvrgi, operis Vogelianis, 1715.

1 p. l., 21 p. 21½ᶜᵐ.

ML166.A2S4

Sendschreiben an die herren verfasser der Freyen urtheile in Hamburg, das Schreiben an den herrn verfasser des Kritischen musikus an der Spree betreffend. Berlin, 1750.

16 p. 21¼ x 17ᶜᵐ.

Signed "A" and dated "Berlin, den 28ten august 1750."

ML275.3.A3

[Sénecé, Antoine Bauderon de] 1643–1737.

Lettre de Clememt Marot [*pseud.*], a Monsieur de * * *, touchant ce qui s'est passé à l'arrivée de Jean Baptiste de Lulli, aux Champs Elisées. A Cologne, chez Pierre Marteau, 1688.

119 p. 13 x 7ᶜᵐ.

ML410.L95S4

Senff, Carl Samuel, *praeses.*

... De cantionibvs fvnebribvs vetervm ... Lipsiæ, typis C. Gvntheri [1689]

16 p. 18½ x 14½ᶜᵐ.

Diss.—Leipzig (G. Wezelius, respondent)

ML169.A2S4

Sense against sound; or, A succedaneum, for Abbey music ... This is (strictly speaking) the clerical widow's sermon at St. James's ... on the disappointment in losing advantages expected from Handel's anniversary ... London, C. Stalker [1788?]

1 p. l., 24 p. 24½ᶜᵐ.

ML64.S36

Serio, Luigi.

See MATTEI, S. Se i maestri di cappella son ... artigiani [1785?]

Sermes, *Sieur* de, *pseud.*

See MERSENNE, MARIN.

Serra, Paolo.

Introduzione armonica sopra la nuova serie de' suoni modulati oggidì e modo di rettamente, e più facilmente intuonarla, di Paolo Serra. Roma, Nella stamperia di S. Michele a Ripa, per il Giunchi, 1768.

xv, [1], 230 p. front., A-D fold. pl. 28^{cm}.

MT44.A2S48

Serre, Jean Adam, *b.* 1704.

Essais sur les principes de l'harmonie, où l'on traite de la théorie de l'harmonie en général, des droits respectifs de l'harmonie & de la melodie, de la basse fondamentale, et de l'origine du mode mineur. Par Monsieur Serre ... Paris, Prault fils, 1753.

4 p. l., 159, [1] p. 2 pl. 19^{cm}.

ML3815.A2S4

Observations sur les principes de l'harmonie, occasionnées par quelques ecrits modernes sur ce sujet, & particuliérement par l'article Fondamental de M. d'Alembert dans l'Encyclopédie, le Traité de théorie musicale de M. Tartini, et le Guide harmonique de M. Geminiani. Par J. A. Serre ... Geneve, H.-A. Gosse et J. Gosse, 1763.

xiii, [3], 206 p. 22^{cm}.

ML3815.A2S48

[Serré *de Rieux*, Jean de]

Les dons des enfans de Latone: La musique et La chasse du cerf, poëmes dédiés au roy. Paris, P. Prault [etc.] 1734.

xij p., 1 l., 330 p., 1 l., 32 p. (music, engr.), [2] p. front., 7 pl. 19$\frac{1}{2}$^{cm}.

Souhart, "Bibl. . . . des ouvr. sur la chasse," 1886, gives a full description of this work and adds that it is practically a translation of Jean Savary's "Venationis cervinæ." In the present copy, the "Remarques sur la musique," 14, 4 p. (engr.) are inserted at p. [14] and 28.

CONTENTS.—Au roy.—Préface.—Apollon, ou L'origine des spectacles en musique, poeme.—La musique, epitre en vers. 3. ed., rev., cor. & augm.—Catalogue chronologique des opera representés en France depuis l'année 1645 . . . jusqu'à présent.—Diane, ou Les loix de la chasse du cerf, poeme.—Dictionaire des termes usités dans la Chasse du cerf.—Nouvelle chasse du cerf, divertissement en musique; composé de plusieurs airs parodiés sur les opera d'Angleterre.—Parodies sur les fanfares.—Tons de chasse et fanfares a une et deux trompes.—Remarques sur la musique.

ML63.S36

[Servan, Joseph Michel Antoine] 1737–1807.

Discours d'un ancien avocat-général, dans la cause du comte de * * [La Suze], et de la Dlle. * * * [Bon], chanteuse de l'Opéra. Lyon, S. Grabit, 1772.

xxiij, 368 p. 17$\frac{1}{2}$^{cm}.

ML420.L2S3

Sévin, Joseph Barnabé Saint-

See SAINT-SÉVIN, JOSEPH BARNABÉ.

Sharp, Granville, 1735–1813.

A short introduction to vocal music. By Granville Sharp. The 2d ed. London: first printed in the year 1767, re-printed in 1777.

iv, 5–32 p. 20^{cm}.

MT870.A2S4

Sherlock, William, *bp. of London, d.* 1707.

A sermon preach'd at St. Paul's cathedral, November 22. 1699. being the anniversary meeting of the Lovers of musick. By W. Sherlock ... London, W. Rogers, 1699.

2 p. l., 27 p. 19½ x 15ᶜᵐ.

ML3001.S43

Shield, William, 1748–1829.

An introduction to harmony, by William Shield. London, Printed for the author & sold by G. G. & J. Robinson, 1800.

3 p. l., 125, [3] p. 31 x 25ᶜᵐ.

Engr. t.-p.

MT50.A2S55

A **short** explication of such foreign words, as are made use of in musick books. London, J. Brotherton, 1724.

93, [3] p. 13½ᶜᵐ.

Appended: "An account of printed musick, for violins, hautboys, flutes and other instruments, by several masters," and "Books printed for J. Brotherton" (24 p.)

ML108.A2S39

See also RULES ... for attaining to play a thorough bass [1715 ?]

Signoretti, P.

Méthode contenant les principes de la musique et du violon, par P. Signoretti. Premiere [-seconde] partie. La Haye, Les freres Williams, 1777.

5 p. l., 3–36 p., 1 l., 41, [1] p. illus., 3 pl. on 2 l. 23½ x 18½ᶜᵐ.

L. of C. copy imperfect, wanting p. 27–30 of part 2 and all of part 3. Ms. signature at end of "Avertissement de l'auteur": P. Signoretti.

MT7.A2S4

Silva, Alberto José Gomes da.

See GOMES DA SILVA, ALBERTO JOSÉ.

Silva, Manuel Nunes da.

See NUNES DA SILVA, MANUEL.

Silva Leite, Antonio da, 1759–1833.

Estudo de guitarra, em que se expoem o meio mais facil para aprender a tocar este instrumento: dividido em duas partes. A primeira contem as principaes regras da musica, e do accompanhamento. A segunda as da guitarra; a que se ajunta huma collecçaõ de minuetes, marchas, allegros, contradanças, e outras peças mais usuaes para desembaraço dos principiantes: tudo com accompanhamento de segunda guitarra ... Por Antonio da Silva Leite ... Porto, Officina typografica de A. Alvarez Ribeiro, 1795.

38, [2], xxiii p. 1 illus. 33½ᶜᵐ.

MT582.A2S53

Rezumo de todas as regras, e preceitos da cantoria, assim da musica metrica, como do canto-chaõ. Dividido em duas partes. Composto por Antonio da Silva Leite ... Para o uso dos seus discipulos. Porto, Officina de A. Alvarez Ribeiro, 1787.

4 p. l., 43, [1] p. 2 pl. (1 fold.) 20½ᶜᵐ.

MT7.A2S58

Simpson, Christopher, *d.* 1669.

A compendium of practical musick in five parts: teaching, by a new, and easie method, 1. The rudiments of song. 2. The principles of composition. 3. The use of discords. 4. The form of figurate descant. 5. The contrivance of canon. By Christopher Simpson ... London, Printed by W. Godbid for H. Brome, 1667.

8 p. l., 176 p. front. (port.) 17½ᶜᵐ.

The 1st edition, London, 1665, has title: The principles of practical musick.

MT40.A2S6

—— A compendium of practical musick in five parts. Teaching, by a new, and easie method, 1. The rudiments of song. 2. The principles of composition. 3. The use of discords. 4. The form of figurate descant. 5. The contrivance of canon. Together with lessons for viols, &c. The 3d editio. By Christopher Simpson ... London, Printed by M. C. for H. Brome, 1678.

7 p. l., 192 p. front. (port.) 17½ᶜᵐ.

"Appendix: Short and easie ayres designed for learners": p. 145–192. .

MT40.A2S63

—— A compendium: or, Introduction to practical musick. In five parts. Teaching, by a new, and easie method, 1. The rudiments of song. 2. The principles of composition. 3. The use of discords. 4. The form of figurate descant. 5. The contrivance of canon. By Christopher Simpson. The 4th ed. with additions: much more correct than any former, the examples being put in the most useful cliffs ... London, Printed by W. Pearson, for J. Cullen, 1706.

7 p. l., 144 p. front. (port.) 17½ᶜᵐ.

MT40.A2S64

—— A compendium; or, Introduction to practical music. In five parts. Teaching, by a new and easy method, 1. The rudiments of song. 2. The principles of composition. 3. The use of discords. 4. The form of figurate descant. 5. The contrivance of canon. By Christopher Sympson. The 6th ed. with additions: much more correct than any former, the examples being put in the most useful cliffs ... London, Printed by W. P. for J. Young, 1714.

7 p. l., 144 p. front. (port.) 18ᶜᵐ.

A slip with printed date 1722 is mounted over imprint date on t.-p.

MT40.A2S66

—— A compendium: or, Introduction to practical music. In five parts. Teaching, by a new and easy method. I. The rudiments of song. II. The principles of composition. III. The use of discords. IV. The form of figurate descant. V. The contrivance of canon. By Christopher Sympson. The 8th ed., with additions: much more correct than any former, the examples being put in the most useful cliffs ... London, Printed by W. Pearson, for A. Bettesworth, and C. Hitch [etc.] 1732.

7 p. l., 144 p. front. (port.) 18ᶜᵐ.

MT40.A2S68

Simpson, Christopher—*Continued.*

—— A compendium, or Introduction to practical music, in five parts. Teaching by a new & easy method, 1.ˢᵗ The rudiments of song. 2.ᵈ The principles of composition.   3.ᵈ The use of discords.   4.ᵗʰ The form of figurate descants.   5.ᵗʰ Yᵉ contrivance of canons.   By Christopher Sympson.   The 9th ed. with material additions, corrected from many gross errors in the former editions, the examples being put in the most useful cliffs . . .   London, Longman, Lukey and co. [1775 ?]

1 p. l., vi, 90 p. front. (port.) 19 x 26ᶜᵐ.

Engraved, with the exception of p. i–vi.

MT40.A2S69

The division-violist: or, An introduction to the playing upon a grovnd: divided into two parts.   The first, directing the hand, with other preparative instructions.   The second, laying open the manner and method of playing ex-tempore, or composing division to a grovnd. To which, are added some divisions made upon grounds for the practice of learners.   By Chr. Simpson.   London, Printed by W. Godbid, and sold by J. Playford, 1659.

5 p. l., 67 p. incl. illus., diagrs. on pl. front. (port.) 30ᶜᵐ.

Pages 51–52 blank in this copy.

The 2d edition, London, 1665, has title: Chelys, minuritionum artificio exornata, sive Minuritiones ad basin, etiam extempore modulandi ratio . . .   The division viol.

MT49.A2S4

See also PLAYFORD, J.   An introduction to the skill of musick.

Smith, Amand Wilhelm.

See SCHMITH, AMAND WILHELM.

Smith, Robert, 1689–1768.

Harmonics, or The philosophy of musical sounds.   By Robert Smith . . .   Cambridge, Printed by J. Bentham, and sold by W. Thurlbourn; [etc., etc.] 1749.

xv, [1], 292, [13] p. xxv fold. pl. (incl. tables, diagrs.) tables (1 fold.) 20½ᶜᵐ.

ML3805.A2S6

—— Harmonics, or The philosophy of musical sounds.   By Robert Smith . . .   2d ed., much improved and augm.   London, Printed for T. and J. Merrill, Cambridge, 1759.

xx, 280, [12] p. xxix fold. pl. (incl. tables, diagrs.) tables (1 fold.) 21ᶜᵐ.

ML3805.A2S62

—— A postscript to Dʳ. Smith's Harmonics, upon the changeable harpsichord: which being supplied with all the useful flat and sharp sounds and tuned in the best manner, is made as harmonious as possible: and yet the execution of music upon this perfect instrument is the same as upon the common harpsichord.   London, Printed for T. and J. Merrill, Cambridge; [etc., etc.] 1762.

12 p. 21ᶜᵐ. (*With his* Harmonics. London, 1759)

ML3805.A2S62

256 LIBRARY OF CONGRESS

Solano, Francisco Ignacio, *d.* 1800.

Dissertação sobre o caracter, qualidades, e antiguidades da musica, em obsequio do admiravel mysterio da Immaculada conceição de Maria santissima, Nossa Senhora, feita por Francisco Ignacio Solano, e por elle recitada no dia 24 de novembro de 1779 para effeito de abrir, e estabelecer nesta corte huma aula de musica theorica, e prática . . . Lisboa, Regia officina typografica, 1780.

27 p. 20½ᶜᵐ.

"Poezias que recitárão na mesma occasião alguns professores musicos": p. 24–27.

ML3800.A2S68

Exame instructivo sobre a musica multiforme, metrica, e rythmica, no qual se pergunta, e dá resposta de muitas cousas interessantes para o solfejo, contraponto, e composiçaõ: seus termos privativos, regras, e preceitos, segundo a melhor pratica, e verdadeira theorica . . . por . . . Francisco Ignacio Solano. Lisboa, Regia officina typografica, 1790.

10 p. l., 289 p., 1 l. 15ᶜᵐ.

MT6.A2S68

Nova arte, e breve compendio de musica para lição dos principiantes, extrahido do livro, que se intitula Nova instrucção musical, ou Theorica pratica da musica rythmica . . . Por . . . Francisco Ignacio Solano. Lisboa, Officina de M. Manescal da Costa, impressor, 1768.

2 p. l., 16 p. 20ᶜᵐ.

MT7.A2S69

—— Nova arte, e breve compendio de musica para lição dos principiantes mais purificada, e accrescentada nesta 2. ed. . . . Por . . . Francisco Ignacio Solano. Lisboa, Officina de S. T. Ferreira, 1794.

16 p. 19ᶜᵐ.

MT7.A2S69

Nova instrucção musical, ou Theorica pratica da musica rythmica, com a qual se fo'rma, e ordena sobre os mais solidos fundamentos hum novo methodo, e verdadeiro systema para constituir hum intelligente solfista, e destrissimo cantor, nomeando as nótas, ou figuras da solfa pelos seus mais proprios, e improprios nomes, a que chamamos ordinarios, e extraordinarios no canto natural, e accidental, de que procede toda a difficuldade da musica . . . Por . . . Francisco Ignacio Solano. Lisboa, Officina de M. Manescal da Costa, impressor, 1764.

30 p. l., 340 p., 1 l., [2], 47, [1] p. illus.; fold. pl. 23 x 17ᶜᵐ.

MT44.A2S68

Novo tratado de musica metrica, e rythmica, o qual ensina a acompanhar no cravo, orgão, ou outro qualquer instrumento, em que se possão regular todas as especies, de que se compõe a harmonia da mesma musica. Demonstra-se este assumpto prática, e theoricamente, e tratão-se tambem algumas cousas parciaes do contraponto, e da composição . . . Por . . . Francisco Ignacio Solano. Lisboa, Regia officina typografica, 1779.

xvi, 301, [1] p. illus. 20½ᶜᵐ.

MT68.A2S68

Soler, Antonio, 1729–1783.

Llave de la modulacion, y antiguedades de la mvsica, en que se trata del fundamento necessario para saber modular: theorica, y práctica para el mas claro conocimiento de qualquier especie de figuras, desde el tiempo de Juan de Muris, hasta hoy, con algunos canones enigmaticos, y sus resoluciones. Su autor el P. Fr. Antonio Solèr . . . Madrid, Oficina de J. Ibarra, 1762.

20 p. l., 272 p. incl. 28 pl. (partly fold.) fold. l. (music) 21 x 16ᶜᵐ.

The plates, each counted as one page only, contain music.

MT52.A2S68

Some observations on Dr. Brown's Dissertation on the rise, union, &c., &c., &c. of poetry and musick. In a letter to Dr. B * * * * * . . . London, W. Johnston, 1764.

2 p. l., 59 p. 24½ x 18½ᶜᵐ.

ML3849.A2B89

Sonnette, Jean Jacques, *pseud.*

See GOUDAR, ANGE.

Sorge, Georg Andreas, 1703–1778.

Anleitung zur fantasie, oder zu der schönen kunst, das clavier, wie auch andere instrumente aus dem kopfe zu spielen; nach theorethischen und practischen grundsåtzen, wie solche die natur des klangs lehret, gestellet von Georg Andreas Sorgen . . . Mit 17. kupfertafeln . . . Lobenstein, Verlag des verfassers [1767]

4 p. l., 80 p. xvii pl. (incl. diagr.) 20½ x 16½ᶜᵐ.

MT68.A2S84

Anweisung zur stimmung und temperatur sowohl der orgelwerke, als auch anderer instrumente, sonderlich aber des claviers. In einem gespräche zwischen einem musico theoretico und seinem scholaren. Mit nöthigen mathematischen beweisthümern versehen, und durch frag und antwort, auch endeckung [!] vieler durch lange praxin erlangter vortheile und handgriffe leicht und deutlich gemacht von Georgio Andrea Sorgen . . . Hamburg, Gedruckt mit Piscators schriften, 1744.

56 p. 18ᶜᵐ.

ML3809.A2S7

Ausführliche und deutliche anweisung zur rational-rechnung, und der damit verknüpfften ausmessung und abtheilung des monochords, vermittelst welcher man die musikalische temperatur . . . nicht nur . . . ausrechnen, sondern auch . . . ausmessen, und folglich auf orgeln und allerhand andere instrumente bringen kan. Nebst einer ausführlichen nachricht von dem neuen Telemannischen intervallen system . . . gesprächs-weise gestellet und ans licht gegeben von Georg Andreas Sorgen . . . Lobenstein, Im verlag des verfassers, 1749.

6 p. l., 308 p. incl. tables. 17½ᶜᵐ.

ML3809.A2S73

258   LIBRARY OF CONGRESS

Sorge, Georg Andreas—*Continued.*

Ausweichungs-tabellen; in welchen auf vierfache art gezeiget wird
wie eine iede tonart in ihre neben-tonarten ausweichen könne / entworffen von herrn Georg Andreas Sorge ...   Nürnberg, J. U. Haffner
[17—]

11 p.   37^cm.

Engraved throughout.   At foot of t.-p.: N.ᵖᵒ LXIV.   Pag. x.

MT52.A2S71

Compendium harmonicum, oder Kurzer begrif der lehre von der
harmonie, vor diejenigen, welche den generalbass und die composition
studiren, in der ordnung welche die natur des klangs an die hand
giebt, verfasset von Georg Andreas Sorge ...   Mit 24. kupfertafeln.
Löbenstein, Im verlag des verfassers, und in commission in Hof bey
Ludwig [1760]

8 p. l., xxiv pl., 121, [3] p.   19½ x 16^cm.

MT50.A2S71

Genealogia allegorica intervallorum octavae diatono-chromaticae,
das ist: Geschlecht-register der intervallen der diatonisch-chromatischen octav in einem verblümten verstande, nach anleitung der klänge
so das grose waldhorn gibt ... von Georgio Andrea Sorgen ...   Hof,
Gedruckt bey J. E. Schultzen auf kosten des auctoris [1741]

4 p. l., 44 p., 1 l.   17^cm.

ML3809.A2S75

Gespräch zwischen einem musico theoretico und einem studioso
musices von der Prätorianischen / Printzischen / Werckmeisterischen
/ Neidhardtischen und Silbermannischen temperatur / wie auch von
dem neuen systemate herrn capellmeister Telemanns / zu beförderung
reiner harmonie entworffen von Georg Andreas Sorgen ...   Lobenstein, Verlag des autoris [1748]

85, [1] p.   16½^cm.

ML3809.A2S8

Der in der rechen- und messkunst wohlerfahrne orgelbaumeister,
welcher die behörige weite und länge aller orgelpfeifen, ihren erforder-
lichen raum, die nöthige metalldicke, die grösse der cancellen und
canäle, die accurate abtheilung der windladen, u. a. m. genau
erforschen und ausmessen kan ... zum nutzen des gemeinen wesens,
wie auch der orgelmacher und probisten neuerbaueter und reparirter
orgelwercke, nebst 5 kupfer-tafeln in folio, beschrieben von Georg
Andreas Sorge ...   [Lobenstein] Auf kosten und im verlag des
verfassers [1773]

ʻ64, [4] p.   diagrs. on v fold. pl.   22 x 18½^cm.

ML552.A2S7

Vorgemach der musicalischen composition, oder: Ausführliche,
ordentliche und vor heutige praxin hinlängliche anweisung zum
general-bass, durch welche ein studiosus musices zu einer gründlichen
erkänntniss aller in der composition und clavier vorkommenden con-
und dissonirenden grund-sätze, und wie mit denenselben natur- gehör-
und kunst-mässig umzugehen, kommen, folglich nicht nur ein gutes

Sorge, Georg Andreas—*Continued.*

clavier als ein compositor extemporaneus spielen lernen, sondern auch in der composition selbst wichtige und gegründete profectus machen kan. Eröffnet von Georgio Andrea Sorgio . . . Lobenstein, Verlag des autoris [1745–47]

3 pt. in 1 v. 98 pl. on 49 l. 21½ x 16¼^{cm}.

Each part has special t.-p. Plates printed on both sides.

MT49.A2S81

Georg Andreas Sorgens . . . Zuverlässige anweisung claviere und orgeln behörig zu temperiren und zu stimmen, nebst einem kupfer, welches die ausmessung und ausrechnung der temperatur, wie auch das Telemannische intervallen-system &c. darstellet; auf veranlassung herrn Barthold Fritzens . . . herausgegebenen Mechanischen art zu stimmen, und zur vertheidigung gegen desselben angrif entworfen . . . Leipzig und Lobenstein, Bey dem autore, und G. F. Authenrieth [1758]

4 p. l., 28 p. fold. pl. 21 x 17½^{cm}.

MT165.A2S6

See also LUDWIG, J. A. J. Eine helle brille [1767]

Sousa Villa Lobos, Mathias de.

Arte de cantochão . . . Composta por Mathias de Sousa Villa-Lobos . . . Coimbra, Officina de M. Rodrigves de Almeyda, 1688.

8 p. l., 214, [4] p. 19 x 14½^{cm}.

MT860.A2S72

South, Robert, 1634–1716.

Musica incantans, sive Poema exprimens musicæ vires, juvenem in insaniam adigentis, et musici inde periculum. Authore Roberto South . . . Oxonii, typis W. H. impensis G. West, 1667.

1 p. l., 19 p. 20 x 15¼^{cm}.

First edition, Oxford, 1655.

ML3920.A2S7

Spangenberg, Johann, 1484–1550.

Qvaestiones mvsicæ in usum scholæ Northusianæ, per Ioann. Spang. Herdess. collectæ. Norimbergæ, apud I. Petreium [1536]

[58] p. 15½^{cm}.

Title vignette: coat of arms. Dedication dated: Northusiæ pridie idus augusti, anno XXXVI. Signatures: A–C in eights, D in five.
"De arte canendi, ex libro decimosexto De subtilitate Hieronymi Cardani Mediolanensis:" [2] p. at end.

ML171.S83

See also AGRICOLA, M. Rvdimenta mvsices, 1539.

Spataro, Giovanni, *d.* 1541.

Tractato di mvsica di Gioanni Spataro mvsico bolognese nel qvale si tracta de la perfectione da la sesqvaltera prodvcta in la mvsica mensvrata exercitate . . . [*Colophon:* Impressa in Vinegia per Maestro Bernardino / de Vitali el di octauo del mese di ottobre M.D.XXXI.]

[118] p. incl. diagrs. 28½^{cm}.

The t.-p., wanting in this copy, is supplied in facsimile. Signatures: 1 l. unsigned, a in two, A in eight, b–h in sixes (except c in seven) i in five.

ML171.S88

Spazier, Johann Gottlieb Carl, 1761–1805, *editor.*

See BERLINISCHE musikalische zeitung, 1794.

Spechtshart, Hugo, *of Reutlingen,* 1285–1359 *or* 60.

Flores Musi ‖ ce omnis cātus ‖ Gregoriani. [*Colophon:* Imp̄ssum Argētine p Johan ‖ nem pryss Anno Mcccclxxxviij]

18½ᶜᵐ.

Hain * 7174 (1)   Proctor 538.
With heliog. facsim. of the "dispositio monocordi," between fol. 27 and 28.
cf. Beck, C., Flores musice . . . neu hrsg., Stuttgart, 1868, p. 8.   Bound in limp vellum (a fragment of a 15th (?) cent. ms. service book)
Of the 2 examples described in Hain, neither agrees with the copy in hand. In this copy the word Argentine in the colophon is printed Argētine, and the last leaf (97) has on verso a full page woodcut.

ML171.H84

Speer, Daniel, *d.* 1693 *or* 4.

Grund-richtiger / kurtz / leicht und nôthiger unterricht der musicalischen kunst / wie man fûglich und in kurtzer zeit choral und figural singen / den general-bass tractiren / und componiren lernen soll. Denen lehr- und lernenden zu beliebigem gebrauch / herauss gegeben von Daniel Speeren . . . Ulm / G. W. Kûhne / 1687.

144 p.   fold. tab.   16½ᶜᵐ.

Running title: Musicalische fragstuck.

MT6.A2S7

Spiess, Meinrad, 1683–1761.

Tractatus musicus compositorio-practicus. Das ist, Musicalischer tractat, in welchem alle gute und sichere fundamenta zur musicalischen composition aus denen alt- und neuesten besten autoribus herausgezogen . . . und deutlich erlâutert werden . . . Samt einem anhang in welchem fast alle . . . in griechisch- lateinisch- welsch- frantzôsisch- und teutscher sprach gebrâuchliche kunst- und andere gewôhnlich-vorkommende wôrter nach ordnung des alphabets gesetzt, und erklâret werden. Hrsg. von r. p. Meinrado Spiess . . . Opus VIII. Augspurg, J. J. Lotters seel. erben, 1746.

8 p. l., 220, [8], 11, [1] p.   front.   33ᶜᵐ.

"Specification aller meiner musicalischen wercken, so im druck heraus seynd": [1] p. at end.

MT40.A2S85

Sponsel, Johann Ulrich, 1721–1788.

Johann Ulrich Sponsels . . . Orgelhistorie.   Nûrnberg, G. P. Monath, 1771.

167 p.   18 x 10½ᶜᵐ.

Title vignette.

ML552.A2S8

[Steffani, Agostino] 1654–1728.

Quanta certezza habbia da suoi principii la musica et ·in qual pregio fosse perciò presso gli antichi.   Amsterdam, 1695.

72 p.   14½ᶜᵐ.

A second title is given on p. 3: Risposta di D. A. Steffani . . . ad vna lettera del Sʳ. marchᵉ. A. G. in difesa d'vna proposizione sostenuta da lui in vna assemblea hannovera sett. 1694.

ML3800.A2S79

[Steffani, Agostino]—*Continued.*

—— D. A. Steffani . . . send-schreiben / darinn enthalten wie grosse gewissheit die music aus ihren principiis, und grund-såtzen habe / und in welchen werthe / und wůrckung sie bey denen alten gewesen / aus dem italienischen ins hochdeutsche befőrdert; dann um der wůrde und nutzen so darinnen enthalten / mit einigen anmerckungen erlåu-tert / und dem druck übergeben von Andr. Werckmeister . . . Qued-linburg und Aschersleben, G. E. Struntz, 1700.

101, [1] p. 16½ᶜᵐ.

ML3800.A2S81

[Steinberg, Christian Gottlieb] 1738–1781.

Betrachtungen über die kirchen-music und heiligen gesånge derer rechtglåubigen, und ihrem nutzen. Breslau und Leipzig, D. Piet-schische buchhandlung, 1766.

125 p. 17½ᶜᵐ.

"Beurtheilung der Allbrechtischen abhandlung von der kirchen-music": p. [7]–19.

ML3001.S73

[Stillingfleet, Benjamin] 1702–1771.

Principles and power of harmony . . . London, Printed by J. and H. Hughs and sold by S. Baker and G. Leigh [etc.] 1771.

vii, [1], 154, [6] p. fold. pl. 22½ x 17ᶜᵐ.

An analysis of Tartini's "Trattato di musica."

ML3836.A2S8

[Stölzel, Gottfried Heinrich] 1690–1749.

Practischer beweiss, wie aus einem nach dem wahren fundamente solcher noten-kůnsteleyen gesetzten canone perpetuo in hypo dia pente quatuor vocum, viel und mancherley, theils an melodie, theils auch nur an harmonie, unterschiedene canones perpetui à 4 zu machen seyn. Der warheit, und einigen music-freunden zu gefallen, dem druck überlassen, von G. H. S. [n. p.] 1725.

[24] p. 20½ x 17ᶜᵐ.

MT59.A2S8

Stohrius, Johannes Mauritius, *praeses.*

. . . Organum musicum, historice extructum . . . Lipsiæ, literis J. Georg [1693]

[16] p. 17½ᶜᵐ.

Diss.—Leipzig (Johannes Schiecke, respondent)

ML64.S86

Straet, Jan van der, *d.* 1605.

Enconivm mvsices quod Sacris Litteris concinnabat Philip. Gallæus. Iconibus exprimebat pictor celeberrimus Io. Stradanus. Versibus illustrabat doctissimus Io. Bochius, urbi Antverp. à secretis. Ant-verpiæ, apud Philippum Gallæum [ca. 1600]

2 p. l., 18 pl. (incl. t.-p.) 25½ x 32½ᶜᵐ.

Straet, Jan van der—*Continued.*

Engr. title, with illustration consisting of 3 figures, Mvsica, Harmonia, and Mensvra; in the background musical instruments, mostly those in use in the 16th century, and in center an open book showing a complete motet for six voices, "Nata et grata polo." The inscription is from Psalm 150, "Laudate Eum. in sono tubæ [etc.]" The title is at top of page, and at foot is the dedication "Amplissimis ornatissimisqve d. d. Edvardo vander Dilft et Carolo Malineo civitatis Antverpiae consvlibvs Philppvs [!] Gallaevs d. d.—Title-page, verso blank.—Preface, "Philippvs Gallævs ad artis mvsicæ stvdiosos," p. 1. [2] r°. Verso blank.—Plates, numbered 3–18, each with Latin hexameter verse paraphrasing a text from the Vulgate at foot.—Unnumbered plate illustrating Luke xv, 7, with the corresponding verse from the Vulgate.

Plates 3–15, 17, are signed: "Ioan. Stradan. inuent. Adrian. Collaert sculp. Phls. Galle excudit" (form of signature varies slightly, and Collaert's name does not appear on pl. 5, 10, 12, 13, 17) On pl. 16: "Ioan. Stradan. inuent. Theodor. Galle sculpsit"; pl. 18: "Ioan. Stradan. inuent." Last pl. has "Marti. de Vos inuen. Phls. Gall. excud."

ML467.A2S7

Strodtmann, Johann Christoph, 1717–1756.

See ABHANDLUNG von den pantomimen, 1749.

Stryk, Elias August, *d.* 1733, *praeses.*

... Disputatio juridica de eo quod justum est, circa ludos scenicos operasqve modernas, dictas vulgò operen ... Kiloni, typis J. Reumanni [1693]

63, [1] p.   18 x 15½ᶜᵐ.

Diss.—Kiel (G. von Bertuch, respondent and author)

ML1703.A2B35

Studien für tonkünstler und musikfreunde. Eine historisch-kritische zeitschrift mit neun und dreissig musikstücken von verschiedenen meistern fürs jahr 1792, in zwei theilen herausgegeben von F. Ae. Kunzen und J. F. Reichardt. Berlin, Im verlage der Neuen musikhandlung, 1793.

2 pt. in 1 v. (2 p. 1., 191, [1], 172 p.)   25 x 21ᶜᵐ.

Reissue with new t.-p. and preface, of two periodicals, the Musikalisches wochenblatt, 1791–92, and the Musikalische monathsschrift, 1792.

ML4.S92

Sueur, Jean François le.

See LE SUEUR, JEAN FRANÇOIS.

Suire, Robert Martin le.

See LESUIRE, ROBERT MARTIN.

Sulzer, Johann Georg, 1720–1779.

Allgemeine theorie der schönen künste, in einzeln, nach alphabetischer ordnung der kunstwörter auf einander folgenden, artikeln abgehandelt, von Johann George Sulzer ... Neue verm. 2. aufl. Leipzig, Weidmannsche buchhandlung, 1792–99.

5 v.   front., illus., fold. pl., 6 fold. 1.   22ᶜᵐ.

The 6 fold. leaves, in vol. 4, contain 39 musical examples.
Ed. by C. F. von Blankenburg. The articles relating to music are by J. A. P. Schulz and J. P. Kirnberger.

ML3845.A2S9

Suremain de Missery, Antoine, 1767–1852.

Théorie acoustico-musicale, ou de la doctrine des sons rapportée aux principes de leur combinaison. Ouvrage analytique et philosophique. Par A. Suremain-Missery . . . Paris, F. Didot, 1793.

9 p. l., [ix]–xxxvj, [37]–404 p. fold. pl. 20^{cm}.

ML3805.A2S9

Sweerts, Pierre François, 1567–1629, *editor.*

See MAGGI, G. De tintinnabvlis liber.

Symmes, Thomas, 1678–1725.

Utile dulci. Or, A joco-serious dialogue, concerning regular singing: calculated for a particular town, (where it was publickly had, on Friday Oct. 12. 1722.) but may serve some other places in the same climate. By Thomas Symmes . . . Boston: Printed by B. Green, for S. Gerrish, in Cornhill, 1723.

1 p. l., ii, 59 p. 15^{cm}.

ML3869.S98

[Tabourot, Jean] 1519–1595.

Orchesographie. Et traicte en forme de dialogve, par leqvel tovtes personnes pevvent facilement apprendre & practiquer l'honneste exercice des dances. Par Thoinot Arbeau [*pseud*] . . . Lengres, Imprimé par Iehan des Preyz [1589]

104 numb. l. illus. 21^{cm}.

Thoinot Arbeau is an anagram for Jehan Tabourot.
Includes a large number of dance tunes, with words fitted to the melodies.

GV1590.T3

Tacet, Joseph.

See COMPLEAT instructions for the German flute.

Tans'ur, William, *d.* 1783.

The elements of musick display'd: or, its grammar, or ground-work made easy: rudimental, practical, philosophical, historical, and technical. In five books. Containing, I. An universal introduction to all the rudiments of musick . . . II. Of time, in all its various moods . . . III. The structure of musical instruments . . . With sacred lessons; songs in parts; and tunes for instruments. IV. The theory of sound . . . with the principles of composition, in all its branches. V. A new musical-dictionary . . . By William Tans'ur, senior . . . London, Printed for S. Crowder; and sold by the author, and his son, 1772.

xiii, [1], 232 p. illus. 21^{cm}.
Preface dated 1766. Books II–V have each special t.-p.

MT6.A2T16

A new musical grammar: or, The harmonical spectator. Containing all the useful theoretical, practical, and technical parts of musick. Being a new and correct introduction to all the rudiments, terms, and characters, and composition in all its branches. With several scales

Tans'ur, William—*Continued.*

for musical instruments; and philosophical demonstrations, on the nature of sound. Laid down in so concise and easy a method, as to be understood by the meanest practitioner, whether vocal or instrumental, by way of question and answer ... By William Tansur ... Printed for the author, and sold by him, and in London, by J. Robinson, 1746.

1 p. l., iv, [2], 156 p. incl. 14 pl., diagrs. 17^{cm}.

MT7.A2T16

—— A new musical grammar, and dictionary: or, A general introduction to the whole art of musick. In four books ... The whole is extracted from the best authors, both ancient, and modern; and methodically digested to every capacity ... 3d ed., with large additions. By William Tans'ur, senior ... London, Printed by R. Brown, for J. Hodges; also sold by the author; and by his son, 1756.

xii, [4], 176 p. illus. 19½^{cm}.

Books II–IV have each special t.-p.

MT6.A2T13

Tapia, Martín de, *b.* 1542?

... Vergel de mvsica ‖ spiritual speculatiua y actiua. del ‖ qual, muchas, diuersas y suaues flores se puedē coger. Dirigi- ‖ do al yllustrissimo y Reuerēdissimo Señor dō Frācisco Tello ‖ de San Doual Obispo de Osmay del Cōsejo de su Magestad ‖ ℂ Autor el Bachiller Tapia Numantino. ‖ ℂ Tratase lo primero con grāde artificio y profundidad, las ‖ alabanças, las gracias, la dignidad, Las virtudes y prerrogati- ‖ uas dela musica y despues, Las artes de Cantollano, Organo y Contrapūto, en suma y en Theorica. ℂ Esta tassado cada volumē en papel A tres Reales. [*Colophon:* ... Se ‖ acabo de imprimir el presēte libro ... el q̄l fue impresso ēla Incly ‖ ta vniuersidad dela Villa del Burgo de Osma por Diego ‖ Fernandez de Cordoua impressor. Acabose a veynte y ocho ‖ dias del mes de Mayo, Año de nuestra redemp ‖ cion de mil y quiniētos y setenta años]

4 p. l., cxx numb. l. diagrs. 19½^{cm}.

Contains three approbations, the first undated, the others dated 1559.
At head of title the arms of the bishops of Osmay, surrounded by quotations from the Psalms (32, 149, 95, 67) within line borders. Printer's mark following colophon on recto of last leaf. Leaves liv and lxxi numbered lv and lxxxvij respectively.

ML171.T17

Tartini, Giuseppe, 1692–1770.

De' principj dell' armonia musicale contenuta nel diatonico genere, dissertazione di Giuseppe Tartini. Padova, Stamperia del Seminario, 1767.

6 p. l., 120 p. 24½^{cm}.

Title vignette; initial; head-piece.

ML3815.A2T19

Tartini, Giuseppe—*Continued.*

Traité des agrémens de la musique, contenant l'origine de la petite note, sa valeur, la maniere de la placer, toutes les differentes especes de cadences, la maniere de les employer, le tremblement et le mordant,˙ l'usage, qu'on en peut faire, les modes ou agrémens naturels, les modes artifficiels qui vont à l'infini, la maniere de former un point d'orgue . . . composé par le célebre Giuzeppe Tartini . . . et tr. par le Sig.ʳ P. Denis. Paris, Chez l'auteur [1782]

1 p. l., 94 p. 23ᶜᵐ.

Engraved throughout.
"Never published in the original Italian."—Vander Straeten, The romance of the fiddle, 1911.

MT80.A2T2

Trattato di musica secondo la vera scienza dell' armonia. Padova, Nella stamperia del Seminario, appresso G. Manfrè, 1754.

4 p. l., 175, [1] p. fold. pl., diagrs. 24½ᶜᵐ.

Title vignette.
Tartini is given as author in a preface by Decio Agostino Trento, who published the work.

ML3805.A2T2

[Tate, Nahum] 1652–1715.

An essay for promoting of psalmody. London, J. Holland, 1710.

5 p. l., 38 p. 16½ᶜᵐ.

Dedication signed: N. Tate.

ML3001.T16

[Tauber von Taubenfurt, Johann Nepomuk, *freiherr*]

Uiber meine violine . . . Wien, Bey Joseph edlen von Kurzböck [1780]

188 p. illus. 17ᶜᵐ.

Title vignette.
"Reflexionen des kapellmeisters": p. 28–188.

ML66.A2T2

Taylor, Dan, 1738–1816.

A dissertation on singing in the worship of God: interspersed with occasional strictures on Mr. Boyce's late tract, entitled, "Serious thoughts on the present mode and practice of singing in the public worship of God." By Dan Taylor . . . London, Printed for the author, and sold by J. Buckland [etc., 1786]

v, 7–72 p. 17½ᶜᵐ.

ML3001.T18

A second dissertation on singing in the worship of God; introduced with two letters to the Revᵈ. Mr. Gilbert Boyce, in defence of a former dissertation on that subject. By Dan Taylor . . . London, J. Buckland [etc.] 1787.

77 p. 18½ᶜᵐ.

ML3001.T183

Taylor, John, 1704–1766.

The music speech at the public commencement in Cambridge, July 6, MDCCXXX. To which is added, an ode designed to have been set to music on that occasion. By John Taylor . . . London, Printed by W. Bowyer, jun., and sold by W. Thurlbourn, Cambridge; [etc., etc.] 1730.

26 p. 19½ᶜᵐ.

Ch. 33

Telemann, Georg Michael, 1748–1831.

Georg Michael Telemanns . . . Unterricht im generalbass-spielen, auf der orgel oder sonst einem clavier-instrumente. Hamburg, M. C. Bock, 1773.

112 p. 20 x 17ᶜᵐ.

MT182.A2T3

Telemann, Georg Philipp, 1681–1767, *editor.*

See HALTMEIER, C. J. F. Anleitung, 1737.

Telemann, Georg Philipp, 1681–1767, *translator.*

See CASTEL, L. B. Beschreibung der augen-orgel, 1739.

[Teller, Wilhelm Abraham] 1734–1804.

Kurze wahrhafte geschichte der ältesten deutschen kirchengesänge, besonders von D. Martin Luther. Zur heilsamen anwendung auf das für die königlich preussischen lande bestimmte allgemeine gesangbuch. Berlin, Bey Unger dem jüngern, 1781.

35 p. 16ᶜᵐ.

Signed: Willhelm Abraham Teller.

Ch.17.1896

[Tempelhof, Georg Friedrich von] 1737–1807.

Gedanken über die temperatur des herrn Kirnberger, nebst einer anweisung, orgeln, claviere, flügel, &c. &c. auf eine leichte art zu stimmen, von G. F. T. einem liebhaber der music. Berlin und Leipzig, G. J. Decker, 1775.

37 p. 17ᶜᵐ.

ML3809.A2T28

Teralbo Timate.

Gl' elementi generali della musica esposti, e spiegati con metodo sistematico per uso de' giovanetti principianti, con diverse figure in rame, da Teralbo Timate, accademico augusto delle buone arti, e socio letterario vmbro; dati in luce da N. N. In grazia de' signori dilettanti. Roma, A. Casaletti, 1792.

xij, 103 p. 7 pl. on 4 fold. l., 2 fold. tab. 18ᶜᵐ.

MT7.A2T58

[Terrasson, Antoine] 1705–1782.

Dissertation historique sur la vielle; où l'on éxamine l'origine & les progrès de cet instrument. Avec une digression sur l'histoire de la musique ancienne & moderne. Dediée à Mademoiselle de * * * par M. * * * Paris, J. B. Lamesle, 1741.

6 p. l., 104, [4] p.   18 x 10ᶜᵐ.

ML760.A2T38

Tessarini, Carlo, *b.* 1690.

A musical grammar which teaches an easy and short method of learning to play to perfection the violin in parts. Divided in two books. With all the necessary figures, lessons, sonnets, for the use of all the tones in music, with the measures and the touches of all the sounds that can possibly be expressed on the violin . . . by Carlo Tessarini . . . Edinburgh, N. Stewart [176– ?]

18 p.   pl.   22½ x 31ᶜᵐ.

Engraved throughout. At end: "End of book first."
Published originally in Italian, Rome, 1741 (?)

MT262.A2T3

Testori, Carlo Giovanni, 1714–1782.

La musica ragionata espressa famigliarmente in dodici passeggiate a dialogo; opera di Carlo Giovanni Testori . . . per cui si giungerà . . . all' acquisto del vero contrappunto. Vercelli, G. Panialis, 1767.

4 p. l., cli, [1] p.   22 pl.   24 x 18½ᶜᵐ.

Title within ornamental border.

MT55.A2T34

—— Primi rudimenti della musica e supplemento alla Musica ragionata, opera di Carlo Giovanni Testori . . . Libro secondo. Vercelli, Nelle stampe di G. Panialis, 1771.

2 p. l., lxx p.   6 pl.   24½ x 19½ᶜᵐ.

The third work in the series was published in 1773 as "Supplemento alla Musica ragionata . . . Libro terzo".

MT55.A2T35

——- L'arte di scrivere a otto reali, e supplemento alla Musica ragionata, opera di Carlo Giovanni Testori . . . Libro quarto. Vercelii, G. Panialis, 1782.

3 p. l., [iii]–lvi p.   26 fold. pl. ("pag. 1–29")   25 x 19½ᶜᵐ.

Added t.-p., engr.: Esempi della Musica ragionata di Carlo Giō Testori.

MT55.A2T37

Tettamanzi, Fabrizio, *b. ca.* 1650.

Breve metodo per fondatamente, e con facilità apprendere il canto fermo. Diuiso in trè libri. Nel primo si pongono breuemente le regole del medesimo canto, con il modo di pratticarle. Nel secondo il modo di cantare l'hore canoniche, all' vso francescano, e romano. Nel terzo si pone l'officio in canto di tutta la Settimana santa. Del padre F. Fabricio Tettamanzi . . . Milano, Per F. Agnelli scultore, e stampatore, 1636 [*i. e.* 1686]

148 p.   illus.   22½ x 17½ᶜᵐ.

MT860.A2T31

Tettamanzi, Fabrizio—*Continued.*

—— Breve metodo per apprendere fondatamente e con facilita' ii canto fermo; diviso in tre libri, nel primo si pongono brevemente le regole del medesimo canto, con il modo di praticarle: nel secondo, il modo di cantare l'ore canoniche; nel terzo, si pone l'officio in canto di tutta la Settimana santa. Del padre F. Fabrizio Tettamanzl . . . Milano, Per B. Sirtori, stampatore arcivescovile, ad istanza di G. Galleazzi libraro, 1756.

155, [1] p. illus. 22 x 16½cm.

3d edition.

MT860.A2T34

Tevo, Zaccaria, b. 1651.

Il mvsico testore del p: bac: Zaccaria Tevo . . . Venezia, A. Bortoli, 1706.

7 p. l., 366, [2] p. illus., 2 pl. 24½ x 17½cm.

Engr. t.-p. with ornamental border. Added t.-p., engr., with port. of the author.

MT6.A2T42

Thalesio, Pedro.

Arte de canto chão, com hvma breve instrvcção pera os sacerdotes, diaconos, subdiaconos, & moços do coro, conforme ao vso romano. Composta, & ordenada' por o mestre Pedro Thalesio . . . Agora nesta segunda impressão nouamente emendada, & aperfeiçoada pello mesmo autor . . . Coimbra, Na impressão de D. Gomez de Louveiro, 1628.

6 p. l., 136 p. illus. 20cm.

Title vignette: ecclesiastical coat of arms.

MT860.A2T42

[Thielo, Carl August] 1702–1763.

Grund-regeln wie man, beÿ weniger information, sich selbst die fundamenta der music und des claviers, lernen kan, beschrieben, mit exempeln in noten gezeiget und verlegt von C. A. T. Erster theil. [Kopenhagen, 1753]

1 p. l., 81 p. 16 x 21cm.

No more published.
According to Fétis this is an abridged translation of Thielo's "Tanker og regler fra grunden af om musiken," Copenhagen, 1746.

MT224.A2T43

Thomas, Christian Gottfried, 1748–1806.

Praktische beyträge zur geschichte der musik, musikalischen litteratur und gemeinen besten, bestehend vorzüglich in der einrichtung eines öffentlichen allgemeinen und ächten verlags musikalischer manuscripte, zum vortheil derer hrn. verfasser und käufer; wie auch in andern litterarischen abhandlungen, die musik betreffend. Hrsg. von Christian Gottfried Thomas . . . Erste sammlung. Leipzig, Verlag des verfassers, 1778.

64 p. 23 x 19cm.

No more published.

ML112.A2T45

Tigrini, Orazio.

Il compendio della mvsica, nel qvale brevemente si tratta dell' arte del contrapunto, diviso in qvatro libri. Del r. m. Oratio Tigrini . . . Nouamente composto, & dato in luce . . . Venetia, R. Amadino, 1588.

6 p. l., 135, [1] p. 21 x 16^{cm}.

Title within ornamental border; title vignette.

ML171.T47

—— Il compendio della mvsica, nel qvale brevemente si tratta dell' arte del contrapvnto, diuiso in quattro libri. Del r. m. Oratio Tigrini . . . Di nouo con diligentia corretto, & ristampato . . . Venetia, R. Amadino, 1602.

4 p. l., 135, [1] p. 21½ x 15½^{cm}.

Title vignette.

MT55.A2T56

Til, Salomon van, 1644–1713.

Digt- sang- en speel-konst, soo der ouden, als bysonder der Hebreen, door een nauwkeurig ondersoek der oudheyd uyt sijn vorige duysterheyt wederom opgeheldert: dienende, om, by wege van een voorlooper, den leser tot een beter verstand der goddelijke Psalmen, en netter begrip van haar ware gebruyk onder de beyde Testamenten op te leyden: door Salomon van Til . . . Dordrecht, D. Goris, 1706.

14 p. l., 533, [15] p. illus. 20½^{cm}.

Title vignette.
1st edition, Dordrecht, 1692.

ML166.A2T55

—— Digt- sang- en speel-konst, soo der ouden, als bysonder der Hebreen, door een nauwkeurig ondersoek der oudheyd uyt sijn voorige duysterheyd wederom opgeheldert: dienende, om, by wege van een voorlooper, den leser tot een beter verstand der goddelijke Psalmen, en netter begrip van haar waare gebruyk onder de beyde Testamenten op te leyden: door Salomon van Til . . . Amsterdam, A. Schoonenburg, 1725.

14 p. l., 533, [15] p. illus., 5 pl. (1 fold.) 20½ x 16^{cm}.

The illustrations are printed from engr. plates.

ML166.A2T57

—— Dicht- sing- und spiel-kunst / so wohl der alten / als ins besonder der Hebreer. Durch neusgierige untersuchung der antiquitåt aus ihrer vorigen dunckelheit wieder auffgeklåret: als vorlaüffer d' göttlichē Psalmen / zu dero besserem verstand dem leser dienend und zum deutlicherm begriff ihres gebrauchs unter beyden Testamenten anleitung zu geben durch Salomon von Til . . . Franckfurt/M. Groot ' 1706.

9 p. l., 478, [16] p. illus., fold. pl. 21 x 16½^{cm}.

ML166.A2T56

Tilesius von Tilenau, Nathanael, 1565–1616.

Christliche vnd gründliche erweisung dass die musica vnd singe-
kunst Gott wolgefellig / vnd mit gleubiger andacht / in kirchen vnd
häusern möge gebraucht werden.   In einer hochzeitpredigt gehandelt
. . .   Gehalten zu Stroppen / den 13. novembris anno 1596, vnd
jetzt . . . in druck verfertiget durch Nathanaelem Tilesium . . .   [n. p.]
Gedruckt im jahr 1599.

[20] p.   19½ᶜᵐ.

ML3001.T57

Tinctoris, Joannes, *d.* 1511.

See FORKEL, J. N.   Allgemeine litteratur der musik, 1792.

Todd, John, *d.* 1812.

An humble attempt towards the improvement of psalmody: the
propriety, necessity and use, of evangelical psalms, in Christian worship.   Delivered at a meeting of the Presbytery of Hanover in Vir-
ginia, October 6th, 1762.   By John Todd . . .   Philadelphia: Printed
by A. Steuart, 1763.

40 p.   16½ᶜᵐ.

[Hazard pamphlets, v. 10, no. 5]

AC901.H3

Töpfer, Johann Christian Carl, *b.* 1740 ?

Anfangsgründe zur erlernung der musik und insonderheit des
claviers, durch eigenen fleiss und erfahrung aufgesetzet und mit einer
kritischen vorrede begleitet von Johann Christian Carl Töpfer . . .
Bresslau, W. G. Korn, 1773.

xii, [13]–44 p.   3 fold. pl. (music)   20 x 16ᶜᵐ.

MT7.A2T6

Tollius, Jacobus, *d.* 1696.

See BACCHINI, B.   De sistris, 1696.

Tomás de Santa María, *d.* 1570.

Libro llamado Arte de tañer fantasia, assi para tecla como para
vihuela, y todo instruméto, en que se pudiere tañer a tres, y a quatro
vozes, y a mas . . .   Elqual por mandado del muy alto Consejo real
fue examinado, y aprouado por el eminête musico de Su Magestad
Antonio de Cabeçon, y por Iuan de Cabeçon, su hermano.   Compuesto por el muy reuerendo padre fray Thomas de Sancta Maria . . .
Valladolid, Impresso por F. Fernandez de Cordoua, 1565.

4 p. l., 90, 124 numb. l.   28½ᶜᵐ.

Title vignette.

ML171.T65

Tomeoni, Florido, 1757 ?–1820.

Théorie de la musique vocale, ou des dix règles qu'il faut connaître
et observer pour bien chanter ou pour apprendre à juger par soi-même
du degré de perfection de ceux que l'on entend; par Florido Tomeoni
. . .   Avec des remarques sur la prononciation des langues française et
italienne, rédigées par un homme de lettres.   Paris, Chez l'auteur
[etc.] an VII [1799]

viij, 138, 2–5 p., 1 l.   19½ᶜᵐ.

MT820.A2T76

Tomeoni, Pellegrino, b. 1729.

Regole pratiche per accompagnare il basso continuo esposte in dialoghi per facilitare il possesso alla principiante gioventù da Pellegrino Tomeoni . . . Firenze, A. G. Pagani, e comp., 1795.

44 p. 22ᶜᵐ.

Pages 17-18, 21-22, 25-26, 31-32, 37-38, 43-44 (musical examples) are printed on leaves 31½ x 21½ᶜᵐ.

MT49.T65

[Toneellief, Willem] *pseud.?*

Missive van een heer in Leijden, aan zyn vriend in's Gravenhaage, vervattende eenige nieuwigheeden, betreffende de Amsteldamsche en Rotterdamsche schouwburgen, benevens een nette origineele lyst en staat der muziciens, acteurs, actrices, dansers . . . enz. zoo als die voor beide de schouburgen geangageert zyn om het toneel te openen, benevens hunne naamen en de characters waar voor zy in't vervolg zullen speelen, gevolgt van iets het geen de Hoogduitsche en Vlaamsche operas betreft.   Monnikendam, By de Gorter; [etc., etc., 1774]

8 p. 18½ᶜᵐ.

Signed: Willem Toneellief. Dated: Leijden den 14 Augustus 1774.

ML1735.3.A2T7

Torino, Illuminato da.

See ILLUMINATO *da Torino*.

Torres Martínez Bravo, José de, 1665–1738.

Reglas generales de acompañar, en organo, clavicordio, y harpa, con solo saber cantar la parte, ó vn baxo en canto figurado.   Distribvidas en tres partes.   En la primera, se enseñan los fundamentos, que deben preceder al acompañar, en la segunda el modo de acompañar, vsando solo de especies consonantes, y en la tercera el modo de practicar las especies falsas . . . Compuestas por Don Joseph de Torres . . . Madrid, Imprenta de mvsica, 1702.

8 p. l., 143, [12] p.   21ᶜᵐ.

MT49.A2T7

—— Reglas generales de acompañar, en organo, clavicordio, y harpa, con solo saber cantar la parte, o un baxo en canto figurado. Distribuidas en tres partes . . . Añadido aora un nuevo tratado, donde se explica el modo de acompañar las obras de musica, segun el estilo italiano. Compuestas por Don Joseph de Torres Martinez Bravo . . . Madrid, Imprenta de musica, 1736.

4 p. l., 124, [3] p.   illus.   21 x 28½ᶜᵐ.

MT49.A2T72

Torres Martínez Bravo, José de, 1665–1738, *editor.*

See NASSARRE, P.   Fragmentos musicos, 1700.

[Toscan, G. L. George] 1756–1826.

De la musique et de Nephté.   Aux manes de l'abbé Arnaud.   Paris, Imprimerie de Monsieur, 1790.

2 p. l., 28 p.   20½ᶜᵐ.

ML3920.A2T7

Tosi, Pietro Francesco, *ca.* 1650–*ca.* 1731.

Opinioni de' cantori antichi, e moderni, o sieno Osservazioni sopra il canto figurato di Pierfrancesco Tosi . . . Dedicate a Sua Eccellenza Mylord Peterborough . . . [Bologna, L. dalla Volpe, 1723]

3 p. l., 118 p. 18ᶜᵐ.

This copy is without imprint and contains the dedication to Lord Peterborough.
For variations in the different copies of this edition *see* Gaspari's catalogue of the
Liceo musicale of Bologna.

MT820.A2T72

—— Observations on the florid song; or, Sentiments on the ancient and modern singers. Written in Italian by Pier. Francesco Tosi . . . Tr. into English by Mr. Galliard . . . To which are added, explanatory annotations, and examples in musick . . . 2d ed. London, J. Wilcox, 1743.

xviii, [2], 184 p. vi fold. pl. 17ᶜᵐ.

"A prefatory discourse giving some account of the author": p. [vii]–xiii.

MT820.A2T73

—— Anleitung zur singkunst. Aus dem italiånischen des herrn Peter Franz Tosi . . . mit erlåuterungen und zusåtzen von Johann Friedrich Agricola . . . Berlin, Gedruckt bey G. L. Winter, 1757.

xvi, 239 p. 21 x 17ᶜᵐ.

Title vignette; head and tail pieces.

MT820.A2T74

Tovar, Francisco.

Libro de mu ‖ sica pratica Compuesto por ‖ mosz Francisco touar: di ‖ rigido al illustrissimo y ‖ reuerédissimo senyor ‖ dō Enrique de Car ‖ dōa obispo d'Bar ‖ celona. y a su insi ‖ gno capitulo. [*Colophon:* ℂ La presente obra fue compuesta por mossen Francisco to ‖ uar de la villa de Pareia Imprimida en la insigne ‖ cibdad de Barçelona por maestre Johan Rosē ‖ bach aleman a. v. de Janero anyo de mil y ‖ quinientos y diez]

4 p. l., xxxv numb. l. diagrs. 28ᶜᵐ.

Title in red; printer's mark at end. The musical notes and clefs are in ms. on printed staves.

ML171.T73

Towerson, Gabriel, *d.* 1697.

A sermon concerning vocal and instrumental musick in the church. As it was delivered in the parish church of St. Andrew Undershaft, upon the 31ᵗʰ of May, 1696, being Whit-Sunday, and the day wherein the organ there erected was first made use of. By Gabriel Towerson, D. D. London, B. Aylmer, 1696.

30 p. 18½ x 15ᶜᵐ.

ML3001.T78

Tractatvs mvsices.

See COMPENDIŨ musices.

[Travenol, Louis] *d.* 1783.

Les entrepreneurs entrepris, ou Complainte d'un musicien opprimé par ses camarades, adressée aux protecteurs et aux protectrices des sciences & des beaux arts. [Paris, Impr. de S. Jorry, 1758]

40 p. 19½ᶜᵐ.

Caption title: Memoire pour le sieur Travenol . . . Contre le sieur Mondon-ville, ex-musicien du roi, le sieur Capperan, ex-musicien de l'Opéra, & la dame Rover, tous trois entrepreneurs & directeurs du Concert spirituel.
This copy has ms. notes and inscription on t.-p.: "A Monsieur l'abbé de la Porte." On fly-leaf at end: "Chanson nouvelle, sur l'air, Or ecoutés petits et grands."

ML1727.8.P2T8

La galerie de l'Académie royale de musique, contenant les portraits, en vers, des principaux sujets, qui la composent en la présente année 1754. Dédiée à Jean Jacques Rousseau . . . Par un zelé partisan de son systême sur la musique françoise. [Paris] 1754.

62 p. 17½ x 10ᶜᵐ.

ML1727.33.T7

Histoire du Théatre de l'opera en France. Depuis l'établissement de l'Académie royale de musique, jusqu'à présent . . . Paris, J. Barbou, 1753.

2 v. in 1 (v. 1: 4 p. l., 264 p.; v. 2: 1 p. l., 221, [3] p.) 20ᶜᵐ.

Vol. 2 dated M.LCC.LIII. Dedication signed: D ✱ ✱ ✱
By Durey de Noinville and Louis Travenol.

ML1727.3.D8

—— Histoire du théatre de l'Académie royale de musique en France, depuis son établissement jusqu'à présent. 2. éd., cor. & augm. des pieces qui ont été représentées sur le Théâtre de l'opera par les musiciens italiens, depuis le premier août 1752. jusqu'à leur départ en 1754. avec un extrait de ces piéces & des ecrits qui ont paru à ce sujet . . . Paris, Duchesne, 1757.

2 v. in 1 (v. 1: 6, [8], 320 p.; v. 2: 1 p. l., 221, [3], 221–222 p., 1 l., 11 p.) 20ᶜᵐ.

Dedication signed: D ✱ ✱ ✱

ML1727.3.A2D82

Œuvres mêlées du sieur ✱ ✱ ✱, ouvrage en vers et en prose, contenant des remarques curieuses sur les mystères de la confrairie des Francs-maçons, sur la Lettre de J. J. Rousseau, contre la musique françoise, & sur le Dialogue de Pégaze & du vieillard, par M. de Voltaire. Amsterdam [*i. e.* Paris] 1775.

xij, 114 p. 21ᶜᵐ.

ML1727.33.T8

Treiber, Johann Friedrich, 1641 or 42–1719.

. . . De cantantium ordinibus Veteris Testamenti: cantico novo Novi Testamenti: ut & de officio civium erga choros, symphoniacum & currentium; & tandem de officio beneficiariorum utriusq̃ chori, in solennitate Catharinali, d. XXVII. novembr. a. r. s. CIↃ.IↃCCV. h. l. q. c. peroraturos sistet m. Joh. Fridericus Treiber . . . Arnstadiæ, literis Meurerianis [1705]

8 p. 19 x 15½ᶜᵐ.

ML166.A2T7

Treiber, Johann Friedrich—Continued.

. . . Orationes de musica Davidica, itemque discursibus per urbem cum musica nocturnis, in solennitate Catharinali d. nov. a. r. s. cɪɔ.ɪɔccɪ. h. l. q. c. habendas intimat M. Jo. Frider. Treiber . . . Arnstadiæ, literis Bachmannianis [1701]

[8] p. 19½ᶜᵐ.

ML63.T7

Treiber, Johann Philipp, 1675–1727.

D. Johann Philipp Treibers . . . sonderbare invention: eine arie in einer einzigen melodey aus allen tonen und accorden / auch jederley tacten / zu componiren / so / dass sie in dem hårtesten accord anfångt / in dem weichsten auffhöret / und dem auffmercker dennoch die abwechselung derer accorde nicht frembde vorkommet. Von welcher invention der autor, besage der vorrede . . . in nachfolgender arie, worinne die regirung Gottes und der obrigkeit mit der music verglichen wird / eine probe abgeleget . . . Jena, C. Junghans, 1702.

[8] p. 12 pl. (music) 30½ x 20ᶜᵐ.

Initial; head-piece.

MT47.A2T85

Trento, Decio Agostino.

See TARTINI, G. Trattato di musica, 1754.

Trew, Abdias, 1597–1669, *praeses.*

Disputatio musica de divisione monochordi et deducendis inde sonorum concinnorum speciebus et affectionibus et tandem tota praxi compositionis musicae . . . Altdorffi, typis Georgi Hagen, 1662.

[32] p. pl. 19 x 15½ᶜᵐ.

Diss.—Altdorff (T. G. Mayr, respondent)

ML3809.A2T8

Trillo, Camille, *pseud.*

See LESUIRE, ROBERT MARTIN.

Tromlitz, Johann George, 1726–1805.

Ausführlicher und gründlicher unterricht die flöte zu spielen, von Johann George Tromlitz . . . Leipzig, A. F. Böhme, 1791.

xxiv, 376, [8] p., 1 l. pl. 24½ x 19ᶜᵐ.

Title vignette.

MT348.A2T84

Ueber die flöten mit mehrern klappen; deren anwendung und nutzen. Nebst noch einigen andern dahin gehörigen aufsåtzen von Johann George Tromlitz . . . Als zweyter theil zu meinem Ausführlichen und gründlichen unterricht die flöte zu spielen. Leipzig, A. F. Böhme, 1800.

x, 140, [4] p. 24½ x 19ᶜᵐ. (*With his* Ausführlicher . . . unterricht. Leipzig, 1791)

MT348.A2T84

Trydell, John.

Two essays on the theory and practice of music. In the first are laid down the principles of the science. In the latter are demonstrated the rules of harmony, composition, and thorough bass. To which is added, a new and short method of attaining to sing by note. By the Rev. John Trydell . . . Dublin, Printed for the editor by B. Grierson, 1766.

xx, 140, 51 p. 21½^{cm}.

"Examples": 51 p., engr.

MT6.A2T87

Tübel, Christian Gottlieb, *d.* 1776.

Korte onderrichting van de musiek, met daar by gevoegde LXXVII. handstukkies, voor het clavier. Beneevens eene korte verhandeling van het contrapunct, door den Heer C. G. Tubel . . . Kurzer unterricht von der music, nebst den dazu gehörigen LXXVII. piecen, fur die ienigen welche das clavecin spielen, nebst eine kurze nachricht von contrapunct . . . Amsterdam, J. Covens [pref. 1766]

1 p. l., 4, 123 p. 17 x 24^{cm}.

Engraved, with the exception of 4 p. following title. Text in German and Dutch, in parallel columns.

MT224.A2T8

Türk, Daniel Gottlob, 1750?–1813.

Klavierschule, oder Anweisung zum klavierspielen für lehrer und lernende, mit kritischen anmerkungen, von Daniel Gottlob Türk . . . Leipzig und Halle, Auf kosten des verfassers, in kommission bey Schwickert in Leipzig [etc.] 1789.

4 p. l., 408, [12], 15 p. 22 x 17½^{cm}.

"Zwölf handstücke zum gebrauche beym unterrichten": 15 p. at end.

MT222.A2T9

Kurze anweisung zum generalbassspielen, von Daniel Gottlob Türk . . . Halle und Leipzig, Auf kosten des verfassers, in kommission bey Schwickert in Leipzig [etc.] 1791.

2 p. l., 307, [1] p. 20½^{cm}.

MT49.A2T8

Von den wichtigsten pflichten eines organisten. Ein beytrag zur verbesserung der musikalischen liturgie, von D. G. Türk. Halle, Auf kosten des verfassers, in kommission bei Schwickert zu Leipzig [etc.] 1787.

211, [1] p. 18½^{cm}.

"Das choralspielen bey den protestanten": p. 6–109.

MT190.A2T9

Turmair, Johannes.

See AVENTINUS *i. e.* JOHANNES TURMAIR, *of Abensberg.*

Turner, William.

Sound anatomiz'd, in a philosophical essay on musick. Wherein is explained the nature of sound, both in its essence and regulation, &c. Contrived for the use of the voice in singing, as well as for those who play on instruments. Together with a thorough explanation of all the different moods used in musick, for regulating time in the different divisions of measures used therein . . . To which is added, a discourse concerning the abuse of musick. By William Turner   London, Printed by W. Pearson for the author, 1724.

3 p. l., 80, 7 p.   pl.   21 x 16^{cm}.

MT7.A2T95

Tyard, Pontus de, 1521–1605.

Les discovrs philosophiqves de Pontvs de Tyard, seignevr de Bissy, et depvis euesque de Chalon.   [Le tout reueu & beaucoup augmenté, depuis la derniere edition]   A Paris, Chez A. L'Angelier, 1587.

368 numb. l., [24] p.   fold. pl., port., diagrs.   24 x 17^{cm}.

Printer's mark on t.-p.

CONTENTS.—Solitaire premier, ov Discours de muses, & de la fureur poëtique.—Solitaire second, ov Discours de la musique.—Mantice, ov Discours de la verité de diuination par astrologie.—Le premier cvrievx, ov Premier discovrs de la natvre dv monde, & de ses parties.—Le second cvrievx, ov Second discovrs de la natvre dv monde, et de ses parties, traitant des choses intellectuelles.—Sceve, ov Discovrs dv temps, de l'an, et de ses parties.

Ch.40

Solitaire second, ov Prose de la musique.   Lion, Par Ian de Tovrnes, 1555.

160, [16] p.   illus. (port.) fold. pl.; diagrs.   22½^{cm}.

Title within ornamental border, in this copy colored by hand; initials.
On verso of t.-p. is a portrait of the author, with inscription "P. D. T. en son an 31" and on p. [161] is a laudatory poem: "G. Altarij Carolatis, ad Pontum Tyardæum endecasyllabi."

ML171.T9

U., B. W.

See NEUE . . . art zu solmisiren, 1763.

Uberti, Grazioso.

Contrasto mvsico.   Opera dilettevole del Signor Gratioso Vberti . . .   Roma, L. Grignani, 1630.

4 p. l., 152 p.   15½^{cm}.

Title vignette.

ML3795.A2U14

Ulloa, Pedro de, 1663–1721.

Musica universal, ó Principios universales de la musica, dispuestos por el padre maestro Pedro de Ulloa . . .   Madrid, En la Imprenta de musica, por B. Peralta, 1717.

6 p. l., 104 p.   2 fold. pl.   22½^{cm}.

MT6.A2U42

Unger, Johann Friedrich von, 1716–1781.

Entwurf einer maschine, wodurch alles was auf dem clavier gespie-
let wird, sich von selber in noten setzt. Im jahr 1752. an die Königl.
akademie der wissenschaften zu Berlin eingesandt, nebst dem mit
dem herrn direktor Euler darüber geführten briefwechsel, und einigen andern diesen entwurf betreffenden nachrichten. Von Johann
Friedrich Unger . . . Mit 8 kupfertabellen. Braunschweig, Fürstl.
Waisenhaus-buchhandlung, 1774.

5 p. l., [3]–52 p. VII (*i. e.* 8) fold. pl. (partly music) 21 x 17cm.

ML1050.A2U5

Uranian society, *Philadelphia.*

See INTRODUCTORY lessons, practised by the Uranian society [1785]

V * * * *, M.

See RÉFLEXIONS sur la musique, 1785.

Valenti-Gonzaga, Silvio, *cardinal,* 1690–1756, *editor.*

See BANDINI, A. M. Commentariorvm de vita . . . Ioannis Bapt.
Doni, 1755.

Vallara, Francesco Maria.

Primizie di canto fermo del padre Francesco Maria Vallara . . .
Modona, Per A. Capponi, stampatore, 1700.

8, 80 p. 23¼ x 18cm. MT860.A2V17

Scuola corale nella quale s'insegnano i fondamenti più necessarii
alla vera cognizione del canto gregoriano, composta dal padre Francesco Maria Vallara . . . Modena, Per A. Capponi, stamp., 1707.

viii, 198 p., 1 l. 24½ x 18½cm.

The frontispiece given by Gaspari is wanting in this copy.

MT850.A2V17

Teorico-prattico del canto gregoriano, dato alla luce dal padre
Francesco Maria Vallara . . . Parma, G. Rosati, 1721.

viij, 140 p. 2 fold. pl. 25½cm.

MT860.A2V19

[Valle, Guglielmo della] 1740 ?–1794 ?

Memorie storiche del p. m. Giambattista Martini, minor conven-
tuale di Bologna, celebre maestro di cappella. Napoli, Stamperia
Simoniana, 1785.

viii, 152 p. 20cm.

ML410.M38V2

Vallière, Louis César de La Baume Le Blanc, *duc* de la.

See LA VALLIÈRE, LOUIS CÉSAR DE LA BAUME LE BLANC, *duc* DE.

Vallotti, Francesco Antonio, 1697–1780.

Della scienza teorica, e pratica della moderna musica libro primo. Opera del p. f. Francescantonio Vallotti . . . Padova, Nella stamperia del Seminario, appresso G. Manfrè, 1779.

xxxi, 168 p.   7 pl. (1 fold.) fold. tab.   25½ x 19¼ᶜᵐ.

. "Non fu pubblicato che questo primo volume; ma tutto il rimanente dell' opera conservasi ms. nella biblioteca de' Min. conv. al Santo di Padova."— Gaspari, Catalogo della bibl. del Liceo musicale di Bologna.

ML3805.A2V2

Vandermonde, Alexandre Théophile, 1735–1796.

Second mémoire sur un nouveau systême d'harmonie applicable à l'état actuel de la musique.   Par M. Vandermonde . . .   [Paris, 1781 ?]

18, 4 p.   27 x 21ᶜᵐ.

Caption title.
Musical illustrations: 4 p., engr.

ML3815.A2V23

See also LA BORDE, J. B. DE.   Mémoires sur les proportions musicales, 1781.

Vanneo, Stefano, *b.* 1493.

Recanetvm de mvsica avrea a magistro Stephano Vanneo Recinensi . . . nuper æditum, & solerti studio enucleatum, Vincentio Rosseto Veronensi interprete.   Romae apvd Valerivm Doricvm Brixiensem, 1533.

4 p. l., 93 numb. l.   illus., diagrs.   28ᶜᵐ.

The Italian original was not published.

ML171.V26

Vaucanson, Jacques de, 1709–1782.

Le mécanisme du fluteur automate, presenté a messieurs de l'Académie royale des sciences.   Par M. Vaucanson, auteur de cette machine.   Avec la description d'un canard artificiel; mangeant, beuvant, digerant & se vuidant, épluchant ses aîles & ses plumes, imitant en diverses manieres un canard vivant.   Inventé par la mesme.   Et aussi celle d'une autre figure, également merveilleuse, jouant du tambourin & de la flute, suivant la relation, qu'il en a donnée dépuis son mémoire écrit.   Paris, J. Guerin, 1738.

11 (*i. e.* 23) p.   front.   25½ x 19½ᶜᵐ.
Last page numbered 11 for 23.

ML1055.A2V19

Vayer, François de La Mothe le.

See LA MOTHE LE VAYER, FRANÇOIS DE.

Vaz Barradas Muitopão e Morato, João, *b.* 1689.

Breve resumo de cantocham, com as regras mais principaes e a fórma que devem guardar, o director do coro para o sustentar firme na corda chamada coral, e o organista quando o acompanha, ordenado ao uso romano, por Joaõ Vaz Barrada Muito Pam, e Morato . . . Lisboa Occidental, Officina da musica, 1735.

2 p. l., 59 p. 19½ᶜᵐ.

MT860.A2V39

Flores musicaes colhidas no jardim da melhor liçaõ de varios autores. Arte pratica de canto de orgao, indice de cantoria para principiantes, com hum breve resummo das regras mais principaes de acompanhar com instrumentos de vozes, e o conhecimento dos tons assim naturaes como accidentaes . . . por Joaõ Vaz Barradas Muito Pam, e Morato . . . Lisboa Occidental, Officina da musica, 1735.

6 p. l., 113, [6] p. incl. pl., tables. 21ᶜᵐ.

MT860.A2V41

[Veal, George]

Musical travels through England. By Joel Collier [*pseud.*] . . . London, G. Kearsly, 1774.

viii, 59 p. 19½ᶜᵐ.

[Miscellaneous pamphlets, v. 1141, no. 1]
A satire on Burney. Attributed also to J. L. Bicknell.

AC901.M5

—— Musical travels through England. By the late Joel Collier . . . 4th ed. London, G. Kearsly, 1776.

2 p. l., vi p., 1 l., 102, 28 p. 20½ᶜᵐ.

ML429.V394

—— Musical travels through England. By the late Joel Collier . . . New ed. London, G. Kearsley, 1785.

xiv, [2], 126, 32 p. 15ᶜᵐ.

ML429.V396

Velasco, Sebastián López de.

See LÓPEZ DE VELASCO, SEBASTIÁN.

Venceslaus Philomathes, *de Nova Domo.*

Venceslai Philomatis de Nova Domo Musicorum libri quatuor . . . [*Colophon:* Impressum Viennæ Pannoniæ per Ioannem Singrenium. Anno M.D.XXIII.]

[43] p. 22ᶜᵐ.

Below title, on t.-p.: "Rvdberti Resch Grecensis . . . epigramma extemporale, musicæ complectens obiter laudem" (14 lines in pentameter) followed by the sentence "Eme lector et gavdebis" in capitals.
Title within woodcut border with printer's mark; initials. Signatures: a–d in fours; e in six. This copy has ms. notes.
The present is the 3d edition. According to Fétis, the 1st edition, Vienna, 1512, has title: Venceslai Philomathis de Nova Domo Musicorum libri quatuor, compendioso carmine elucubrati.

ML171.V36

Venezia, Giacinto.

Esercizio accademico sulla musica pubblicamente esposto da cherici delle scuole pie nel collegio della duchesca sotto la direzione del padre Giacinto Venezia . . .   Napoli, 1792.

26 p.   23 x 18½^{cm}.

ML64.V3

Venini, Francesco, 1737–1820.

De i principi dell' armonia musicale, e poetica, e sulla loro applicazione alla teoria e alla pratica della versificazione italiana.   Dissertazione dell' abate Francesco Venini.   Parigi, G. C. Molini, l'an 6me — (1798)

2 p. l., 3–165 p.   21½^{cm}.

2d edition. 1st edition, Paris, 1784.

PC1505.V5

Verato, Giovanni Maria.

Il Verrato insegna con noua e breuissima inuentione facile per imparare per tutte le chiaue, à leggere le notte, cantare & portar la batuda, con cinque sole regole, in dialogo cioue maestro, & discepolo . . . Con vn epilogo breue per li maestri che insegnano.   Di f. Gio. Maria Verrato . . .   Novamente stampata.   Venetia, B. Magni, 1623.

1 p. l., 18 p.   23^{cm}.

MT44.A2V35

Veridicus Gratus, *pseud.*

See PRINTZ, W. C.   Phrynis Mitilenæus, 1696.

Verissimo dos Martyres, 1699 ?–1767.

Director ecclesiastico das ceremonias da Cinza, Ramos, e de toda a Semana santa, conforme as rubricas do Missal romano, e decretos da S. Congregação de ritos, com todo o canto-chaõ que nos sobreditos dias se deve cantar . . . Pelo R. padre Fr. Verissimo dos Martyres . . .   Lisboa, Offic. de J. da Costa Coimbra, 1755.

4 p. l., 407, [1] p.   19½^{cm}

MT860.A2V51

Director funebre de ceremonias na administraçaõ do sagrado viatico, extrema-unçaõ aos enfermos, enterro, officio dos defuntos, procissaõ das almas, e outras funçoẽs pertencentes aos mortos, com o canto, que em todas se deve observar . . . Dedicado ao . . . Senhor Luiz Cesar de Menezes, ii. conde de Sabugosa . . . pelo R. P. Fr. Verissimo dos Martyres . . .   Lisboa, J. da Costa Coimbra, 1749.

7 p. l., 289 p.   20^{cm}.

MT860.A2V5

Veritophilus, *pseud.*

See RAUPACH, CHRISTOPH.

Vermehrter / und nun zum zweytenmal in druck beförderter kurtzer jedoch gründlicher wegweiser / vermittelst welches man nicht nur allein aus dem grund die kunst / die orgel recht zu schlagen / sowol was den general-bass, als auch was zu dem gregorianischen choralgesang erfordert wird / erlernen . . . sondern auch weiland herrn Giacomo Carissimi Sing-kunst / und leichte grund-regeln / vermittelst welcher man die jugend . . . in der music perfectioniren kan / zu finden seyn. Wobey auch die eigentliche unterweisung / den choral-gesang zu begreiffen / alle desselben thon zu erkennen / und sich nach denselben in den introitibus, Kyrie, hymnis, psalmis, Benedictus, Magnificat, &c. wissen auf der orgel mit den præambulis zu richten. Deme hinzu gefügt ein in kupffer verfertigter ubungs-plan / bestehend in allerhand præambulis, interambulis, versen, toccaten, tastaten, variationen, fugen, und dergleichen . . . Allen / so geist- als weltlichen / welche nothwendig den choral-gesang verstehen sollen . . . absonderlich denen / so der lateinischen sprach unerfahren / zu lieb in teutsch hervor gegeben / und in druck verfertiget. Augspurg, J. Koppmayer, 1693.

48, 55 p. 1 illus. 16 x 20½cm.

"Præambula, variationen, &c.": 55 p.

MT35.A2K87

See also CARISSIMI, G. G. Ars cantandi, 1693.

Verschuere-Reynvaan, Joos, 1739–1809.

Muzijkaal kunst-woordenboek, behelzende, de verklaaringen, alsmede het gebruik en de kracht der kunstwoorden, die in de muzijk voorkomen, door J. Verschuere Reynvaan . . . [1. deel] Amsteldam, W. Brave, 1795.

xxii, [2], 618 p. fold. plates. 21½cm.

Cover dated 1796. Several of the plates are printed on both sides.
Only the first part was published, covering the letters A–M.

Versuch einer systematischen entwickelung der tactarten und vorschläge zu neuen tactzeichen.

(*In* Deutsches magazin. [Altona?] 1792. 17 x 10cm. märz, p. [231]–264)

Detached copy.

ML432.A2V5

Vicentino, Nicola, *b.* 1511.

L'antica mvsica ridotta alla moderna prattica, con la dichiaratione, et con gli essempi de i tre generi, con le loro spetie. Et con l'inventione di vno nvovo stromento, nel qvale si contiene tvtta la perfetta mvsica, con molti segreti mvsicali. Nuouamente mess' in luce, dal reverendo M. Don Nicola Vicentino. Roma, A. Barre, 1555.

146 numb. l., [10] p., 1 l. illus. (port.) 31½cm.

Title vignette. Leaf 105 numbered 106.

ML171.V43

Vierling, Johann Gottfried, 1750–1813.

Versuch einer anleitung zum präludiren für ungeübtere, mit beispielen erläutert, von Johann Gottfried Vierling . . . Neue ausg. Leipzig, Breitkopf und Härtel [1794]

28 p. 25ᶜᵐ.

MT68.A2V66

Viéville, Jean Laurent Le Cerf de la.

See LE CERF DE LA VIÉVILLE, JEAN LAURENT, *seigneur de Freneuse.*

Villa Lobos, Mathias de Sousa.

See SOUSA VILLA LOBOS, MATHIAS DE.

Villasagra, Pedro de.

Arte, y compendio del canto llano. Brevissimo en su inteligencia para los que quieran aprender con facilidad: con algunas antiphonas, y missas para la practica. Su autor el P. Fr. Pedro de Villasagra . . . Valencia, Impr. de la viuda de J. de Orga, 1765.

2 p. l., 136 p. 1 illus. 21ᶜᵐ.

Appended: "Adicion al Compendio del arte de canto llano . . . La escribia Don Manuel Narro," Valencia, 1766. 12 p.

MT860.A2V6

Ville sur Illon, Bernard Germain Étienne de la, *comte de Lacépède.*

See LACÉPÈDE, BERNARD GERMAIN ÉTIENNE DE LA VILLE SUR ILLON, *comte* DE.

Villers, Clémence de.

Dialogues sur la musique, par Mˡˡᵉ de Villers, adressés a son amie. Paris, Vente, 1774.

64 p. 17ᶜᵐ.

ML1727.35.V7

Vincent, William, 1739–1815.

Considerations on parochial music. By William Vincent . . . 2d ed., with additions. London, T. Cadell, 1790.

iv, 43 p. 20½ᶜᵐ.

ML3001.V77

Vinet, Élie, 1509–1587.

See DISCOURS non plus melancoliqves qve divers, 1557.

Viotti, Giovanni Battista, 1753–1824.

Mémoire au roi, concernant l'exploitation du privilege de l'Opéra, demandé par le sieur Viotti. [Paris ? 1789 ?]

50 p. 20ᶜᵐ.

Dated "29 avril 1789."

ML1727.8.P2V5

Virdung, Sebastian.

See LUSCINIUS, O. Mvsvrgia, 1536.

[**Vismes, Alphonse Denis Marie de,** *called* **de Saint-Alphonse**]
1746–1792.

Lettre a Madame de *** , sur l'opéra d'Iphigénie en Aulide.
A Lausanne, 1774.

23 p. 18½ᶜᵐ.

For authorship *see* Pougin's supplement to Fétis' Biographie universelle des
musiciens.

ML1727.35.V74

Vives, Vincenzo Requeno y.

See REQUENO Y VIVES, VINCENZO.

Vockerodt, Gottfried, 1665–1727.

Missbrauch der freyen künste / insonderheit der music / nebenst
abgenöthigter erörterung der frage: was nach d. Luthers und anderer
evangelischen theologorum und politicorum meinung von opern und
comödien zu halten sey? Gegen hn. d. Wentzels / hn. Joh. Christian
Lorbers / und eines weissenfelsischen hof-musicantens schmäh-schrifft-
ten . . . vorgestellet / und mit einer zugabe: darinne enthalten: I.
Eine erinnerung an die censores dieser schrifft: II. Das von den pasquillanten angefochtene programma: III. Der hochlöblichen Theol.
facultät zu Giessen bedencken: IV. Vorstellung des . . . beginnens des
weissenfelsischen pasquillanten . . . hrsg. von Gottfried Vockerodt . . .
Franckfurt / Bey J. D. Zunnern, 1697.

176 p., 1 l. 19 x 15½ᶜᵐ.

The program has special t.-p.: . . . De falsa mentium intemperatarum medicina . . . Litteris Reyherianis.

ML194.A2V6

Gottfried Vockerodts . . . Wiederholetes zeugnüs der warheit
gegen die verderbte music und schauspiele / opern / comödien und
dergleichen eitelkeiten / welche die heutige welt vor unschuldige mit-
teldinge will gehalten wissen: abgenöthiget durch die andere von
einem weissfelsischen hof-musicanten / im jahr 1697. herausgegebene
schmäh-schrifft . . . Hierzu komt als eine zugabe / nebenst andern
. . . materien / des herrn von Chanteresme gründliches . . . bedencken
von denen heutigen schau-spielen; wie auch des . . . hn. Armand von
Bourbon, printzens von Conty, herrliches tractätlein von denen pflichten grosser herren. Franckfurt und Leipzig / Bey J. Bielcken / 1698.

6 p. l., 148, 59, [1] p. 19 x 15½ᶜᵐ. (*With his* Missbrauch der freyen künste.
Franckfurt, 1697)

The "tractätlein" has special t.-p.

ML194.A2V6

Vogelsang, Joannes.

Mvsicæ rv- ‖ dimenta, per Ioan. ‖ Vogelsangum Lindauiensem, tam ‖ fideliter quam compendiose ‖ congesta. ‖ Ioan. Pedionevs Rhæ- ‖ tus, ad literarum tyrunculos. ‖ Qui cupis in teneris, statim perdiscere cantum, ‖ Annis, hæc musæ prima clementa para: ‖ Quæ tibi cui nomen cantus fœcere uolucrum ‖ Succincto tradit colligit atq̜ libro. [*Colophon:* Auguste Vindelicorum per Va- ‖ lentinum Otthmar]

[88] p. 14½ᶜᵐ.

Dedication dated 1542. Signatures: A–E in eights, F in four.

ML171.V64

Vogler, Georg Joseph, *abt,* 1749–1814.

Georg Joseph Vogler's . . . Stimmbildungskunst. Mannheim, Kuhrfürstliche hofbuchdruckerei, 1776.

[7] p. 4 fold. l. (music) 18½ᶜᵐ.

Leaves printed on both sides.

MT820.A2V6

Vogler's Tonschule, tonwissenschaft und tonsezkunst. Nebst beyspielen . . . Offenbach a/M, J. André [n. d.]

2 v. in 1. fold. tab., fold. diagr. 17½ᶜᵐ.

A reissue, with André's engr. t.-p. added, of Vogler's:

Kuhrpfälzische tonschule. Auf kosten des verfassers. Mannheim, In commission bei herrn C. F. Schwan, und bei herrn M. Götze [1778]

2 v. in 1 (v. 1: viii, 96 p.; v. 2: 4 p. l., 206 p.) fold. tab., fold. diagr. 17½ᶜᵐ.

CONTENTS.—1. th. Tonkunst. Clavierschule. Stimmbildungskunst. Singschule. Begleitungskunst.—2. th. Tonwissenschaft. Tonsezkunst. Nuzbarkeit des tonmases. Gebrauch der harmonie. Tonlehre.

From this it appears that the "Nuzbarkeit des tonmases" does not constitute a third part to the work, as is stated in Barclay Squire's "Catalogue of printed music (1487-1800) in the British museum."

The "Zweiter theil" is apparently a reissue with the original t.-p. of "Georg Joseph Vogler's . . . Tonwissenschaft und tonsezkunst," Mannheim, 1776.

The "beyspiele" refer to the "Gründe der Kuhrpfälzischen tonschule in beispielen" following.

MT40.A2V88

—— Gründe der Kuhrpfälzischen tonschule in beispielen: als vorbereitung zur Mannheimer monat-schrift, und zu den herausgaben des Öffentlichen tonlehrers. [Mannheim, 1778]

xxx p. 30 x 24ᶜᵐ.

Engraved throughout.

MT40.A2V883

Verbesserung der Forkel'schen verånderungen über das englische volkslied God save the King. Nebst acht kupfertafeln. Frankfurt am Main, Varrentrapp und Wenner, 1793.

2 v. (v. 1: 48 p. fold. tab.; v. 2: 10 p.) 19ᶜᵐ (v. 2: 35ᶜᵐ)

Preface signed: A. V.

Vol. 2, engraved throughout, has title: Kontrapunktische bearbeitung des englischen volkslieds God save the King.

MT64.A2V6

See also ERSTE-musikalische preisaustheilung, 1794.

Vogt, Moritz Johann, 1669–1730.

Conclave Thesauri magnæ artis musicæ [in quo tractatur. Præcipuè de compositione pura, musicæ theoria, anatomia sonori, musica enharmonica, chromatica, diatonica, mixta, nova, & antiqua: terminorum musicorum nomenclatura: musica authenta, plagali, chorali, figurali: musicæ historia . . . &c. . . . Authore R. P. Mauritio Vogt]
. . . Vetero-Pragæ, typis Georgij Labaun, 1719.

8 p. l., 223, [3] p., 1 l. illus., diagrs. 33½ᶜᵐ.

Supposed by some authorities to have been written by Tomáš Baltazar Janovka and merely edited by Vogt.

MT7.A2V75

[Voigt, C.]

Gespräch von der musik, zwischen einem organisten und adjuvanten, darinnen nicht nur von verschiedenen missbräuchen, so bey der musik eingerissen, gehandelt, sondern auch eines und das andere beym clavier- und orgel-spielen angemerket wird . . . an das licht gestellet von einem, der von jugend auf christlich vnterrichtet, und oeffentlich die wahrheit an den tag gegeben. In iv. unterredungen. Erfurth, J. D. Jungnicol, 1742.

5 p. l., 140 p. front. 20 x 17ᶜᵐ.

Preface by Lorenz Mizler.

ML3001.V89

[Voisenon, Claude Henri de Fusée, *abbé* de] 1708–1775.

Réponse du coin du roi au coin de la reine. 2. ed. cor. & augm.
[n. p., 1753]

No. 1 in a volume of pamphlets lettered Quere[lle] des Bouffo[ns]

ML1727.33.A1

See also GRIMM, F. M., *freiherr* VON. Le petit prophète [1753 ?]

Voltaire, François Marie Arouet de, 1694–1778.
See HERTEL, J. W. Sammlung musikalischer schriften, 1757–58.

Voye Mignot, de la.
See LA VOYE MIGNOT, DE.

Wagenseil, Johann Christoph, 1633–1705.

Joh. Christophori Wagenseilii De Sacri rom. imperii Libera civitate noribergensi commentatio. Accedit, De Germaniæ phonascorvm, von der meister-singer / origine, præstantia, vtilitate, et institvtis, sermone vernacvlo liber. Altdorfi Noricorvm, typis impensisqve J. W. Kohlesii. 1697.

4 p. l., 7–576 (*i. e.* 588) p. front., vign., plates (partly fold.) ports., fold. plan, tab. 21 x 16¼ᶜᵐ.

Between p. 554 and 555 is "Der meisterliche hort, in vier gekrönten thönen," [12] p.
"Vrbs Norimberga carmine heroico illvstrata per Helivm Eobanvm Hessvm": p. [393]–432.

ML183.A2W3

Walder, Johann Jacob, 1750–1817.

Anleitung zur singkunst in kurzen regeln für lehrer und in stuffenweyser reyhe von uebungen und beyspielen für schüler, zum gebrauch der vaterländischen schulen. Von J. J. Walder. Zürich, Orell, Gessner, Füssli und compagnie, 1788.

xx, 60 p.   20½ x 17½^{cm}.

MT935.A2W26

Walker, Joseph Cooper, d. 1810.

Historical memoirs of the Irish bards. Interspersed with anecdotes of, and occasional observations on, the music of Ireland. Also, an historical and descriptive account of the musical instruments of the ancient Irish. And an appendix . . . By Joseph C. Walker . . . Dublin, Printed for the author, by L. White, 1786.

xii, 166, 124, [6] p.   front. (port.) illus.   27 x 21^{cm}.

Appendix: no. i. Inquiries concerning the ancient Irish harp . . . By the Rev. Edward Ledwich.—no. ii. A letter . . . on the style of the ancient Irish music. From the Rev. Edward Ledwich.—no. iii. An essay on the poetical accents of the Irish: by William Beauford.—no. iv. Dissertazione del Signor canonico Orazio Maccari di Cortona, sopra un' antica statuetta di marmo, rappresentante un suonator di cornamusa.—no. v. Memoirs of Cormac Common.—no. vi. The life of Turlough O'Carolan.—no. vii. An account of three brass trumpets, found near Cork: with remarks thereon.—no. viii. An essay on the construction and capability of the Irish harp, in its pristine and present state. By William Beauford.—no. ix. Select Irish melodies.

ML287.W18

Wallin, Georg, 1686–1760.

See WERNSDORF, G.   De prudentia [1723]

Wallis, John, 1616–1703.

See SALMON, T.   A proposal to perform musick, 1688.

Wallis, John, 1616–1703, *translator.*

See PTOLEMAEUS, CLAUDIUS.   Ἁρμονικῶν βιβλία γ', 1682.

Walter, Thomas, 1696–1725.

The grounds and rules of musick explained: or, An introduction to the art of singing by note. Fitted to the meanest capacities . . . Recommended by several ministers. [n. p., 17—]

iii, [1], 25 p., 20 l. (music)   12½ x 18^{cm}.

Imperfect, wanting t.-p. and plate 4. Title taken from that of the 1st edition, 1721, as given in "Catalogue of the American library of . . . Mr. George Brinley," Hartford, 1881. According to Mr. Metcalf, however, our copy is not of the 1st edition, but was published probably about 1740.

Contains (1) "A recommendatory preface," dated Boston, April 18, 1721, and signed by Increase and Cotton Mather and 13 other ministers. iii p. (2) Explanation of musical characters. [1] p. (3) "Some brief and very plain instructions for singing by note." 25 p. (4) Music (engraved) consisting of "Rules for tuning the voice" (leaf 1) followed by hymn tunes arranged for 3 parts (l. 2–20)

M2116.W23

Walter, Thomas—*Continued.*

—— The grounds and rules of musick explained: or, An introduction to the art of singing by note. Fitted to the meanest capacities. By Thomas Walter ... Boston: Printed for, and sold by T. Johnston, 1764.

1 p. l., 25 p., 24 l. (music) 11½ x 17^{cm}.

The first 20 l. of music in this issue correspond to those in the foregoing.

M2116.W24

The Sweet psalmist of Israel. A sermon preach'd at the lecture held in Boston, by the Society for promoting regular & good singing, and for reforming the depravations and debasements our psalmody labours under, in order to introduce the proper and true old way of singing. Boston, J. Franklin, for T. Fleet, 1722.

3 p. l., 6+ p. 16°.

Imperfect, wanting p. 7-28.

Ch. 17.1063

Walther, Johann Gottfried, 1684–1748.

Musicalisches lexicon, oder Musicalische bibliothec, darinnen nicht allein die musici, welche so wol in alten als neuern zeiten, ingleichen bey verschiedenen nationen, durch theorie und praxin sich hervor gethan, und was von jedem bekannt worden, oder er in schrifften hinterlassen, mit allem fleisse und nach den vornehmsten umstånden angeführet, sondern auch die in griechischer, lateinischer, italiånischer und frantzösischer sprache gebräuchliche musicalische kunst- oder sonst dahin gehörige wörter, nach alphabetischer ordnung vorgetragen und erklåret, und zugleich die meisten vorkommende signaturen erläutert werden von Johann Gottfried Walthern ... Leipzig, W. Deer, 1732.

7 p. l., 659, [7] p. xxii fold. pl. 22^{cm}.

ML100.A2W2

Weaver, John, 1673–1760.

An essay towards an history of dancing, in which the whole art and its various excellencies are in some measure explain'd. Containing the several sorts of dancing, antique and modern, serious, scenical, grotesque ... London, J. Tonson, 1712.

4 p. l., 172 p. 17^{cm}.

GV1601.W36

The history of the mimes and pantomimes, with an historical account of several performers in dancing, living in the time of the Roman emperors. To which will be added, a list of the modern entertainments that have been exhibited on the English stage, either in imitation of the ancient pantomimes, or after the manner of the modern Italians; when and where first performed, and by whom composed. By John Weaver ... London, J. Roberts [etc.] 1728.

56 p. 20^{cm}.

[Miscellaneous pamphlets, vol. 31, no. 6]

AC901.M5

[Webb, Daniel] 1719?–1798.

Observations on the correspondence between poetry and music. By the author of An enquiry into the beauties of painting . . . London, J. Dodsley, 1769.

vii, 155 p. 17½^{cm}.

ML3849.A2W3

Weidling, Christian, 1660–1731, *praeses.*

. . . Exercitatio philologica de instrumentis Ebræorum musicis חנגינות והנחילות ex psalmo IV. & V. . . . Lipsiæ, literis J. Coleri [1686]

[20] p. 17½ x 14½^{cm}.

Diss.—Leipzig (J. A. Glaser, respondent and author)

ML166.A2G56

Weimar, Georg Peter, 1734–1800.

Versuch kurzer praktischer uebungs-exempel allerley art für schüler, die im gesange zum sogenannten notentreffen oder vom blatt-singen angeleitet werden sollen; ein pendant zu Hillers kürzeren und erleichterten singeanweisung . . . von Georg Peter Weimar . . . Leipzig, Breitkopfische musikhandlung [1795]

1 p. l., 110 p. 22 x 17½^{cm}.

MT870.A2W3

Weissbeck, Johann Michael, 1756–1808.

Protestationsschrift, oder Exemplarische widerlegung einiger stellen und perioden der kapellmeister Voglerischen Tonwissenschaft und tonsetzkunst, von Johann Michael Weissbeck, d. r. g. b. Erlangen, Gedruckt mit Kunstmannischen schriften, 1783.

1 p. l., 17, [5] p. 21½ x 18^{cm}.

Title vignette.
Contains another t.-p., undated, and with different vignette, under which the motto: Ich werde keinen spruch und keine prüfung scheuen. Weissbeck is here designated as "juris stud."
"Anhang zur Protestations-schrift . . . Im februar 1784": [4] p. at end.

MT40.A2W45

Werckmeister, Andreas, 1645–1706.

Andreæ Werckmeisters . . . Cribrvm mvsicvm, oder Musicalisches sieb, darinen einige mängel eines halb gelehrten componisten vorge-stellet, und das böse von dem guten gleichsam ausgesiebet und abge-sondert worden, in einem sendschreiben an einem [!] guten freund dargestellet, dann denen unzeitigen componisten zur nachricht und fleissigern nachsinnen zum druck befördert durch Johann Georg Carln . . . Quedlinburg und Leipzig, T. P. Calvisius, 1700.

4 p. l., 60 p. 19½ x 16^{cm}.

Pages 42–60 contain an extract from Johann Kuhnau's "Der musikalische quack-salber," Dresden, 1700.

MT55.A2W48

Werckmeister, Andreas—*Continued.*

Harmonologia musica, oder Kurtze anleitung zur musicalischen composition, wie man vermittels der regeln und anmerckungen bey den general-bass einen contrapunctum simplicem . . . durch drey sätze oder griffe componiren / und extempore spielen: auch dadurch im clavier und composition weiter zu schreiten und zu variiren gelegenheit nehmen könne: benebst einen unterricht / wie man einen gedoppelten contrapunct und mancherley canones oder fugas ligatas, durch sonderbahre griffe und vortheile setzen und einrichten möge / aus denen mathemathischen und musicalischen gründen aufgesetzet und zum drucke heraus gegeben durch Andream Werckmeistern . . . Franckfurth und Leipzig / In verlegung T. P. Calvisii, Qvedlinburg, 1702.

13 p. l., 142 p.   20½ x 16½^{cm}.

MT55.A2W5

Hypomnemata musica, oder Musicalisches memorial / welches bestehet in kurtzer erinnerung dessen / so bisshero unter guten freunden discurs-weise / insonderheit von der composition und temperatur möchte vorgangen seyn / zu eigener nachricht auffgesezzet / und denen musical-lernend- und liebenden zum besten / den druck übergeben von Andrea Werckmeister . . .   Qvedlimburg, In verlegung T. P. Calvisii, 1697.

4 p. l., 44, [3] p.   20 x 15½^{cm}.

ML3809.A2W37

Musicæ mathematicæ hodegus curiosus. Oder, Richtiger musicalischer weg-weiser / das ist, wie man nicht alleine die natürlichen eigenschafften der musicalischen proportionen / durch das monochordum, und ausrechnung erlangen / sondern auch vermittels derselben / natürliche und richtige rationes über eine musicalische composition vorbringen könne. Benebenst einem allegor-moralischem / von der music entspringendem anhange . . . Von Andrea Werckmeistern . . . Franckfurt und Leipzig, In verlegung T. P. Calvisii, 1687.

4 p. l., 160, [12] p.   20 x 15½^{cm}.

ML3809.A2W3

Musicalische paradoxal-discourse, oder Ungemeine vorstellungen / wie die musica einen hohen und göttlichen uhrsprung habe / und wie hingegen dieselbe so sehr gemissbrauchet wird. Dann wie dieselbe von den lieben alten mit grosser schwürig- und weitläufftigkeit / welche uns zum theil noch anhanget / ist fortgesetzet worden / und wie man hingegen in vielen stücken / in heutiger musica practica eines nähern weges und vortheils sich bedienen könne. &c. So wohl denen so ihre music zur ehre Gottes gedencken anzuwenden / auch andern Gott- und kirchen-music liebenden zum weitern nachdencken mathematicè, historicè, und allegoricè, durch die musicalischen proportional-zahlen entdecket / und vorgestellet von Andrea Werckmeister . . . Qvedlinburg / T. P. Calvisius, 1707.

120, [2] p.   19½ x 16^{cm}.

Imperfect, wanting p. 27–28.

ML3800.A2W4

Werckmeister, Andreas—*Continued.*

Die nothwendigsten anmerckungen / und regeln wie der bassus continuus, oder general-bass wohl kônne tractiret werden / und ein jeder / so nur ein wenig wissenschafft von der music und clavier hat / denselben vor sich selbst erlernen kônne. Aus dem wahren fundament der musicalischen composition denen anfângern zu besserer nachricht aufgesezet / u. aniezo merckich [!] vermehret / und mit vielen exempeln erklâret durch Andreas Werckmeistern / m. u. o. z. S. M. i. H. Andere aufl. Aschersleben / G. E. Struntz, 1715.

75, [1] p. 19 x 16½ᶜᵐ.

MT49.A2W48

—— Die nothwendigsten anmerckungen / und regeln wie der bassus continuus, oder general-bass wol kônne tractiret werden und ein jeder so nur ein wenig wissenschafft von der music und clavier hat denselben vor sich selbst erlernen kônne. Aus dem wahren fundament der musicalischen composition denen anfângern zu besserer nachricht auffgesezet und aniezzo mercklich vermehret / und mit vielen exempeln erklâret / durch Andreas Werckmeistern / m. u. o. z. S. M. i. H. Aschersleben / G. E. Struntze [n. d.]

72, [4] p. 18 x 15ᶜᵐ.

As most of the errata in this edition are also in the edition of 1715, it is not possible to determine which is the earlier. Various authorities date the 1st edition 1698 and describe as the third an undated edition.

MT49.A2W47

. . . Organum gruningense redivivum, oder Kurtze beschreibung des in der grüningischen schlos-kirchen berühmten orgel-wercks, wie dasselbe anfangs erbauet und beschaffen gewesen: und wie es anitzo . . . ist renoviret und mercklich verbessert worden . . . von Andreas Werckmeister. Quedlinburg und Aschersleben / G. E. Struntz [pref. 1705]

[36] p. 19 x 15½ᶜᵐ.

ML594.G7

Andreæ Werckmeisters . . . erweiterte und verbesserte Orgel-probe / oder Eigentliche beschreibung / wie und welcher gestalt man die orgel-wercke von den orgelmachern annehmen / probiren / untersuchen und denen kirchen liefern kônne; auch was bey verdüngniss eines neuen und alten wercks / so da zu renoviren vorfallen môchte / nothwendig in acht zu nehmen sey . . . jetzo von dem autore selbst übersehen / mit gründlichen uhrsachen bekrâfftiget / und zum druck befordert. Qvedlinburg, In verlegung T. P. Calvisii, 1698.

8 p. l., 84, [4] p. 19ᶜᵐ.

Added t.-p., engr., in this copy colored by hand.

ML552.A2W4

—— Andreæ Werckmeisters . . . erweiterte und verbesserte Orgel-probe / oder: Eigentliche beschreibung wie und welcher gestalt man die orgelwercke von den orgelmachern annehmen / probiren / untersuchen und denen kirchen liefern kônne; auch was bey verdüngniss eines neuen und alten wercks / so da zu renoviren vorfallen môchte / nothwendig in acht zu nehmen sey . . . jezo von dem autore .selbst

Werckmeister, Andreas—*Continued.*

übersehen / mit gründlichen ursachen bekråfftiget / und zum druck befördert. Quedlinburg und Aschersleben / G. E. Struntz / 1716.

12 p. l., 85, [3] p.   21 x 16½ᶜᵐ.

Added t.-p., engr.

ML552.A2W41

—— Andreas Werkmeisters erweiterte und verbesserte Orgelprobe. Leipzig, J. M. Teubner, 1754.

110 p.   front.   17ᶜᵐ.

ML552.A2W42

Werckmeister, Andreas, 1645–1706, *translator.*

See STEFFANI, A.   Send-schreiben, 1700.

[Wernich, Johann Carl Gustav] *d.* 1796.

Versuch einer richtigen lehrart die harfe zu spielen, wobey die grundsåtze nach welchen dieses instrument erlernet werden muss, mit der grössten deutlichkeit, und solchergestalt vorgetragen werden, dass der liebhaber desselben eine hinlångliche geschicklichkeit darauf erlangen könne, von J. C. G. W.   Berlin, G. L. Winter, 1772.

8 p. l., 43 p.   1 illus.   21½ x 17ᶜᵐ.

Dedication signed: J. C. G. Wernich.

MT540.A2W57

Wernsdorf, Gottlieb, 1668–1729, *praeses.*

. . . De prudentia in cantionibus ecclesiasticis adhibenda . . .   Wittenbergae, literis vidvae Gerdesiae [1723]

76 p.   19ᶜᵐ.

Diss.—Wittenberg (Georg Wallin, respondent and author)

ML3001.W49

Wiedeburg, Michael Johann Friedrich, *b. ca.* 1735.

Musikalisches charten-spiel ex G dur, wobey man allezeit ein musikalisches stück gewinnet, zum vergnügen und zur uebung der clavierspieler und zum gebrauch der organisten in kleinen stådten und auf dem lande. Erstes spiel. Von Mich. Joh. Fridr. Wideburg . . . Aurich, A. F. Winter, 1788.

8, 48 p.   22½ x 19ᶜᵐ.

No more published.

MT68.A2W4

Der sich selbst informirende clavierspieler, oder Deutlicher und leichter unterricht zur selbstinformation im clavierspielen . . . so deutlich und mit fleiss weitlåuftig abgefasset, dass die liebhaber . . . sich selbst so weit bringen können, nach noten ein lied auf dem clavier zu spielen, nebst dreyssig bekannten liedermelodien und einer aria, wie auch einer kurzen anweisung alle lieder auch nach dem generalbass spielen zu lernen, aufgesetzet von Michael Johann Friedrich Wiedeburg . . . Halle und Leipzig, Verlag der buchhandlung des Waisenhauses, 1765–75.

3 v. in 4.   2 pl. (1 fold.)   24½ x 19½ᶜᵐ.

Wiedeburg, Michael Johann Friedrich—*Continued*.

Vols. 2 and 3 have special t.-p.: (v. 2) Anderer theil des Sich selbst informi-
renden clavier-spielers, oder Deutlicher und gründlicher unterricht zur selbst-
information im general-bass . . . Von Michael Johann Friedrich Wideburg . . .
Halle, Gedruckt und verlegt im Waisenhause, 1767. (v. 3) Dritter theil . . .
worin gezeiget wird, wie ein liebhaber der music bey fleissiger selbst-information
nicht allein . . . zum fantasiren auf der orgel und dem clavier, sondern auch zu
einer geschicklichkeit, allerley musicalische stücke . . . zu verfertigen und zu
componiren, gelangen kan . . . Halle, Im verlag des Waisenhauses, 1775.

MT248.A2W64

[Wiese, Christian Ludwig Gustav, *freiherr* von] 1732–1800.

Discours analytique sur la cohérence imperturbable de l'unité du
principe des trois premieres parties intégrantes de la théorie musicale,
et qui sont: 1.) La partie canonique . . . 2.) La partie mélodique . . .
3.) La partie harmonique . . . Ouvrage enrichi de cinq tables formu-
laires . . . Par le B. de W. . . . Dresde, Chez les freres Walther,
1795.

38 p. 5 fold. pl. 22½ x 19ᶜᵐ.

ML3805.A2W5

Versuch eines formularisch und tabellarisch vorgebildeten leit-
fadens im bezug auf die quelle des harmonischen tönungsausflusses;
ferner auf die mechanisch ausführbare stimmungsübertragung der
sowohl rationalstimmung, als auch ungleichschwebenden fixen tem-
peraturstimmung auf der orgel und den tastenjnstrument . . . Dresden, P. C. Hilscher [1791]

1 p. l., 33 p. 24 x 36ᶜᵐ.

Engraved in part.

ML3809.A2W6

Wilisch,

See NACHGEDANKEN herrn m. Joh. Gottl. Biedermanns, 1750.

Wilke, Johann Georg Leberecht von, 1730–1810.

See MUSIKALISCHES handwörterbuch, 1786.

Wöchentliche nachrichten und anmerkungen die musik betreffend.
1. jahrg. 1. jul. 1766–22. jun. 1767; 3. jahrg., 4. jul. 1768–26. jun.
1769; 4. jahrg., 1. jan.–24.dec. 1770. Leipzig, Im verlag der Zei-
tungs-expedition, 1766–70.

3 v. 24½ x 19ᶜᵐ.

Each quarter-year has t.-p. 4. jahrg. has title: Musikalische nachrichten und
anmerkungen auf das jahr 1770. 1. [-52.] stück. (Signatures: IV. jahrg.)
J. A. Hiller, editor.
L. of C. set lacks 2. jahrg. and 24 numbers published July 10–Dec. 25, 1769, as
anhang to the 3. jahrg.

ML4.W6

Wolf, Ernst Wilhelm, 1735–1792.

Auch eine reise, aber nur eine kleine musikalische, in den monaten
junius, julius und august 1782 zum vergnügen angestellt und . . .
beschrieben und herausgegeben von Ernst Wilhelm Wolf . . . Weimar, C. L. Hoffmanns sel. wittwe und erben, 1784.

64 p. 16ᶜᵐ.

ML275.3.W75

Wolf, Ernst Wilhelm—*Continued.*

Musikalischer unterricht. Vom ton; von den tonleitern; von den kon- und dissonirenden tönen; denen daraus entstehenden akkorden u. s. w.; von den fortschreitungen der töne und akkorde; von ihren ausweichungen, auflösungen und den daraus entstehenden verschiedenen kadenzen; vom takt ... vom tempo; von der melodie ... vom generalbass, und von der harmonischen modulazion; vom kontrapunkt ... von der nachahmung ... von der fuge ... alles durch praktische beyspiele erläutert; vom ausdruk, und etwas von der einrichtung musikalischer tonstükke ... geschrieben und hrsg. von Ernst Wilhelm Wolf. Dresden, Hilschersche musikverlage, 1788.

2 v. (v. 1: 2 p. l., 76 p.; v. 2: 1 p. l., 54 p.) 34½ᶜᵐ.

Vol. [2], "Praktische beyspiele," is engraved throughout.

MT40.A2W85

Wolf, Georg Friedrich, 1762–1814.

Kurzgefasstes musikalisches lexikon, zusammengetragen von Georg Friedrich Wolf ... Halle, J. C. Hendel, 1787.

xiv, 192 p. 20ᶜᵐ.

ML100.A2W8

Georg Friedrich Wolfs ... Unterricht im klavierspielen ... Halle, J. C. Hendel, 1799.

2 v. in 1 (v. 1: 104 p.; v. 2: 96 p.) 20ᶜᵐ.

Part 1: 4., verb. und verm. aufl. Part 2: Zweiter theil, welcher die anfangsgründe des generalbasses enthält. 2., verb. und verm. aufl.

MT220.A2W85

Georg Friedrich Wolfs Unterricht in der singekunst. Halle in Sachsen, J. C. Hendel, 1784.

123, [1] p. 20½ᶜᵐ.

Title vignette.

MT820.A2W7

Wollick, Nicolas.

Opus Aureum. ‖ Musice castigatissimū ‖ de Gregoriana et Figuratiua atcḥ con ‖ trapūcto simplici percōmode tra ‖ ctans ōm̄ibↄ cantu oblectan ‖ tibus vtile et necessa- ‖ rium e diuersis ‖ excerptum ‖ Fata regunt finem, spero dij cepta secundent ‖ Qui ducis vultus &non legis ista libenter ‖ Omnibus inuideas, liuide nemo tibi ‖ [*Colophon:* ℭ Explicit opusculū musices oībↄ volentibↄ cantum ‖ vtrūqↄ scire necessariū fausto fine Impressum Colo- ‖ nie in edibus honesti viri Henrici Quentell. Anno ‖ domini. M.ccccc.iiij]

[78] p. 1 illus., diagr. 21ᶜᵐ.

Signatures: A⁶, B⁴, C⁶, D–E⁴, F⁶, G⁴, H⁶ (one leaf, to complete signature H, wanting)

In four parts, of which only the first two, treating of the Gregorian choral, are by Wollick; the last two, dealing with florid song, are by Malcior of Worms.

The staves alone are given for the musical examples of the third and fourth parts.

On the last page is a letter headed: Nicolaus wollick de Serouilla Artiū magister dño Ade Popardiensi sacre pagine licentiato ac in gymnasio Corneliano regenti Salutē. P. D.

According to Fétis this is a reissue of the 1st edition, Cologne, 1501, with new t.-p.

ML171.W75

Wollick, Nicolas—*Continued.*

—— ℂ Enchiridiō musices Nicolai wolici ‖ Barroducensis de gregoriana et figu ‖ ratiua atᴄ̨ cōtrapūcto simplici ᴘcom- ‖ mode tractās / omnibus cantu oblectā ‖ tibus perutile et necessarium. ‖ ℂ Distichon. ‖ Fata regunt musas placidum pertingere callem ‖ Annuet optanti cepta canora deus. ‖ [printer's mark] ‖ ℂ Distichon in zostum. ‖ Liuidus americos liuenti murmure tractus. ‖ Vadat: vt inuidiam liuor acerbus edat. [*Colophon:* ℂ Impressum Parisii impensa . . . Johānis ‖ Parui ad ītersigniū leonis argentei. ⸀ Francisci Regnault ad in- ‖ tersigniū diui Claudii cōmorātiū. Anno virginei partus. 1512. 14. ‖ kalendas Nouembris]

[163] p. illus. 19ᶜᵐ.

Signatures: a–i⁸, k⁶, l⁴. Gothic type; rubricated. Lettered: Thesaurus melodiæ.

ML171.W86

Wonnegger, Johann Ludwig.

See GLAREANUS. Musicæ epitome [1559]

Young, Matthew, *bp. of Clonfert,* 1750–1800.

An enquiry into the principal phænomena of sounds and musical strings. By Matthew Young . . . London, G. Robinson, 1784.

3 p. l., 203 p. pl., diagrs. on fold. pl. 22ᶜᵐ.

QC225.Y8

Yzo,

Lettre sur celle de M. J. J. Rousseau, citoyen de Geneve, sur la musique. Par M. Yzo . . . [Paris] 1753.

24 p. 16ᶜᵐ.

Addressed to "Monsieur Breun de Larcherie, Américain."

ML1727.33.Y97

See also Iso.

Zacconi, Giulio Cesare, *in religion* **Lodovico,** 1555–1627.

Prattica di mvsica vtile et necessaria si al compositore per comporre i canti suoi regolatamente, si anco al cantore per assicurarsi in tutte le cose cantabili. Divisa in qvattro libri. Ne i qvali si tratta delle cantilene ordinarie, de tempi de prolationi, de proportioni, de tuoni, et della conuenienza de tutti gli istrumenti musicali. S'insegna a cantar tvtte le composizioni antiche, si dichiara tutta la messa del Palestina titolo Lomè armè, con altre cose d'importanza & diletteuole. Vltimamente s'insegna il modo di fiorir una parte con uaghi & moderni accenti. Composta dal r. p. f. Lodovico Zacconi . . . Venetia, B. Carampello, 1596.

6 p. l., 218 numb. l. illus. 29ᶜᵐ.

Title vignette. Leaves 30, 67, 124, 130, 188 numbered 29, 140, 130, 122, 194 respectively.

Leaf inserted before leaf 50, bearing also the number 50, and having on recto the alto, etc.: Beatus author seculi, in measured notation; on verso, canto etc.: Gloria tibi domine, in black choral notation. The original leaf has on recto the alto, etc.: Beatus author seculi, in black choral notation, and on verso, text.

According to Gaspari this edition is the same, t.-p. excepted, as the edition of 1592.

A second part was published at Venice in 1622.

ML171.Z23

Zanger, Johann.

Practicae mv- ‖ sicae praecepta, ‖ pveritiae institvendae ‖ gratia, ad certam metho- ‖ dum reuocata, per ‖ Ioannem Zange- ‖ rum Oenipontanum. ‖ Lipsiae, ‖ In officina Typographica ‖ Georgij Hantzsch. ‖ Anno ‖ 1554.

[154] p. 1 illus. 20^{cm}.

Signatures: A–S in fours, T in six (last leaf blank)   Guidonian hand on verso of B2.

ML171.Z26

De **zangkunst** gemaklijk gemaakt; of, Musykaal handboek; met behulp van 't welke men alle de gronden dier loflijke kunst zonder meester kan leeren: benevens eene duidelijke verklaaring van de hoogstnuttige transpositie: opgehelderd met veele voorbeelden, op uitslaande plaaten, zeer zindelyk in 't koper gegraveerd. Amsterdam, H. Gartman, 1788.

40 p.   front., 9 fold. pl.   19½^{cm}.

Introduction signed: D. v. H.
A new edition of Dirk van der Hooch's Grondslag van 't vocaalmuzijk?

MT870.A2Z2

Zanotti, Francesco Maria, 1692–1777.

Lettere del Sig. Francesco Maria Zanotti, del pad. Giambatista Martini, MIN. CON., del pad. Giovenale Sacchi, C. R. B., accademici dell' Istituto di Bologna, nelle quali si propongono, e risolvono alcuni dubbj appartenenti al trattato: Della divisione del tempo nella musica, nel ballo, e nella poesia, pubblicato in Milano l'anno 1770 nella stamperia Malatesta; e all' altro: Delle quinte successive nel contrappunto, e delle regole degli accompagnamenti, pubblicato nella medesima stamperia, l'anno 1780. Milano, Stamperia de' fratelli Pirola, 1782.

2 p. l., [3]–59 p.   23^{cm}.

Pages 9–10, 39–40 (half-titles?) do not appear in this copy.
The treatises in question were written by Sacchi.

MT55.A2Z2

Zapata, Maurizio, 1640–1709.

Ristretto, overo breve discorso sopra le regole di canto fermo, di D. Mavrizio Zapata . . .   Parma, G. dall' Oglio, e I. Rosati, 1682.

64 p.   21^{cm}.

MT860.A2Z2

Zarlino, Gioseffo, d. 1590.

De tvtte l'opere del r. m. Gioseffo Zarlino . . . ch' ei scrisse in bvona lingva italiana; già separatamente poste in luce; hora di nuouo corrette, accresciute, & migliorate, insieme ristampate . . . Venetia, Francesco de' Franceschi Senese, 1588–89.

4 v. in 3.   illus., diagrs. (1 fold.)   30½^{cm}.

Printer's mark on t.-p.   Title varies.

CONTENTS.—1. v. L'istitvtioni harmoniche. 1589.—2. v. Le dimostrationi harmoniche. 1589.—3. v. Sopplimenti mvsicali . . . ne i quali si dichiarano molte cose contenute ne i due primi volumi, delle istitutioni e dimostrationi; per essere state mal' intese da molti; e si risponde insieme alle loro calonnie. 1588.—4. v. Il trattato della patientia, Il discorso del vero anno, & giorno della morte di Christo, L'origine de i r. p. Capuccini, et Le risolutioni d'alcune dimande fatte intorno la correttione del calendario di Giulio Cesare. 1589.

ML171.Z33

Zarlino, Gioseffo—*Continued.*

Dimostrationi harmoniche del r. m. Gioseffo Zarlino ... Nelle quali realmente si trattano le cose della musica: & si risoluono molti dubij d'importanza. Opera molto necessaria à tutti quelli, che desiderano di far buon profitto in questa nobile scienza. Con la tauola delle materie notabili contenute nell' opera ... Venetia, Francesco de i Franceschi Senese, 1571.

4 p. l., 312, [10] p., 1 l. illus., diagrs. 30^{cm}.

Printer's mark on t.-p.

ML171.Z37

Le istitvtioni harmoniche di m. Gioseffo Zarlino da Chioggia; nelle quali; oltra le materie appartenenti alla mvsica; si troùano dichiarati molti luoghi di poeti, d'historici, & di filosofi; si come nel leggerle si potrà chiaramente vedere ... Venetia, 1558.

6 p. l., 347 p. diagrs. 30½^{cm}.

Printer's mark (?) on t.-p., with legend: Excubo ac vigilo. Text, preface and table of contents printed in italics. Page 95 wrongly numbered 87.

ML171.Z35

—— Istitvtioni harmoniche del rev. messere Gioseffo Zarlino ... di nuouo in molti luoghi migliorate, & ... ampliate. Nelle quali; oltra le materie appartenenti alla mvsica; si trouan dichiarati molti luoghi di poeti, historici, & di filosofi; si come nel leggerle si potrà chiaramente vedere. Con due tauole; l'vna che contiene le materie principali: & l'altra le cose più notabili, che nell' opera si ritrouano ... Venetia, Francesco de i Franceschi Senese, 1573.

6 p. l., 428, [20] p. illus., diagrs. 30^{cm}.

Printer's mark on t.-p.
Bound with the "Dimostrationi harmoniche" and "Sopplimenti musicali."

ML171.Z37

Sopplimenti mvsicali del rev. m. Gioseffo Zarlino ... Ne i quali si dichiarano molte cose contenute ne i due primi volumi, delle Istitutioni & Dimostrationi; per essere state mal' intese da molti; & si risponde insieme alle loro calonnie. Con due tauole, l'una che contiene i capi principali delle materie, & l'altra le cose più notabili, che si trouano nell' opera. Terzo volume ... Venetia, Francesco de' Franceschi, Sanese, 1588.

8 p. l., 330, [20] p. illus. (incl. coat of arms) diagrs. (1 fold.) 30^{cm}.

Printer's mark on t.-p.
Bound with "Dimostrationi harmoniche" and "Istitutioni harmoniche."

ML171.Z37

See also CERONE, D. P. El melopeo, 1613.

Zeidler, Carl Sebastian, 1719–1786.

Dissertatio epistolica de vetervm philosophorvm stvdio mvsico, qvam ... domino Erhardo Andreae Frommanno in anniversario Academiae altdorffinae sacro A. D. XXIX. ivnii MDCCXLV. dignitatem philosophicam impetranti gratvlationis cavssa dicat Carolvs Sebastianvs Zeidler ... Norimbergae, typis A. Bielingii [1745]

12 p. 20 x 16½^{cm}.

ML168.Z34

See also GRUBER, J. S. Beyträge zur litteratur der musik.

Zeidler, Johann Georg, *b. ca.* 1590, *praeses.*

. . . Ternarius musicus . . .   Jena[e] typis Henri[ci Rauchmauls?
1615]

[8] p.   18 x 15ᶜᵐ.

Diss.—Jena (U. Fritsch respondent)
Imperfect, part of t.-p. torn off.

ML64.Z34

Zeno, Apostolo, 1668–1750.

See ALLACCI, L.   Drammaturgia, 1755.

Zuccari, Carlo.

The true method of playing an adagio made easy by twelve examples, first, in a plain manner with a bass, then with all their graces,
adapted for those who study the violin; composed by Carlo Zuccari
. . .   London, Printed by R: Bremner [17—]

1 p. l., xii p.   24 x 33ᶜᵐ.   (*With* Pasquali, Nicolo. The art of fingering, the
harpsichord. London [17—])

Engraved throughout.

MT252.A2P31

[Zumbag de Koesfelt, Coenraad] 1697–1780.

Institutiones musicæ, of Korte onderwyzingen rakende de practyk
van de musyk; en inzonderheid van den generaalen bas. of bassus
continuus, benevens de daer úit sprúitende gronden van de compositie. Úitgegeven door een liefhebber van deze kunst. Leyden,
G. Potvliet, 1743.

4 p. l., 74, [2] p.   viii pl.   18½ᶜᵐ.

Engr. t.-p. Dedication signed: Coenraad Zumbag de Koesfelt, m. d.
Based on a work left in ms. by his father, Lothar Zumbag de Koesfelt
(1661–1727)

MT49.A2Z8

INDEX TO ANONYMOUS WORKS.

Including references to special contents.

A B C Dario musico. *See* Title.
A. G. Kaestners . . . schreiben. *See* Bollioud-Mermet.
Der aberwitzige pickelhering Jean Rebhu. *See* Printz' Phrynis Mitilenaeus.
Abhandlung vom schalle. *See* Belz' Dissertation sur le son et sur l'ouie.
Abhandlung von den pantomimen. *See* Title.
Abrégé de l'histoire de la Ménestrandie. *See* Bêche.
Abstract of the laws . . . of the Fund for the support of decayed musicians.
See Burney's Account.
An account of printed musick. *See* A short explication.
An account of the institution and progress of the Academy of ancient
music. *See* Hawkins.
An account of three brass trumpets, found near Cork. *See* Walker.
Adicion al Compendio del arte de canto llano. *See* Villasagra.
Aggiunta di alcune messe proprie de santi. *See* La Feillée's Il cantore ecclesiastico.
Alcuni essempi della più antica musica. *See* João IV.
Alguns hymnos selectos. *See* Bernardo da Conceição.
Allgemeine musikalische zeitung. *See* Title.
Almanach des Theaters in Wien. *See* Title.
Als unverhoetz. *See* Papius.
Altri documenti musicali nel canto fermo. *See* Banchieri's Cartella musicale.
Alypii Introductio musica. *See* Meibom.
Die an der kirchen Gottes gebauete satans-capelle. *See* Fuhrmann.
Analyse critique de Tarare. *See* Title.
Ancient songs from the time of King Henry the Third. *See* Ritson.
Anecdotes dramatiques. *See* Clément, J. M. B.
Anecdotes of . . . Handel . . . and . . . Smith. *See* Coxe.
Aneddoto forense. *See* Mattei.
Anleitung zum selbstunterricht in der musikalischen composition. *See*
Daube's Anleitung zur erfindung der melodie.
Anmerkungen ueber die musik ueberhaupt. *See* Hertel's Sammlung.
L'anti-scurra. *See* Title.
Apologia delle opere drammatiche di Metastasio. *See* Franceschi.
Apologie de la musique françoise. *See* Laugier.
Apologie du goût françois. *See* Caux de Cappeval.
Arguments to prove the obligation of the duty, by Mr. Bradbury. *See* Practical discourses.
Ariette, mise en musique par M. l'abbé Dugué. *See* Fournier.
Ἀριστείδου Κοϊντιλιανοῦ Περὶ μουσικῆς βιβλία. *See* Meibom.
Aristidis Quintiliani De musica libri III. *See* Meibom.
Aristoxeni Harmonicorum elementorum libri III. *See* Meibom.
Armonici erudimenti. *See* Title.
Arrest de la Cour de Parlement. *See* France.

Compendium musice. *See* Cantorinus.
Compendiū musices. *See* Title.
Compendium regularum generalium cantus. *See* Title.
Compleat instructions for the German flute. *See* Title.
The compleat tutor for the fife. *See* Title.
The compleat tutor for the German flute. *See* Title.
The compleat tutor for the harpsichord or spinnet. *See* Title.
La constitution de l'opéra. *See* Chevrier's Constitution du Patriarche de l'opera.
Constitution du Patriarche de l'Opera. *See* Chevrier.
Le correcteur des Bouffons. *See* Jourdan.
Cours de jeux instructifs pour la jeunesse. *See* Gaultier.
Der Critische musicus an der Spree. *See* Marpurg.
Crotalogía; ó, Ciencia de las castañuelas. *See* Fernández de Rojas.
The dancing-master. *See* Title.
De arte canendi. *See* Spangenberg.
De arte medendi apud priscos musices. *See* Michell.
De cantionibus funebribus veterum. *See* Senff.
De excellentia musicae antiquae Hebraeorum. *See* Bretagne.
De i vizj, e de i difetti del moderno teatro. *See* Bianchi.
De l'art du théâtre en général. *See* Nougaret.
De la musique considérée en elle-même. *See* Chabanon.
De la musique et de Nephté. *See* Toscan.
De principijs musice tractatus I[-II] *See* Reisch.
De sono et tono. *See* Funk.
De templo musicae. *See* Fludd.
De Venise. Rémarques sur la musique & la danse. *See* Goudar, *Mme.* Sara.
De veteris Graecorum musices. *See* Title.
Declaration du public. *See* Title.
Déclaration du roi. *See* France.
Declaration oder weitere erklaerung der Refutation. *See* Printz' Phrynis Mitilenaeus.
Deliciae theatrales. *See* Lambranzi.
Dialogue sur la musique des anciens. *See* Châteauneuf.
Dictionnaire de danse. *See* Compan.
Dictionnaire des théatres de Paris. *See* Parfaict.
Difesa della musica moderna. *See* João IV.
Directions for playing on the flute. *See* Prelleur.
Directions for the right performance of the duty of singing, by Mr. Newman. *See* Practical discourses.
Discours analytique sur la cohérence imperturbable. *See* Wiese.
Discours d'un ancien avocat-général. *See* Servan.
Discours non plus melancoliques que divers. *See* Title.
Discours préliminaire de l'opéra de Tarare. *See* Beaumarchais.
Discours sceptique sur la musique. *See* La Mothe Le Vayer.
Discours sur l'harmonie. *See* Gresset.
Discurs des herrn Quanz ueber das clavieraccompagnement. *See* Marpurg's Clavierstuecke.
Disputatio juridica de eo quod justum est. *See* Stryk.
Disputatio medica ordinaria de musica. *See* Franck de Franckenau.
Disputatio musica de divisione monochordi. *See* Trew.
Dissertation historique sur la vielle. *See* Terrasson.
Dissertation on the origin of the violoncello. *See* Gunn.
Dissertation on the songs ... of the ancient English. *See* Ritson.

An essay on the construction . . . of the Irish harp . . . **By William Beauford.** *See* Walker.

An essay on the poetical accents of the Irish: by **William Beauford.** *See* Walker.

An essay towards an history of dancing. *See* Weaver.

An essay upon tune. *See* Maxwell.

Etat actuel de la musique du roi. *See* Title.

Euclidis Introductio harmonica. *See* Meibom.

Euterpe. *See* Dorat.

Examen de deux principes avancés par M. Rameau. *See* Rousseau's Traités.

Examen de la lettre de M. Rousseau, sur la musique françoise. *See* Bâton.

Examen d'un passage de Platon. *See* Fraguier.

Exemples de quelques antiennes et respons. *See* Nivers.

Exemplum omnium regularum. *See* Galliculus.

Exercitatio philologica de instrumentis Ebraeorum musicis. *See* Weidling.

Exercitatio qua musices origo prima. *See* Schlick.

Exhortation to singing, by Mr. Gravener. *See* Practical discourses.

Exposition de quelques nouvelles vues mathematiques. *See* Title.

Extrait d'une reponse du petit faiseur. *See* Rousseau's Traites.

Des herrn Frerons critik . . . *See* Hertel.

La galerie de l'Académie royale de musique. *See* Travenol.

Gaudentii . . . Introductio harmonica. *See* Meibom.

Gedanken eines liebhabers der tonkunst. *See* Leopold.

Gedanken ueber die temperatur des herrn Kirnberger. *See* Tempelhof.

Gedanken ueber die welschen tonkuenstler. *See* Title.

Gedanken und konjekturen zur geschichte der musik. *See* Leopold.

Gedanken von den tragoedien der Griechen. *See* Hertel.

Gespraech von der musik. *See* Voigt.

Gespraech zwischen Lulli, Rameau und Orpheus. *See* Riedel.

Der gestuertzte und wieder erhoehte Nebucadnezar (libretto) *See* Hunold.

Le gratie d' Amore. *See* Negri.

Grund-regeln wie man . . . sich selbst die fundamenta der music . . . lernen kan. *See* Thielo.

Guazzabuglio filosarmonico. *See* Mattei.

La guerre de l'opera. *See* Cazotte.

Harmonie theorico-pratique. *See* Blainville.

The harpsichord illustrated. *See* Prelleur.

The harpsichord illustrated and improv'd. *See* Title.

The harpsichord preceptor. *See* Title.

Eine helle brille. *See* Ludwig.

Histoire anecdotique et raisonnée du Théâtre italien. *See* Desboulmiers.

Histoire de l'opera bouffon. *See* Contant d'Orville.

Histoire du théatre de l'Académie royale de musique. *See* Durey de Noinville.

Histoire du théatre de l'Opéra comique. *See* Desboulmiers.

Histoire du théatre de l'opera en France. *See* Durey de Noinville.

L'Hopital musicien. *See* Title.

Ici sont ecrits les vingt-un chapitres de la prophétie. *See* Grimm.

Das in unsern opern-theatris und comoedien-buehnen siechende christenthum. *See* Fuhrmann.

Inquiries concerning the ancient Irish harp . . . by . . . Ledwich. *See* Walker.

Institutiones musicae, of Korte onderwyzingen. *See* Zumbag de Koesfelt.

Institutionis musicae practicae. *See* Falck's Idea boni cantoris.

Instructions upon the hautboy. *See* Prelleur.

An introduction to singing. *See* Prelleur.

Lettre de M. * * * négociant de Paris. *See* Title.
Lettre de M. Camille Trillo. *See* Lesuire.
Lettre de M. de * * * à Madame de * * * *See* Title.
Lettre d'un amateur de l'Opera. *See* Title.
Lettre d'un Parisien. *See* Title.
Lettre d'un sage a un homme très respectable. *See* Lamorlière.
Lettre sur la musique, a Monsieur le comte de Caylus. *See* Arnaud.
Lettre sur la musique moderne. *See* Moyria.
Lettre sur les drames-opera. *See* Du Roullet.
Lettres a Madame la marquise de P. *See* Mably.
Lettres de Mr. G . . . à Milord Pembroke. *See* Goudar, *Mme.* Sara.
Lettres et chansons, de Cephise et d'Uranie. *See* Lévesque.
Lettres patentes du roi. *See* France.
Lettres sur la musique françoise. *See* Fréron.
La libertà del cantare. *See* Cattaneo.
Libro llamado Arte de tañer fantasia. *See* Tomás de Santa María.
The life of Turlough O'Carolan. *See* Walker.
Liliũ musice plane. *See* Keinspeck.
Liturgia Ambrosiana. *See* Regole d'alcuni capi necessarj.
Lobspruch . . . Jo. Ernestus Saur. *See* Bulyovszky.
Joh. Friedr. Loewens Anmerkungen ueber die geistliche cantatenpoesie. *See* Hertel's Sammlung.
Joh. Friedr. Loewens Anmerkungen ueber die odenpoesie. *See* Hertel's Sammlung.
Lully, musicien. *See* Le Prévost d'Exmes.
Lumi primi del canto fermo. *See* Erculeo's Il canto ecclesiastico.
Magazin der musik. *See* Title.
Le Magazin des modernes. *See* Title.
Manuductio ad cantum choralem. *See* Title.
Martiani Capellae De musica liber IX. *See* Meibom.
Melody—The soul of music. *See* Title.
Mémoire justificatif des sujets de l'Académie royale de musique. *See* Paris.
Mémoire, lettres patentes et arrêts. *See* France.
Memoire pour le sieur de Lanove. *See* Title.
Memoire pour le sieur Iso. *See* Iso.
Memoire pour le sieur Travenol. *See* Travenol.
Mémoire pour servir l'histoire de la comédie italienne. *See* Le nouveau théatre italien.
Memoire sur l'autorité des musiciens en matiere de plainchant. *See* Burette's Extrait d'une lettre.
Memoires anecdotes pour servir a l'histoire de M. Duliz. *See* Desforges.
Mémoires historiques sur Raoul de Coucy. *See* La Borde.
Mémoires pour servir a l'histoire de la révolution opérée . . . par . . . Gluck. *See* Title.
Memoires pour servir a l'histoire des spectacles de la foire. *See* Parfaict.
Mémoires sur les proportions musicales. *See* La Borde.
Memoirs of Cormac Common. *See* Walker.
Memoirs of the life of the late George Frederic Handel. *See* Mainwaring.
Memorie storiche del p. m. Giambattista Martini. *See* Valle.
Le Mercure galant devalisé. *See* La musique du diable.
Methode de musique selon un nouveau systême. *See* Démotz de La Salle.
Methode du chant ecclesiastique. *See* Alexis de Sainte Anne.
Metodo per suonare il flauto. *See* Title.
Missa in coena Domini. *See* Gerbert.

Missive van een heer in Leijden.   *See* Toneellief.
Modelles pour la transposition.   *See* Rousseau's Traité de la viole.
The modern musick-master; or, the universal musician.   *See* Prelleur.
Il modo di solfeggiare all' uso francese.   *See* Larghi.
Mon dernier mot.   *See* Latour de Franqueville.
Morceaux de musique du 16ᵉ et 17ᵉ siècle.   *See* La Borde's Essai.
Motetes y obras diferentes al Santissimo y à Nra Sra.   *See* Roel del Río.
Motets pour les principales fêtes de l'année.   *See* La Feillée.
Mozarts leben.   *See* Schlichtegroll.
Museum musicum theoretico-practicum.   *See* Majer.
Musica libris quatuor demonstrata.   *See* Le Fèvre.
Musica parabolica.   *See* Neuss.
La musica, poemetto.   *See* Olio.
Musicae, id est, artis canendi libri duo.   *See* Heyden.
A musical directory for the year 1794.   *See* Title.
Musical phaenomena.   *See* Clagget.
Musical travels through England.   *See* Veal.
Musicalische discurse.   *See* Bähr.
Musicalische strigel.   *See* Fuhrmann.
Musicalischer-trichter.   *See* Fuhrmann.
Musices choralis medulla.   *See* Title.
Musicus αὐτοδίδακτος.   *See* Eisel.
Musicus curiosus, oder Battalus.   *See* Printz.
Musicus magnanimus, oder Pancalus.   *See* Printz.
Musicus theoretico-practicus.   *See* Hartong.
Musik.   *See* Title.
Der Musikalische dillettante, eine wochenschrift.   *See* Title.
Musikalische monathsschrift.   *See* Title.
Musikalische real-zeitung.   *See* Title.
Musikalischer almanach . . .   *See* Title.
Musikalischer und kuenstler-almanach.   *See* Title.
Musikalisches handwoerterbuch oder kurzgefasste anleitung.   *See* Title.
Musikalisches kunstmagasin.   *See* Title.
Musikalisches wochenblatt.   *See* Title.
La musique du diable, ou Le Mercure galant devalisé.   *See* Title.
La musique rendue sensible par la méchanique.   *See* Choquel.
Musomachia, id est Bellum musicale.   *See* Sartorius.
Nachgedanken herrn m. Joh. Gottl. Biedermanns.   *See* Title.
Nachricht von Georg Friedrich Haendel's lebensumstaenden.   *See* Burney.
Neue melodien zu einigen liedern des neuen hamburgischen gesangbuchs
    (C. Ph. E. Bach)   *See* Kellner's Treuliches unterricht, 7. aufl.
Neue und erleichterte art zu solmisiren.   *See* Title.
New and complete instructions for the fife.   *See* The compleat tutor for the fife.
New and complete instructions for the harpsichord.   *See* Title.
A new and easie method to learn to sing by book.   *See* Title.
New instructions for the German flute.   *See* Compleat instructions.
New instructions for the violin.   *See* Geminiani's Compleat instructions for the
    violin.
The newest method for learners on the German flute.   *See* Prelleur.
Nicomachi Geraseni, Pythagorici, harmonices manuale.   *See* Meibom.
Le nouveau théatre italien.   *See* Title.
Nouvelle méthode où Traité théorique et pratique du plain-chant.   *See*
    Poisson.
Nouvelle méthode pour aprendre le plain-chant.   *See* Title.

La Rameïde. *See* Rameau, J. F.

Recueil d'édit, arrêt du Conseil du roi. *See* France.

Reflections on antient and modern musick. *See* Brocklesby.

Reflexions d'un patriote sur l'opera françois. *See* Rochemont.

Reflexions d'un peintre sur l'opera. *See* Gauthier de Montdorge.

Réflexions sur la musique dramatiques. *See* Garcin.

Reflexions sur la musique, ou recherches sur la cause des effets qu'elle produit. Par M. V * * *. *See* Title.

Reflexions sur l'opera. *See* Rémond de Saint-Mard.

Réfutation . . . des principes de M. Rousseau de Genève. *See* Aubert.

Refutation des Satyrischen componisten. *See* Printz' Phrynis Mitilenaeus.

Reglas y advertencias generales. *See* Minguet é Irol.

Reglemens pour l'Académie royale de musique. *See* Paris.

Réglement pour l'Académie royale de musique. *See* France.

Regles de composition. *See* Blainville's Harmonie.

Regole d'alcuni capi necessarj. *See* Title.

Regole le principali . . . per bene apprendere. *See* Belli's Dissertazione sopra li preggi del cantō gregoriano.

Regole musicali per li principianti di cembalo. *See* Title.

Remarks on Mr. Avison's Essay on musical expression. *See* Hayes.

Remarques curieuses sur l'art de bien chanter. *See* Bacilly's L'art de bien chanter.

Remarques sur l'art de bien chanter. *See* Bacilly's L'art de bien chanter.

Der [!] herrn Remond von St. Mard Betrachtungen ueber die oper. *See* Hertel's Sammlung.

Réponse critique d'un académicien de Rouen. *See* Castel.

Réponse de M. l'abbé Roussier. *See* La Borde's Mémoires sur les proportions musicales.

Réponse du coin du roi au coin de la reine. *See* Voisenon.

Des representations en musique anciennes et modernes. *See* Menestrier.

Requeste de deux actrices d'Opera a Momus. *See* Couppé.

Requeste présentée à Momus. *See* Couppé.

A review of some short directions. *See* Lowe.

Risposta di un' anonimo al celebre Sig. Rousseau. *See* Title.

Rules and directions for singing the psalms. *See* Playford, John.

Rules; or a short and compleat method. *See* Title.

Ruth, an attempt towards an oratorio. *See* Davy's Letters.

Saggio per costruire e suonare un flauto traverso. *See* Orazi.

Sammlung einiger nachrichten von beruehmten orgel-wercken. *See* Meyer.

Sanctissimi in Christo patris . . . Clementis . . . papae XIII constitutio . . . *See* Clemens XIII.

Die . . . satans-capelle. *See* Fuhrmann.

Satire a Monsieur le marquis D . . . *See* Robbé de Beauveset.

Schreiben an den herrn von L * s * r. *See* Hertel.

Schreiben an die herren verfasser der Freyen urteile. *See* Title.

La science et la pratique du plain-chant. *See* Jumilhac.

Seconde lettre du correcteur des Bouffons. *See* Jourdan.

Select Irish melodies. *See* Walker.

Sendschreiben an die herren verfasser der Freyen urtheile. *See* Title.

Sense against sound; or, A succedaneum, for Abbey music. *See* Title.

Sentiment d'un harmoniphile. *See* Laugier.

Short and easie ayres designed for learners. *See* Simpson's Compendium, 1678.

A short explication of . . . foreign words. *See* Title.

A short treatise on harmony. *See* Pepusch.

ADDENDA

(Entries for books received too late for insertion in the main alphabet)

Artusi, Giovanni Maria, *d.* 1613.

L'Artvsi, ouero Delle imperfettioni della moderna mvsica ragionamenti dui. Ne' quali si ragiona di molte cose vtili, & necessarie alli moderni compositori. Del r. p. d. Gio. Maria Artvsi da Bologna. Canonico regolare nella congregatione del Saluatore. Nouamente stampato. In Venetia, Appresso Giacomo Vincenti, 1600.

4 p. l., 71 numb. l. diagrs. 26½ᶜᵐ.

Title vignette: ecclesiastical coat of arms.
"Un motetto à quattro voci del re. Costanzo Porta:" l. 70 v°–l. 71.

ML171.A83

[Freillon Poncein, Jean Pierre]

La veritable maniere d'apprendre a jouer en perfection du haut-bois, de la flute et du flageolet. Avec les principes de la musique pour la voix et pour toutes sortes d'instrumens. Paris, J. Collombat, 1700.

5 p. l., 74 (*i. e.* 81) p. illus. 16½ x 23½ᶜᵐ.

The epistle dedicatory is signed: Freillon Poncein.
Printer's mark on t.-p.; paging irregular. Contains, in addition to the usual examples, the author's 6 part "L'embarras de Paris," based on the street cries of Paris, and "Bruits de guerre pour toutes sortes d'instruments."

MT362.F8

Gando, Nicolas, *d. ca.* 1767.

Observations sur le Traité historique et critique de Monsieur Fournier le jeune, sur l'origine et les progrès des caractères de fonte, pour l'impression de la musique. Par MM. Gando, pere et fils. A Berne, et se trouve à Paris, chez Moreau, 1766.

27, [1] p. 25 x 19ᶜᵐ. (*With* Fournier, P. S. Traité historique et critique. Berne, 1765. Copy 2)

"Six morceaux d'ancienne musique . . . pour démontrer les progrès de cette partie de l'art typographique en France, jusqu'en 1695:" [1] p. at end.

Yudin coll.

[Goudar, *Mme.* Sara] *d. ca.* 1800.

Osservazioni sopra la musica, ed il ballo, ossia Estratto di due lettere di Mr. G . . . a Milord P . . . tradotte dal francese. Milano, G. Motta [17—]

110 p. 21ᶜᵐ.

The original was published at Venice, in 1773, under title: "De Venise. Rémarques sur la musique & la danse." The translator is given as "F. T." in a ms. copy dated Venice, 1773, belonging to the Liceo musicale of Bologna.

ML3845.A2G693

Musikalische charlatanerien. Von F. W. V. Berlin und Leipzig, 1792.

23 p. 16½ᶜᵐ.

Observations sur la musique, la flute, et la lyre des anciens . . . Paris, Flahault, 1726.

34 p., 1 l. pl. 17½ᶜᵐ. (*With* Châteauneuf, F. de Castagnères, *abbé* de. Dialogue sur la musique. Paris, 1725. Copy 2)

A criticism of the Abbé de Châteauneuf's "Dialogue sur la musique des anciens." Printed also in "Bibliothèque française, ou Histoire littéraire de la France," Amsterdam, 1723–42, vol. v, p. 107–125. *cf.* Fétis, Biog. univ. des musiciens.

Regole d'alcvni capi necessarii, e più frequenti per l'osseruanza delle sacre cerimonie, e del canto fermo Ambrosiano. Stampate d'ordine di Monsig. illustrissimo, e reuerendissimo Federico cardinal Borromeo arciuescouo di Milano. Con privilegio. In Milano, Per gli her. di Pacifico Pontio, & Gio. Battista Piccaglia. stampatori archiepiscopali.1622.

46 p. 23ᶜᵐ.

Title vignette.

O

THE LIBRARY OF CONGRESS

CATALOGUE

OF

EARLY BOOKS
ON MUSIC

(*before* 1800)

SUPPLEMENT

(BOOKS ACQUIRED
BY THE LIBRARY 1913–1942)

By

HAZEL BARTLETT

Principal Cataloger

Descriptive Cataloging Division

WITH A LIST OF BOOKS ON MUSIC
IN CHINESE AND JAPANESE

Washington

1944

TABLE OF CONTENTS

II

PREFATORY NOTE

Thirty years have gone by since the Library of Congress Catalogue of Early Books on Music, prepared by Julia Gregory of the Catalogue Division, was issued under the direction of the late O. G. T. Sonneck, then chief of the Music Division. That catalog listed, besides the pre-1800 printed books, neither numerous nor important, that he had found in the general collection of the Library at the time of his appointment as chief in 1902, the almost incredibly larger number that he had been able to gather together in the next 10 years. The total came to nearly 1,500 books. In his preface to the Gregory catalog, he estimated that these constituted "probably more than a third of the entire output before 1800." While he complained that "in the short space of ten years it was, of course, impossible to acquire every rare book of moment and in some cases this was due less to rarity than to prohibitive cost," the time was still favorable for the play of his exceptional energy, discrimination, and enthusiasm; since then, with the spread of collector's fever, and the entrance of many rare books into permanent collections, prices have become still more prohibitive and wanted books more difficult to find.

The present supplement to the Gregory catalog contains roughly 500 entries. They are almost all for works in the ML and MT classifications (literature of music and instruction in its theory and practice), although a few books classified in M (music) have been included because of the introductory matter that they contain. Two prized tablature books, Judenkünig and Neusiedler, are included, but others, such as Narváez and Cabezón, have been omitted. (For a list of tablatures, printed and manuscript, see the report of the Librarian of Congress for 1928 and the following years.) A few works in classifications other than music have been admitted when their musical interest seemed enough to warrant inclusion, but there are doubtless many other books in the Library, dealing incidentally with music and listed by bibliographers among works on music, that might as well have been included. It was proposed to include more of the early encyclopedic works, such as Valla, that contain sections on music, but before they could be picked out and cataloged, the contents of the Rare Book Room had been removed from the Library for safe keeping during the war.

A recent important accession of early books, the Dayton C. Miller collection of works on the flute, acquired by the Library in 1941, was sent away to be kept in protective custody before it had even been completely unpacked. A few of the items were cataloged and appear in the body of this supplement, but descriptions of about 50 more were copied verbatim from the catalog of the collection printed in 1935, and form an appendix to this supplement. For copying the Miller catalog entries, and for assistance in preparing this supplement for the press, I thank Dr. Helen E. Bush.

The style of the supplement is, in general, modeled on that of the Gregory catalog, but inconsistencies and variations undoubtedly appear in a catalog whose items have been prepared over a period of 30 years. It has not been possible to check any discrepancies with the books, for the Music Division's treasures, like those of the Rare Book Room, have been sent away.

The entries in the supplement are, in general, uniform with the Library's printed cards, except that they omit subject headings, but occasional modifications have been made. Numbers printed at the lower left of each entry are the serial numbers of printed cards.

It is possible that a few undated publications later than 1800 have been included. When attempting to determine imprint dates, especially of the swarm of eighteenth century instruction books, the cataloger's thoughts turn with a shade of rancor to the early music publisher who is credited with the dictum, so widely followed, that music, like women, should not be dated.

This supplement, like the preceding catalog, is a descriptive list merely, and by its nature unconcerned with appraising the cultural or historical value of the works it describes. The section of "Books on East Asiatic Music," prepared by two former members of the Asiatic Division, is of a different character, and presents an informing and interesting account of the development of Chinese and Japanese music and musical instruments, serving at the same time as a reminder of the valuable and extensive resources of the Library's Asiatic Division.

I regret any mistakes in this catalog and desire to be informed of them. If any typographical errors have escaped notice, I hope that the user of the catalog may be as indulgent as Thomas Jefferson, who wrote in 1816 of another Library of Congress catalog: "There are some errors of the press, but such a number of titles in so many different languages could not be expected to be otherwise."

                                                HAZEL BARTLETT.

WASHINGTON, D. C., *September 1943.*

Catalogue *of*
Early Books on Music

A. B.
See [BAILLIE, A.] *supposed author.* An introduction to the knowledge and practice of the thoro' bass. 1717.

A. B., *Philo-Mus.*
See SYNOPSIS of vocal musick. 1680.

Aaron, Pietro.
Toscanello in musica di messer Piero Aron ... Nuouamente stăpato con la gionta da lui fatta & con diligentia corretto ... [*Colophon:* Stampato in Vineggia per Marchio Sessa nelli anni del Signore M.D.XXXIX. a di XIX. marzo]

[72] p. illus. (incl. music) tables, diagr. 29½^{cm}.

Signatures: A–I⁴.
Printer's mark on t.-p.; initials; title within ornamental border. On verso of Aii a full-page illustration of Aaron in his lecture room.
Limp vellum binding.
25–21743   ML171.A133

Académie de musique de Troyes.
Reglemens de l'Academie de musique de Troyes, capitale de Champagne; établie le septième de décembre 1728. Troyes, P. Michelin, 1729.

12 p. 25 x 19½^{cm}.

42–5442   ML270.3.T75R3

Adam, Louis, 1758–1848.
Methode ou principe général du doigté pour le forté-piano, suivie d'une collection complette de tous les traits possibles avec le doigté, en commençant par les plus aisés jusqu'aux plus difficiles: terminée par un dictionnaire de passages aussi doigtés tirés des auteurs les plus célèbres. Par L. Adam ... et Lachnith ... Paris, Sieber [1798?]

vii, 149, 2–99 p., 1 l. 34½^{cm}.

Engraved, with exception of the Introduction (p. iii–vii)
13–7406   MT222.A2A21

Adams, Zabdiel, 1739–1801.
The nature, pleasure and advantages of church-musick. A sermon preached at a lecture in the First parish of Lancaster, on Thursday April 4th. 1771. By Zabdiel Adams ... Published at the request of the choir ... Boston: Printed by Richard Draper. 1771.

2 p. l., 3–38 p. 18½^{cm}.
27–1419   ML3001.A31

Affillard, Michel l'.
See L'AFFILLARD, MICHEL, *fl.* 1700.

1

Agatho Cario, *pseud.*

See NISLEN, TOBIAS.

Agazzari, Agostino, 1578–1640.

Del sonare sopra 'l basso con tvtti li stromenti e dell' vso loro nel conserto, dell ill[re] sig[r] Agostino Agazzari, Sanese, Armonico intronato. Siena, D. Falcini, 1607.

12 numb. l. illus.´(music) 23[cm].
Engraved throughout, on rectos only.
Title within illustrated border (musical instruments)
37–37928   MT49.A25D4

Agricola, Martin, 1486–1556.

Musica instru- ‖ mētalis deudsch ‖ inn welcher begrif- ‖ fen ist: wie man ‖ nach dem gesange auff mancherley ‖ Pfeiffen lernen sol / Auch wie auff ‖ die Orgel / Harffen / Lauten / Gei- ‖ gen / vnd allerley Instrumenten vnd ‖ Seitenspiel / nach der recht- ‖ gegrůndten Tabel- thur ‖ sey abzusetzen. Mart. Agric. Anno. 1542. [*Colophon:* Ge- druckt zu Wittemberg ‖ durch Georgen Rhaw. M.D.XLII.]

lvi numb. l., 4 l. illus. (part col.) 14[cm].
Signatures: A–G[8], H[4].
Leaves xxxij, xlvij, liij numbered xxxiij, 47, liiij, respectively.
In verse.
Leaf xxv torn; a few words partly or entirely wanting.
Signature on leaf xiij: Georgius Rhaw.
42–304   ML171.A26 1542

Agus, Enrico, *b.* 1749.

See DURIEU, ——. Nouvelle methode de musique vocale.

Alembert, Jean Lerond d', 1717–1783.

Elémens de musique, théorique et pratique, suivant les principes de m. Rameau, éclaircis, développés et simplifiés, par m. d'Alembert ... Nouv. éd., rev., cor. & considérablement augm. Lyon, J.-M. Bruyset, pere & fils, 1779.

2 p. l., xxxvi, 236, [4] p. 10 fold. pl. (incl. music) 20½[cm].
"Réponse à une lettre imprimée de m. Rameau" (p. 211–231) was first printed in Le Mercure, March, 1762, as "Lettre à m. Rameau, pour prouver que le corps sonore ne nous donne et ne peut nous donner par lui-même aucune idée des proportions."
29–5994   ML3815.A52 1779

[Algarotti, Francesco, *conte*] 1712–1764.

Saggio sopra l'opera in musica ... [n. p., 1754?]

35 p. 16½[cm].
The dedicatory epistle, "Al signor barone di Svertz", is dated "Mira- bello 6. ottobre 1754."
Signatures: a[6], b[12].
Includes the outline of an opera, "Enea in Troja" (p. 31–35) but not "Ifigenia in Aulide", which, according to the text, should be appended. The catalogue of the W. Wolffheim collection (II, no. 905) describes this as a rare 1st edition, apparently a private print. The 90-page edi- tion dated 1755 is the earliest listed in Eitner and Gaspari.
29–28714   ML3858.A369

Algarotti, Francesco—Continued.

—— Essai sur l'opéra, traduit de l'italien du comte Algarotti; par m.***. A Pise; & se trouve a Paris, chez Ruault, 1773.

viii, 190 p. 21^{cm}.

Translated by the Marquis de Chastellux.

Includes Algarotti's outline of an opera, "Enée à Troye", and the full text (in prose) of a second, "Iphigénie en Aulide", written by him in French.

29–28715

ML3858.A393

—— Versuche über die architectur, mahlerey und musicalische opera, aus dem italiänishchen des grafen Algarotti übersetzt von R. E. Raspe ... Cassel, J. F. Hemmerde, 1769.

9 p. l., [3]–300, [2] p. 17^{cm}.

"Die folgenden abhandlungen stehen im zweyten bande der zu Livorno im 1764. jahre ... zusammengedruckten werke des verfassers."—Vorbericht.

13–13846

N7420.A5

Allen, Richard.

See MARLOW, I. The controversie of singing brought to an end.

Almanach musical ... 1781–82; 1783, ptie. II. Paris, Au Bureau de l'abonnement littéraire, 1781–83.

3 v. 14½^{cm}.

"Cet ouvrage a été commencé en 1775; il a paru successivement en 1776, 1777, 1778 & 1779 ... Des raisons particulières ont empêché jusqu'ici de publier l'Almanach musical de 1780: on donne aujourd'hui ceux de 1780, 1781 & 1782."—Avis de l'auteur in vol. for 1781.

1783 was issued in 2 parts.

The earlier numbers were edited by Mathon de la Cour; the last 3 years, 1781–1783, by Luneau de Boisjerman. *cf.* Grand-Carteret, Almanachs français, no. 543; Alm. musical, 1783, pt. 2, p. 228.

ML20.A56

Ancient music, Concerts of.

See CONCERTS of ancient music, *London*.

André, Yves Marie, 1675–1764.

Essai sur le beau, par le pere André J., avec un Discours preliminaire, et des reflexions sur le gout, par mr. Formey. Amsterdam, J. H. Schneider, 1759.

5 p. l., cxxxi, [3], 192 p. 16½^{cm}.
"Le beau musical": p. 114–171.

17–854

N63.A55 1759

—— Essai sur le beau. Nouv. éd., augmentée de six discours, sur le modus, sur le decorum, sur les graces, sur l'amour du beau, sur l'amour désintéressé; par le feu pere André ... Paris, L. E. Ganeau, 1770.

vii, [5], 501 p. 17^{cm}.

Edited by the Abbé Guillaume Germain Guyot.
"Sur le beau musical": p. 131–198.

17–816

N63.A55 1770

André, Yves Marie—Continued.

—— Versuch über das schône da man untersucht, worinnen eigentlich das schône in der naturlehre, in der sittenlehre, in den werken des witzes und in der musik bestehe. Aus dem französichen ins deutsche übersetzt von Ernst Gottlieb Baron ... Altenburg, Richter, 1757.

8 p. l., 184 p.   19½ᶜᵐ.

"Des herrn Gresset ... Rede ... von dem uralten adel und nutzen der musik": p. [131]–184.

21–3016   N63.A57

Anfossi, Pasquale, 1736?–1797.

See CORFE, J.   A treatise on singing.   [*ca.* 1800]

Anglo-Italiny.

See A LETTER from a gentleman in the town.   1727.

L'Anti-Scurra, *pseud.*

See EPITRE aux Bouffonnistes.

Aprile, Giuseppe, 1738–1814.

The modern Italian method of singing, with a variety of progressive examples, and thirty six solfeggi, by Sigʳ. D. G. Aprili.   London, Printed by R. Birchall [1795?]

1 p. l., 53 p.   23 x 32½ᶜᵐ.

Engraved throughout.
First published in 1791 (London, Broderip)

35–21814   MT845.A81

Arauxo, Francisco Correa de.

See CORREA DE ARAUJO, FRANCISCO.

Aristoteles.

Aristotle's treatise on poetry, translated: with notes on the translation, and on the original; and two dissertations, on poetical, and musical, imitation.   By Thomas Twining, M. A.   London, Payne and son; [etc., etc.] 1789.

xix, [1], 565, [31] p.   27½ᶜᵐ.

14–22494   PN1040.A7T8   1789

Aron, Piero.

See AARON, PIETRO.

Ein **aufrichtiger** music-freund.

See RUDIMENTA panduristæ.

Avison, Charles, *d.* 1770.

An essay on musical expression. By Charles Avison ... 2d ed., with alterations and large additions. To which is added, A letter to the author, concerning the music of the ancients, and some passages in classic writers, relating to that subject [by J. Jortin]. Likewise, Mr. Avison's Reply to the author [W. Hayes] of Remarks on the Essay on musical expression. In a letter from Mr. Avison, to his friend in London. London, C. Davis, 1753.

5 p. l., 152, 43 p., 2 l., 53 p. 3 fold. pl. (music) 20^{cm}.

Mr. Avison's " Reply to the author of Remarks on the Essay on musical expression " (53 p. at end) has special t.-p.
Imperfect? wanting half-title?
28–12679. ML3847.A95 1753

—— An essay on musical expression. By Charles Avison ... With alterations and large additions. To which is added, A letter to the author concerning the music of the ancients, and some passages in classic writers, relating to that subject [by J. Jortin]. Likewise, Mr. Avison's Reply to the author [W. Hayes] of Remarks on the Essay on musical expression. In a letter from Mr. Avison to his friend in London. The 3d ed. London, L. Davis, 1775.

viii, 221 p. 4 fold. pl. (music) 18^{cm}.

20–10873 ML3847.A95 1775

—— A reply to the author of Remarks on the Essay on musical expression. In a letter from Mr. Avison, to his friend in London ... London, C. Davis, 1753.

2 p. l., 53 p. 4 fold. pl. 20½^{cm}.

Detached from the author's Essay on musical expression, 2d ed., 1753 ?
A reply to William Hayes' anonymous " Remarks on Mr. Avison's Essay on musical expression."
ca 17–183 Unrev'd ML3847.A95H25

B., A.

See [BAILLIE, A.] *supposed author.* An introduction to the knowledge and practice of the thoro' bass. 1717.

B., A., *Philo-Mus.*

See SYNOPSIS of vocal musick. 1680.

B. von W.

See WIESE, C. L. G., *freiherr* VON.

Bacchius, *senior.* Εἰσαγωγὴ τέχνης μουσικῆς.

See MERSENNE, M. Quæstiones celeberrimæ in Genesim.

Bacilly, Bénigne de, *ca.* 1625–*ca.* 1690.

Remarqves cvrievses svr l'art de bien chanter, et particulierement pour ce qui regarde le chant françois. Ouvrage fort vtile à ceux qui aspirent à la methode de chanter, sur tout à bien prononcer les paroles auec toute la finesse & toute la force necessaire; & à bien obseruer la quantité des syllabes, & ne point confondre les longues & les brefues, suivant les regles qui en sont établies dans ce traité. Par m. B. de Bacilly. Paris, Chez l'autheur et chez monsieur Ballard, 1668.

9 p. l., 428, [2] p. 15 x 8½ᶜᵐ.

Colophon: A Paris, De l'imprimerie de C. Blageart, 1668.

Added t.-p., engraved: Remarques curieuses sur l'art de bien chanter ... par le sieur B. D. B. Paris, 1668.

An issue of the same year (1668) published under the author's initials, B. D. B., with imprint Paris, Chez l'autheur et chez Ballard, is listed in the Wolffheim cat. (II. 744) as "seltene erste ausgabe". British museum lists another 1668 issue, also published under the initials B. D. B., but with imprint. Paris, L'autheur & P. Bien-fait. *cf.* Brit. mus. Gen. cat. VIII (1934). According to Fétis, there is still another 1668 issue (Paris, Ballard) with neither name nor initials of the author.

40–21213   MT820.A2B2 1668

[Baillie, Alexander] *supposed author.*

An introduction to the knowledge and practice of the thoro' bass. Humbly inscrib'd to the Right Honourable the Lord Colvill. By A. B. Edinburgh, 1717.

11 p. 33 ᶜᵐ.

Followed by "Institutions of musick, wherein are sett forth the practicall principles of musical composition in two parts": [22] p. of ms., with musical illustrations.

"The author of the printed portion was probably Alexander Baillie who in 1735 published in oblong 4ᵗᵒ 'Air for the flute, with a thorough bass for the harpsichord ...' This was a presentation copy from the author to Robert third & last Lord Colville ... Whether he or Baillie or some one else was the author of the ms. treatise that follows is uncertain. Mr. D. Laing never heard of another copy than the present of the printed tract."—Ms. note by J. Maidment, on fly-leaf.

Manuscript note by Thomas Taphouse quotes a reference by David Laing to this work in "Additional notes and illustrations to Johnston's Scots musical museum".

Manuscript note from John Graham Dalzell inserted.

Armorial book-plate of James Maidment.

22–11221   MT49.A2B18

Banchieri, Adriano, *d.* 1634.

Lettere armoniche del r. p. d. Adriano Banchieri bolognese, abbate oliuetano, & academico dissonante, intrecciate in sei capi. Di dedicatione, ragguaglio, congratulatione, buone feste, ringratiamento, piaceuolezza ... Bologna, G. Mascheroni, 1628.

8 p. l., 160 p. illus. 15ᶜᵐ.
13–24945   ML194.A2B2

[Banister, John] 1630–1679, *supposed author.*

The most pleasant companion, or Choice new lessons for the recorder or flute, being a new collection of new lessons, set forth by dots and notes. To which is added, plain and easie rules and instructions for young beginners, by J. B., gent. London, J. Hudgebutt, 1681.

2 p. l., 8 p.; 2 l., [18] p. (music) front. 10½ x 21ᶜᵐ.

The music, engraved, includes 26 tunes in tablature, with caption: Lessons for the recorder.

"Prepared by Banister."—Miller, Dayton C. Catalogue of books relating to the flute. 1935, p. 60 (under Hudgebut); *cf.* also entry for present work, p. 15 of the Miller catalogue.

Manuscript notes on fly-leaves.

42–26032   MT342.B25M6 Miller coll.

Bannius, Joannes Albertus, 1597 *or* 8–1644.

Joannis Alberti BannI Dissertatio epistolica de musicæ natura, origine, progressu, & denique studio bene instituendo. Ad incomparabilem virum Petrum Scriverium ... Lugduni Batavorum, ex officina Isaaci Commelini, 1637.

60 p. 13ᶜᵐ. [*With* Grotius, Hugo. Hugonis Grotii et aliorum De omni genere studiorum rectè instituendo dissertationes. Lugduni Batavorum, 1637]
21–20026   AZ200.G8

[Baretti, Giuseppe Marco Antonio] 1719–1789.

The voice of discord; or, The battle of the fiddles. A history of a seditious attempt upon the lives and properties of fifty singers and fiddlers. La voix de la discorde; ou, La bataille des violons. Histoire d'un attentat seditieux, et atroce contre la vie et les biens de cinquante chanteurs et violinistes ... London, W. Owen and T. Snelling, 1753.

55 p. 18ᶜᵐ.

English and French on opposite pages; dedication in Italian.
Burlesque reply to the author's anonymous "Scheme for having in London an Italian opera of a new taste." Occasioned by a quarrel between the impresario Vanneschi and musicians of his opera company.
20–14647   ML1731.3.B2

Baron, Ernst Gottlieb, 1696–1760, *translator.*

See ANDRÉ, Y. M. Versuch über das schône. 1757.

Bartoli, Daniello, 1608–1685.

Del svono de' tremori armonici e dell' udito. Trattati del p. Daniello Bartoli ... Bologna, A spese di P. Bottelli, 1680.

6 p. 1., 330 p. diagrs. 20ᶜᵐ.
Second edition.
29–6576   ML3805.B29 1680

Battell, Ralph, 1649–1713.

The lawfulness and expediency of church-musick asserted, in a sermon preached at St. Brides-church, upon the 22ᵈ· of November, 1693. Being the anniversary meeting of Gentlemen, Lovers of musick. By Ralph Battell ... London, Printed by J. Heptinstall, for J. Carr, 1694.

1 p. 1., 25 p. 18½ᶜᵐ. [*With* Reading, J. A sermon lately delivered at the cathedral church of Canterbury, concerning church musick. London, 1663. 19½ᶜᵐ]
17–31228   ML3001.R31 copy 2

Baurans, Pierre, 1710–1764.

See ELOGE de m. Baurans. [176–?]

Bayly, Anselm, *d.* 1794.

The sacred singer, containing an essay I. On grammar. II. Just speaking. III. The requisites of singing. IV. The ornaments

v. Their application. VI. On cathedral compositions ... By Anselm
Bayly ... London, Printed by S. Towers and sold by J. Rivington,
1771.

iv, 16, 99 p. illus. (music) 23½ᶜᵐ.

Published also under title: A practical treatise on singing and playing.

17–31241   ML3166.A2B2

Beattie, James, 1735–1803.

Essays. On the nature and immutability of truth, in opposition
to sophistry and scepticism. On poetry and music, as they affect the
mind. On laughter, and ludicrous composition. On the utility of
classical learning. By James Beattie ... Edinburgh, W. Creech, 1776.

1 p. l., xiv, [3]–757, [1] p. 27ᶜᵐ.

24–19522   B1403.B53E7 1776

—— Essays: on poetry and music, as they affect the mind; on laugh-
ter, and ludicrous composition; on the utility of classical learning.
By James Beattie ... Edinburgh, Printed for E. and C. Dilly, in
London; and W. Creech, Edinburgh, 1778.

vi p., 2 l., [3]–555 p. 21ᶜᵐ.

13–18287   PN1055.B4

—— Essays: on poetry and music, as they affect the mind; on
laughter, and ludicrous composition; on the usefulness of classical
learning. By James Beattie ... 3d ed., cor. London, Printed for
E. and C. Dilly; and W. Creech, Edinburgh, 1779.

5 p. l., [3]–515 p. front. (port.) 22ᶜᵐ.

20–10861   ML60.B41

—— Essai sur la poésie et sur la musique, considérées dans les affec-
tions de l'ame, traduit de l'anglais, de James Beattie ... Paris, H.
Tardieu; [etc., etc.] an viᵉ [1798?]

2 p. l., [iii]–xxiv, 342 p., 2 l. 22ᶜᵐ.

42–30518   ML60.B41E4

Beer, Georg Alexander, *respondent.*

See KIRCHMAIER, T., *praeses.* Schediasma physicum.

Bemetzrieder, Anton, 1743?–1817.

Exemples des principaux élémens de la composition musicale, addi
tion au Nouvel essai sur l'harmonie, par m. Bemetzrieder ... Paris,
Chez l'auteur et chez Onfroy, 1780.

viii p.; 20 p. (music) 21 x 26½ᶜᵐ.

Music engraved.

29–6569   MT40.A2B48

Traité de musique, concernant les tons, les harmonies, les accords &
le discours musical ... par m. Bemetzrieder. Paris, Chez l'auteur,
et chez Pissot, 1776.

4 p. l., xxxvii, [3], 261 p., 2 l., viii, 80 p. 20½ᶜᵐ.

"Exemples du Traité de musique": 2 p. l., viii, 80 p. at end.
The "Exemples" are engraved and have special t.-p.
Autographed by the author.

29–5993   MT50.B418

Benelli, Alemanno, *pseud.*
See MELONI, ANNIBALE, *16th cent.*

Bernis, François Joachim de Pierre de, *comte de Lyon, cardinal,* 1715–1794.
See MEUSNIER DE QUERLON, A. G. Reglement pour l'Opera.

Bertalotti, Angelo Michele.
Regole vtilisime per apprendere con fondamento, e facilità il canto fermo, dato alle stampe per comodo delli giovani delle scuole pie di Bologna & à beneficio commune ... da Angelo Michele Bertalotti ... Bologna, M. Siluani, 1706.

35, [1] p. illus. (music) 22½ᶜᵐ.
Title vignette (arms of Cardinal Giacomo Boncompagni)
Also published under title: Regole facilissime ...

22–901   MT860.A2B52

Besard, Jean Baptiste, *b. ca.* 1567.
See DOWLAND, R. Varietie of lute-lessons.

[Béthisy, Jean Laurent de] 1702–1781, *supposed author.*
Effets de l'air sur le corps humain, considérés dans le son; ou Discours sur la nature du chant. Par m. ***. Amsterdam: et se trouve à Paris, chez Lambert [etc.] 1760.

2 p. l., vii, [1], [9]–71 p. front. 14½ᶜᵐ.
Ascribed in an obituary notice communicated to the "Journal encyclopédique ou universel", 1783, t. 1, p. 330, to "Eugène-Eléonore de Béthisi, marquis de Mezières, lieutenant-général des armées du roi", etc. For a note on Jean Laurent de Béthisy, "professeur de musique à Paris", see T. A. Dufour, Recherches bibliographiques sur les œuvres imprimées de J.-J. Rousseau. Paris, 1925, v. 1, p. 24.
                                          ML1727.33.B56E3

Exposition de la théorie et de la pratique de la musique, suivant les nouvelles découvertes. Par m. de Bethizy. Paris, M. Lambert, 1754.

xvj, 296, [4] p.; 60 p. (music) 20ᶜᵐ.
Music engraved.
31–23118   MT6.A2B55

Bevin, Elway, *fl.* 1575–1631.
A briefe and short instrvction of the art of mvsicke, to teach how to make discant, of all proportions that are in vse: very necessary for all such as are desirous to attaine to knowledge in the art; and may by practice, if they can sing, soone be able to compose three, foure, and five parts: and also to compose all sorts of canons that are usuall, by these directions of two or three parts in one, upon the plain-song. By Elway Bevin. London, Printed by R. Young, 1631.

3 p. l., 52 p. 23ᶜᵐ.
Signatures: A–G⁴, H² (A₁ (blank?) wanting)
Title vignette (printer's mark); head-piece.
Principally musical examples.
Full vellum binding, gold border.
31–4481   MT6.A2B6

Biedermann, Johann Gottlieb, 1705–1772.

See MATTHESON, J. Sieben gespräche der Weisheit und Musik. 1751.

Billings, William, 1746–1800.

The singing master's assistant, or Key to practical music. Being an abridgement from the New-England psalm-singer; together with several other tunes, never before published. Composed by William Billings, author of the New-England psalm-singer ... Boston: (New-England.) Printed by Draper and Folsom. 1778.

32 p.; 104 p. (music)   12 x 19½^{cm}.

Music engraved. *Colophon:* Engrav'd by Benj^a Pierpont jun^r Roxbury
1778.   M2116.B59S4   1778

—— —— [Another issue] Boston: (New-England.) Printed by Draper and Folsom. 1778.

29, [1] p.; 104 p. (music)   11½ x 19½^{cm}.

Without the "Encomium on music," p. [31]–32 in the preceding copy.
The text in the two copies differs typographically.
41–18174   M2116.B59S4   1778a

Billington, *Mrs.* **Elizabeth (Weichsel)** *afterwards* Mme. Félissent, 1768?–1818.

See MEMOIRS of Mrs. Billington. 1792.

The **bird** fancyer's delight; or, Choice observations, and directions concerning ye teaching of all sorts of singing-birds, after ye flagelet & flute, if rightly made as to size & tone, with a method of fixing ye wett air, in a spung or cotton, with lessons properly composed, within ye compass & faculty of each bird, vizt for ye wood-lark, black-bird, throustill, house-sparrow, canary-bird, black-thorn-linnet, garden-bull-finch, and starling. London, R. Meares, 1717.

8 numb. l.; 18 numb. l. (music)   illus. (music)   10½ x 20^{cm}.

Engraved throughout.
Pictures of two birds ("canary-bird" and "bull-finch") and of a bird flageolet on t.-p.
From the Miller collection.
"Only known copy of this early edition."—Miller, Dayton C., Catalogue of books ... relating to the flute. Cleveland, 1935.
42–836   MT345.B57 Miller coll.

Bisse, Thomas, *d.* 1731.

A rationale on cathedral worship or choir-service. A sermon preach'd in the cathedral church of Hereford, at the anniversary meeting of the choirs of Worcester, Glocester, and Hereford, Sept. 7, 1720. By Tho. Bisse ... The 2d ed. Publish'd at the request of the audience. London, W. and J. Innys, 1721.

61 p.   18^{cm}.
13–21146   ML3001 B6

Blakemore, Thomas, *joint author.*

See JONES, WILLIAM. Clavis campanalogia. 1788.

New campanalogia. [1796]

Blavet, Michel, 1700–1768. *See* Éloge de monsieur Blavet.

Bode, Johann Joachim Christoph, 1730–1793, *translator.*
See Burney, C. Carl Burney's ... Tagebuch seiner musikalischen reisen. 1772–73.

[Boemus, Johann] *fl.* 1500.
⟨In hoc libello continentur ‖ ⟨Liber Heroicus de Musicæ laudi⸗ bus. ‖ ⟨Carmen Sapphicum / de laude & situ Vl⸗ ‖ mæ / ciuitatis Imperialis Sueuiæ. ‖ ⟨Oratiunculæ item Metricæ sex, ad sex san⸗ ‖ ctissimas personas: quæ nostræ redemptio ‖ ni interfuerunt. ‖ ⟨Quæstio quædam Theologica / quatuor ‖ anni partes cum studijs suis cõplectens. ‖ ⟨Elegiæ duæ / quarũ prima quatuordecim ‖ beatæ virginis Mariæ gaudia: altera ‖ tercentum eiusdem vir⸗ ginis ‖ nomina comprehen ‖ dit. Cum multis ‖ alijs Epigrã ‖ mati⸗ ‖ b9 ‖ [Augustæ Vindelicorum, 1515]
[43] p. 20½ᶜᵐ.
Colophon: In officina excusoria Ioannis Miller ‖ Augustæ Vindelicorum: quar ‖ tadecima die mensis De ‖ cembris. Anno vir- ‖ ginei partus. ‖ M.D.XV. ‖
Signatures: a–d⁴, e⁶ (e₍₁₎ signed c; eᵥ signed e₁₁₁₁)
Title within ornamental border; initials.
Author's name in dedication, captions, etc.
Book-plate: Georgius Kloss, M. D., Francofurti ad Moenum.
29–15441   ML64.B7

Boethius, *d.* 524.
See Le Fèvre, J. Arithmetica et Musica.

Boissy, Louis de, 1694–1758. Le triomphe de l'intérêt.
See Desforges.

Bonanni, Filippo.
See Buonanni, Filippo, 1638–1725.

Bonaventura *da Brescia, fl.* 1500.
Regula musice plane venerabi ‖ lis fratris Bonauenture ‖ de Brixia ordinis ‖ Minorum. [Venetiæ, 1527]
[62] p. illus. (incl. music) 15ᶜᵐ.
Colophon: Stampato in Venetia per Elisabetta de Rusconi. M.CCCCCXXVII. A di otto de mazo.
Signatures: A–D⁸ (last leaf (blank?) wanting)
Woodcut on t.-p.; Guidonian hand on verso of A₁₁₁₁; printer's mark on verso of D₇₁₁.
First edition published at Brescia in 1497 under title: Breviloquium musicale.
35–21831   ML171.B72

Bononcini, Giovanni Maria, 1640–1678.
Mvsico prattico che brevemente dimostra il modo di giungere alla perfetta cognizione di tutte quelle cose, che concorrono alla composizione de i canti, e di ciò ch' all' arte del contrapunto si ricerca. Opera ottava di Gio: Maria Bononcini ... In Bologna, Per G. Monti. Si vendono da M. Siluani, 1688.
156 p. illus. (music) 22ᶜᵐ.
Dedication signed by the publisher, Marino Silvani.
30–3285.

Bordier, Louis Charles, *d.* 1764.

Nouvelle methode de musique, par m^r. Bordier ...   Paris, Le Clerc [176–?]

1 p. l., 118 p.   32 x 25^{cm}.

Engraved throughout.

A new edition was published in 1781 under title: Méthode pour la voix.

21–20005   MT870.A2B72

Bossler, Heinrich Philipp Carl, *d.* 1812.

Elementarbuch der tonkunst zum unterricht beim klavier für lehrende und lernende, mit praktischen beispielen. Eine musikalische monatschrift ... herausgegeben von H. P. Bossler ... Speier, Gedrukt mit Enderesischen schriften, 1782–89.

2 v. in 1.   front., plates.   20^{cm}.

——Praktische beiträge zu dem Elementarbuch der tonkûnst. Speier, 1782.

2 v. in 1.   30½^{cm}.

Engraved throughout.

22–10948–9   MT224.A2B68

Bossler, Heinrich Philipp Carl, *d.* 1812, *editor.*

See MUSIKALISCHE korrespondenz der Teutschen filarmonischen gesellschaft.

[Bottrigari, Ercole] 1531–1612.

Il Desiderio overo, De' concerti di uarij strumenti musicali, dialogo, di Alemanno Benelli [*pseud.*]; nel quale anco si ragiona della participatione di essi stromenti, & di molte altre cose pertinenti alla musica. Venetia, R. Amadino, 1594.

6 p. l., 51 p.   illus. (music) diagrs.   22^{cm}.

Signatures: *⁶, A–E⁴, F⁶ (verso of last leaf blank).

Title within woodcut border, with illustrations of musical instruments, etc.   Title vignette (an organ) Sidenotes.

Without the errata found on verso of last leaf in some copies, and on an added leaf in others.

Dialogue between "Gratioso Desiderio" and "Alemanno Benelli." The latter name is an anagram of the name of Bottrigari's friend Annibale Meloni (Anniballe Melone) for whom the work was later claimed by G. B. Artusi. An edition was issued under Meloni's name in 1601. *cf.* Catalogo della biblioteca del Liceo musicale di Bologna compilato da G. Gaspari. I, 68–71; 88.

Limp vellum binding.

26–18545   ML171.B747

Brady, Nicholas, 1659–1726.

Church-musick vindicated. A sermon preach'd at St. Bride's church, on Monday, November 22. 1697. Being St Cæcilia's day, the anniversary feast of the Lovers of musick. By Nicholas Brady ... London, J. Wilde, 1697.

2 p. l., 23 p.   18½^{cm}.   [*With* Reading, J. A sermon lately delivered in the cathedral church of Canterbury, concerning church musick. London, 1663. 19½^{cm}]

17–312266   ML3001.R31   copy 2

Breitkopf, Johann Gottlob Immanuel, 1719–1794.

See BREITKOPF & HÄRTEL, *Leipzig.* Verzeichniss musicalischer werke.

Breitkopf & Härtel, *Leipzig.*

Verzeichniss musicalischer werke allein zur praxis, sowohl zum singen, als für alle instrumente, welche nicht durch den druck bekannt gemacht worden; in ihre gehörige classen ordentlich einge-theilet; welche in richtigen abschriften bey Joh. Gottlob Immanuel Breitkopf [2. ausg.: bey Bernh. Christoph Breitkopf u. sohn] in Leipzig, um beystehende preisse zu bekommen sind. 1.[–2.] ausg. ... Leipzig, 1761–64.

2 v. 19½^{cm}.

> On t.-p. of v. 1: Erste ausgabe, und des Musicalischen bücher-ver-zeichnisses dritte ausgabe.
> "Vorbericht," v. 1, signed: J. G. I. Breitkopf.
> Complete in 4 "ausgaben," 1761–80.
> ca 28–487 Unrev'd.   ML145.B832

Brookbank, Joseph, *b.* 1612.

The well-tuned organ, or, An exercitation; wherein, this question is fully and largely discussed, whether or no instrumental and or-ganical musick be lawful in holy publick assemblies? Which query is made good in the affirmativ, by sufficient arguments; the objections refelled; and directions given for the safe and profitable practice thereof. By the blessing of God upon the industry of Joseph Brook-bank, minister of Gods Holy Word and sacraments; intended for the glory of God, the quiet and peace of these nations. London, Printed anno Domini, 1660.

2 p. 1., 67, [1] p. 18½ x 14^{cm}.

> Bound in mottled calf; book-plate of William Hayman Cummings.
> 35–21819   ML3001.B87

Brossard, Sébastien de, *d.* 1730.

Dictionaire de musique, contenant une explication des termes grecs, latins, italiens, & françois, les plus usitez dans la musique. Par m. Sebastien de Brossard ... 2. ed., conforme à celle in-folio, faite en 1703. Paris, C. Ballard, 1705.

> xij, 5–380 p. illus. (music) 2 fold. tab. 19^{cm}.
> 39–19786   ML108.A2B62

—— Dictionaire de musique, contenant une explication des termes grecs, latins, italiens & françois les plus usitez ... A l'occasion desquels on rapporte ce qu'il y a de plus curieux & de plus ne-cessaire à sçavoir; tant pour l'histoire & la theorie, que pour la composition, & la pratique ... de la musique ... Ensemble, une table alphabetique des termes françois qui sont dans le corps de l'ouvrage ... Un traité de la maniere de bien prononcer, sur tout en chantant, les termes italiens, latins & françois. Et un catalogue de plus de 900. auteurs, qui ont écrit sur la musique ... Par m. Sébastien de Brossard ... 3. ed. Amsterdam, Aux dépens d'E. Roger [17—]

> 388 p. illus. (music) 2 tab. (1 fold.) 19½^{cm}.
> 35–21816   ML108.A2B64

Brossard, Sébastien de—Continued.

—— A musical dictionary: containing a full explanation of all the terms made use of in ... music: also explanations of the doctrines of ancient music, and ... inquiries into the nature of sound ... together with a full description of all the various kinds of musical instruments ... abstracted from the best authors in the Greek, Latin, Italian, French, and English languages, by James Grassineau ... New ed., to which is added an Appendix, selected from the Dictionnaire de musique of M. Rousseau ... London, J. Robson, 1769.

v (*i. e.* vii), 347 p., 2 l., 52 p. illus. ,(music) 21^{cm}.

Appendix has special t.-p. and separate paging.
Translated, with additions, from the French of Sébastien de Brossard, probably under the supervision of Dr. Pepusch. First edition published 1740.

20–19875   ML108.A2B73

Brown, Isaac.

Disquisitio medica inauguralis, de sonorum modulatorum vi in corpora humana: quam ... ex auctoritate ... Gulielmi Wishart ... Academiae edinburgenae praefecti ... pro gradu doctoratus ... eruditorum examini subjicit Isaacus Brown, Anglus. Ad diem 3 maii [1751] ... Edinburgi, apud Hamilton, Balfour, et Neill, 1751.

iv, 48 p. 20^{cm}.

35–17698   ML3920.B7D5 Toner coll.

Buc'hoz, Pierre Joseph, 1731–1807, *editor.*

See MARQUET, F. N. Nouvelle méthode ... pour connoitre le pouls.

Buonanni, Filippo, 1638–1725.

Gabinetto armonico pieno d'istromenti sonori indicati, e spiegati dal padre Filippo Bonanni ... Roma, Nella stamperìa di G. Placho, 1722.

8 p. l., 170 p. front., cxlviii (*i. e.* 152) pl. (1 fold.)   25½^{cm}.
Armorial bookplate of Dogmersfield library.

ML460.B612

—— Gabinetto armonico pieno d'instrumenti sonori indicati, spiegati, e di nuovo corretti, ed accresciuti dal padre Filippo Bonanni ... Roma, Nella stamperìa di G. Placho, 1723.

8 p. l., 170 p. front., cxlviii (*i. e.* 152) pl. (1 fold.)   24^{cm}.
Plates numbered irregularly.
Another issue, with different t.-p., of the 1722 edition.
Second edition, Rome, 1776, has title: Descrizione degl' istromenti armonici.

18–4313   ML460.A2B613

Burchard, Ulrich.

Hortulus musices. Practice omibus diuino Gregoriani concentus modulo se oblectaturis tam iucūdus q͵ proficuus. Decastichon Joannis Langij in Hortulū musices Udalrici Burchardi. [*10 lines of verse*] ... Lipsiae, ex officina Melchiaris Lottheri. [1518]

[28] p. illus. (music) 20^{cm}.
Dated at end: Anno. xviij.
Signatures: A⁶, B⁸.
Title in red and black.
Dedicatory letter dated: Lipsie kalendis aprilis. Anno salutis millesimo quingentesimo decimoquarto.

40–21467   ML171.B82 1518

Burney, Charles, 1726–1814.

A general history of music, from the earliest ages to the present period. To which is prefixed, a dissertation on the music of the ancients. By Charles Burney ... London, Printed for the author, 1776–89.

4 v. fronts. (incl. port.) illus. (incl. music) 9 pl. (part fold., incl. music) 28 x 22^{cm}.

First edition. A 2d edition of v. 1 was published in 1789.

Vol. 2, printed, like the other 3 vols., with the long s, and with a leaf of "corrections and additions" at end, differs in these and other particulars from a later printing, also dated 1782, but printed with the modern s, as is the 2d edition of v. 1.

Some of the musical illustrations are engraved.

"Chronological list of the principal books published on the subject of music in England, during the present century": v. 4, p. [687]–688.

With vol. 4 is bound the author's An account of the musical performances in Westminster-abbey, and the Pantheon ... in commemoration of Handel ... London, 1785.

36–34066 ML159.B958

The present state of music in France and Italy: or, The journal of a tour through those countries, undertaken to collect materials for a general history of music. By Charles Burney ... 2d ed., cor. London, T. Becket and co. [etc.] 1773.

1 p. l., [v]–viii, 409, [10] p. 21^{cm}.

15–11225 ML195.B961

—— Carl Burney's ... Tagebuch seiner musikalischen reisen ... Hamburg, Bode, 1772–73.

3 v. illus. (music) 17½^{cm}.

Vol. 1 has title: Carl Burney's ... Tagebuch einer musikalischen reise durch Frankreich und Italien, welche er unternommen hat um zu einer allgemeinen geschichte der musik materialien zu sammlen. Aus dem englischen übersetzt von C. D. Ebeling.

Vols. 2–3 translated by J. J. C. Bode. cf. Gerber, E. L. Hist.-biog. lex. der tonkünstler.

Translation of "The present state of music in France and Italy" and "The present state of music in Germany, the Netherlands, and United Provinces."

CONTENTS.—1. bd. Durch Frankreich und Italien.—2. bd. Durch Flandern, die Niederlande und am Rhein bis Wien.—3. bd. Durch Böhmen, Sachsen, Brandenburg, Hamburg und Holland. Mit einigen zusätzen und anmerkungen zum zweyten und dritten bande.

40–37371 ML195.B9655

Burney, Charles, 1726–1814, *translator.*

See TARTINI, G. A letter from the late Signor Tartini. 1779.

Burtius, Nicolaus.

See BURZIO, NICCOLÒ, 1450–1518.

Burzio, Niccolò, 1450–1518.

Opusculum musices cum defensione Guidonis Aretini. Bononiæ, Ugo Rugerius, 30 Ap. 1487. 4° (21½^{cm})

fol. [1] (a₁₁)^{recto}: Nicolai Burtij parmensis: musices professoris: ac ‖ iuris pontificij studiosissimi: musices opusculu₃ inci ‖ pit: cum defensione Guidonis aretini: aduersus que‖ndam hyspanum veritatis preuaricatorem. ‖ Pauperibus clericis: ac religiosis: Nicolaus bur ‖ tius.

Burzio, Niccolò—Continued.

S. P. D. || fol. [67] ([i₄₁₁₃])ʳᵉᶜᵗᵒ, l. 27, *colophon:* Impēsis Bñdicti libzarij bonoñ. ac suma industria || Ugonis de rugerijs: qui pzopatissimus huius artis || exactoz impſsus Bonōie. Año dñi. m.cccc.lxxxvij. || die vltima apzilis. ||

Signatures: a–h⁸, i⁴ (a₁, blank, wanting). 67 printed leaves without foliation or catchwords.
Woodcut music and diagrams. Initial spaces blank or with indicators.
Hain-Copinger 4145; Proctor 6565; Pellechet 3098.
27–25066   ML171.B87

Butler, Charles, *d.* 1647.

The feminin' monarchi', or The histori of bee's. Shewing their admirable natur', and propertis; their generation and colonis; their government ... &c. Together with the right ordering of them from tim' to tim': and the sweet' profit arising ther'of. Written ... by Charls Butler, Magd. ... Oxford, Printed by William Turner, for đe author, 1634.

8 p. l., 182 (*i. e.* 180) p. illus., diagrs. 19½ᶜᵐ.

Third edition. First edition published 1609.
Printed according to the system of orthography proposed by the author in his English grammar, published 1633.
Nos. 113–114 omitted in paging.
" Melissomelos, or Bee's madrigall" (the song of the bees at swarming) :
4 pages of table-music (p. 78–81)

SF525.B8

Cacciò, Giovanni Batista, *editor.*

See INDICE de' teatrali spettacoli.

[Cailleau, André Charles] 1731–1798.

Le Waux-hall populaire; ou, Les fêtes de la guinguette, poeme grivois et poissardi-lyri-comique, en cinq chants; enrichi de rondes de table & vaudevilles nouveaux; parodiés sur les ariettes les plus jolies. Dédié a mˡ. de Voltaire. A la Gaité, Chez le compere La Joie. [Paris, Cailleau, etc., 1769]

2 p. l., [3]–127, [1] p. 17ᶜᵐ.

With book-plate of Edmond de Goncourt.
42–6138   ML1950.C25W2

Calckman, Jan Jacob, *17th cent.*

Antidotvm, tegen-gift vant Gebruyck of on-gebruyck vant orgel inde kercken der Vereenighde Nederlanden ... Door I. I. Calckman. 's Gravenhage, A. Meuris, 1641.

213, [1] p. 14½ᶜᵐ.

A criticism of Huygens' " Gebruyck of ongebruyck van 't orgel in de kerken der Vereenighde Nederlanden."
13–24959   ML3001.C2

Calvör, Caspar, 1650–1725.

See SINN, C. A. Die aus mathematischen grûnden richtig gestellete musicalische temperatura practica. [1717?]

[Campion, François] *fl.* 1703–1738.

Lettre de monsieur l'abbé Carbasus [*pseud.*], a monsieur de ***
auteur du Temple du goust, sur la mode des instrumens de musique,
ouvrage curieux & interressant pour les amateurs de l'harmonie ...
Paris, Chez la veuve Allouel, 1739.

2 p. l., [7]–45, [1] p. fold. pl. (music) 16^{cm}.

42–6136   ML760.C27L3

Campion, Thomas, 1567–1620.

See PLAYFORD, J. A brief introduction to the skill of musick.
1667.
An introduction to the skill of musick. 1672.

Cantone, Gerolamo.

Armonia gregoriana in cui con breuità, e chiarezza si spiegano
tutte le regole più importanti del canto fermo, col modo di cantare
le passioni, lamentationi, e profetie, nuouamente gionto. Data in
luce dal padre Gerolamo Cantone ... 4. impressione. Torino, Per
G. B. Boetto & G. B. Guigonio, a spese di G. B. Vernoni, 1701.

48 (*i. e.* 44) p. illus. (music) 17½ x 23½^{cm}.

Pages 41–44 numbered 45–48.
30–3277   MT860.C2 1701

Cantorinus.

See COMPÉDIUM musices. 1538.

Cappeval,   de Caux de.
See CAUX DE CAPPEVAL,   DE.

Carbasus, *Abbé, pseud.*
See CAMPION, FRANÇOIS.

Cardano, Girolamo, 1501–1576.

See SPANGENBERG, J. Qvæstiones musicæ in vsvm scholæ Northusianæ. 1563.

Cario, Agatho, *pseud.*
See NISLEN, TOBIAS.

Carli, Giovanni Rinaldo, *conte*, 1720–1795.

Osservazioni sulla musica antica, e moderna. (*In* Carli, G. R.,
conte. Delle opere. Milano, 1784–94. 19 v. 21^{cm}. t. XIV. 1786.
p. [329]–450)

AC43.C3

————————— Copy 2, detached.
With a frontispiece, detached from vol. I.

ML159.C2

Carmelites.

Directorivm chori, vna cvm processionali, ivxta ordinem, ac ritvm fratrum B. Mariæ Virginis de Monte Carmeli, continens ea, quæ ad sacra officia cantu persoluenda pertinent. [Iussu] Reverendissimi patris magistri Matthaei Orlandi, generalis carmelitarum, denuo impressum. Romæ, typis Iacobi Fei Andreæ filij, 1668.

4 p. l., 151 p.   1 illus.   22ᶜᵐ.

Printer's device on last page.

27–7065   M2148.7.O7 1668

Caroso, Marco Fabrizio.

Nobiltà di dame del sʳ. Fabritio Caroso da Sermoneta, libro, altra volta, chiamato Il ballarino. Nuouamente dal proprio auttore corretto, ampliato di nuoui balli, di belle regole, & alla perfetta theorica ridotto: con le creanze necessarie à caualieri, e dame. Aggiontoui il basso, & il soprano della musica: & con l'intauolatura del liuto à ciascun ballo. Ornato di vaghe & bellissime figure in rame ... In Venetia, Presso il Muschio, 1600. Ad instantia dell' auttore.

10 p. l., 370, [6] p.   illus. (incl. ports.)   24½ᶜᵐ.

Title within engraved architectural border ornamented with vignettes of instrumentalists, a portrait of the author, etc. Head and tail pieces; initials. The illustrations consist of 10 full-page engravings by Giacomo Franco; 8 of them, figures of dancers, occur from 2 to 7 times each.

Part 2 has special half-title: Della Nobiltà di dame ... libro secondo, nelquale s'insegnano varie sorti di balletti, cascarde, tordiglione, passo e mezzo, pauaniglia, canario, & gagliarde ...

The music, through p. 148, is in both tablature and ordinary notation; throughout the rest of the book, in tablature only.

Second edition. The 1st edition was published 1581 under title: Il ballarino. An edition (evidently a reissue of the 2d) entitled "Raccolta di varij balli fatti in occorenze di nozze, e festini" appeared in 1630.

30–3284   MT950.C182

Casoni, Giovanni Agostino, *17th cent.*

Manvale choricanvm ab vtrivsqve sexvs choricistis concupitum, clericis omnibvs necessarium, & maximè ivvenibvs. Per f. Io: Augustinum Casonū de Spedia min. ref. prou. Genuæ annotatū, collectū, dispositum. Genvæ, ex officina Farroni, 1649.

8 p. l., 247, [6] p. incl. front.   11½ x 9ᶜᵐ.

29–9151   MT860.C382

[Castel, Louis Bertrand] 1688–1757.

Lettres d'un academicien de Bordeaux sur le fonds de la musique, a l'occasion de la lettre de m. R * * * contre la musique françoise ... Tome premier.   A Londres, et se trouvent à Paris, chez C. Fosse, 1754.

1 p. l., 74 p.   17ᶜᵐ.

No more published.
Occasioned by Rousseau's Lettre sur la musique française.

39–19788   ML270.3.C34L4

Castoldi, Giovanni Giacomo.

See GASTOLDI, GIOVANNI GIACOMO, *fl.* 1582–1609.

Catholic church. *Pope, 1691–1700 (Innocentius)*

Editto sopra la musica ... Roma, Stamperia della reuerenda Camera apostolica, 1698.

broadside. illus. (coat of arms) 42½^{cm}.

Printed on one side of a sheet of customs service blanks.

29–28719 ML291 1698

Catholic church. *Pope, 1700–1721 (Clemens XI)*

Editto per le donne, acciò non imparino il canto, ed il suono dagl'huomini, nè questi l'insegnino ... Roma, Stamperia della reuerenda Camera apostolica, 1703.

broadside. illus. (incl. coat of arms) 37½^{cm}.

29–28720 ML291 1703

Caus, Isaac de, *fl.* 1644.

New and rare inventions of water-works shewing the easiest waies to raise water higher then the spring. By which invention the perpetual motion is proposed, many hard labours performed, and varieties of motions and sounds produced ... First written in French, by Isaak de Cavs ... and now translated into English by John Leak. London, Printed by J. Moxon, 1659.

3 p. l., 34 p. illus., xxvi pl. (part fold.) 32^{cm}.

Title engraved, within architectural border. Caption and running title: The theorie of the conduct of water.
Signatures: 1 leaf, B–K², L¹ (E₁ lettered D)
Translation of Isaac de Caus, "Nouvelle invention de lever l'eau", 1644, the text and plates of which were based on Salomon de Caus, "Les raisons des forces movvantes auec diuerses machines", Francfort, 1615. Includes descriptions and illustrations of various musical automata and of a hydraulic barrel-organ.
Full calf binding, stamped with arms of an earl (Coningsby?) with motto: Vestigia nulla retrorsum.

TJ144.C37

Caus, Salomon de, *d.* 1626.

See CAUS, I. DE. New and rare inventions of water-works.

Caux de Cappeval, de, *d.* 1774, *supposed author.*

See EPITRE aux Bouffonnistes.

Cerbellón de la Vera, Eustaquio.

Dialogo harmonico, sobre el Theatro critico vniversal [de B. Feijóo]: en defensa de la musica de los templos ... Compuesto por d. Eustaquio Cerbellon de la Vera ... Madrid, Se hallará en la libreria de F. Lopez, 1726.

10 p. l., 64 p. 19½^{cm}.

24–28809 ML3001.C25

Chastellux, François Jean, *marquis* de, 1734–1788, *translator.*

See ALGAROTTI, F. Essai sur l'opéra. 1773.

[Châteauneuf, François de Castagnères, *abbé* de] *d.* 1709.
Dialogue sur la musique des anciens. A monsieur de * * *
Nouv. ed. Paris, La veuve Pissot, 1735.

4 p. l., 127, [5] p. vii pl. (1 fold.) 18 x 10¼ᶜᵐ.

Published, with a preface, by Jacques Morabin.

24–24666   ML169.A2C42

[Chevrier, François Antoine] 1721–1762, *supposed author.*
La constitution de l'Opera. Amsterdam [*i. e.* Paris?] 1736.

16 p. 19ᶜᵐ.

Colophon: Donné à Cythéropolis, en notre siège patriarchal, ce ɪ. novembre, l'an de grace 1736, & de notre patriarchat le 30ᵐᵉ. Signé, Pancrace. Et plus bas, Mariette, directrice de l'Opéra.
Published in 1754 under title: Constitution du Patriarche de l'Opera.
Armorial bookplate of mʳ. von der Mulhen; anonymous book-plate of Edmond de Goncourt ("Ex-libris du cabinet d'un vieux bibliophile")

41–25461   ML1720.3.C52C5

Cid, Francisco Xavier.

Tarantismo observado en España, con que se prueba el de la Pulla, dudado de algunos, y tratado de otros de fabuloso: y memorias para escribir la historia del insecto llamado tarántula, efectos de su veneno en el cuerpo humano, y curacion por la música con el modo de obrar de esta, y su aplicacion como remedio á varias enfermedades. Su autor don Francisco Xavier Cid ... [Madrid] En la imprenta de M. Gonzalez, 1787.

2 p. l., 324 p. 3 pl. (2 fold.: music) 22ᶜᵐ.

Agr 4–3394   ML3920.A2C5

Cionacci, Francesco, 1633–1714.
See Coferati, M. Il cantore addottrinato. 1682.

The **clarinet** instructor, by which playing on that instrument is rendered easy to any one unacquainted with music, as it contains a compleat scale of all the notes with the graces, also a dictionary explaining such words as occur in music, with several favorite airs; the whole by a capital performer on the above instrument. To which is added several duos for two clarinets and a quintetto for horns, clarinets and a bassoon ... London, Longman & Broderip [17—]

1 p. l., 34 p. front., fold. pl. 18½ x 25ᶜᵐ.

Engraved throughout.

13–21150   MT388.C7

The **clarinet** preceptor, or The whole art of playing the clarinet rendered easy to every capacity, wherein every instruction relative to that instrument is elucidated in the most clear and simple manner, and by which any one may without the assistance of a master learn to play with taste & judgement in a short time. To which is added a valuable selection of favorite airs, song tunes and duetts. London, Printed by C. Wheatstone [*ca.* 1800]

[42] p. fold. pl. 17 x 24½ᶜᵐ. [*With* Granger, F. Gentlemen's pocket companion. Boston, New York [*ca.* 1805]]

M288.G35

Cochlaeus, Johannes, 1479–1552.

Tetrachordū musices Joannis Coclei Norici ... Nurnbergæ æditum: pro iuuentute laurentiana in primis: dein pro ceteris quoq̦ musarum tyrunculis ... Hvivs Tetrachordi qvatvor tractatus, quorū quilibet decem capita complectitur. Primus, De musices elementis; secundus, De musica gregoriana; tertius, De octo tonis meli; quartus, De musica mensurali. [*Colophon:* Finis Tetrachordi musices Nurnbergæ impressi in officina excusoria Friderici Peypus anno salutis 1516]

[59] p. illus. (music) 19½ᶜᵐ.

Signatures: A–B⁶, C–E⁴, E iii–[iv], F⁴.

First edition published, Nuremberg, 1511. Said to be based on the author's "Musica", Cologne, 1507.

42–891 ML171.C66 1516

Coferati, Matteo.

Il cantore addottrinato, ovvero Regole del canto corale, oue con breue, e facil metodo s'insegna la pratica de' precetti più necessari del canto fermo; il modo di mantenere il coro sempre alla medesima altezza di voce; di ripigliare doue resta l'organo; d'intonare molte cose, che fra l'anno si cantano; e in particolare tutti gl' inni. Opera di Matteo Coferati ... Firenze, Il Vangelisti, 1682.

20 p. l., 306, [14] p. illus. (incl. music) 15ᶜᵐ.

Coat of arms on half-title.
"Dell' origine, e progressi del canto ecclesiastico, discorso proemiale di Francesco Cionacci": prelim. leaves 12–20.

31–23117 MT860.A2C66

—— Cantore addottrinato in tutte le regole del canto corale; ovvero Modo facile, e breve per la pratica de' precetti piu necessarj del canto fermo, per mantenere il coro alla medesima altezza di voce, e di ripigliarla dove resta l'organo. Con l'intonazione di molte singolari cose, che fra l'anno si cantano. In specie inni, invitatorj con il lor salmo, e offizio parvo della B. Vergine, e de' morti, con tutte le seguenze, e antifone da cantarsi alla distribuzione delle candele, e palme. 3. ed. ampliata. Opera data in luce dal molto rev. sig. Matteo Coferati ... Firenze, Per M. Nestenus, e A. Borghigiani, ad instanza di G. A. Scaletti, 1708.

xvi, 391 p. illus. (incl. music) 15½ᶜᵐ.

30–3278 MT860.C671

—— Manuale degli invitatorj co' suoi salmi da cantarsi nell' ore canoniche per ciascheduna festa, e feria di tutto l'anno: nell' ufizio parvo della Beatissima Vergine, e de' morti. Coll' aggiunta delle sequenze, e lor canto, e antifone da cantarsi alla distribuzione delle candele, e delle palme. Opera raccolta dal molto rev. sig. Matteo Coferati ... 2. ed. Firenze, Per M. Nestenus, ad istanza di S. Scaletti, 1718.

viii, 200 p. 15½ᶜᵐ. [*With his* Cantore addottrinato. Firenze, 1708]

30–3279 MT860.C671

—— Scolare addottrinato nelle prime regole più necessarie a sapersi del canto fermo, estratte dal Cantore addottrinato del molto rev. sig. Matteo Coferati ... per più facilità de' principianti. Opera

data in luce da Jacopo Antonio Mariottini ... con nuova aggiunta.
7. impressione. In Firenze, Per M. Nestenus, e A. Borghigiani. Si
vendono da D. Piazini, 1714.

> 32 p. illus. (incl. music) 15ᶜᵐ.
> 35–21823 MT860.C671S3 1714

Compēdium musices confectū ad faciliorē instructionē cantum
choralē discentiū : necnō ad ītroductionē huius libelli : q̄ Cantorinus
intitulat : oīb⁹ diuino cultui deditis perutilis ꝭ necessari⁹ : vt in
tabula hic immediate sequēti latius apparet. [*Vignette: Agnus Dei*]
Venetijs, sub Signo Agnus Dei, 1538.

> 32 p., 88 numb. l. illus. 15½ᶜᵐ.
> *Colophon:* Finis Cantorini romani: anno salutis. 1538. Venetijs. Apud
> Petrū Liechtenstein Coloniensem Germanum. Registrum. A ... N. Omnia
> sunt quaterna.
> The Cantorinus has caption : De principijs horay̶ Cantorinus ...
> Rubricated ; gothic type; initials. Printer's mark at end.
> 13–24943 MT860.A2C76

[Compleat instructions for the German flute]

New instructions for the German flute ... To which is added a
favorite collection of minuets, marches, song tunes, duets, &c.
Also the method of double tongueing, and a complete scale and
description of of [!] the German-flute with all the additional keys,
invented by Mʳ. Tacet. London, Longman & Broderip [178–?]

> 1 p. l., 36 p. front., illus. (incl. music) fold. pl. 17½ x 25ᶜᵐ. [*With* New
> instructions for the German-flute. London, J. Preston [178–?]]
> Engraved throughout.
> 20–18773 MT342.A2N39

——New instructions for the German-flute ... to which is added a
favorite collection of minuets, marches, song tunes, duets &c. Also
the method of double tongueing and a complete scale & description
of a new invented German flute with the additional keys such as
play'd on by two eminent masters, Florio and Tacet. London,
J. Preston [178–?]

> 1 p. l., 34 p. front., illus. (music) 17½ x 25ᶜᵐ.
> Engraved throughout.
> 20–18774 MT342.A2N39

The compleat tutor for the German flute, containing the best and
easiest instructions for learners to obtain a proficiency, translated
from the French. To which is added a choice collection of yᵉ most
celebrated airs, curiously adapted to that instrument. London,
H. Waylett [*ca.* 1745]

> 2 p. l., 34 p. illus. (music) 24½ᶜᵐ.
> Engraved throughout.
> Music: p. 1–2 (fold. pl.), 14–34.
> Apparently a much altered edition of "The newest method for learners
> on the German flute" which forms the third part of Peter Prelleur's
> "Modern musick-master," London, 1738. The "Newest method" is itself
> a free translation from Hotteterre's "Principes de la flute traversière,"
> Amsterdam, 1708.
> The preliminary text and musical examples are the same as in editions
> published by J. Simpson [17—] (Library of Congress copy: MT342.A2C76)
> and by J. Johnson [17—] (MT342.A2C78) The selection of airs is different
> in each case.
> 17–22470 MT342.A2C77

The **compleat** tutor for the German flute ... to which is added a favorite collection of song tunes, minuets, marches, duets &c. Also the method of double tongueing, and a concise scale & description of a new invented German flute with additional keys, made by T. Cahusac, such as play'd on by the two celebrated masters, Tacet and Florio. London, T. Cahusac [178-?]

> 1 p. l., 40 p., 1 l. front., illus. (incl. music) pl. 17½ x 25ᶜᵐ. [*With* New instructions for the German-flute. London, J. Preston [178-?]]
> Engraved throughout.
> Caption title: New instructions for the German flute.
> 20–18772   MT342.A2N39

The **compleat** tutor for the harpsichord or spinnet, wherein is shewn the Italian manner of fingering, with suits of lessons for beginners & those who are already proficients on that instrument & the organ: with rules for tuneing the harpsichord or spinnet. London, J. Johnson [176-?]

> 1 p. l., 33 p. front., fold. pl. 24½ᶜᵐ.
> Engraved throughout.
> Label mounted below imprint: Sold by Michael Hillegas, in Second street, Philadelphia.
> Forms the sixth part of Peter Prelleur's "Modern musick-master," London, 1738, where it appears under title "The harpsichord illustrated and improv'd." In the present edition the "Rules for attaining to play a thorough bass" are omitted. The selection of airs differs somewhat in the three Library of Congress editions.
> 22–11205   MT252.A2C77

—— The **compleat** tutor for the harpsichord or spinnet, wherein is shewn the Italian manner of fingering with suits of lessons for beginners & those who are already proficients on that instrument & the organ: with rules for a thorough bass, and tuning. London, Printed for & sold by Cˢ. & Sˡ. Thompson [176-?]

> 1 p. l., 36 p. front., illus. (music) fold. pl. 25½ᶜᵐ.
> Engraved throughout.
> "A dictionary explaining such Greek, Latin, Italian and French words as generally occur in musick": p. 36.
> 42–6754   MT252.A2C78

See also NEW instructions for playing the harpsichord.

The **compleat** tutor for the hautboy, containing the best and easiest instructions for learners to obtain a proficiency, to which is added a choice collection of the most celebrated Italian, English and Scotch tunes, also the favorite rondeau perform'd at Vauxhall, by Mʳ. Fisher ... London, Printed for C. & S. Thompson [17—]

> 1 p. l., 32 p. front., illus. (music) 23½ᶜᵐ. [*With* [Prelleur, Peter] Directions for playing on the flute ... London [173-?]]
> Engraved throughout.
> "A dictionary explaining such Italian, French and other words as generally occur in music": p. 31.
> 42–6757   MT342.P87

—— New and complete instructions for the oboe or hoboy, containing the easiest & most improv'd rules for learners to play, to which is added a select collection of airs, marches, minuets, duets, &c., also the favorite rondeau perform'd at Vauxhall, by Mr. Fischer ... London, T. Cahusac [17—]

> 1 p. l., 36 p. front., illus. (music) 17½ x 26ᶜᵐ.
> Engraved throughout.
> 41–34402   MT362.N38

The **compleat** tutor for the violin, containing the best and easiest instructions for learners to obtain a proficiency. To which is added a choice collection of the most celebrated Italian, English, and Scotch tunes. With several choice pieces for 2 violins. London, J. Simpson [174–?]

34 (*i. e.* 36) p. incl. fold. diagr. front., illus. (music)   24ᶜᵐ

Engraved throughout. Two blank versos omitted in numbering.
41–18176   MT262.C66

Compleat tutor for the violin.

See also GEMINIANI, F.

The **compleat** violist. Or An introduction to yᵉ art of playing on yᵉ bass viol wherein the necessary rules & directions are laid down in a plain & familiar method. With a collection of the psalm tunes set to the viol, as they are now in use in the churches where there are organs. To which are added some select aires & tunes, set according to yᵉ divers manners of playing by the G sol re ut cliff, the C sol fa ut cliff, & yᵉ fa ut cliff, also several lessons, viz. almans, sarabands, courants, iiggs, &c. compos'd for that instrument by yᵉ late famous master Mʳ. Benjamin Hely. London, I. Hare [etc., *ca.* 1700]

4 p. l., 16 numb. l.   18 x 23ᶜᵐ.

Engraved throughout.
31–4472   MT338.H4

Complete instructions for the bassoon, containing the most useful directions & examples for learners to obtain a proficiency; to which is annexed ... a selection of the most admired songs, airs, duetts &c. London, Preston & son [179–?]

1 p. l., 32 p. front., illus. (incl. music)   18 x 25½ᶜᵐ.
Engraved throughout.
Songs, airs, etc.: p. 11–30.
21–6994   MT402.A2C6

Concerts of ancient music, *London.*

Concerts of ancient music. [The performances for the season[s] 1785–1848] ... London, W. Lee [etc., 1785–1848]

64 v. fronts. (1797–1810)   16½–18½ᶜᵐ.

Title varies slightly.
Publisher, 1785–1811, W. Lee; 1812–1838, G. Wilding; 1839–1848, Henry Field.
Annual books of programs with words, containing lists of directors, performers, subscribers, etc.
"A sketch of the rise and progress of Her Majesty's Concerts of ancient music, by John Parry": vol. for 1847, p. [iii]–xii.
The "Concert of antient music" was established in 1776; the last concert took place June 7, 1848.
20–10875   ML28.L8A57

Cooke, Benjamin, *fl.* 1730.

See DIRECTIONS for playing on the flute. [173–?]

Cordeiro, Antonio.

See MARTÍNEZ, J. Arte de canto chão. 1612.

Corfe, Joseph, -1740–1820.

A treatise on singing, explaining ... all the rules for learning to sing by note, without the assistance of an instrument, with some observations on vocal music, interspersed with original examples, solfeggi, airs, duettos &c. &c. ... (particularly some ... pieces of sacred music, from the M.S.S. of Iomelli and Sacchini, never before published. In the collection of the late Iames Harris & W. B. Earle esq.ʳ, Salisbury) ... By Joseph Corfe ... To be had at the principal music shops in London & Bath, & at Mʳ Corfe's, Salisbury [*ca.* 1800]

2 p. l., 11, 40 p.   23 x 34ᶜᵐ.

Engraved with exception of text (preface, on 2d prelim. leaf, and "Treatise on singing," which occupies 1st page group) Preface autographed by Corfe.
Includes compositions by Jommelli, Sacchini, and Anfossi.
17–17447   MT830.C78

Corominas, Juan Francisco de.

Aposento anti-critico, desde donde se ve representar la gran comedia, que en su Theatro critico regaló al pueblo el rr. p. m. Feijoo, contra la musica moderna, y uso de los violines en los templos, ò carta, que en defensa de uno, y otro escribió d. Juan Francisco de Corominas ... Salamanca, Impr. de la Santa cruz [1726?]

3 p. l., 32 p.   14½ᶜᵐ.

Occasioned by discourse xiv, "Musica de los templos", in v. 1 of Feijóo y Montenegro's Theatro critico universal.
27–20890   ML3001.F28C7

Cantaridas amigables para remedio de sueños desvariados, y consejos de Corominas à Torres dormido, sobre el Montante, que manejó en la pendencia musica soñada. [Salamanca? 1727?]

8 p.   14½ᶜᵐ.

Polemic occasioned by v. 1 of Feijóo y Montenegro's Theatro critico universal.
27–20891   ML3001.F28C71

See also TORRES Y VILLARROEL, D. DE. Montante christiano.

Correa de Araujo, Francisco.

Libro de tientos y discvrsos de mvsica practica, y theorica de organo, intitulado Facultad organica: con el qual, y con moderado estudio y perseverancia, qualquier mediano tañedor puede salir aventajado en ella; sabiendo diestramente cantar canto de organo, y sobretodo teniendo buen natural. Compvesto por Francisco Correa de Arauxo ... Alcala, Impresso por A. Arnao, 1626.

4 p. l., 26 numb. l., 204 numb. l. (music) 29ᶜᵐ.

Signatures: § ⁴, A–N ², A–Z ⁴, Aa–Zz ⁴, Aaa–Eee ⁴.
Engraved title vignette (coat of arms)
Music in tablature.
Leaves 33–36 numbered 39–42; other errors in numbering.
30–3280   MT182.C7

Corrette, Michel, 1706 or 7–1795.

L'art de se perfectionner dans le violon, ou l'on donne à étudier des leçons sur toutes les positions des quatre cordes du violon et les différens coups d'archet ... Cet ouvrage fait la suite de l'Ecole d'Orphée, methode pour le violon. Par m^r. Corrette ... Paris, L'auteur [1783?]

> 1 p. l., 90 p., 1 l. front. 30^{cm}.
>
> Engraved throughout.
> 22–11220   MT271.A2C7

La belle vielleuse, methode pour apprendre facilem^t. à jouer de la vielle, contenant des leçons ou les doigts sont marqués pour les commençans; avec des jolis airs et ariettes en duo, deux suittes avec la basse et des chansons, par m^r. Corrette ... Paris, Chez les marchands assortis [ca. 1780]

> 1 p. l., 50 p. front., illus. (music) diagrs. 28½^{cm}.
>
> Published in 1763 under title: Méthode de vielle.
> Engraved throughout.
> Music: p. 14–50.
> Imperfect: p. 45–46 wanting.
> Bound in a fragment of manuscript. Inscribed on cover: Principes pour la vielle. Le 16 juin 1787. A madame Quiche.
> 31–21440   MT338.C8

Coste, César.

See MALOUIN, P. J., *praeses.*   An ad sanitatem musice?

Cotton, John, 1585–1652.

Singing of Psalmes a gospel-ordinance. Or A treatise, wherein are handled these foure particulars. 1. Touching the duty it selfe. 2. Touching the matter to be sung. 3. Touching the singers. 4. Touching the manner of singing. By John Cotton, teacher of the church at Boston in New-England. London, Printed by M. S. for Hannah Allen [etc.] 1647.

> 1 p. l., 72 p. 18½^{cm}.
>
> Bound by W. Pratt for H. Stevens, 1872. Full blue calf, gilt; double line inside borders.
> 41–9084   BV290.C6

Couperin, François, 1668–1733.

L'art de toucher le clavecin, par monsieur Couperin, organish [!] du roi ... Paris, Chés l'auteur [etc.] 1717.

> 3 p. l., 71, [1] p., 1 l. illus. (music) 33^{cm}.
>
> Engraved throughout.
> Includes eight preludes by Couperin.
> 20–10859   MT228.A2C6

Croci, Antonio, *fl.* 1642.

Geminato compendio, ouero Dvplicata gvida altretanto curiosa, quanto necessaria per giungere facilmente alla perfettione del canto piano, ouer fermo, e d'imparare il modo di ben ordinare l'vffitio prescritto nelle rubriche del Breuiario romano, tradotte in lingua

volgare con quelle de santi min. conu. di san Francesco ... Opera
qvinta. Di fra Antonio Croci ... Venetia, Presso il Ginami, 1642.

168 p. illus. (music) 17^{cm}.

Music: p. 31–59.
17–31243

MT860.A2C8

Crome, Robert.

The fiddle new model'd, or A useful introduction for the violin,
exemplify'd with familiar dialogues, by Robert Crome ... London,
Printed by J. Tyther [174—?]

1 p. l., 70 p. illus. (music) fold. plates. 24^{cm}.

Engraved throughout.
35–21818

MT262.C75F5

—— The fiddle new model'd, or A useful introduction to the violin,
exemplify'd with familiar dialogues, between the master & scholar,
by Robert Crome ... London, S. A. & P. Thompson [178–?]

1 p. l., 68 p. illus. (music) fold. plates. 23½^{cm}.
Engraved throughout.
41–18177

MT262.C75F54

Danby, John, 1757–1798.

La guida alla musica vocale, containing various progressive examples & duetts calculated for the use of beginners, by J. Danby.
Op. 2. London, Printed for the author—to be had at Blands [1787?]

1 p. l., 34 p. illus. (music) 25 x 34^{cm}.

Engraved throughout; ornamental t.-p. in terra-cotta.
Contains the following duets: Arise sweet messenger of morn; The
virgin when soften'd by May; Gentle Zephir with thy wing; O take this
wreath my hand has wove; Now the snowdrops lift their heads; If
those who live in shepherds bow'r.
29–6570

MT870.A2D27

Dandrieu, Jean François, 1684–1740.

Principes de l'acompagnement du clavecin exposez dans des tables
dont la simplicité et l'arangement peuvent, avec une mediocre aten-
tion, faire conoître les règles les plus sures et les plus nècèssaires
pour parvenir à la téorie et à la pratique de cète sience. Dèdiez a
monseigneur le duc de Noailles par m^r. Dandrieu ... Paris, Chez
l'auteur [etc., 1719]

2 p. l., 6 p., 68 l., [1], 18 p., 1 l. 28 x 36½^{cm}.
Engraved throughout; title within ornamental border.
Includes a collection of "brunètes" (18 p. at end)
Second edition published 1727; 3d edition, 1777.
29–725

MT49.D26

Davidson, Thomas, 17th cent.

See FORBES, J. Cantus, songs and fancies. 1682.

Demantius, Christoph, 1567–1643.

Isagoge artis musicae ad incipientium captum maxime accommodata. Kurtze anlaitung recht- vnnd leicht singen zu lernen.

Auctore Christophoro Demantio ... Ed. 5. OnoldsbachI, ex typographéo Pauli Bohemi, 1611.

[127] p. 16ᶜᵐ.

With musical examples.
Latin and German on opposite pages.
22–11219   MT870.A2D35

Demar, Sébastien, 1763–1832.

Nouvelle méthode pour la clarinette, faite d'une manière très facile avec le doigté et tous les principes indispensables pour bien jouer de cet instrument, par S. Demar. Paris, B. Pollet; Orléans, L'auteur [180–]

1 p. l., 2 l. illus. 34½ᶜᵐ.

38–35339   MT382.A2D36

Desaugiers, Marc Antoine Madeleine, 1772–1827, *translator.*

See MANCINI, G. B. L'art du chant figuré. 1776.

Descartes, René, 1596–1650.

Renati Des-Cartes Musicæ compendium. Amstelodami, apud Joannem Janssonium juniorem, 1656.

2 p. l., 34 p. illus. (music) diagrs. 22½ᶜᵐ.

Title vignette.
24–31349   ML3805.A2D24

——— Copy 2. 21ᶜᵐ. [*With his* Geometria. Amstelædami, 1659–61]
                                                  QA33.D43   1659

Traité de la mechaniqve, composé par monsievr Descartes. De plvs l'Abregé de mvsique dv mesme autheur mis en françois. Avec les eclaircissemens necessaires. Par N. P. [*i. e.* N. J. Poisson] ... Paris, C. Angot, 1668.

127, [1] p. illus., diagrs. 23½ x 18ᶜᵐ.

10–18430   QC123.D5

[Desforges,   ]

Mémoires anecdotes des avantures galantes de m. Duliz, devenuës tragiques, après la catastrophe de celle de mademoiselle Pélissier, actrice de l'Opéra de Paris. Avec Le triomphe de l'intérêt, comédie. Lisbonne, Imprimerie de la Juiverie, 1752.

1 p. l., 206 p., 1 l., 66 p. front. 16½ᶜᵐ.

Title vignette.
"Le triomphe de l'intérêt, comédie, sur les avantures galantes de m. Duliz" by Louis de Boissy (1 l., 66 p.) has special t.-p. with same imprint as the preceding "Mémoires."
41–27529   ML429.D88D32

Deutsche filarmonische gesellschaft.

See MUSIKALISCHE korrespondenz der Teutschen filarmonischen gesellschaft.

Devienne, François, 1759–1803.

Méthode de flûte, par Devienne. Nouv. ed., augm. de petits airs, de six nouveaux duos et des gammes pour la flûte à petites clefs ... Ecrit et gravé par Joannès. Paris, B. Pollet; [etc., etc., n. d.]

1 p. l., 113 p. 33^{cm}.

Engraved throughout.
First edition: Paris, Imbault, 1795.
18–12268   MT342.A2D2

Dezais, ——, *joint author.*

See FEUILLET, R. A. Chorégraphie. 1713.

Directions for playing on the flute, with a scale for transposing any piece of musick to ye properest keys for that instrument. To which is added a choice collection of minuets, jiggs, song-tunes & aires in two parts. London, B. Cooke [173–?]

1 p. l., 2–30, 3 p. front., illus. (music) fold. pl. (music) 25½^{cm}.

Folded plate numbered as p. 14.
Engraved throughout.
Music: p. 14–30.
"Benjamin Cooke, the publisher, and probably the author, of this curious book was the father of the illustrious musician Dr. Benjamin Cooke."—Ms. note by Wm. Hayman Cummings on fly-leaf of Library of Congress copy.
17–31246   MT342.A2D3

See also PRELLEUR, P. Directions for playing on the flute.

Diruta, Girolamo, *fl.* 1574–1609.

Il Transilvano, dialogo sopra il vero modo di sonar organi, & istromenti da penna. Del r. p. Girolamo Dirvta ... Nel quale facilmente, & presto s'impara di conoscere sopra la tastatura il luogo di .ciascuna parte, & come nel diminuire si deueno portar le mani, & il modo d'intendere la intauolatura; prouando la verità, & necessità delle sue regole, con le toccate di diuersi eccelenti organisti, poste nel fine del libro. Opera nuouamente ritrouata, vtilissima, & necessaria a professori d'organo ... Venetia, A. Vincenti, 1625, '22.

2 v. in 1. illus. (music) 35½^{cm}.

Collation: pt. 1: 63, [1] p.; pt. 2 (4 books): 2 p. l., 2–21 p.; 36 p.; 12 p.; 25, [1] p. Signatures: A^{32}; A–B^{12}, Bb^6, C^6, D^{14} (last leaf blank).
Part 2 has title: Seconda parte del Transilvano, dialogo diviso in qvattro libri ... Nel quale si contiene il vero modo, & la vera regola d' intauolare ciascun canto ... Venetia, A. Vincenti, 1622.
Titles within floreated borders.
The 1st edition of pt. 1 was published in 1593. (*cf.* Wadding, L. Scriptores Ordinis minorum. Suppl. (by Sbaraglia) Ed. nova. pars 1, Romæ, 1908, p. 364). Other editions appeared in 1597 and 1612. The earliest edition of pt. 2 is dated 1609.
Includes compositions by G. Diruta, C. Merulo, A. Gabrieli, G. Gabrieli, L. Luzzaschi, A. Romanini, P. Quagliati, V. Bell'haver, G. Guami, A. Mortaro, G. Fatorini, A. Banchieri.
26–21062   MT182.A2D46

Dodwell, Henry, 1641–1711.

A treatise concerning the lawfulness of instrumental musick in holy offices. By Henry Dodwell, M. A. To which is prefixed, a preface in vindication of Mr. Newte's sermon, concerning the lawfulness and use of organs in the Christian church, &c. From the exceptions of an anonymous letter, to a friend in the country, concerning the use of instrumental musick in the worship of God, &c. London, W. Hawes [etc.] 1700.

1 p. l., [46], 82 p. 19^{cm}.

Irregularities in paging: p. 34–48 not in consecutive order.
Preface signed: J. Newte.

21–7000   ML3001.D6

See also A LETTER to a friend in the country, concerning the use of instrumental musick in the worship of God.
NEWTE, J. The lawfulness and use of organs.

Domingos do Rosario, *frey.*

Theatro ecclesiastico. Em que se acham muitos documentos de canto chaõ para qualquer pessoa dedicada ao culto divino nos officios de coro, e altar ... Exposto por seu autor fr. Domingos do Rosario ... Dado ao prélo por Jozé Gomes de Oliveira. Lisboa, Officina joaquinianna da musica de d. B. Fernandez Gayo, 1743.

16 p. l., 262, [3], 263–383 p. 21^{cm}.

35–21824   MT860.D76

Don * * *

See METHODE pour aprendre a jouër de la guitarre.

[Dorat, Claude Joseph] 1734–1780.

La déclamation théâtrale, poëme didactique en trois chants, précédé d'un discours. Paris, Impr. de S. Jorry, 1766 [i. e. 1767]

198 p. front., 4 pl. 19½^{cm}.

"La danse, chant quatrième du poëme de La déclamation, précédée de notions historiques sur la danse, & suivie d'une réponse à une lettre écrite de province" (p. [129]–182) has special t.-p. with imprint date 1767.

CONTENTS.—Chant I. La tragédie.—Chant II. La comédie.—Chant III. L'opera.—Chant IV. La danse.

43–28173   PQ1981.D35A64 1767

—— La déclamation théâtrale, poëme didactique en quatre chants, précédé d'un discours, et de notions historiques sur la danse. Nouv. ed. Paris, Impr. de S. Jorry, 1767.

176 p. 5 pl. 19½^{cm}.

CONTENTS.—Chant I. La tragédie.—Chant II. La comédie.—Chant III. L'opéra.—Chant IV. La danse.

42–51416   PQ1981.D35A64a

Douland, Robert.

See DOWLAND, ROBERT, 1586 (*ca.*)–1641.

Dowland, John, 1563–1626.

See DOWLAND, R. Varietie of lute-lessons.

Dowland, Robert, 1586 (*ca.*)–1641.

Varietie of lute-lessons: viz. fantasies, pauins, galliards, almaines, corantoes, and volts: selected out of the best approued avthors, as well beyond the seas as of our owne country. By Robert Douland.

Whereunto is annexed certaine obseruations belonging to lvte-playing: by Iohn Baptisto Besardo of Visonti. Also a short treatise thereunto appertayning: by Iohn Douland batcheler of musicke. London, Printed for Thomas Adams, 1610.

[72] p. illus. (music) diagr. 33½ᶜᵐ.

Signatures: A–S².
Title within ornamental border.
Caption title: Necessarie observations belonging to the lute, and lvte-playing, by John Baptisto Besardo ... with choise varietie of lvte-lessons, partly inuented, and partly collected out of the best avthors, by Robert Douland, and Iohn Douland ...
Music in tablature.
Bound in full vellum, gilt, double line border and corner ornaments, gilt edges, by F. Bedford. Christie-Miller arms in gold on front and back cover.

29–9159   MT640.D7

Drechssler, Johann Gabriel, *d.* 1677, *praeses.*

לדוד כנור sive De cithara Davidica ... Lipsiæ, litteris Colerianis, 1712.

98 (*i. e.* 38) p. 19½ᶜᵐ.

Diss.—Leipzig, 1670 (C. Felmer, respondent)

27–7074   ML166.A2D73

[Du Boccage, Marie Anne (Le Page) Fiquet] 1710–1802.

Lettre de madame * * * à une des ses amies sur les spectacles, et principalement sur l'Opera comique. [n. p.] 1745.

44 p. 15½ᶜᵐ.

41–25463   ML1727.3.D78L3

Dumont, ——, *supposed author.*

See [MAYEUR DE SAINT PAUL, F. M.] Le vol plus haut.

Dupuit, Baptiste.

See DUPUIT, JEAN BAPTISTE.

Dupuit, Jean Baptiste.

Principes pour toucher de la viele avec six sonates pour cet instrument qui conviennent aux violon, flûte, clavessin &c. ... Composés par mʳ. Bap. Dupuit ... Œuvre ɪ. Paris, L'auteur [etc., 1741]

2 p. l., xi p.; 35 p. (music); [1] p. illus. (music) diagrs. 40ᶜᵐ.

Engraved throughout. Title within ornamental border.
"Privilege général" dated 1741.

29–6567   MT338.D8

[Duran, Domingo Marcos]

Estes es vn excelente tra ‖ ctado dela musica lla ‖ mado Lux bella. q̃ ‖ tracta muy larga ‖ mête del arte de ‖ cãto llano biê ‖ emendado y ‖ corregido. ‖ [Seuilla, J. Cromberger, 1518]

[27] p. diagrs. 21ᶜᵐ.

Gothic type. Signatures: a⁶, b⁸ (verso of last leaf blank)
Colophon: La presente obra fue impressa ‖ enla muy noble muy leal ciudad de Seuilla a ho ‖ nor y gloria de dios, y a prouecho delos que ‖ quisieren aprender de cantar: por Jaco- ‖ bo cromberger aleman. Enel año ‖ de nuestra saluacion de mill ? ‖ quinientos y diez y ‖ ocho años. ‖

Duran, Domingo Marcos—Continued.

Verso of t.-p.: Lux bella d' cãto llano corregida: emēdada y aprobada, puesta ē ordē y estilo muy breue: cierto ᴣ copioso, la q̃l ordēo ᴣ cōpuso el bachiller domīgo marcos durã ...

Music (p. [13]–[26]) has caption: Incipiunt octo toni artis musice: a patre sanctissimo Gregorio ordinati ᴣ cōposti ...

Two earlier editions are known: one, supposed to have been printed at Salamanca near the end of the 15th century; one printed in Seville "por quatro alemanes" in 1492. A commentary on the Lux bella by its author was published in 1498 ("Comiença una Glosa del bachiller Domingo Marcos Duran ... sobre el arte de canto llano compuesta por el mesmo llamado Lux bella"). cf. Riaño, Critical and bibliographical notes on early Spanish music, London, 1887, p. 73–74, 76–77.

Bound in full brown morocco; inside borders.

On label: Biblioteca de Juan M. Sánchez. Unico ejemplar conocido.

Armorial book-plate.

23–4270　　　　　　　　　　　　　　　　　　　　ML171.D97

Durieu,

Nouvelle methode de musique vocale; concernant les principes de cet art, démontré par des leçons, et accompagné d'exemples qui en applanissent toutes les difficultés. Adoptée par l'Institut national de musique, chant et déclamation ... Par le citoyen Durieu. Paris, L'auteur [1793]

2 p. l., 107 p. illus. (music) diagrs. 35ᶜᵐ.

Engraved throughout; title within historiated border containing the author's (?) portrait.

"La seconde partie est composée de quarante quatre leçons variées sur la même gamme, et de vingt cinq autres leçons sur tous les tons, composées par le citoyen Agus."—Avertissement.

29–15436　　　　　　　　　　　　　　　　　　　MT835.D99

Ebeling, Christoph Daniel, 1741–1817, *translator.*

See BURNEY, C. Carl Burney's ... Tagebuch seiner musikalischen reisen. 1772–73.

Eccles, Solomon, 1618–1683.

A musick-lector: or, The art of musick (that is so much vindicated in Christendome) discoursed of, by way of dialogue between three men of several judgments: The one a musician, and master of that art, and zealous for the Church of England; who calls musick the gift of God. The other a Baptist, who did affirm it to be a decent and harmless practice. The other a Quaker (so called) being formerly of that art, doth give his judgment and sentence against it; but yet approves of the musick that pleaseth God. Written by Solomon Eccles ... London, Printed in the year, 1667.

28 p. 20ᶜᵐ.

19–7338　　　　　　　　　　　　　　　　　　　　ML64.E33

Einicke, Georg Friedrich, 1710–1770.

See MATTHESON, J. Sieben gespräche der Weisheit und Musik. 1751.

Éloge de m. Baurans. [n. p., 176–?]

p. [115]–125. 16½ᶜᵐ.

Half-title.
Detached from an unidentified publication ("Le Nécrologe des hommes célèbres de France"?)

ML423.B296E4

Éloge de monsieur Blavet. [Paris, 1770]

p. 335–343. 16½ᶜᵐ.

Caption title.
From "Le Nécrologe des hommes célèbres de France," edited by Palissot de Montenoy, Poinsinet de Sivry, Francois de Neufchâteau, and others. Ascribed by Fétis to "M. François." cf. Biog. univ. des musiciens, 2. éd., v. 1, p. 440.
42–310

ML410.B638

Entire new and compleat tutor for the violin.

See GEMINIANI, F.

Epitre aux Bouffonnistes. [n. p., 1753]

8 p. 19½ᶜᵐ.

Caption title.
Signed "L'Anti-Scurra" and dated "A Paris 12 février 1753".
In verse.
By Caux de Cappeval? cf. Fétis, Biog. univ. des musiciens, supp., II, 450.
30–3275

ML1727.33.E7

Estienne, Henri, 1460?–1520, translator.

See LE FÈVRE, J. Arithmetica et Musica. 1514.

Eximeno y Pujades, Antonio, 1729–1808.

Duda de d. Antonio Exîmeno sobre el Ensayo fundamental practico de contrapunto del m. r. p. m. fr. Juan Bautista Martini: traducida del italiano a nuestro idioma por d. Francisco Antonio Gutierrez ... Madrid, Imprenta real, 1797.

xiv, 313, [1] p. 19½ᶜᵐ.

34–17783

MT55.E92

Risposta al giudizio delle Efemeridi letterarie di Roma ... sopra l'opera di d. Antonio Eximeno circa l'origine e le regole della musica. [Roma, Bouchard e Gravier, 1774]

42 p. 26½ᶜᵐ.

Four papers, with caption titles, "Risposta," "Seconda risposta," etc., in reply to articles which appeared in the Efemeridi on March 19 and 26 and April 2 and 9, 1774.
21–7946

ML159.E9R4

Faber, Jacobus, Stapulensis.

See LE FÈVRE, JACQUES, d'Étaples, d. 1537.

Falletti, Girolamo, *conte di Trignano,* 1518?–1564.

Le lodi della mvsica tradotte da i versi latini del conte Girolamo Faletti in ottaua rima da Giouan Mario Verdezzotti. All' illustrissimo & eccellentissimo signore d. Alfonso ii. duca di Ferrara v. Con due sonetti del sudetto fatti nell' entrata, che fece in Venetia sua Eccellentia l'anno 1562. Di nuouo corretti e ristampati. Venetia, N. Beuilacqua, 1563.

[31] p. 22^{cm}.

Signatures: A–D⁴.
Title vignette (printer's mark)
35–21827   ML64.F3L6

Feijóo y Montenegro, Benito Jerónimo, 1675–1764.

See CERBELLÓN DE LA VERA, E.   Dialogo harmonico.
COROMINAS, J. F. DE.   Aposento anti-critico.
Cantaridas amigables.
TORRES Y VILLARROEL, D. DE.   Montante christiano.

Felmer, Caspar, *fl.* 1670, *respondent.*

See DRECHSSLER, J. G., *praeses.*   ...   De cithara Davidica.

Fenaroli, Fedele, 1730–1818.

...   Cours complet d'harmonie et de haute composition ...   Nouv. ed., soigneusement cor.   Paris, Vve Launer [17—?]

1 p. l., ix, 167 p.   port.   34½^{cm}.

Publisher's plate no.: 500.
Italian and French in parallel columns.
Translated and edited by Emanuele Imbimbo.
First edition, Naples, 1775, published under title: Regole musicali per 1 principianti di cembalo.
18–12267   MT49.F35

Ferandiere, Fernando, *18th cent.*

Arte de tocar la guitarra española por música, compuesto y ordenado por d. Fernando Ferandiere ...   Madrid, Impr. de P. Aznar, 1799.

4 p. l., 32 p.   17 pl. (music)   20^{cm}.

"Diálogo ... sobre el contrapunto y composicion": p. 19–30.
"Catálogo de la música compuesta para guitarra por d. Fernando Ferandiere": p. 31–32.
35–21834   MT582.F35

[Ferrer, Pedro]

Intonario general para todas las yglesias de España.   Corregido y en muchos lugares emēdado.   Enel qual se hã añadido los ocho tonos / o modos de Miravete / y las prefaciones q̃ se cantan enla missa / y el Pater noster / Cõ otras cosas muchas y muy necessarias para los sacerdotes q̃ fueren zelosos de saber cantar las cosas que incumben a su profession ...   [Zaragoza] Con priuilegio imperial, 1548.

6 l., lviii numb. l.   1 woodcut illus.   19½^{cm}.

Colophon: ... Fue impresso el presente Intonario enla muy noble y leal ciudad de Caragoça en casa de Pedro Bernuz. Acabose a siete dias di mes de mayo. Año de mil y quinientos y quarenta y ocho. [*Device of Pedro Bernuz. cf.* Haebler, Span. u. port. bücherzeichen. Strassburg, 1898, pl. ii a (error for ii o: *cf.* p. vi. col. 2)]

Ferrer, Pedro—Continued.

Signatures: ✝⁶, A–F⁸, G¹⁰.
Printed in red and black. Arms of Don Hernando de Aragón, archbishop
of Saragossa, at head of title.
Author's name in superscription of dedication, verso of t.-p.

36–23941   MT860.F365

Feuillet, Raoul Auger, *fl.* 1700.

Chorégraphie, ou L'art de décrire la dance par caracteres, figures
et signes desmonstratifs avec lesquels on apprend facilement de soy
même toutes sortes de dances. Par m^rs Feuillet et Dezais ... Paris,
Chez le s^r Dezais, 1713.

3 p. l., 95 p. incl. diagrs. 24^cm.

Engraved throughout.
Contains music.
With this are bound the author's Recueil de dances ... Paris, 1709, and
Recueil de dances, composées par m. Pecour ... et mise [!] sur le papier par
m. Feuillet ... Paris, 1709.
In ms. on fly-leaf: Ce livre appartien a son mestre qui nest ni capeusin
ni pretre mais en tout cas de perdition—Mathurin terrade est son nom.

14–2127   GV1590.F5

—— Orchesography; or, The art of dancing by characters and
demonstrative figures. Wherein the whole art is explain'd; with
compleat tables of all steps us'd in dancing, and rules for the motions
of the arms, &c. Whereby any person (who understands dancing)
may of himself learn all manner of dances. Being an exact and just
translation from the French of Monsieur Feuillet. By John Weaver,
dancing master. The 2d ed. N. B. To this edition is added, the
Rigadoon, the Louver, & the Brittagne, in characters, with the contents, or index: the whole engraven: and likewise may be had where
these are sold, 20 dances in characters, by Mr Isaac, in one vollume.
London, In°. Walsh [*ca.* 1715?]

3 p. l., 120 p. incl. diagrs. 27^cm.

The Rigadoon, the Louver, & the Brittagne, by Mr. Isaac (p. 101–120)
consist of diagrams of dance figures, with tunes.
Engraved throughout.
Bound in mottled calf, paneled, with gold tooling.

22–22367   GV1590.F6

—— Choregraphie, das ist/Die kunst einen tantz durch cha-
racteres, figuren und andere zeichen zu beschreiben ... von mons.
Feüillet ... (*In* Taubert, Gottfried. Rechtschaffener tantzmeister.
Leipzig, 1717. 21½ x 17^cm. p. 745–915 incl. plates (diagrs.))

With reproduction of title-page of French edition of 1701.

GV1590.T4

Recueil de contredances mises en chorégraphie, d'une maniére si
aisée, que toutes personnes peuvent facilement les apprendre, sans le
secours d'aucun maître et même sans avoir eu aucune connoissance de
la chorégraphie. Par m^r. Feuillet ... Paris, L'auteur, 1706.

16 p. l., 192 p. diagrs. 14¼^cm.

Engraved throughout.
Contains music.
24–27846   MT950.A2F49

Recueil de dances, composées par m^r. Feuillet ... Paris, L'auteur,.1709.

1 p. l., 84 p. of diagrs. (part fold) 24^{cm}. [*With his* Chorégraphie, ou L'art de décrire la dance par caracteres ... Paris, 1713]

Engraved throughout.
Full-page diagrams; at head of each, the tune for the dance figure represented.

14–2126   GV1590.F5

Recueil de dances composées par m. Pecour ... et mise [!] sur le papier par M. Feuillet ... Paris, L'auteur, 1709.

1 p. l., 72 p. of diagrs. 24^{cm}. [*With his* Chorégraphie, ou L'art de décrire la dance par caracteres ... Paris, 1713]

Engraved throughout.
Full-page diagrams; at head of each, the tune for the dance figure represented.

14–2125   GV1590.F5

Fischer, Johan Philip Albrecht, *d.* 1778.

Kort en grondig onderwys, van de transpositie, beneffens eenige korte aenmerkingen over de musiek der ouden, de onnodigheit van eenige modis, en het ut, re, mi, als mede de subsemitonia, of gesneede klavieren. Waer noch bygevoegt is, eene korte en gemakkelyke methode, om een klavier gelyk te stemmen. Door J. P. A. Fischer. Utrecht, W. Stouw, 1728.

1 p. l., 34 p. fold. diagr. 21^{cm}.

Musical examples: p. 31–34.

22–10951   MT68.A2F47

Korte en noodigste grond-regelen van de bassus-continuus, beneffens verscheydene aenmerkingen, over desselfs behandelinge, voorgestelt, ende met eenige exempels verklaert. Door J. P. A. Fischer ... Utrecht, W. Stouw, 1731.

4 p. l., 52 p., 1 l. illus. (music) 21 x 16½^{cm}.

27–20889   MT49.A2F4

Verhandeling van de klokken en het klokke-spel; waer in behalven de opkomst van het klokkespel, alles wat omtrent de klokken aenmerkelyk is, als: de stoffe, gewigt, grootte, en klank der zelve, mitsgaders de compositie regels voor de ton, en de nodige wetenschap van't versteeken, wort voorgestelt; benevens een kort bericht van de outheit, gebruyk, misbruyk, en doopen der klokken, als ook van zogenaemde wonderklokken, door J. P. A. Fischer. Utrecht, W. Kroon, 1738.

4 p. l., 108 p., 1 l. front., illus. (music) 3 fold. pl. 21 x 17^{cm}.

38–35470   ML1039.F52V51

Fischer, Johann Christian, 1733–1800.

See The COMPLEAT tutor for the hautboy.

[Forbes, John] *d.* 1675, *publisher.*

Cantus, songs and fancies, to severall musicall parts. Both apt for voices and viols. With a brief introduction to musick, as is taught into the Musick-school of Aberdeen. The 3d ed., exactly cor.

and enl. Together also, with severall of the choisest Italian-songs, and new English-ayres, all in three parts, (viz.) two treebles and a bass ... Aberdeen, Printed by Iohn Forbes, printer to the ancient city of Bon-Accord, anno Dom. 1682.

[116] p. illus. 15 x 18½ᶜᵐ.

Signatures: 2 leaves unsigned, A–O⁴.
Added t.-p. (with woodcut illustrations): Cantus, songs and fancies, to three, four or five parts, both apt for voices and viols. With a brief introduction to musick. As is taught in the Musick-school of Aberdeen. The 3d ed., much enl. and cor. Printed in Aberdeen by Iohn Forbes, and are to be sold at his printing-house above the Meal-market, at the sign of the Towns-armes. 1682.
The photolithographic facsimile issued in the New club series, Paisley, A. Gardner, 1879, contains the illustrated t.-p. only.
In the 1st and 2d editions the "Brief introduction to musick" is given as by Thomas Davidson.
"Several of the choisest Italian songs composed by Giovanni Giacomo Castoldi [i. e. Gastoldi] da Carravaggio. Together also, with some of the best new English-ayres ... ": p. [99]–[116]
The English composers named are Henry Lewis [i. e. Lawes], Simon Ives, William Webb, John [i. e. Jeremy] Savile and Dr. Wilson.
Armorial book-plate: Bibliotheca Lindesiana.
Bound in full morocco, gilt, gilt edges, by Zaehnsdorf.

29–6571 M1490.F69

Formenti, Lorenzo, *editor.*
See INDICE de' teatrali spettacoli.

Formey, Jean Henri Samuel, 1711–1797, *editor.*
See ANDRÉ, Y. M. Essai sur le beau. 1759.

France.
Declaration du roy, portant reglement pour les fonctions des jurez syndics en titre d'office de la Communauté des maistres à danser, & joüeurs d'instrumens tant hauts que bas, & hautbois de la ville & fauxbourgs de Paris, & des droits attribuez à leurs charges; avec confirmation des statuts de ladite communauté. Donnée à Versailles le 2. novembre 1691. Registrée au Parlement. Paris, E. Michallet, 1692.

8 p. 24½ x 19ᶜᵐ.

ML271 1692

Extrait de l'arrest definitif de la Cour de Parlement prononcé en la grande chambre le 7. may 1695. En faveur des compositeurs de musique, organistes & professeurs de clavecin. Contre les jurez de la Communauté des maistres à danser & joüeurs d'instrumens tant hauts que bas & haut-bois. [Paris, 1695]

3 p. 23ᶜᵐ.

Caption title.

ML271 1695

Franches et courtes réflections sur un mémoire au roi; publié nouvellement par m. Viotti, 10 mai 1789. [Paris? 1789?]

15 p. 21ᶜᵐ.

On Viotti's Mémoire au roi, concernant l'exploitation du privilege de l'Opéra.

ML1727.8.P2V52

Francœur, Louis Joseph, 1738–1804.

Diapason général de tous les instrumens à vent avec des observations sur chacun d'eux au quel on a joint un projet nouveau pour
simplifier la maniere actuelle de copier. Dédié à m. de La Borde ...
Par m. Francœur neveu ... Paris, Des Lauriers [ca. 1782?]

2 p. l., 82 p.   illus. (music)   33ᶜᵐ.

Engraved throughout.
First published 1772. *cf.* Choron's preface to the edition of 1813.
Items in publisher's " Catalogue " in this copy indicate that it is a reissue,
about 1782.
An edition with additions by Choron, and omitting the " projet nouveau ",
was published in 1813 under title: Traité général des voix et des instru-
ments d'orchestre.
Imperfect: pages 57–60 wanting.

29–9156   MT70.F78

François de Neufchâteau, Nicolas Louis, *comte,* 1750–1828, *supposed author.*

See Éloge de monsieur Blavet.

Francus, Theodorus, *Herbipolensis.*

See Theodorus *Herbipolensis.*

Frezza *dalle Grotte,* **Giuseppe.**

Il cantore ecclesiastico per istruzione de' religiosi minori conventuali, e beneficio comune di tutti gl' ecclesiastici, del p. Giuseppe
Frezza dalle Grotte ... 2. impressione. Padova, Nella stamperia
del Seminario, appresso G. Manfrè, 1713.

164, [7] p.   illus. (music) fold. pl.   24ᶜᵐ.

Illustrated half-title; title vignette.

30–3276   MT860.F895

—— Il cantore ecclesiastico per istruzione de' religiosi minori
conventuali, e benefizio comune di tutti gli ecclesiastici, del p. Giuseppe Frezza dalle Grotte ... Tomo primo. 3. impressione. Padova,
Nella stamperia del Seminario, appresso G. Manfrè, 1733.

164, [7] p.   illus. (music) fold. pl.   25ᶜᵐ.

Illustrated half-title, title vignette.
Complete, although designated " tomo primo ". In the 1st edition, 1698,
another part was promised, but, according to Gaspari, it never appeared.

20–19881   MT860.F9

Frick, Philipp Joseph, 1740–1798.

Ausweichungs-tabellen worinne gezeiget wird, wie man aus einer
tonart in eine andere, sie sey nahe, oder weit entfernet, geschwind
übergehen könne; zum beliebigen gebrauch für clavier und orgel-
spieler, verfertiget und heraus gegeben von Philipp Joseph Frick ...
I. th. Wien, J. Kurzböck, 1772.

[3] p.; [24] p. (music); 1 l.   33 x 21½ᶜᵐ.

22–3342   MT68.A2F74

A Friend to church-music.
See OF the use and abuse of music. 1753.

Fries, Johann Henrich Hermann.
Johann Henrich Hermann Fries Abhandlung vom sogenannten pfeifer-gericht, so in ... Frankfurt am Main, von uralten zeiten her ... aljårlich einmal gehalten zu werden pflegt: welcher eine kurze nachricht vom wahren ursprung der beiden dasigen von alters her berûmten reichs-messen einverleibet, samt einigen andern zufålligen anmerkungen und einem sendschreiben des hôchstberûmten freiherrn von Senkenberg ... an den verfasser. Frankfurt am Main, W. C. Multz, 1752.

7 p. l., 16, 248, [8] p. front. 18¼ᶜᵐ.

9–11406   JN3259.F8

[Frison, A.]
Éloge de la musique. [Paris, 1762]

4 p. 25½ x 20ᶜᵐ.
Caption title.
Signed at end: A. Frison, maître de musique.
"Cet éloge est inséré dans le Mercure de France, année 1762, page 54."—
Foot-note, p. [1]

ML3847.F75E8

Fux, Johann Joseph, 1660–1740.
Salita al Parnasso, o sia Guida alla regolare composizione della musica con nuovo, e certo metodo non per anche in ordine sì esatto data alla luce, e composta da Giovanni Giuseppe Fux ... Fedelmente trasportata dal latino nell'idioma italiano dal sacerdote Alessandro Manfredi ... Carpi, Nella Stamperia del pubblico per il Carmignani, 1761.

5 p. l., 140 (*i. e.* 240) p. front., illus. (incl. music) 39ᶜᵐ.

Title in red and black; initials. Engraved frontispiece, title vignette, head-pieces, illustration. Many full pages of music, engraved.
Pages 103–104 and 105–106 duplicated. Last page wrongly numbered.

29–6566   MT40.F994

Gaffurio, Franchino, 1451–1522.
Theoricum opus musice discipline. Neapolis, Franciscus di Dino, 8 Oct. 1480. 4° (18½ᶜᵐ.)

fol. [1] ʳᵉᶜᵗᵒ blank. fol. [1] ᵛᵉʳˢᵒ —fol. [2] ʳᵉᶜᵗᵒ: [Tabula] fol. [2] ᵛᵉʳˢᵒ: CLARISSIMI AC PRESTANTISSI ‖ MI MVSICI FRANCHINI GAFORI ‖ LAVDENSIS Theoricum opus musice ‖ discipline ... fol. [115], line 14, *colophon* : FRANCHINI Gafori Laudensis Musices ‖ pfessoris theoricum opus armonice discipli ‖ ne Explicit. Impressum Neapolis per Magi ‖ strum Fråciscū di dino florentinum. Anno dñi M.CCCC.LXXX. Die octauo octo ‖ bris. Inuictissimo Rege Ferdinando regnan ‖ te. Anno regni eius vigessimo tertio. ‖ fol. [115] ʳᵉᶜᵗᵒ: Incipit Registrū huius libri.
116 leaves without foliation or signatures. 4 prelim. leaves, [a–oᵃ] ([a₁] and [o₃], blank, wanting).
Woodcut illustrations and diagrams. On fol. [102] ʳᵉᶜᵗᵒ (21ᶜᵐ., lower margin folded), cut of a cleric (Gaffurio?) at the keyboard of an organ, the pipes of which represent the gamut.
Hain-Copinger 7404; Proctor 6721; Gaspari, Cat. della Biblioteca del Liceo musicale di Bologna, I, p. 216–217.
Full vellum binding.

Vollbehr collection

Gaffurio, Franchino—Continued.

—— Theorica musice. Mediolani, Philippus Mantegatius, 15 Dec. 1492. 2° (28½^{cm})

fol. [1] ^{recto}: THEORICA MVSICE FRANCHINI GAFVRI ‖ LAVDENSIS ‖ [*Woodcut*] fol. [68] ([kⱽ₁₁ⱼ]) ^{recto}, 1. 17, *colophon:* Impressum mediolani per Magistrum Philippum Man ‖ tegatium dictum Cassanum opera & impensa Magistri ‖ Ioannis Petri de lomatio anno salutis M.cccc.Lxxxxii. ‖ die xv Decembris. ‖

Signatures: 4 leaves unsigned, a⁸, b–i⁶, k⁸ (verso of [kⱽ₁₁ⱼ] blank) 68 leaves without foliation or catchwords.
Woodcut illustrations and diagrams, the t.-p. cut showing Gaffurio (?) at the keyboard of an organ. Initial spaces with indicators.
Revised edition of Theoricum opus musice discipline, Naples, 1480.
Hain-Copinger 7406; Proctor 6055; Panzer II, 69, no. 391; Gaspari, Cat. della Biblioteca del Liceo musicale di Bologna, I, p. 216–217.
Book-plate: From the library of George Dunn of Woolley Hall near Maidenhead.

27–20861   ML171.G14

—— —— Another copy.   Vollbehr collection.

See also VEGIUS, M. Quae in hoc opere continentur. Maphei Vegij ... Pompeana [*etc.*] ... [1521]

Galilei, Vincenzo, *d.* 1591.

Dialogo della musica antica e moderna, di Vincentio Galilei nobile fiorentino. In sva difesa contro Ioseffo Zerlino. Fiorenza, Per F. Givnti, 1602.

1 p. l., 149, [9] p. illus. (incl. music) diagrs. (1 fold.) 32½^{cm}.

Signatures: 1 leaf unsigned, A–M⁶, N⁸.
Printer's mark on t.-p. and (in another form) at end.
Second edition.
Armorial book-plates: (1) "Ex libris marchionis Salsae". (2) With motto "Comme je fus."

35–21822   ML171.G15 1602

Discorso di Vincentio Galilei nobile fiorentino, intorno all' opere di messer Gioseffo Zarlino da Chioggia, et altri importanti particolari attenenti alla musica ... Fiorenza, G. Marescotti, 1589.

134 p., 1 l. 16^{cm}.

Title vignette: device of Marescotti.
Signatures: A–H⁸, I⁴.

41–9132   ML171.G15D5

Galliard, John Ernest, 1687?–1749, *translator.*

See TOSI, P. F. Observations on the florid song. 1742.

[Gallimard, Jean Edme] 1685–1771.

Arithmetique des musiciens, ou Essai qui a pour objet diverses espéces de calcul des intervalles; le développement de plusieurs sistêmes de sons de la musique; des expériences pour aider à discerner quel est le véritable; c'est-à-dire celui de la voix; la description de celui qu'on suppose l'être sur quelques instrumens [etc.] ... On y a ajoûté une explication des propriétés les plus connues des logarithmes par celle qu'ils ont de mesurer les intervalles ... Paris, 1754.

1 p. l., 30 p. tables, diagrs. 20^{cm}.

20–19887 ML3809.A2G16

La theorie des sons applicables a la musique, où l'on démontre dans une exacte précision les rapports de tous les intervales [*sic*] diatoniques, & chromatiques de la gamme. Par m. Gallimard. Paris, Ballard [etc.] 1754.

2 p. l., 14 p. 19½^{cm}.

40–21201 ML3809.A2G168 1754

Gantez, Annibal, *d. ca.* 1670.

L'entretien des mvsiciens, par le sievr Gantez ... Avxerre, Iacqves Bovquet, 1643.

6 p. l., 295 p. 13½^{cm}.

20–21477 ML270.2.A2G2

Gaphurianus, Franchinus.

See GAFFURIO, FRANCHINO, 1451–1522.

Garzia, Antonio, *translator.*

See IRIARTE Y OROPESA, T. DE. La musica. 1789.

Gasparini, Francesco, 1668–1727.

L'armonico pratico al cimbalo. Regole, osservazioni, ed avvertimenti per ben suonare il basso, e accompagnare sopra il cimbalo, spinetta, ed organo. Di Francesco Gasparini ... 5. impressione. Venezia, A. Bortoli, 1764.

viii, 86 p., 1 l. illus. (music) 24^{cm}.

Title vignette.
Folded leaf, with table on verso, numbered as p. 83–86.

20–18803 MT68.A2G176

Gastoldi, Giovanni Giacomo, *fl.* 1582–1609.

See FORBES, J. Cantus, songs and fancies. 1682.
SYNOPSIS of vocal music. 1680.

[Gauthier, François Louis] 1696–1780.

Traité contre les danses et les mauvaises chansons, dans lequel le danger & le mal qui y sont renfermés sont démontrés par les témoignages multipliés des Saintes Ecritures, des ss. pp. des conciles, de plusieurs evêques du siécle passé & du nôtre, d'un nombre de théologiens moraux & de casuistes, de jurisconsultes, de plusieurs ministres protestans, et enfin des païens même. Paris, A. Boudet, 1769.

lij, 286, viij, 120, [4] p. 17½ x 10^{cm}.

20–10856 ML3920.A2G18

Geminiani, Francesco, 1687–1762.

The art of accompaniament, or A new and well digested method to learn to perform the thorough bass on the harpsichord, with propriety and elegance, by F. Geminiani. Opera 11th ... London, Printed for the author by J. Johnson [1755]

2 v. in 1. 33½^{cm}.

Engraved throughout.
Exercises.
Vol. 2 has title: The art of accompaniament ... Opera 11th. Part the 2^{d}. Treating of position and motion of harmony, and the preparation and resolution of discords.

20–19878   MT49.A2G42

The compleat tutor for the violin ... with some useful directions, lessons, graces, &c. by Geminiani. To which is added a favourite collection of airs, marches, minuets, song tunes, and duetts ... London, S., A. & P. Thompson [178–?]

1 p. l., 33, [1] p. incl. fold. pl. front., illus. (music) 17½ x 25^{cm}. [*With* New instructions for the German-flute. London, J. Preston [178–?]]

Engraved throughout.
Caption title: New instructions for the violin.

20–18776   MT342.A2N39

—— The entire new and compleat tutor for the violin, containing the easiest and best methods for learners to obtain a proficiency, with some useful directions, lessons, graces, &c., by Geminiani. To which is added a favourite collection of airs, marches, minuets, song tunes, &c. London, J. Preston [178–?]

1 p. l., 34 p. front., illus. (music) fold. pl. 17½ x 25^{cm}. [*With* New instructions for the German-flute. London, J. Preston [178–?]]

Engraved throughout.
Caption title: New instructions for the violin.

20–18775   MT342.A2N39

—— New and compleat instructions for the violin ... with some useful directions, lessons, graces, &c. by Geminiani. To which is added a favourite collection of airs, marches, minuets, &c., with several excellent p.^{s} for two violins ... London, Longman and Broderip [178–?]

1 p. l. 38 p. incl. fold. pl. front., illus. (music) 17½ x 25^{cm}. [*With* New instructions for the German-flute. London, J. Preston [178–?]]

Engraved throughout.
Caption title: New instructions for the violin.

20–18777   MT342.A2N39

Gérard de Rayneval, Joseph Mathias, 1736–1812, *translator.*

See MANCINI, G. B. Réflexions pratiques sur le chant figuré. [1796]

Gerber, Christian, 1660–1731.

See MOTZ, G. Die vertheidigte kirchen-music.

Gerson, Joannes, 1363–1429.

Collectorium super Magnificat. [Esslingae, Conradus Fyner] 1473.

169 l. 2° (27½^{cm})

fol. [1] ^{recto}: [C]ollectoɪiũ suɒ magnificat particulas habet expositas ‖, non semp eodē oɪdine quo sũt in cantico ... ‖ fol. [167] ^{recto}, line 30 *colophon:* Et sic terminat hec ɔpilacio deuota egregij ‖ ɪ famosi mgɪi iohãnis gerson sacre pagine ‖ doctoɪ eximij cancellarij parisiensis Anno ‖ dñi. M°. cccc°.lxx. iij. ‖

Rubricated throughout; initial spaces partly blank, partly filled in in red. On recto of fol. 4, five square musical notes, without the staff, supposed to be the first printed music. They are usually said to have been printed with a stamp after the printing of the text. For a contrary opinion see J. Mantuani (Über den beginn des notendruckes. Wien, 1901) who holds that they were printed with improvised type at the same time as the text.

Hain *7717; Pellechet 5140; Proctor 2458 (9 Esslingen 1–1); Brit. mus., pt. 2, p. 512, B 8911.

Pellechet describes this edition as one of 168 leaves, the final leaf blank. Leaves 168–169 ("Rubrice" and "Registrum") supplied in facsimile in Library of Congress copy (supplied in ms. in Brit. mus. copy as leaves 1–2)

ML171.G37

Gesellschaft auf dem Musiksaal, *Zurich.*

See NEUJAHRSGESCHENK ab dem Musiksaal.

Gibert, Paul César, 1717–1787.

Solfeges ou leçons de musique sur toutes les clefs, dans tous les tons, modes et genres, avec accompagnement d'une basse chiffrée, tres utile aux personnes qui veulent apprendre l'accompagnement de clavecin, et qui desirent acquerir l'usage de s'accompagner elle mêmes. Avec un précis des regles de la musique. Dédiés a mademoiselle de Langeac. Et composés par P. C. Gilbert ... Paris, Chez l'auteur [1783]

139 p. 25½ x 33½^{cm}.

Engraved throughout.

13–12852   MT870.A2G52

[Ginguené, Pierre Louis] 1748–1816.

Instruction du procès, entre les premiers sujets de l'Académie royale de musique & de danse. Et le s^r de Vismes, entrepreneur, jadis public, aujourd'hui clandestin, & directeur de ce spectacle. Pardevant la tournelle du public. Extrait de quelques papiers qui n'ont pas cours en France. [Paris, 1779]

44 p. 19^{cm}.

Signed: Duval, lecteur, greffier & buvetier.

For a key *cf.* Barbier, Dict. des ouvr. anon. 3. éd., t. 5 (1874) col. 993.

42–311   ML1727.3.G55 I 6

Greeting, Thomas, *fl.* 1667.

The pleasant companion; or, New lessons and instructions for the flagelet. By Thomas Greeting. The 2d ed., with large additions. London, J. Playford, 1673.

1 p. l., [12] p.; [54] p. (music) 10 x 16^{cm}.

Signatures: title-page (verso blank), A₃–A₍₈₎, A–F⁴, G³.

Greeting, Thomas—Continued.

The music, in tablature, with caption, "Lessons for the flagilett," is engraved. The 1st edition apparently contained 20 leaves of music, extending through sig. E, the last page in which is marked "Finis."
"Books lately printed and sold by John Playford ": page preceding first leaf of music.

17–22435   MT359.G84

—— The pleasant companion: or, New lessons and instructions for the flagelet. By Thomas Greeting, gent. London, J. Playford, 1680.

1 p. l., [8] p.; [64] p. (music)   front.   10 x 16½^{cm}.

Signatures: title-page (verso blank) unsigned, A⁴, A–H⁴.
The music, 70 tunes in tablature, with caption, "Lessons for the flagilett," is engraved.   The 1st ed. apparently contained 20 leaves of music, extending through sig. E, the last page in which is marked "Finis." The 2d ed. (1673) added 8 leaves of music, extending through sig. G, the last page in which is marked "Finis." This edition adds 4 leaves of music, through sig. H, the last page in which is also marked "Finis."
Quotation in manuscript from Pepys's Diary, Feb. 28, 1666–67 and manuscript note concerning 1682 edition on fly-leaves.

42–26035   MT359.G86 Miller coll.

—— The pleasant companion: containing variety of new ayres and pleasant tunes for the flagelet. To which is added plain and easie instructions for beginners. By Thomas Greeting, gent. The 6th ed., with several new tunes not published before. London, J. Playford, 1683.

1 p. l., [8] p.; [72] p. (music)   front.   10 x 16^{cm}.

Signatures: title-page (verso blank) unsigned, A⁴, A–I⁴.
The music, in tablature, with caption, "Lessons for the flagilett", is engraved.
"The little volume ... entitled 'The pleasant companion' ... is of general interest on account of the connexion of the author with Samuel Pepys, the famous diarist ... Kidson's British music publishers ... [gives] the following dates for various editions. 1661–66–72–75–80–82–83–88."—Welch, C. Six lectures on the recorder, 1911, p. 60ff.

27–3929   MT359.G88

Gresset, Jean Baptiste Louis, 1709–1777.

Des herrn Gresset, mitgliedes der Königl. gesellschaft der wissenschaften zu Paris, Rede, die er in öffentlicher versammlung daselbst von dem uralten adel und nutzen der musik im jahr 1751 gehalten. Aus dem französischen ins deutsche übersetzt von Ernst Gottlieb Baron ... (*In* [André, Y. M.] Versuch über das schöne. Altenburg, 1757. 19½^{cm}. p. [131]–184)

21–3017   N63.A57

Gruber, Johann Sigmund, 1759–1805.

Litteratur der musik, oder Systematische anleitung zur kenntnis der vorzüglichen musikalischen bücher, für liebhaber der musikalischen litteratur bestimmt. Herausgegeben von d. Johann Siegmund Gruber ... 2. verb., stark verm. und mit einem vollständigen register versehene aufl. Frankfurt und Leipzig, 1792.

5 p. l., [7]–122, [20] p.   17½^{cm}.

15–570   ML111.A2G82

Guidetti, Giovanni, 1532–1592.

Directorivm chori ad vsum omnium ecclesiarum, tam cathedralium, quam collegiatarum, nuper restitutum, & nunc secundo in lucem editum. Opera Ioannis Guidetti ... [*Publisher's device*] Romæ, apud Franciscum Coattinum, 1589.

8 p. l., 606, [1] p. 16½ᶜᵐ.

Rubricated.

27–7064. M2148.7.G92 1589

——Directorivm chori ad vsum omnium ecclesiarum cathedralium, & collegiatarum a Ioanne Gvidetto olim editum, et [n]vper ad novam Romani [breui]arij correctionem ex præcepto Clementis [vi]ii. impressam restitutum, & plurimis in locis auctum, & emendatum. [Access]erunt h[ui]c postremæ editioni quamplures hymnorum, & antiphonarum toni, qui in præcedentibus desiderabantur. Romæ, apud Andream Phæum, 1624.

4 p. l., 619, [3] p. 15½ᶜᵐ.

Rubricated.
Title-page mutilated.

27–3938 M2148.7.G92 1624

Guido *Aretinus, d.* 1050?

See BURZIO, N. Opusculum musices cum defensione Guidonis Aretini. 1487.

Gunn, John, *ca.* 1765–*ca.* 1824.

The art of playing the German flute, on new principles, calculated to increase its powers, and give to it greater variety, expression, and effect. To which are added, copious examples ... a compleat system of modulation, the art of varying simple passages, and a new method of tonguing. By John Gunn ... [London] Sold by the author, and at Birchall's music shop [1793]

1 p. l., 32, 53 p. 32ᶜᵐ.

Title-page and music (53 p.) engraved.

13–21151 MT342.A2G9

Gutiérrez, Francisco Antonio, d. 1828, *translator.*

See EXIMENO Y PUJADES, A. Duda ... sobre el Ensayo fundamental practico de contrapunto del m. r. p. m. fr. Juan Bautista Martini. 1797.

Guyot, Guillaume Germain, 1724–1800, *editor.*

See ANDRÉ, Y. M. Essai sur le beau. 1770.

H., J. Three treatises.

See [HARRIS, J.] Three treatises.

Händel, Georg Friedrich, 1685–1759.

See LANGHORNE, J. The tears of Music. 1760.

[MAINWARING, J.] Georg Friedrich Håndels lebensbeschreibung.

Hafenreffer, Samuel, 1587–1660.

Monochordon symbolico-biomanticum. Abstrusissimam pulsuum doctrinam, ex harmoniis musicis dilucidè, figurisq; oculariter demonstrans, de causis & prognosticis inde promulgandis fideliter instruens, & jucundè per medicam praxin resonans; pulsatum per Samvelem Hafenreffervm ... Ulmæ, typis & impensis Balthasari Kûhnen, 1640.

7 p. l., 146 p. fold. plates, fold. tab., diagrs. 15½ᶜᵐ.
Title vignette.
Bound in a fragment of manuscript music.
Armorial stamp on t.-p.: Bibl. Buxheim:
9–9185 RC74.H2

Hales, William, 1747–1831.

Sonorum doctrina rationalis et experimentalis, ex Newtoni, optimorumque physicorum scriptis, methodo elementaria congesta. Cui præmittitur disquisitio de aere et modificationibus atmosphæræ. Auctore Guilielmo Hales ... Dublinii, impensis Guil. Hallhead, 1778.

151 p. fold. diagr. 23½ x 18ᶜᵐ.
QC222.H3
—— —— Copy 2.
10–8140 ML3805.A2H15 1778

Hanbury, William, 1725–1778.

See HAYES, W. Anecdotes of the five music-meetings.

[Hanway, Jonas] 1712–1786.

Thoughts on the use and advantages of music, and other amusements most in esteem in the polite world, and the means of improving them to make our proper happiness and our pleasures but one object. In nine letters. In answer to a letter relating to modern musical entertainments, &c. London, J. Dodsley, 1765.

2 p. l., 116 p. front. 20½ᶜᵐ.
18–4318 ML60.H18

[Harris, James] 1709–1780.

Three treatises. The first concerning art. The second concerning music, painting, and poetry. The third concerning happiness. By J. H. London, J. Nourse and P. Vaillant, 1744.

3 p. l., [3]–357 p. 20½ᶜᵐ.
20–23787 ML60.H17

—— Three treatises; the first concerning art, the second concerning mvsic, painting and poetry, the third concerning happiness, by Iames Harris, esq. The 2d ed. rev. and cor. London, I. Novrse and P. Vaillant, 1765.

2 p. l., [3]–377, [18] p. front. 21ᶜᵐ.
1–2704 BH181.H2 1765

—— Three treatises; the first concerning art, the second concerning mvsic, painting and poetry, the third concerning happiness, by Iames Harris, esq. The 3d ed., rev. and cor. London, I. Novrse and P. Vaillant, 1772.

3 p. l., [3]–377, [19] p. front. 21½ᶜᵐ.
1–2705 BH181.H2 1772

Havingha, Gerardus, *b.* 1722.

Oorspronk en voortgang der orgelen, met de voortreffelykheit van Alkmaars groote orgel, by gelegentheit van deszelfs herstellinge opgestelt door Gerhardus Havingha ... Alkmaar, By J. van Beyeren, 1727.

27 p. l., 147 (*i. e.* 247) p. illus. 16^{cm}.

Last page wrongly numbered.
Interleaved; manuscript notes.
Imperfect: p. 193-194 wanting.

40-15277 ML582.H2806

Havingha, Gerardus, *b.* 1722, *translator.*

See KELLNER, D. Korte en getrouwe onderregtinge van de generaal bass. 1751.

[Hawkins, *Sir* **John]** 1719-1789, *supposed author.*

Memoirs of the life of Sig. Agostino Steffani, some time master of the Electoral chapel at Hanover, and afterwards bishop of Spiga. [London ? 17—]

1 p. l., viii p. 22¼ x 29^{cm}.

" The following memoirs were collected for the private satisfaction of their author ... They were printed in the manner in which they now appear, the better to adapt them to the size and form of the books in which manuscript copies of duets, cantata's, and songs are usually made; and the title ... was intended to connect it, not only with the author's, but with any other collection of Steffani's duets, before which it might be thought worthy to be placed."—Advertisement.

16-2091 ML410.S813H3

Haydn, Joseph, 1732-1809.

Gioco filarmonico, o sia Maniera facile per comporre un infinito numero di minuetti et trio anche senza sapere il contrapunto, da eseguirsi per due violini e basso, o per due flauti e basso, del sign. Giuseppe Haidn. Napoli, L. Marescalchi [1793 ?]

7 p. 31^{cm}.

Caption title.
Music (p. 3-7) engraved.
In manuscript on fly-leaf at end: In Roma, Si vende da Bouchard e Gravier ...
Haydn's authorship is questioned. *cf.* Schnerich, A. Joseph Haydn. 2. aufl. (Zürich [etc., 1926]) p. 264.

32-5346 MT41.H29

Hayes, William, 1706-1777.

Anecdotes of the five music-meetings, on account of the charitable foundations at Church Langton: in which many misrepresentations, and gross falsehoods, contained in a book, intitled, The history of the above foundations, are fully detected, and confuted, upon indubitable evidence. With an appendix, containing several original letters with remarks. By W. Hayes ... Oxford, Printed by W. Jackson; London, Sold by J. Fletcher & co.; [etc., etc.] 1768.

1 p. l., 71 p. 20½^{cm}.

The book referred to is W. Hanbury's History of the rise and progress of the charitable foundations at Church Langton.

22-3336 ML416.H19

See also Avison, C. An essay on musical expression.
A reply to the author of Remarks on the Essay
on musical expression.
Warton, T. Ode for music.

Heck, Johann Caspar, *b.* 1740.

The musical library and universal magazine of harmony, containing curious, entertaining and interesting subjects relative to the
history and practice of music ... The whole being interspersed with
a great variety of compositions in various styles, vocal & instrumental, selected from the works of some of the most celebrated
masters who flourished in this century ... By John Caspar Heck.
Book I. London, Printed for the proprietor, and sold by J. Welcker
[177–?]

1 p. l., 36 p. 35^{cm}.

Engraved throughout.
No more published?

20–19914 ML390.H32

Hely, Benjamin.
See The Compleat violist. [*ca.* 1700]

Hensel, Johann Daniel, 1757–1839.

Ausübende klavierschule. Erster gang. Von Johann Daniel
Hensel. Erstes[–drittes] heft. Hirschberg, Auf kosten des verfassers und in kommission bei Breitkopf and Härtel in Leipzig
[1796?–97?]

3 v. in 1. 30 x 33^{cm}.

"Vorerinnerung" of pt. 1 dated 1796; of pt. 2, 1797; pt. 3 undated.
4. heft wanting in Library of Congress copy.

29–727 MT222.A2H36

Herbst, Johann Andreas, 1588–1666.

Musica practica sive Instructio pro symphoniacis, das ist: Eine
kurtze anleitung / wie die knaben / vnd andere / so sonderbare lust
vnd liebe zum singen tragen / auff jetzige italienische manier ...
kŏnnen informiret vnd vnterrichtet ;werden. Dessgleichen denen
anfahenden instrumentisten / auff allerhand musicalischen instrumenten ... zu gebrauchen. Alles auss' den fŭrnembsten / vnd dieser
zeit bewårtesten italienischen authoribus ... zusammen getragen /
auch mit vielen clausulis vnd variationibus gezieret vnd vermehret /
allen liebhabern dieser kunst ... publiciret, vnd zum druck verfertiget:
durch Johann Andream Herbst ... [Nŭrnberg] In verlegung
Jeremiæ Dŭmlers, 1642.

4 p. l., 55 p. 20½ x 16^{cm}.

First edition.

35–21830 MT915.H2

Hess, Joachim, 1730–1810 *or* 11.

Korte en eenvoudige handleyding tot het leeren van 't clavecimbel
of orgel-spel, opgesteld ten dienste van leerlingen, door Joachim

Hess ... 2. druk, vermeerderd en verbeterd. Gouda, J. vander Klos, 1768.

2 p. l., 28 p. illus. (music) fold. pl. (music) 20½ x 16½^{cm}.

40–15278 MT252.A2H58 1768

See KNOCK, N. A. Dispositien der merkwaardigste kerk-orgelen.

Hickman, Charles, 1648–1713.

A sermon preached at St. Bride's church, on St. Cæcilia's day, Nov. 22, 1695. Being the anniversary feast of the Lovers of musick. By Charles Hickman ... London, W. Kettelby, 1696.

3 p. l., 22 p., 1 l. .19^{cm}. [*With* Reading, J. A sermon lately delivered in the cathedral church of Canterbury, concerning church musick. London, 1663]

17–31227 ML3001.R31 copy 2

Hiller, Johann Adam, 1728–1804, *editor.*

See MUSIKALISCHE nachrichten und anmerkungen. 1766–70.

Hilliger, Johann Zacharias, 1693–1770, *praeses.*

... De ἀυληταῖς sive tibicinibvs in fvnere adhibitis ad illvstrandvm Matthaei cap. ix comma xxiii ... Witebergae, typis Christiani Schroederi [1717]

[32] p. 18 x 15¼^{cm}.

Diss.—Wittenberg (" respondente Godofredo Iaspide chemnicensi ")

42–5443 ML935.H56 Miller coll.

Hizler, Daniel, 1576–1635.

Extract auss der Neuen musica oder Singkunst. M. Danielis Hizleri ... Zu förderlichem vnd doch gründlichem vntericht der jugend. Nürmberg, Gedruckt durch A. Wagenmann, 1623.

5 p. l., 85 p. incl. tab. illus. (incl. music) 14½^{cm}.

21–7022 MT895.A2H44

Hodermann, Georg Caspar.

Beknopt onderwys in de muzyk, voor de eerstbeginnenden; hoe dezelven, op eene zeer gemaklyke wyze het clavier kunnen leeren speelen; met vier-en-twintig handstukjes, en de bygevoegde vinger-zetting: uit het hoogduitsch van den heere Georg Caspar Hodermann. Amsterdam, C. N. Guerin, 1788.

1 p. l., 19, [1] p.; 18 p. (music) 18 x 24¼^{cm}.

35–24560 MT224.H6B4

[Holbach, Paul Henri Thiry, *baron* **d']** 1723–1789.

Lettre a une dame d'un certain age, sur l'etat présent de l'opéra. En Arcadie, aux dépens de l'Académie royale de musique. [Paris] 1752.

1 p. l., 17 p. 17^{cm}.

38–6121 ML1727.33.H6L4

Holden, John, *18th cent.*

An essay towards a rational system of music.   By John Holden. [Calcutta, 1799]

1 p. l., iii, [5], 148 p. xiii pl. (music)   18 x 24^{cm}.

Preface signed: A. U.
First edition published 1770.
Contents.—pt. i. The rudiments of practical music.—pt. ii. The theory of music.

20–19876   MT50.A2H727

Hotteterre, Jacques, *d.* 1760 *or* 61.

Principes de la flute traversiere, ou flute d'Allemagne.   De la flute à bec, ou flute douce, et du haut-bois, divisez par traitez.   Par le sieur Hotteterre-le-Romain ...   Paris, C. Ballard, 1707.

2 p. l., 50, [2] p. illus. (music) 7 pl. (6 fold.) port. 25 x 19^{cm}.

Signatures: 2 leaves unsigned, A–F^4, G^2.
Folded plate D, scale for the flûte à bec, wanting.

41–26826   MT342.H74 Miller coll.

—— Principes de la flute traversiere, ou flute d'Allemagne; de la flute à bec, ou flute douce; et du haut-bois, divisez par traitez.   Par le sieur Hotteterre-le-Romain ...   Nouv. ed.   Paris, C. Ballard, 1713.

2 p. l., 50, [2] p. front. (port.) illus. (music) 7 pl. (6 fold.) 25 x 19^{cm}.

Signatures: 2 leaves unsigned, A–F^4, G^2.

Portrait frontispiece and folded plates A and B, giving fingerings for transverse flute, wanting. Plate C laid in.

41–26827   MT342.H74 1713 Miller coll.

—— Principes de la flute traversiere, ou flute d'Allemagne; de la flute à bec, ou flute douce; et du haut-bois; divisez en differents traitez.   Par le sieur Hotteterre-le-Romain ...   Nouv. ed.   Paris, J. B. C. Ballard, 1722.

54, [2] p. front. (port.) illus. (music) 7 pl. (6 fold.) 26 x 20^{cm}.

Signatures: A–G^4.

41–26828   MT342.H74 1722 Miller coll.

—— Grond-beginselen over de behandeling van de dwars-fluit. In een duidelyke verhandeling over het recht gebruik, in een korte leeroeffening van dien vervat.   Door den heer Hotteterre den Romein ...   Overgezet door Abraham Moubach.   Amsterdam, M. C. Le Cene, 1728.

4 p. l., 47 p. illus. (music) 3 fold. pl., port. 20½ x 14½^{cm}.

42–440   MT342.H743 Miller coll.

—— The rudiments or principles of the German flute.   Explaining after an easy method every thing necessary for a learner thereon, to a greater nicety than has been ever taught before.   Wrote in French by the Sieur Hotteterre le Romain ... & faithfully translated into English.   To which is added a collection of familiar airs for examples.   London, Printed for and sold by I: Walsh at y Harp &

Hoboy in Catherine street in the Strand, and Ioseph Hare at the Viol and hoboy in Cornhill near the Royal exchange [1729]

1 p. l., 36 numb. l., 1 l.   fold. front. (port.) illus. (music) 2 fold. pl.   14 x 23½^{cm}
On leaf 24: Finis.   Leaves 25 to 36 are music.   Last leaf contains "A catalogue of choice musick for the German flute.   Printed for I: Walsh."
From the Miller collection.   "As far as can be traced, this is a unique work not found in any other library."—Miller, Dayton C.   Catalogue of books ... relating to the flute.   Cleveland, 1935.

42–26033   MT342.H744   Miller coll.

[Hudgebut, John] *fl. 17th cent.*

A vade mecum for the lovers of musick, shewing the excellency of the rechorder: with some, rules and directions for the same.   Also, some new ayres never before published.   London, Printed by N. Thompson for John Hudgebut, 1679.

[10] p.; 36 p. (music)   10 x 20^{cm}.
Signatures: A^6, B–C^6, D[₁], C₂-[₄], D₃-[₄]
Errors in paging: p. 29 numbered 33 (?); p. 33 numbered 29.
Preface signed: John Hudgebut.
From the Dayton C. Miller collection.
"This is the earliest known book of instructions for the recorder ...   The work ... is a very rare book, only one other copy being known to exist; this second copy is in the Bodleian library at Oxford university."—Miller, Dayton C.   Catalogue of books ... relating to the flute.   Cleveland, 1935.
Contemporary full mottled calf binding.

42–26034   MT348.H83V2   Miller coll.

Huygens, Constantijn, *heer van Zuilichem,* 1596–1687.
See CALCKMAN, J. J.   Antidotvm.

Idées sur l'opéra, avec un projet d'établissement d'une véritable Académie de musique, qui auroit la direction de l'Opéra & de l'Opéra comique: projet suivant le quel les auteurs seroient mieux récompensés & les principaux acteurs encouragés, en les faisant partager aux profits.   [n. p.] 1764.

1 p. l., 38 p.   16^{cm}.

By Le Texier?   *cf.* Bibl. dram. Soleinne, v. 5, no. 327.   A work of the same title, published 1790, is listed under Le Texier in Quérard, France litt.; a translation into English, also dated 1790, is entered under Le Texier in the Catalogue of the British museum.

27–25046   ML1727.8.I 3

Imbimbo, Emanuele, *d.* 1839, *translator.*
See FENAROLI, F.   Cours complet d'harmonie.   [17—]

Indice de' teatrali spettacoli ...
Milano [G. Bianchi, 17
v. fronts. (incl. ports.)   14^{cm}.

From   –1785/86, title reads: Indice de' spettacoli teatrali.   Several numbers (1780, 1782, 1785) are labeled on back of cover: Lunario teatrale.   According to Manoel de Carvalhaes, an index of the same character was published at Venice in 1764 under title: Il labirinto degli amanti.
Title of 1795/96 reads: Indice de' teatrali spettacoli di tutto l'anno, dalla primavera 1795, a tutto il Carnevale 1796.   Con aggiunta dell' elenco de' signori virtuosi cantanti, e ballerini; dei capi delle comiche compagnie

Indice—Continued.

italiane, e dello stato personale componente le compagnie istesse: de' signori pittori teatrali, e finalmente della nota di tutte le opere serie, e buffe
italiane scritte di nuova musica da' rispettivi signori maestri di cappella, ed
in quali teatri ...
Editors :   –1784/85, G. B. Cacciò.—1785/86–   L. Formenti.
    Published for the most part at Milan, first by Agnelli, later by Bianchi,
whose name appears in imprint of part of the numbers.
    Vols. for 1790/91–1795/96 numbered as pts. 6–11 (of the series edited by
Formenti)
    Complete, according to Carvalhaes, in about 30 vols. (the series edited
by Formenti is complete in 15) L. C. set (14 vols., all published by Bianchi) wants numbers published 1767–68 and any others which may have
appeared before 1780; also numbers for 1781/82, 1787/88–1788/89, 1796/97–
1799/1800.
    Frontispiece of vol. for 1784/85 is a portrait of Anna Morichelli Bosello.

    22–22329   ML1733.3.I 6

Institutions of musick.

    See [BAILLIE, A.] *supposed author.* An introduction to the
knowledge and practice of the thoro' bass. 1717.

Intonario general para todas las yglesias de España. 1548.

    See FERRER, P.

Iriarte y Oropesa, Tomás de, 1750–1791.

La musica, poema di d. Tommaso Iriarte, tradotto dal castigliano
dall' abate Antonio Garzia ... Venezia, Stamperia di A. Curti q.
Giacomo, 1789.

    1 p. l., [46], 149, xxxiv p.   plates.   24ᶜᵐ.

    24–24664   ML3800.A2 I 84

Isaac, ——, *dancing master.*

    See FEUILLET, R. A.   Orchesography.
    WEAVER, J.   A collection of ball-dances.

Jackson, William, 1730–1803.

Observations on the present state of music, in London.   By
William Jackson, of Exeter.   Dublin, A. Grueber [etc.] 1791.

    32 p.   23½ᶜᵐ.

    17–31247   ML286.8.L5J2

—— Observations on the present state of music, in London.   By
William Jackson, of Exeter.   London, Harrison and co., 1791.

    2 p. l., [7]–33 p.   21½ x 13ᶜᵐ.

    41–40857   ML286.8.L5J21

Jaspis, Gottfried, *respondent.*

    See HILLIGER, J. Z., *praeses.*   De αὐλητaῖς.

Jommelli, Niccolò, 1714–1774.

    See CORFE, J.   A treatise on singing.   [*ca.* 1800]

Jones, William.

Clavis campanalogia; or, A key to the art of ringing ... By William Jones, John Reeves & Thomas Blakemore ... London, Printed for the authors, and sold by T. Blakemore; [etc., etc.] 1788.

2 p. l., iii–xvi, 298, [2] p. 18^{cm}.

Engraved t.-p.
"A list of the peals of twelve and ten bells, that are in the kingdom at this present time": p. 272–276.

16–7632   MT710.J78

—— New campanalogia, or A key to the art of ringing, with considerable additions, dedicated to the lovers of the art in general; being the result of many years study, diligent application & constant practice, by William Jones, John Reeves & Thomas Blakemore ... London, R. S. Kirby [1796]

1 p. l., xx, 283 p. 20$\frac{1}{2}$^{cm}.

Engraved t.-p.
Also published under titles: " Clavis campanalogia ; or, A key to the art of ringing " and " A key to the art of ringing."
"A list of peals of ten and twelve bells ": p. 260–270.

41–40354   MT710.J78N4

Jordanus Nemorarius, *fl.* 1230.

See LE FÈVRE, J. Arithmetica et Musica.

Jortin, John, 1698–1770.

See AVISON, C. An essay on musical expression.

[Jourdan, Jean Baptiste] 1711–1793.

Lettre critique et historique sur la musique françoise, la musique italienne, & sur les Bouffons. A madame D. ... [Paris, 1753]

20 p. 15$\frac{1}{2}$^{cm}.

Caption title.
Half-title: Lettre sur les Bouffons.
Signed: * * *
Ascribed by Fétis to Jourdan.
With autograph of Edmond de Goncourt.

41–25464   ML1727.33.J7L3

Journal de musique, par une société d'amateurs. 1773– Paris, Ruault [1773]–

v. 20^{cm}. monthly.

Appeared, with interruptions, 1773–1777. *cf.* Freystätter, Die musikalischen zeitschriften. Library of Congress has nos. 1–6, 1773.

ca 12–944 Unrev'd   ML4.J4

Judenkünig, Hans, *d.* 1526.

- 1 - 5 - 2 - 3 - ‖ Ain schone ‖ kunstliche vnder- ‖ weisung in disem ‖ büechlein / leychtlich zu be- ‖ greyffen den rechten grüd ‖ zu lernen auff der Lautten ‖ vnd Geygen / mit vleiss ge- ‖ macht dürch Hans Juden ‖ künig / pirtig von Schwe- ‖ bischen Gmünd Lutenist / ‖ yetz zu Wień in Österreich. [*Colophon:* Vollendet vnd getrückht

zu Wień yn Osterreich ‖ dürch Hanns Singryener. im. 1 . 5 . 2 . 3.
Jar.]

[91] p.   illus.   21¼ᶜᵐ.

Signatures: a–k⁴, 2 leaves unsigned, l⁴.

Title within architectural border; initials. Following the t.-p., a full-page
woodcut of a lutenist (Judenkünig?) and a viol-player.

Title of book 2 (leaf 37, sig. k[ı], recto): Item das ander puechlein
zuuer- ‖ nemen. darinnen du vnderzichtt ‖ wierdest / den gesang zůuer-
steen was ayn yedliche ‖ noten oder pawss bedeüt / vnder aynem yedli-
chen ‖ zaichen welcher nit singen kan / auch wie ain yedli- ‖ cher gesang
anfecht / auff der Lautten oder Geygen ‖ vnd wieuil / ain yedliche noten /
in den Ligereturen ‖ an ainander gepunden / gilt / darnach wie du zwo ‖
oder drey stym zůsamen setzen soldest auss dem ge- ‖ sang / in die
Tabalatur vnder ain mensur einge- ‖ taylt / vnd gerechnet muess werden.
Vnd wie ‖ die noten / vnuolkumen gemacht werden / ‖ in den volkhumen
zaichen / vnd welche ‖ gealterieret wierdt / das ist ainē yedli- ‖ chen nutz
zůwissen / Wiewol es jetzt ‖ wenig der gebrauch ist in dē ge- ‖ sang / noch
ist germainiklich der ‖ aller pesst gesang / in mani- ‖ cherlay zaichen ver-
fatzt / ‖ darumb ist es dier ‖ von nōten zů ‖ wissen. ‖

Includes a collection of song and dance tunes (in tablature)
From the library of Dr. Werner Wolffheim.
Bound in full crimson morocco.

29–11866   MT640.J9

Jürrns, J. F.

Grondig onderwys in de gregoriaansche choorzang of choral, nevens
eenige aanmerkingen over de zang-konst. Bestaande in dertien
lessen, ten dienste der beminnaars en beminnaresen deezes gezangs,
en wel byzonderlyk der organisten. In het licht gegeeven door J. F.
Jürrns ... Amsterdam, F. J. van Tetroode, voor rekening van den
autheur, 1789.

4, [2], 50 p.   illus. (music)   22½ x 18½ᶜᵐ.

24–6399   MT860.J87

Junker, Karl Ludwig, d. 1797, editor.

See MUSIKALISCHER almanach auf das jahr 1784.

Карманная книжка для любителей музыки на 1796 годъ.   Съ доз-
воленія Управы благочинія. Въ Санкпетербургѣ, Ижди. кни-
гопр. I. Д. Герстенберга съ товар. печат. въ типогр. I. К.
Шнора [1796]

1 v.   plates (part fold.: music)   18 cm.

Two vols. were published, for 1795 and 1796 respectively. Library of Congress
has 1796 only.
Imperfect: p. 49–50 wanting.

ML20.G38

Keinspeck, Michael, fl. 1500.

Lilium Musice plane. Ulmæ, J. Schäffler, 1497. 8° (20½ᶜᵐ)

fol. [1] ([Aı]ʳᵉᶜᵗᵒ): Lilium Musice plane Michaeł ‖ Keinspeck musici Alexandrini. ‖ [Woodcut]

fol. [2] (Aıⱼʳᵉᶜᵗᵒ): ❡ Prologus ‖ mUsica ars modulatiua ‖
fol. [15] ([Bᵥₗₗ]ʳᵉᶜᵗᵒ), colophon: ❡ Explicit Lilium Musice plane Michaelis
‖ Keinspeck de Nůrnberga Musici Alexan- ‖ drini benemeriti Vna cuჳ psalmodie vtriusq̃ ‖ tam maioris q̃ minoris intonatōe. secundum ‖ omnes tonos. et

Keinspeck, Michael—Continued.

exercicio solmisandi Nouiter ‖ adiunctis. Impressum Vlme per Johãnem ‖ Schãffler. Anno salutis. M.cccc.xcvii. ‖
  Signatures: A–B⁸ ([Bᵥₙ] ᵛᵉʳˢᵒ and [Bᵥₙₙ] blank) 15 printed leaves (last verso blank) without pagination or catchwords. Gothic type. 30 lines to a full page. Woodcut music; a few initial indicators (fol. Aₙ)
  Hain *9761; Proctor 2590.

40–21468   ML171.K33

Kellner, David, *d.* 1748.

... Korte en getrouwe onderregtinge van de generaal bass, of bassus continuus. Naa de 2. druk uit het hoogduits vertaalt, en met eenige aanmerkingen, benevens een opdragt, en voorreden vermeerdert, door Gerhardus Havingha ... Amsterdam, J. Covens, junior, 1751.

16 p. l., 171, [9] p. 7 pl. (4 fold., incl. tables, diagrs.) 21ᶜᵐ.

At head of title: D. Kelner.

13–21136   MT49.A2K32

Kepler, Johann, 1571–1630.

Ioannis Keppleri Harmonices mvndi libri v. qvorvm primus geometricvs, de figurarum regularium, quæ proportiones harmonicas constituunt, ortu & demonstrationibus. secundus architectonicvs, seu ex geometria figvrata, de figurarum regularium congruentia in plano vel solido: tertius propriè harmonicvs, de proportionum harmonicarum ortu ex figuris; deque naturâ & differentiis rerum ad cantum pertinentium, contra veteres: quartus metaphysicvs, psychologicvs & astrologicvs, de harmoniarum mentali essentiâ earumque generibus in mundo; præsertim de harmonia radiorum, ex corporibus cœlestibus in terram descendentibus, eiusque effectu in natura seu anima sublunari & humana: quintus astronomicvs & metaphysicvs, de harmoniis absolutissimis motuum cœlestium, ortuque eccentricitatum ex proportionibus harmonicis. Appendix habet comparationem huius operis cum Harmonices Cl. Ptolemæi libro ɪɪɪ, cumque Roberti de Fluctibus, dicti Flud. medici oxoniensis speculationibus harmonicis, operi de Macrocosmo & microcosmo insertis. Accessit nvnc propter cognationem materiæ eiusdem authoris liber ante 23. annos editus Tubingæ, cui titulus Prodromus, seu Mysterium cosmographicum, de causis cœlorum numeri, proportionis motuumque periodicorum, ex quinque corporibus regularibus. [*Ornament*] ... Lincii Austriæ, sumptibus Godofredi Tampachii, excudebat Ioannes Plancvs, 1619.

4 p. l., 66 (*i. e.* 64), 255 p. illus. (music) 5 pl., diagrs. 29½ᶜᵐ.

Books 1–2 are paged continuously, as are books 3–5. Books 1, 4 and 5 have special title-pages, included in the paging.

8–9734   QB41.K38

——— Ioannis Keppleri Harmonices mvndi libri v ... Appendix habet comparationem huius operis cum Harmonices Cl. Ptolemæi libro ɪɪɪ. cumque Roberti de Fluctibus, dicti Flud. medici oxoniensis speculationibus harmonicis, operi de Macrocosmo & microcosmo insertis.

[*Ornament*] ... Lincii Austriæ, sumptibus Godofredi Tampachii excudebat Ioannes Plancvs, 1619.

4 p. l., 66 (*i. e.* 64), 255 p. illus. (music) 4 pl., diagrs. 30½^{cm}.

The issue of same date, described above, has fuller title, and different ornament on t.-p., and two full-page plates which are wanting in the present copy. The present copy has 1 plate (facing p. 286) which is wanting in the other issue. Two typographical errors in the other issue (p. 171, 1st line, and p. 205, catch-word) are corrected in this.

22–13574   MT6.A2K36

Kircher, Athanasius, 1602–1680.

Athanasii Kircheri ... Neue hall- vnd thon-kunst / oder Mechanische geheim-verbindung der kunst und natur / durch stimme und hall-wissenschafft gestifftet / worinn ingemein der stimm / thons / hall- und schalles natur·/ eigenschafft / krafft und wunderwürckung / auch deren geheime ursachen / mit vielen neu- und ungemeinen kunst-wercken und proben vorgestellt werden. Ingleichem wie die sprach- und gehôr-instrumenta, machinen und kunst-wercke / vorbildender natur / zur nach-ahmung / so wohl die stimm / hall und schall / an weit-entlegene ort zu fûhren / als auch in abgesonderten geheimzimmern / auff kunst-verborgene weise / vertreulich und ungefâhr sich mit-einander zu unterreden / sollen verfertigt werden. Endlich / wie solche schône erfindung zu kriegszeiten nutzlichen kônne angebracht und gebraucht werden. In unsere teutsche mutter-sprach übersetzet von Agatho Carione [*pseud.*] Nôrdlingen / Gedruckt bey F. Schultes / In verlegung A. Heylen / buchhåndlers in Elwangen / 1684.

3 p. l., 162, [16] p. front., illus. (incl. music) fold. pl., diagrs. 31^{cm}.
Translation, by T. Nislen, of Kircher's Phonurgia nova.

18–23001   ML3805.A2K482

Kirchmaier, Theodor, *fl.* 1659–1677, *praeses.*

Schediasma physicum de viribus mirandis toni consoni ... Wittenbergæ, literis Wendianis excud. D. Schmatz, 1672.

[28] p. 18 x 15^{cm}.
Diss.—Wittenberg (Georg Alexander Beer, respondent)

21–7016   ML3920.A2K47

Kirnberger, Johann Philipp, 1721–1783.

Johann Philipp Kirnbergers clavierûbungen, mit der Bachischen applicatur, in einer folge von der leichtesten bis zu den schwersten stücken. Erste[–dritte] sammlung. Berlin, F. W. Birnstiel, 1761–63.

3 v. in 1. 21½ x 34^{cm}.
Includes several compositions by Händel and one by Holland.
Book 4, 1766, wanting in Library of Congress copy.

29–6577   MT225.A2K59

Construction der gleichschwebenden temperatur, herausgegeben von Johann Philipp Kirnberger. Berlin, Gedruckt bey F. W. Birnstiel [1760]

8 p. fold. diagr. 21½ x 17½^{cm}.
Head-piece.

41–40867   ML3809.K58

Knock, Nicolaas Arnoldi, 1759–1794.

Dispositien der merkwaardigste kerk-orgelen, welken in de provincie Friesland, Groningen en elders aangetroffen worden. Kunnende dit werk verstrekken tot een vervolg van het werk van den heer J. Hess. Door Nicolaas Arnoldi Knock ... Groningen, P. Doekema, 1788.

2 p. l., 77, [3] p. 21 x 17^{cm}.

13–24939   ML582.A2K7

Köllig (*i. e.* Röllig), J. (!) L.

See RÖLLIG, KARL LEOPOLD.

Königsperger, Marianus, 1708–1769.

Der wohl-unterwiesene clavier-schůler / welchem nicht nur die wahre und sichere fundamenta zum clavier auf eine leichte art beygebracht, sondern auch VIII. præambula, XXIV. versette und VIII. arien oder galanterie-stůcke aus allen tonen zur weitern ubung vorgelegt werden. von r. f. Mariano Königsperger ... Augspurg, J. J. Lotters seel. erben, 1761.

43 p. 18½ x 22½^{cm}.

29–6578   MT222.K8

L. * *, M., *avocat.*

See LACOMBE, JACQUES, 1724–1811.

Lachnith, Louis Wenceslas, 1746–1820, *joint author.*

See ADAM, L. Methode ou principe général du doigté. [1798?]

[Lacombe, Jacques] 1724–1811.

Dictionnaire portatif des beaux-arts, ou, Abregé de ce qui concerne l'architecture, la sculpture, la peinture, la gravure, la poésie & la musique; avec la définition de ces arts, l'explication des termes & des choses qui leur appartinennet ... Par M. L. * *. avocat. Paris, La veuve Estienne & fils [etc.] 1752.

2 p. l., viii, 707, [3] p. 17^{cm}.
Later editions published under author's name.

13–3492   N33.L3

Le spectacle des beaux arts, ou considérations touchant leur nature, leurs objets, leurs effets & leurs régles principales; avec des observations sur la maniere de les envisager; sur les dispositions nécessaires pour les cultiver; & sur les moyens propres pour les étendre & les perfectionner. Par m. Lacombe, avocat. Paris, Vincent [etc.] 1761.

xix, [3], 374 p. 17½^{cm}.

41–35033   BH182.L3

L'Affillard, Michel, *fl.* 1700.

Principes tres-faciles pour bien apprendre la musique, qui conduiront promptement ceux qui ont du naturel pour le chant jusqu'au point de chanter toutes sortes d'airs proprement, & à livre ouvert ... Par le sieur l'Affillard ... 2. ed., rev., cor. & augm. Paris, C. Ballard, 1697.

    4 p. l., 3–133, [5] p. 2 fold. pl. 13 x 18¼ᶜᵐ.

    Music: p. 5–133.

    35–21813   MT870.L18

—— Principes tres-faciles pour bien apprendre la musique, qui conduiront promptement ceux qui ont du naturel pour le chant jusqu'au point de chanter toute sorte de musique proprement, & à livre ouvert; par le sʳ. l'Affillard ... 6. éd. rev., cor., & augm. Paris, C. Ballard, 1705.

    2 p. l., 3–171, [5] p. 2 fold. pl. 13 x 19ᶜᵐ.

    Music: p. 9–171.

    17–5234   MT870.A2L2

Lancelot, Claude, 1615?–1695.

L'art de chanter; ou, Metode facile, pour apprendre en fort peu de temps les vrays principes du plein chant & de la musique, & pour les mettre surement en pratique. Par monsieur Lancelot ... Paris, A. Pralard, 1685.

    6 p. l., 41, [2] p. illus. (music) 20½ᶜᵐ.

    First edition ·(Paris, 1668) published under title: Nouvelle méthode de plain-chant, plus facile et plus commode que l'ancienne.

    20–19898   MT860.A2L18

Langhorne, John, 1735–1779.

The tears of Music. A poem, to the memory of Mʳ. Handel. With an Ode to the river Eden. By the Reverend J. Langhorne. London, R. Griffiths, 1760.

    vi, [7]–23 p. 26ᶜᵐ.

    31–23132   ML410.H13L17

Laporte, Nicolas de.

Traité theorique et pratique de l'accompagnement du clavecin, avec l'art de transposer dans tous les tons et sur tous les instrumens. Dedié à mademoiselle Le Duc, par mʳ de Laporte ... Paris, L'auteur [17—]

    4 p. l., 75 p. 33ᶜᵐ.

    Engraved throughout.
    "Gravé par P. L. Charpentier. Imprimé par Petitbled fils." Another issue, "Imprimé par Lorraine", was published in 1753. (cf. Eitner, Quellen-lex.)

    22–11233   MT68.A2L16

Latta, James, 1732–1801.

A discourse on psalmody: in which it is clearly shewn, that it is the duty of Christians to take the principal subjects and occasions of their Psalms, hymns, and spiritual songs from the gospel of Christ.

By James Latta ... Philadelphia: Printed for the author, by William W. Woodward, at Franklin's head, no. 41, Chesnut-street. 1794.

xv, [17]–146 p. 22^{cm}.

19–16946 BV310.L3

The **lawfulness,** excellency and advantage of instrumental music, A second edition of.

See A SECOND edition, < with necessary improvements ... > of The lawfulness, excellency and advantage of instrumental music.

Leak, John, *fl.* 1640, *translator.*

See CAUS, I. New and rare inventions of water-works. 1659.

Leducq, Albert.

Examen de ces deux questions: L'Opéra est-il nécessaire à la ville de Paris? Faut-il en confier l'administration ou l'entreprise à une société? Par Albert Leducq, homme de loi. [Paris? Impr. de F. V. Poncillon, 178–?]

1 p. l., 25 p. 21^{cm}.

Caption title. ML1727.3.L28E9
42–6749

Le Fèvre, Jacques, *d'Étaples, d.* 1537.

Arithmetica et Musica. Parisiis, Joannes Higman et Wolfgangus Hopyl. 22 Jul. 1496. 2° (28^{cm})

fol. 1 (sig. [a₁])^{recto}: In hoc opere contenta. ‖ Arithmetica decem libʒis demonstrata ‖ Musica libʒis demonstrata quattuoʒ ‖ Epitome ī libʒos arithmeticos diui Seuerini Boetij ‖ Rithmimachie ludus q̓ ʑ pugna nūeroʏ appellaƚ. ‖ ... fol. 1 (sig. [a₁])^{verso}: Noua ɔmentatio in Joʒdanū per Jacobum fabʒū stapulēsem laboʒata ‖ ... fol. 2 (sig. a₂)^{recto}: ℂ Joʒdani Nemoʒarij Clarissimi viri Elementa Arithmetica: cū demõstratiõibus ‖ Jacobi Fabʒi Stapulensis ... fol. 41 (sig. f₁)^{recto}: ℂ Jacobi Fabʒi Stapulensis Elementa Musicalia ... fol. 62 (sig. [h₆])^{verso}, line 53: ℂ Quarti elementoʒum Musices Jacobi Stapulensis finis. fol. 72 (sig. [i₈])^{verso}, line 21, *colophon:* ℂ Has duas Quadriuij partes et artium liberalium pʒecipuas atqɜ duces cum quibusdam āmini- ‖ cularijs adiectis: curarunt vna foʒmulis emendatissime mandari ad studioʒum vtilitatem Joannes ‖ Higmanus ‖ et Volgangus Hopilius suis grauissimis laboʒibus ʑ impensis Parhisij Anno salutis ‖ domini: qui oĩa in numero atqɜ harmonia foʒmauit 1496 absolutūqɜ reddiderunt eodem anno: die ‖ vicesima secunda Jullij suos laboʒes vbicunqɜ valebunt semper studiosis deuouentes. Et idem quoqɜ ‖ facit Dauid Lauxius Bʒytannus Edinburgensis: vbiɜ ex archetypo diligens operis recognitoʒ. ‖ line 27, col. 1: Registrum pʒesentis operis. ‖ a b c d e f g h i ‖ Omnes quaterni. ‖ ...
Signatures: a–i⁸ (recto of [h₇] blank) 72 leaves without foliation.
Gothic type. Tables in the text; diagrams in the text and in margins. Capital spaces blank or with initial indicators.
Frequently cited under the name of Jordanus Nemorarius.
Proctor 8137; Hain-Copinger 9436; Panzer II, p. 312, no. 378; Thacher 742; Paris, Conservatoire nat., Catalogue bibliog. (Weckerlin)
Engraved portrait of Le Fèvre mounted on fly-leaf.
Book-plates of Julian Marshall and of William Hayman Cummings.

27–1435 ML171.L38

—— In hoc opere contenta Arithmetica decem libris demonstrata. Musica libris demõstrata quatuor. Epitome in Libros arithmeticos diui Seuerini Boetij. Rithmimachie ludus qui et pugna numerorū appellatur. Hęc secundaria superiorū operum æditio / venalis habetur Parisijs: in officina Henrici Stephani [1514]

[144] p. incl. illus., tables, diagrs. 28½^{cm}.

Title within woodcut border. Forming the outer part of the border are the words: ℂ Haec secvndaria est et castigatissima ex officina aemissio.
Initials. Gothic type. Signatures: a–i⁸.
The "Arithmetica" is by Jordanus Nemorarius.
Colophon: ℂ Has duas Quadriuij partes et artium liberalium precipuas atⱥ duces cū quibusdam amminicularijs adiectis: curauit ex secunda recognitione vna formulis emēdatissime mandari ad studiorum vtilitatem Henricus Stephanus suo grauissimo labore et sumptu Parhisijs anno salutis domini; qui omnia in numero atⱥ harmonia formauit 1514 absolutumⱥ reddidit eodē anno; die septima septembris / suum laborem vbicunⱥ valet semper studiosis deuouens.

11–5444   QA32.L5

—— Musica libris quatuor demonstrata. Parisiis, apud Gulielmum Cauellat, 1551.

44 numb. l. diagrs. 18½^{cm}.
Signatures: A–L⁴. Printer's mark on t.p.

25–21745   ML171.L39

Le Fèvre de La Boderie, Guy, 1541–1598.

See MERSENNE, M. Quæstiones celeberrimæ in Genesim.

Legipont, Oliver, 1698–1758.

R. p. Oliverii Legipontii, cœnobitæ benedictini, Dissertationes philologico-bibliographicæ, in quibus de adornandâ, & ornandâ bibliothecâ; nec non de manuscriptis, librisque rarioribus, & præstantioribus; ac etiam de archivo in ordinem redigendo, veterûmque diplomatum criterio; déque rei nummariæ, ac musices studio, & aliis potissimùm ad elegantiores literas spectantibus rebus disseritur. In usum bibliothecariorum, & philobiblorum publicæ luci commissæ. Norimbergæ, impensis P. Lochneri & Mayeri, 1747.

5 p. l., 327 p. 22^{cm}.

3–8869   Z670.L51

Lemarié,   *avocat.*

See TRAVENOL, ANTOINE, *plaintiff.* Memoire signifié ... Contre le sieur Arrovet de Voltaire ...

Leone,

Methode raisonnée pour passer du violon à la mandoline et de l'archet a la plume, ou Le moyen seur de jouër sans maître en peu de temps par des signes de convention assortis à des exemples de musique facile. Contenant xxiv airs dansants à deux mandolines, vi menuets avec accompagnement, ii duo, i sonate avec la basse et plusieurs airs connus variés, par mʳ Leone de Naples, maître de mandoline de S. A. S. monseigneur le duc de Chartres ... Paris, Chez mʳ Bailleux [ca. 1750?]

1 p. l., 67 p. front., illus. (music) 33^{cm}.
Engraved throughout.
Pages 11–14 bound between p. 18 and 19.

42–6752   MT608.L58M4

[Léris, Antoine de] 1723–1795.

Dictionnaire portatif des théatres, contenant l'origine des différens théatres de Paris; le nom de toutes les piéces qui y ont été représentées depuis leur établissement, & des piéces jouées en province, ou qui ont simplement paru par la voie de l'impression depuis plus de trois siécles; avec des anecdotes & des remarques sur la plûpart: le nom & les particularités intéressantes de la vie des auteurs, musiciens & acteurs; avec le catalogue de leurs ouvrages, & l'exposé de leurs talens: une chronologie des auteurs, des musiciens & des opéra; avec une chronologie des piéces qui ont paru depuis vingt-cinq ans. Paris, C. A. Jombert, 1754.

xl, 557, [3] p. 17^{cm}.

31–25821 ML128.04L5

Le Sueur, Jean François, 1760–1837.

Exposé d'une musique une, imitative, et particuliere à chaque solemnité; où l'on donne les principes généraux sur lesquels on l'établit, & le plan d'une musique propre à la fête de Noël. Essai par m. Le Sueur ... Paris, Veuve Hérissant, 1787.

xiv, [15]–72, 48 p. illus. (music) 19$\frac{1}{2}$^{cm}.

—— Suite de l'Essai sur la musique sacrée et imitative, où l'on donne le plan d'une musique propre à la fête de Pâque. Par m. Le Sueur ... Paris, Veuve Herissant, 1787.

103 p. 21$\frac{1}{2}$^{cm}.

" Motet pour la veille de Pâque: La résurrection " (words only, Latin and French) : p. [29]–39.

—— Exposé d'une musique une, imitative, et propre à chaque solemnité; où l'on donne une dissertation sur ses effets, & le plan d'une musique particuliere à la solemnité de la Pentecôte. Suite de l'Essai. Par m. Le Sueur ... Paris, Veuve Herissant, 1787.

67 p. 19^{cm}.

—— Exposé d'une musique une, imitative, et particuliere à chaque solemnité; où l'auteur, à la suite de ce qu'il a déja publié à ce sujet, donne à ceux de ses eleves qui se destinent à composer la musique de nos temples, les préceptes qu'il leur a cru nécessaires pour mettre le plus de poésie, de peinture & d'expression possible dans leurs ouvrages. Il y donne aussi le plan d'une musique propre à la fête de l'Assomption. Suite de l'Essai, par m. Le Sueur ... Paris, Veuve Hérissant, 1787.

109 p. 19^{cm}.

9–2097 Revised ML3075.L25

Le Texier, ——, *supposed author.*
See IDEES sur l'opéra. 1764.

A **letter** from a gentleman in the town to a friend in the country; containing reflections upon the present time, with a very impartial judgment on our most famous performers in musick; and a new

A letter from a gentleman—Continued.

project how to cultivate musick in Great Britain, without being in need of such performers of Italy, or other countries. London, Printed by A. Moore, 1727.

1 p. l., 27 p. 19^{cm}.

English and French. The English version is signed: Anglo-Italiny; the French (which has special t.-p.) : Anglo Italûs.

18–4312 ML1731.3.A2L3

A letter to a friend in the country, concerning the use of instrumental musick in the worship of God : in answer to Mr. Newte's sermon preach'd at Tiverton in Devon, on the occasion of an organ being erected in that parish-church. London, A. Baldwin, 1698.

1 p. l., 94 p. 20½^{cm}.

17–31229 ML3001.L38

See also NEWTE, J. The lawfulness and use of organs in the Christian church.

Lettre d'un gentilhomme de la ville.

See A LETTER from a gentleman in the town. 1727.

Lettre d'une comédienne, a une danseuse de l'Opera. (*In* Trés-humbles remontrances adressées à monseigneur le contrôleur général. [Paris, *ca.* 1789] 17^{cm}. p. 13–17)

With [Giraud, Claude Marie] La Pr.....ade. Londres [*i. e.* Paris] 1754. Caption title.

1–F3702 PQ1985.G58A75

—— **Lettre** d'une comédienne, a une danseuse de l'Opera. [n. p., *ca.* 1789]

11 p. 16½^{cm}.

Caption title.
" Réponse d'une danseuse de l'Opera, a une comédienne " : p. 6–11.
With autograph and book-plate of Edmond de Goncourt.

ML1727.3.L38

Listenius, Nicolaus, *16th cent.*

Rvdimenta mvsicae, in gratiam studiosæ iuuentutis diligēter comportata. A. m. Nicolao Listenio. Excvsvm Avgvstæ Vindelicorum, per Henricum Steyner, 1540.

[46] p. illus. (music) 16^{cm}.

Colophon (and full title imprint) : Excvsvm Avgvstæ Vindelicorum, per Henricum Steyner, mense iulio, anno M.D.XXXX.
Signatures: A–C^8 (last leaf blank)
Title vignette; tail-piece (A[viii] verso)
First edition published at Wittenberg, 1533.

25–21744 ML171.L44

—— Mvsica Nicolai Listenij, ab authore denuo recognita, multisq̃; nouis regulis & exemplis adaucta. Vitebergae, apud Georgium Rhau. Anno. 1537.

[95] p. illus. (music) 15½^{cm}.

Signatures: A–F^8.
Title within ornamental border.
A revision of the author's Rudimenta musicae.

41–18759 ML171.L45

Listenius, Nicolaus—Continued.

—— Mvsica Nicolai Listenii, ab avthore denuo recognita, multisq̃ nouis regulis et exemplis adaucta. Norimbergae, apud Iohan. Petreium, 1549.

[86] p. illus. (music) 15^{cm}.

Signatures: a–e⁸, f⁴ (last leaf blank)

22–918 ML171.L46

—— Mvsica Nicolai Listenii, ab avthore denuo recognita, multisq̃ nouis regulis & exemplis adaucta. Norimbergæ, apud Iohan. Petreium, 1550.

[86] p. illus. (music) 15½^{cm}.

Signatures: a–e⁸, f⁴ (last leaf blank)

41–23963 ML171.L47

Locke, Matthew, 1630?–1677.

Melothesia: or, Certain general rules for playing upon a continued-bass. With a choice collection of lessons for the harpsichord and organ of all sorts: never before published. All carefully reviewed by M. Locke ... The first part. London, J. Carr, 1673.

9 p., [2] p. (music), [1] p., 84 p. (music) 12 x 23^{cm}.

Only pt. 1 was published.

17–31238 MT49.A2L6

Observations upon a late book, entituled, An essay to the advancement of musick, &c. Written by Thomas Salmon ... By Matthew Locke ... London, Printed by W. G. and are to be sold by J. Playford, 1672.

2 p. l., 39 p. illus. (music) 16½^{cm}.

Salmon replied to this criticism with his Vindication of An essay to the advancement of musick.

19–7359 ML432.A2S27

Lodi caratteristiche del celebre cantore signor Luigi Marchesi ... Siena, Nella stamperia di V. Pazzini Carli e figli, 1781.

x p. 20½^{cm}.

Engraved title vignette and head-piece.

32–19108 ML420.M318

Long, Roger, 1680–1770.

The music speech, spoken at the public commencement in Cambridge, July the 6th, 1714. By Roger Long ... 3d ed. London, T. Payne; [etc., etc., 1714?]

32 p. 21½^{cm}.

No. 6 in a volume lettered: Musical pamphlets.

Brief Latin address, followed by a satirical poem, beginning: The humble petition of the ladies.

20–19903 ML64.M97

Loulié, Étienne.

Elements ou principes de musique, mis dans un nouvel ordre ... & divisez en trois parties. La premiere pour les enfans. La seconde pour les personnes plus avancez en âge. La troisiéme pour ceux qui sont capables de raisonner sur les principes de la musique. Avec l'estampe, la description & l'usage du chronometre ... par le moyen duquel, les compositeurs de musique pourront desormais marquer le veritable mouvement de leurs compositions, & leurs ouvrages marquez par rapport à cet instrument, se pourront executer en leur absence comme s'ils en battoient eux-mesmes la mèsure. Par m. Lovlié. Paris, C. Ballard, 1696.

2 p. l., 3–96 p. illus. (music) fold. pl. 18½^{cm}.

20–19897   MT7.A2L9

Ludus melothedicus, ou Le jeu de dez harmonique, contenant plusieurs calculs par lesquels toute personne composera differents menuets avec l'accompagnement de basse en jouant avec deux dez même sans sçavoir la musique ... Gravé par J. P. Oger ... Paris, Mr de la Chevardière, editeur, successeur de m^r le Clerc; [etc., etc., 176–?]

15 p. illus. (music). 23½ x 20^{cm}.

41–40880   MT41.L85

Lunario teatrale.

See INDICE de' teatrali spettacoli.

Luneau de Boisjermain, Pierre Joseph François, 1732–1801, *editor.*

See ALMANACH musical, 1781–83.

Lustig, Jacob Wilhelm, 1706–1796.

Inleiding tot de muziekkunde; tweede druk: in bevalliger vormen gegooten, door Jacob Wilhelm Lustig ... Groningen, Voor den auteur, by H. Vechnerus, boekdrukker, 1771.

8 p. l., 301, [11] p. 21^{cm}.

First edition published 1751.
"Lyst van de geschriften door J. W. Lustig": p. [312]

40–15280   MT6.A2L97 1771

Lustig, Jacob Wilhelm, 1706–1796, *translator.*

See MARPURG, F. W. Aanleiding tot het clavier-speelen. 1760.

Luther, Martin, 1483–1546.

Deudsche messe vnd ord- ‖ nung Gottis ‖ diensts. ‖ Wittemberg [1526]

[47] p. 19½^{cm}.

Signatures: A–F^4 (verso of last leaf blank)
Title within ornamental border.
Folio 47 ([Fiv])^{recto}, l. 14: ... Amen ‖ Martinus Luther ‖ Gedruckt zu Wittemberg. ‖ M.D.XXVI. ‖ Correctur. ‖ E.ij bald nach dem deudschen sanctus ist aus- ‖ gelassen dis stuck. Darnach folget die Collecten ‖ mit den segen. ‖

Luther, Martin—Continued.

Contains music, including the hymn, "Jesaia dem propheten das ge-
schach" (Ei^{verso}-Eii^{recto})
Printed by Michael Lotther, Wittenberg.
First edition. *cf.* Luthers werke. Kritische gesammtausg. (Weimar, 1883–) v. 19 (1897) p. 60.

27–7072   ML171.L96

Lyceum der schönen künste. 1. bd. (1.–2. th.) Berlin, J. F. Unger,
1797.

1 v. in 2. front. (port., v. 2) illus. (music) 21½ x 12½^{cm}.

Supersedes "Déutschland."
Edited by J. F. Reichardt and F. von Schlegel.
No more published.   N3.L9
43–31136

The **lyric** muse revived in Europe; or, A critical display of the
opera in all its revolutions. London, L. Davis and C. Reymers, 1768.

1 p. l., vi, 147 p. 17^{cm}.
Mainly compiled from Dr. John Brown, V. Martinelli, and others.

27–25058   ML1704.A2L9

M. L. * *, *avocat.*

See LACOMBE, JACQUES, 1724–1811.

Madin, Henri, 1698–1748.

Traité, du contrepoint simple, ou du chant sur le livre. Par
m.^{r} H. Madin ... Gravé par Labassée ... A Paris, Chés Au mont
Parnasse [etc.] 1742.

1 p. l., 35, [1] p. illus. (music) 25½ x 21^{cm}.
38–35334   MT55.M33T76

[Mainwaring, John] *d.* 1807.

Georg Friedrich Händels lebensbeschreibung, nebst einem
verzeichnisse seiner ausübungswerke und deren beurtheilung;
übersetzt, auch mit einigen anmerkungen, absonderlich über den
hamburgischen artikel, versehen vom legations-rath Mattheson ...
Hamburg, Auf kosten des übersetzers, 1761.

5 p. l., 156, [8] p. front. (port.) 17½^{cm}.
Translation of Memoirs of the life of the late George Frederic Handel.

29–9163   ML410.H13M22

Malcior, *of Worms.*

See WOLLICK, N. Opus Aureum. 1501.

Malcolm, Alexander, *b.* 1687.

Malcolm's Treatise of music, speculative, practical, and historical,
corrected and abridged, by an eminent musician ... London, J.
French, 1776.

1 p. l., 104 p. illus. (music) 22½ ^{cm}.
First edition published at Edinburgh, 1721.
"This work is neither corrected, abridged nor improved ... It consists
of entire chapters taken verbatim from the original, omitting only the most
useful."—Ms. note on t.-p., signed : E. H. (Edward Hodges)
                                                    MT6.A2M26

Malcolm, Alexander—Continued.

—— —— Copy 2. (*With* New musical and universal magazine, v. 1, London, 1774)

20–18780   ML4.N49

Malouin, Paul Jacques, 1701–1777, *praeses.*

... An ad sanitatem musice? [Parisiis, typis Quillau, 1743]

8 p. 24^{cm}.

Diss.—Paris (Louis René Marteau, respondent)
Caption title.
The actual author of this dissertation was César Coste of Arles. *cf.*
Fétis, F. J. Biog. univ. des musiciens. 2. éd., t. 5, p. 421.

21–7015   ML3920.A2M15

Mancini, Giovanni Battista, 1716–1800.

L'art du chant figuré de J. B. Mancini ... traduit de l'italien par M. A. Desaugiers ... A Vienne, et se trouve à Paris, chez Cailleau [etc.] 1776.

1 p. l., [v]–viij, 64 p. fold. pl. (music) 10 p. (music) 19½ ^{cm}.

An adaptation of Mancini's Pensieri, e riflessioni pratiche sopra il canto figurato (Vienna, 1774), an enlarged edition of which was published in 1777 under title: Riflessioni pratiche sul canto figurato.

21–7948   MT845.A2M34

—— Réflexions pratiques sur le chant figuré; par J. B. Mancini ... Traduites sur la 3. éd. italienne. Paris, Du Pont, l'an troisième de la république [1796]

viij, 231, [1] p., 1 l. 4 fold. pl. (music) 19½^{cm}.

Translated by J. M. Gérard de Rayneval.

15–464   MT845.A2M4

Mancini, J. B.

See MANCINI, GIOVANNI BATTISTA.

Manfredi, Alessandro, *translator.*

See FUX, J. J. Salita al Parnasso. 1761.

[Marcello, Benedetto] 1686–1739.

Il ‖ Teatro ‖ alla Moda ‖ o sia ‖ Metodo sicuro, e facile per ben comporre, ed esequire ‖ l'Opere Italiane in Musica all' uso moderno. ‖ Nel quale ‖ Si danno Avvertimenti utili, e necessarj a Poeti, Compo- ‖ sitori di Musica, Musici dell' uno, e dell' altro sesso, ‖ Impressarj, Suonatori, Ingegneri, e Pittori di Sce- ‖ ne, Parti buffe, Sarti, Paggi, Comparse, Suggeri- ‖ tori, Copisti, Protettori, e Madri di Virtuose, ed ‖ altre Persone appartenenti al Teatro. ‖ Dedicato ‖ dall' Autore del Libro ‖ al Compositore di esso. ‖ [*Vignette*] ‖ Stampato ne' Borghi di Belisania per Aldivi-‖ va Licante; all' Insegna dell' Orso in Peata. ‖ Si vende nella Strada del Corallo alla ‖ Porta del Palazzo d'Orlando ‖ E si ristamperà ogn' anno con nuova aggiunta. [Venezia, ca. 1720]

64 p. 17½ cm.

Page 16 wrongly numbered 18.
According to Tessier (Preface to his reprint, 1887) the 1st edition, mentioned in a letter of Apostolo Zeno, dated April 2, 1721.

17–1396 ML65.M25

—— Il ‖ Teatro ‖ alla Moda, ‖ o sia ‖ Metodo sicuro, e facile per ben comporre, & esequire ‖ l'Opere Italiane in Musica all' uso moderno, ‖ Nel quale ‖ Si danno Avvertimenti utili, e necessarij a Poeti, Compositori ‖ di Musica, Musici dell' uno, e dell' altro sesso, Impresarj, ‖ Suonatori, Ingegneri, e Pittori di Scene, Parti buffe, ‖ Sarti, Paggi, Comparse, Suggeritori, Copisti, ‖ Protettori, e Madri di Virtuose, & altre ‖ Persone appartenenti al Teatro. ‖ Dedicato ‖ dall' Auttore del Libro ‖ al Compositore di esso. ‖ [*Vignette*] ‖ Stampato ne Borghi di Belisania per Aldiviva ‖ Licante, all' Insegna dell' Orso in Peata. ‖ Si vende nella Strada del Corallo alla ‖ Porta del Palazzo d'Orlando. ‖ E si ristamperà ogn' anno con nuova aggiunta. ‖ [n. p., n. d.]

64 p. 17ᶜᵐ.

The title of this edition corresponds to that of the 2d edition as given by Tessier in the reprint of Venice, 1887, but the paging is the same as that of Tessier's 1st edition, except that p. 16 of Tessier is wrongly numbered 18.

15–11212 ML65.M26

—— Il Teatro ‖ alla Moda ‖ o sia ‖ Metodo sicuro, e facile per ben comporre, ed eseguire ‖ l'Opere Italiane in Musica all' uso moderno, ‖ Nel quale ‖ Si danno Avvertimenti utili, e necessarj a Poeti, Compositori ‖ di Musica, Musici dell' uno, e dell' altro sesso, Impresarj, ‖ Suonatori, Ingegneri, e Pittori di Scene, Parti buffe, ‖ Sarti, Paggi, Comparse, Suggeritori, Copisti, ‖ Protettori, e Madri di Virtuose, ed altre ‖ Persone appartenenti al Teatro. ‖ Dedicato ‖ dall' Auttore del Libro ‖ al Compositore di esso. ‖ [*Vignette*] ‖ Stampato ne Borghi di Belisania per Aldiviva ‖ Licante, all' Insegna dell' Orso in Peata. ‖ Si vende nella Strada del Corallo alla ‖ Porta del Palazzo d'Orlando. ‖ Come pure in Milano da Francesco Agnelli. ‖ Stampandosi ogn' anno con nuova aggiunta. [n. p., 17—]

72 p. 15½ cm.

According to Tessier this is regarded as the 3d edition, the 1st and 2d editions having appeared in 1720 or 21 and 1733 respectively.

17–1397 ML65.M27

Marchesi, Luigi, 1755–1829.

See Lodi caratteristiche del celebre cantore signor Luigi Marchesi. 1781.

Marcou, Pierre, *d. ca.* 1820.

Élemens théoriques et pratiques de musique; par m. Marcou ... A Londres, et se trouve à Paris, Chez la veuve Ballard & fils; [etc., etc.] 1782.

iv, [5]–58 p. illus. (music) 17ᶜᵐ.

38–35358 MT7.M19

Mariottini, Jacopo Antonio.

See COFERATI, M. Scolare addottrinato. 1714.

Marlow, Isaac.

The controversie of singing brought to an end. Or, a treatise in three parts. The first is a tract on singing. The second hath some remarks on Mr. Richard Allen's book, called An essay, &c., with answers to them. And the third containeth several queries presented to divers elders and ministers, with other matters, to the baptized churches about London. By Isaac Marlow. London, Printed for the author, 1696.

3 p. l., 82, [4] p. 17^{cm}.

21–2990 BV290.M23

[Marmontel, Jean François] 1723–1799.

Essai sur les révolutions de la musique, en France. [Paris? 1777?]

1 p. l., 38 p. 20½^{cm}.

Privilege dated 19 avril 1777.
Appears also in " Memoires pour servir à l'histoire de la révolution opérée dans la musique par m. le chevalier Gluck," Naples et Paris, 1781 (p. 153–190)
Another copy in [Pièces de théâtre] PQ1213.P55 vol. 85, no. 5

34–15148 ML1727.3.M28E7

Marpurg, Friedrich Wilhelm, 1718–1795.

Aanleiding tot het clavier-speelen, volgens de hedendaagsche luisterryker manier van uitvoering; opgestelt door den beroemden Friedrich Wilhelm Marburg ... Met zeven nooten-tabula's. Uit het hoogduitsche vertaalt en met ophelderende byvoegselen voorzien door Jacob Wilhelm Lustig ... Amsteldam, J. J. Hummel, 1760.

3 p. l., 48, [2] p. VII pl. 24 x 20½^{cm}.

13–21141 MT224.A2M37

Marquet, François Nicolas, 1687–1759.

Nouvelle méthode facile et curieuse, pour connoitre le pouls par les notes de la musique, par feu m. F. N. Marquet. 2. éd., augm. de plusieurs observations et réflexions critiques, & d'une dissertation en forme de thèse sur cette méthode; d'un mémoire sur la manière de guérir la mélancolie par la musique, & de l'Éloge historique de m. Marquet. Par m. Pierre-Joseph Buchoz ... À Amsterdam, et se trouve à Paris, chez P. F. Didot, 1769.

1 p. l., vi. 216 p. 6 fold. pl. 17^{cm}.

9–5597 RC74.M3

Marteau, Louis René, *respondent.*

See MALOUIN, P. J., *praeses.* An ad sanitatem musice?

Martínez, Juan.

Arte. de canto chão, posta et redvzida em sua enteira perfeição, segũdo a pratica delle, muito necessaria para todo o sacerdote, pessoas q̃ hão de saber cantar. Ordenada por Ioão Martinz sacerdote, & a que mais se vsa em toda a christandade. Vay em cadahũa das regras seu exemplo apontado com as entoações. Agora de nouo reuista, & emmendada de cousas muyto necessarias, por o padre Antonio Cordeiro, sochãtre na see de Coimbra. Com licença da Santa inquisicão. [Coimbra] Por N. Carualho, impressor da Vniuersidadè de Coimbra, 1612.

[80] p. diagr. 15ᶜᵐ.

Signatures: A–E⁸.
Initials, tail-pieces, diagram of the Guidonian hand, musical examples.
The Vasconcellos Catalogue, 1898, no. 83, mentions 9 editions of this work, in the original Spanish or in Portuguese. According to Riaño, the 1st edition was published at Alcalá de Henares in 1512 (Catalina García in his bibliography of Alcalá imprints, "Ensayo de una tipografía complutense", 1889, lists only the edition of 1532) Editions are listed of Seville, 1530, and of Coimbra, the same year.
Armorial book-plate of Sir John Stainer.

27–1417   MT860.A2M385

Martínez de Bizcargui, Gonçalo.

❡ Arte de canto llano y contrapunto y canto de Organo con proporciones y modos breuemēte compuesta y nueuamente añadida y glosada por Gonçalo martinez de Bizcargui. [*Colophon:* ❡ Esta presente arte de Canto llano ... Fue impressa enla muy noble y mas leal ciudad de Burgos: por Juan de Junta. Acabose a .xj. dias del mes de Dezi bre. de .M.D.XXXV. Años]

[72] p. illus. (music) diagrs. 19½ᶜᵐ.

Signatures: a–d⁸, e⁴.
Gothic type; initial; woodcut of Guidonian hand, within ornamental border, on t.-p.

20–10867   MT860.A2M38

Martini, Giovanni Battista, 1706–1784.

See EXIMENO Y PUJADES, A. Duda ... sobre el Ensayo fundamental practico de contrapunto del m. r. p. m. fr. Juan Bautista Martini. 1797.

Martini, Jean Paul Égide, 1741–1816.

Mélopée moderne; ou, L'art du chant, réduit en principes, composé ... par m.ʳ Martini ... Cet ouvrage qui traite généralement de l'exécution de la musique, est également utile aux personnes qui apprennent á s'accompagner sur le forte-piano: on y trouvera aussi la vrai maniere d'accorder le piano et la harpe. Paris, Boyer; Lyon, Garnier [1792?]

88 p. 34ᶜᵐ.

Original imprint (except words "A Paris") covered by label of Cochet, luthier et mᵈ de musique. At foot of p. 83: A Paris, Chez Boyer.
Engraved throughout. Title within ornamental border. At foot of t.-p.: Ecrit par Ribiere.
"Partition pour accorder les forte-piano" and "Partition pour accorder la harpe": p. 83–88.

38–35363   MT820.M2

Masson, Charles, *fl.* 1680.

Nouveau traité des regles pour la composition de la musique, par lequel on apprend à faire facilement un chant sur des paroles; à composer à 2. à 3. & à 4. parties, &c. Et à chiffrer la basse-continuë, suivant l'usage des meilleurs auteurs. Ouvrage très-utile à ceux qui joüent de l'orgue, du clavecin & du théorbe. Par. C. Masson ... 4. ed., rev. & cor. Amsterdam, E. Roger [1710?]

2 p. l., 148 p. illus. (music) 20 x 11½ᶜᵐ. [*With* Rousseau, Jean. Methode claire, certain et facile pour aprendre à chanter la musique. 5. ed. Amsterdam [1710?]]

Signatures: 2 leaves unsigned, A–H⁸, I¹⁰.

41–26825   MT7.RS5   Miller collection

—— Nouveau traité des regles pour la composition de la musique, par lequel on apprend à faire facilement un chant sur des paroles; à composer à 2. à 3. & à 4. parties, &c. et à chiffrer la basse-continuë, suivant l'usage des meilleurs auteurs. Ouvrage trés-utile à ceux qui joüent de l'orgue, du clavecin, &c. Par C. Masson ... 4. & nouv. ed. Paris, Impr. de J. B. C. Ballard, 1738.

4 p. l., 127, [1] p. illus. (music)   20ᶜᵐ.

22–21544   MT40.A2M43

Mattheson, Johann, 1681–1764.

De eruditione musica, ad virum plurimum reverendum, amplissimum atque doctissimum, Joannem Christophorum Krüsike ... schediasma epistolicum Joannis Matthesonii. Accedunt ejusdem literæ ad v. c. Christophorum Friedericum Leisnerum de eodem argumento scriptæ. Hamburgi, apud Felgineri viduam, 1732.

16 p.   20½ᶜᵐ.

First edition.

17–8873   ML63.A2M175

Der neue gôttingische aber viel schlechter / als die alten lacedâmonischen / urtheilende Ephorus, wegen der kirchen-music eines andern belehret von Io. Mattheson, nebst dessen angehângtem / merckwürdigen lauten-memorial ... Hamburg, In verlag des verfassers / und zu bekommen bey J. C. Kissern; [etc., etc.] 1727.

2 p. l., 124 p.   20½ x 17ᶜᵐ.

Reply to Joachim Meyer's Unvorgreiffliche gedancken über die neulich eingerissene theatralische kirchen-music.
Caption title: Matthesonii Ephorus göttingensis.

32–5339   ML3001.M45

Sieben gesprâche der Weisheit und Musik samt zwo beylagen; als die dritte dosis der panacea, mitgetheilet von Mattheson ... Hamburg, J. A. Martini, 1751.

2 p. l., [26], 207, [1] p.   17ᶜᵐ.

"Erste beylage. Von der musik in ewigen leben": p. 145–180. "Zwote beylage. Schreiben des herrn Georg Friedrich Einike ... betreffend die Vitam musicam": p. 181–192.

35–24820   ML63.M18S5

Mattheson, Johann, 1681–1764, *editor and translator.*

See [Mainwaring, J.] Georg Friedrich Håndels lebensbeschreibung.

Mauburnus, Joannes, *d.* 1502 *or* 1503.

Rosetum exercitiorum spiritualium et sacrarum meditationum. [Zwolle, Petrus Os] 1494. 2°. (30ᶜᵐ.)

Includes a section ("Titulus quintus") on music, entitled "Chiropsalteriū", illustrated by a cut of the Guidonian hand (fol. xvi)
Campbell 1224; Hain *13995; Proctor 9144.
Ex libris Paul Schmidt.   Incunabula.

—— Rosetum exercitiorum spiritualiū et sacrarum meditationum: in quo etiam habetur materia predicabilis per totius anni circulum. Recognitum penitus et auctum multis. Presertim primo et vltimo titulis: per ipsius authorem (qui dum vita manebat temporalis nominari noluit) Venerabilem patrem Joannem Mauburnum ... [*Mark of Iehan Petit*] Instauratum est hoc religiosissimu3 opus Impēsis Joãnis parui ⁊ Joãnis Scabelerij vulgo dicti wettenschire. Venditurq₃ ab eis sub Leone argēteo ⁊ insigni Basileeñ. in vico sancti Jacobi. [1510]

[687] p. illus., diagr. 29½ᶜᵐ.
Colophon: Imp2essum est autem p2esens opus in inclyta parrhisio2ū academia opera quidem Ascensiana: sed impensis optimo2ū biblyoholarū [!] Joannis parui ⁊ Johannis Scabeleri: Anno salutis nostre MDX. Ad Idus Augusti ...
Signatures: AA⁶, a–s⁸, t⁶, v–z⁸, A–Q⁸, R⁶, S⁸, T⁶, V⁸ (verso of last leaf blank)
Two columns to the page; gothic type; initials; title in red and black; diagram of the harmonic hand on k111j verso; woodcuts (musical instruments, etc.) l1j–l11j verso; music ("modulus seu nota hymni precedentis ...") v[1] recto.
First edition published at Basel in 1491.
25–15598   ML171.M19

[Maugars, André] *17th cent.*

Discovrs svr la mvsiqve d'Italie, et des opera. (*In* [Saint Glas, Pierre de] *ed.* Divers traitez d'histoire, de morale et d'eloqvence. Paris, 1672. 15ᶜᵐ. p. 154–179)

Originally published under title: Response faite à vn curieux svr le sentiment de la mvsiqve d'Italie. Escrite à Rome le premier octobre 1639. [Paris? 1639?]
           AC20.S3

[Mayeur de Saint Paul, François Marie] 1758–1818.

Le vol plus haut, ou L'espion des principaux théatres de la capitale; contenant une histoire abrégée des acteurs & actrices de ces mêmes théâtres, enrichie d'observations philosophiques & d'anecdotes récréatives. Dédié aux amateurs ... A Memphis, chez Sincere, libraire réfugié au Puits de la Vérité. [Paris] 1784.

viij, [9]–142 p. 17½ᶜᵐ.
"Je ne ... présente que l'histoire du Concert spirituel & de l'Opéra."— Avis de l'éditeur.
This piece is evidently by the same authors as "Le chroniqueur désœuvré" (Mayeur de Saint Paul, Thévenot de Morande, and Poultier d'Elmotte) It has been attributed to the actor Dumont, author of "Le désœuvré mis en œuvre", a work opposed to the other two. *cf.* Lacroix, Bibl. Soleinne.
26–19683   ML1727.3.A2M29

Meloni, Annibale, *16th cent., supposed author.*

See [BOTTRIGARI, E.] Il Desiderio. 1594.

Memoirs of Mrs. Billington, from her birth: containing a variety of matter, ludicrous, theatrical, musical, and ——; with copies of several original letters, now in the possession of the publisher, written by Mrs. Billington, to her mother, the late Mrs. Weichsel: a dedication; and a prefatory address ... London, J. Ridgway, 1792.

4 p. l., xv, 78 p.   23^{cm}.

A scurrilous attack upon Mrs. Billington.
Imperfect: wanting portrait.

5–42735   ML420.A2B56

Merbach, George Friedrich.

Clavierschule für kinder, von George Friedrich Merbach.   Nebst einer kupferplatte.   Leipzig, Zu finden bey dem verfasser, 1782.

2 p. l., 55 (*i. e.* 61), [3] p. pl. (music)   21 x 26^{cm}.

Page 61 incorrectly numbered 55.

36–23937   MT746.M55

Mersenne, Marin, 1588–1648.

F. Marini Mersenni ... Qvæstiones celeberrimæ in Genesim, cvm accvrata textvs explicatione.   In hoc volvmine athei, et deistæ impvgnantvr, & expugnantvr, & Vvlgata editio ab hæreticorum calumnijs vindicatur.   Græcorum, & Hebræorum musica instauratur. Francisci Georgii Veneti cabalistica dogmata fvsè refellvntvr, quæ passim in illivs Problematibvs habentvr.   Opvs theologis, philosophis, medicis, iurisconsultis, mathematicis, musicis verò, & catoptricis præsertim vtile.   Cum indice quadruplici, videlicet locorum Scripturæ Sacræ, quæ in toto libro explicantur, concionatorio, quæstionum, & rerum quæ passim agitantur.   Lvtetiæ Parisiorvm, sumptibus Sebastiani Cramoisy, 1623.

12 p. l., 1916 (*i. e.* 1956) col., 1 l., [36] p., 2 l., 450 (*i. e.* 440) col. illus. (incl. music) diagrs. 36^{cm}.

Title in red and black. Cramoisy's device on t.-p.
Numbering of columns irregular, some leaves being numbered as pages: last column numbered 450 instead of 440. One unnumbered leaf, "Errata potiora " of col. 1–1828, inserted after col. 1827–8.
Commentary on chapters I–VI only. The 2d part was never published; the manuscript is preserved in the Bibliothèque nationale (Fonds latin nos. 17261–2)
" Qvæstio LVI. Qvænam fverint instrvmenta harmonica, quibus tam Hebræi, quàm Græci, cæteræque nationes vtuntur, aut etiam antiquitus vtebantur": col. 1515–1530.
"Quæstio [LVII] De vi mvsicæ tvm antiqvorvm, tum nostræ" (col. 1530–1712) includes an account of the Académie de musique et de poésie founded by J. A. de Baïf and Thibault de Courville.
"Paralipomena ... ea, quæ in quæstione de musica omissa sunt" (col. 1853–1916) include part of the 4th " cercle " of La Galliade, a didactic poem by Guy Le Fèvre de La Boderie, first published at Paris in 1578, and the first edition of the Εἰσαγωγὴ [τέχνης μουσικῆς] Βακχείου τοῦ γέροντος.
Contemporary armorial binding (arms of Mathieu Molé, seigneur de Champlâtreux, 1584–1656, stamped in gold on front and back covers) Book-plates of the Rev. Jonathan Boucher, A.M., and of Wm. Hayman Cummings.

22–12666   BS1235.M43

Méthode pour apprendre a lire les notes sur toutes les clefs ...
Paris, Lecomte [etc.] 1788.

1 p. l., 23 p. fold. pl. 20^{cm}.

Ms. notes.
13–24961 MT35.A2M4

Methode pour aprendre a jouër de la guitarre par don * * * ...
Paris, Le Menu; Madrid, J. Guerrero [ca. 1750?]

1 p. l., 30 p. 1 illus. 27 x 21^{cm}.

"Gravé par Melle Vendôme."
"Premier[–troisieme] duo pour la guitarre": p. 22–30.
26–22260 MT582.A2M6

[Meusnier de Querlon, Anne Gabriel] 1702–1780.

Reglement pour l'Opera de Paris. Avec des nottes [sic] historiques.
A Utopie, chez Thomas Morus. [Paris] 1743.

1 p. l., 68 p. 16^{cm}.

Engraved t.-p.
Also published under title: Le code lyrique ([Paris] 1743)
"Point de vue de l'Opera. Fragment anonyme. En forme de découpure."
(By Bernis): p. 7–31.
Book-plate of Edmond de Goncourt.
41–25465 ML1727.8.P2M58

Meyer, Joachim, 1661–1732.

See MATTHESON, J. Der neue göttingische ... Ephorus. 1727.

Mézières, Eugene Eléonor de Béthisy, *marquis* de, 1709–1782.
Effets de l'air sur le corps humain.
See BÉTHISY, JEAN LAURENT DE, *supposed author.*

Milioni, Pietro, *17th cent.*

Corona del primo, secondo, e terzo libro d'intavolatvra di chitarra
spagnola di Pietro Millioni. Nuouamente stampata dal medesimo con
l'accrescimento di molte lettere false per poter sonar sonate senza mai
far lettere ordinarie. Vna regola per imparar' il modo d'accordare
dodici chitarre per poterle sonare insieme in concerto ciascheduna per
differente chiaue, ouero lettera; & anco l'alfabeto, & accordatura per il
chitarrino, ouero chitarra italiana. Roma, G. Facciotti, 1631.

62 p. 1 illus. 10½ x 16½^{cm}.
29–9157 MT582.M7C7

[Milizia, Francesco] 1725–1798.

Del teatro. Venezia, Giambatista Pasquali, 1773.

viij, 100 p. vi fold. pl. (plans) 25½^{cm}.

Engraved title vignette (printer's device)
Dedication signed: Giambatista Pasquali.
First edition published 1771. *cf.* Pref. According to Melzi (Diz. di opere
anon. e pseudon. III, 129) the 1st edition appeared in 1772 at Rome. There
were several other editions, including one entitled "Discorso sul teatro"
(Venice, 1789) and one, published under the author's name, entitled
"Trattato completo, formale e materiale del teatro" (Venice, 1794)
"Dell' opera in musica," "Dell' argomento dell' opera," etc.: p. 32–52.
25–25489 PN1654.M5 1773

Milizia, Francesco—Continued.

——Trattato completo, formale e materiale del teatro, di Francesco Milizia. Venezia, Stamperia di P. q. G. B. Pasquali, 1794.

104 p.　6 fold. pl.　(plans)　22 x 17^{cm}.

Engraved title vignette (printer's device)
"Dell' opera in musica," "Dell' argomento dell' opera," etc.: p. 38–58.
Book-plate of James E. Matthew.

9–14651　　　　　　　　　　　　　　　　　PN1654.M5　1794

Miller, Edward, 1731–1807.

Thoughts on the present performance of psalmody in the Established church of England. Addressed to the clergy. By Edward Miller ... London, Printed for W. Miller, 1791.

2 p. l., 40 p.　20^{cm}.

20–10864　　　　　　　　　　　　　　　　　ML3166.A2M45

Millet, I.

See MILLET, JEAN, ca. 1620–ca. 1682.

Millet, Jean, ca. 1620–ca. 1682.

Directoire dv chant gregorien. Par I. Millet ... Lyon, Iean Gregoire, 1666.

6 p. l., 176, [4] p.　illus. (music)　23½ x 17½^{cm}.

24–27858　　　　　　　　　　　　　　　　　M2148.7.M63

Millioni, Pietro.

See MILIONI, PIETRO, 17th cent.

[Minguet é Irol, Pablo] d. 1801?

Reglas, y advertencias generales que enseñan el modo de tañer todos los instrumentos mejores, y mas usuales, como son la guitarra, tiple, vandola, cythara, clavicordio, organo, harpa, psalterio, bandurria, violin, flauta travesera, flauta dulce, y la flautilla, con varios tañidos, danzas, contradanzas, y otras cosas semejantes ... [Madrid, El autor? 1774?]

[58] p.　front., 29 engr. pl. (incl. music)　14½ x 20^{cm}.

Contains a general introduction ("Indice, y explicacion de toda la obra") and 6 parts, each with special title-page bearing author's name:
(1) Reglas, y advertencias generales para tañer la guitarra, tiple, y vandola ... Compuestas, y corr. en esta ultima impresion por Pablo Minguet y Yrol, gravador de sellos, laminas, firmas, y otras cosas. Madrid, Impr. del dicho autor, 1774. ([16] p. 10 pl.)
(2) Reglas ... para acompañar ... Madrid, J. Ibarra [n. d.] ([10] p. 9 pl.)
(3) Reglas ... para tañer el psalterio ... Madrid, J. Ibarra, 1754. ([8] p. 2 pl.)
(4) Reglas ... para tañer el bandurria ... Madrid, J. Ibarra, [n. d.] ([8] p. 1 pl.)
(5) Reglas ... para tañer el violin ... Madrid, J. Ibarra. [n. d.] ([8] p. 2 pl.)
(6) Reglas ... para tañer la flauta traversera, la flauta dulce, y la flautilla ... Madrid, Impr. de J. Ibarra, 1754. ([4] p. 3 pl.)
Introduction and part 3 are the same as in another Library of Congress copy, which contains parts 1 to 4 only.

MT582.M32　Miller collection

Monnet, Jean, 1703–1785.

Supplement au Roman comique [de Scarron], ou Mémoires pour servir à la vie de Jean Monnet, ci-devant directeur de l'Opéra-comique à Paris, de l'Opéra de Lyon, & d'une Comédie françoise à Londres. Ecrits par lui-même ... Londres, 1772.

2 v. front. (port.) 17½^{cm}.

18–12283 ML429.M67 1772

Monserrate, Andrés de.

Arte breve, y compendiosa de las dificvltades qve se ofrecen en la mvsica practica del canto llano ... Compvesta por Andres de Monserrate ... Valencia, P. P. Mey, 1614.

123, [1] p. illus. (music) 21½^{cm}.

Signatures: A–G⁸, H⁶.
Title vignette (woodcut of the Virgin of Monserrat)

25–21740 MT860.A2M6

Morabin, Jacques, 1687–1762.

See [CHÂTEAUNEUF, F. DE CASTAGNÈRES, *abbé de*] Dialogue sur la musique des anciens. 1735.

Moraes Pedroso, Manuel de.

Compendio musico, ou Arte abbreviada em que se contèm as regras mais necessarias da cantoria, acompanhamento, e contrapunto ... Por Manoel de Moraes Pedroso ... Porto, Na officina de A. A. Ribeiro Guimaraens, 1769.

2 p. l., 47 p. illus. (music) 19½^{cm}.

25–21737 MT40.A2M84

Morande, Charles Thévenot de, *b.* 1748, *joint author.*

See [MAYEUR DE SAINT PAUL, F. M.] Le vol plus haut.

Morland, *Sir* **Samuel,** *bart.,* 1625–1695.

Tuba stentoro-phonica, an instrument of excellent use, as well at sea, as at land; invented and variously experimented in the year 1670. And humbly presented to the Kings Most Excellent Majesty Charles II. In the year 1671. By S. Morland. The instruments (or speaking-trumpets) of all sizes and dimensions, are made and sold by Mr. Simon Beal, one of His Majesties trump⁸: in Suffolk-street. London, Printed by W. Godbid, and are to be sold by M. Pitt, 1671.

1 p. l., 14 p. front. (port.) illus., diagrs. 30½^{cm}.

41–26615 ML990.T8M6 1671. Miller collection

—— —— [Another issue] London, Printed by W. Godbid, and are to be sold by M. Pitt, 1672.

1 p. l., 14 p. illus., diagrs. 30½^{cm}.

18–8061 ML990.T8M6 1672

[Mott, Hermann]

... Musices choralis medulla; siue, Totius cantus gregoriani succincta ac fundamentalis traditio. Coloniæ, apud Wilhelm Friessem, 1670.

3 p. l., 160 (*i. e.* 150) 88 p.   12 x 7^{cm}.

Engraved t.-p., with ornamental border.
Error in paging: nos. 102–111 omitted.
Dedication signed: F. Hermannus Mott.
"Hymnus in festo s. Petri de Alcantara": 1 leaf inserted after p. 45, 1st group of pages.
"Processionale ad normam missalis ac ritualis, auctoritate apostolica reformatorum concinnatum. In usum FF. minorum recollectorum": 88 p. at end.

35–21832   MT860.M79M8

—— Musices choralis medulla, sive Cantus gregoriani fundamentalis traditio, una cum tonis communibus, hymnis, antiphonis, lectione mensali, &c. Ad usum Fratrum minorum strictioris observantiæ, provinciæ Saxoniæ S. Crucis, ordinis seraphici patris S. Francisci. Paderbornæ, typis Joachimi Friderici Buch, 1714.

1 p. l., 146, 92, 4 p.   13½ x 7½^{cm}.

"Processionale ad normam missalis ac ritualis, auctoritate apostolica reformatorum concinnatum. In usum FF. minorum strictioris observantiæ": 92 p. at end.

9–11093 Revised   MT860.M79M8   1714

Motz, Georg, 1653–1733.

Die vertheidigte kirchen-music, oder Klar und deutlicher beweis/ welcher gestalten hr. m. Christian Gerber ... in seinem buch/ welches er Unerkandte sünden der welt nennet/In dem LXXXI. cap. da er von dem missbrauch der kirchen-music geschrieben/zu verwerfung der musicalischen harmonie und bestraffung der kirchen-music zu weit gegangen ... Von Georgio Motzen ... [Tilsit?] 1703.

5 p. l., 3–264 p.   1 illus. (music) diagr.   17½ x 10^{cm}.

A continuation, "Abgenöthigte fortsetzung", was published in 1708.
Book-plate: Carl Gottlob Stoll. Org. in Schleiz.

29–28717   ML3001.M7

Moubach, Abraham, *translator.*

See Hottetterre, J. Grond-beginselen over de behandeling van de dwars-fluit. 1728.

Mozart, Leopold, 1719–1787.

Leopold Mozarts ... Gründliche violinschule, mit vier kupfertafeln und einer tabelle. 3. verm. aufl. Augsburg, J. J. Lotter und sohn, 1787.

3 p. l., 268, [8] p. front. (port.) illus. (music) 4 pl. (1 fold.: music) 20½ x 15½^{cm}.

First published in 1756 under title: Versuch einer gründlichen violinschule.

41–18183   MT262.M925

Mozart, Leopold—Continued.

———— ... Grondig onderwys in het behandelen der viool, ontworpen door Leopold Mozart ... Met 4 konst-plaaten en een tafel van de regelen der strykmanier enz. voorzien. Haerlem, J. Enschede, 1766.

10 p. l., 259 p. front. (port.) illus. (incl. music) 3 pl., tab. 27 x 21^{cm}.

Translation of Versuch einer gründlichen violinschule.
Second edition; 1st edition published in 1756.
Imperfect: table wanting, margin of last leaf trimmed.

29–724 MT262.M95

Müller, Heinrich, 1631–1675.

Hymnologia sacra, das ist, d. Heinrich Mûllers ... zehen andåchtige Betrachtungen von geistlichen liedern, nebst einer besondern vorrede von dem so genannten Gregorius-fest und liedern, aufs neue heraus gegeben von Johann Caspar Wetzeln ... Nûrnberg, J. D. Taubers sel. erben, 1728.

47, [1], 160, [8] p. 17½^{cm}.

The "Betrachtungen" are reprinted from Müller's "Geistliche seelen-musik", the 1st edition of which appeared in 1659. *cf.* Vorrede.

29–28718 ML3186.M8

Musagetes, Volupius Decorus, *pseud.*

See SCHOENSLEDER, WOLFGANG, 1570–1651.

Muscovius, Johann, 1635–1695.

Gestraffter missbrauch der kirchen-music / und kirchhôfe / aus Gottes wort zur warnung und besserung vorgestellet durch Johannem Muscovium, pastorem primarium und inspectorem der kirchen und schulen in Lauben [!] [Lauban] Gedruckt im jahr 1694.

110, [2] p. 16½^{cm}.

"Lauben", on t.-p., is a misprint for "Lauban". *cf.* Errata.
"Gegen Christn. Schiff gerichtet."—Eitner, Quellen-lex. (*cf.* also Gondolatsch, Ein oberlausitzer beitrag zum streit um die evangelische kirchen-musik (Zeitsch. f. musikwissenschaft, Feb. 1932, p. 278–90)
29-28716 ML3001.M8

The **Musical** library and universal magazine of harmony.

See HECK, J. C.

The **Musical** magazine.

See The NEW musical and universal·magazine.

Musicalische neu-erbauete schåfferey / oder Keusche liebes-beschreibung, von der verliebten nymfen Amaena vnd von jhrem lobwůrdigem schåffer Amandvs. Auffs neue ûbersehen / etwas in der gebundenen rede corrigiret / mit unterschiedlichen sententien und sprichwôrtern vermehrt / vñ die darin befindende oden mit neuen melodien / nach anbegehren etlicher musicalischen freunde / beseelet von einem sonderlichen liebhaber der teutschen poesie / und der edlen musike / Nebenst angehenckter kurtzen anleitung / wie man anmuthige teutsche brieffe / nach heutigem gebrauch / recht zierlich / und kurtz stellen kônne. Kônigsberg, Bey P. Håndeln [1641?]

Musicalische neu-erbauete schäfferey—Continued.

4 p. l., 306, [58] p. 16$^{cl\cdots}$.

Dedication signed: G. C. V. G., A. S. D. D. sonst geheissen Schindscher-sitzky.
The "Kurtze anleitung wie anmutige, teutsche brieffe ... zu stellen" has special t.-p.
Added t.-p., engr.: Newe musicalische schafferey, oder Keusche liebes beschreibungh, von der verliebten nimfen Amœna vnd dem lobwûrdigen schâffer Amandvs ...

12–78   ML3925.A2M9

Musikalische korrespondenz der Teutschen filarmonischen gesellschaft ... 7. julius 1790–28. dez. 1791. Speier, Expedizion dieser Musikal. korrespondenz [1790–91]

2 v. 19½–23^{cm}.

Edited by H. P. C. Bossler.
Preceded by Musicalische real-zeitung (July 1788–June 1790)
Published July 7, 1790–Dec. 26, 1792. Library of Congress set wants all of 1792.

—— Notenblâtter zur Musikalischen korrespondenz der Teutschen filarmonischen gesellschaft. Speier, 1790–91.

2 v. 19½–23^{cm}.

Library of Congress set wants 1792.

                                                                                          ML4.M48

Musikalische nachrichten und anmerkungen. [1.–4. jahrg.]; 1. julius 1776–24. dec. 1770. Leipzig, Im verlag der zeitungs-expedition, 1766–70.

4 v. 24x19^{cm}. weekly.

Each quarter year has title-page.
Includes music.
Title varies:
July 1766–Dec. 1769, Wôchentliche nachrichten und anmerkungen die musik betreffend.
Jan.–Dec., 1770, Musikalische nachrichten und anmerkungen.
Edited by J. A. Hiller.
Vol. 1 issued July 1766–June 1767; v. 2, July 1767–June 1768; v. 3, July 1768–June 1769, with "Anhang", July–Dec. 1769; v. 4, Jan.–Dec. 1770. No more published.

Library of Congress set incomplete: v. 2 wanting.

12–18593 Revised   ML4.M47

Musikalischer almanach auf das jahr 1784. Freyburg [1784?]

14 p. l., [35]–144 p. front. 15½^{cm}.

Added t.-p.: Musikalisches taschenbuch auf das jahr 1784.
Ascribed to Karl Ludwig Junker.
Two previous volumes were published, for 1782 and 1783 respectively.
The almanac for 1783 has title: Musikalischer und kûnstler-almanach auf das jahr 1783.

                                                                                          ML20.M62

Musikalisches taschenbuch auf das jahr 1784.

See MUSIKALISCHER almanach auf das jahr 1784.

Musikgesellschaft zur Deutschen schule, *Zürich*.
See NEUJAHRSGESCHENK an die zürcherische jugend.

N. P.

See POISSON, NICOLAS JOSEPH, 1637–1710.

Naish, Thomas, *d.* 1755.

A sermon preach'd at the cathedral church of Sarum, Novemb. 22. 1700. Before a society of lovers of musick. By Thomas Naish ... London, Awnsham and J. Churchill, 1701.

2 p. l., 28 p. 19½ᶜᵐ.

36–32697   ML64.N3S4

A sermon preach'd at the cathedral church of Sarum, November the 30th, 1726. Being the anniversary day appointed for the meeting of the Society of lovers of musick. By Thomas Naish ... London, J. Lacy; [etc., etc.] 1726.

vi, 7–23 p. incl. front. 24ᶜᵐ.

20–19899   ML64.N14

Nares, James, 1715–1783.

A concise, and easy treatise on singing, addressed to the delettanti in music, who are desirous of performing duets, or any vocal music in parts ... with a set of English duets for beginners, by Dʳ. Nares ... London, Printed for the author, and sold by J. Preston [178–?]

1 p. l., 2–33 p. 26½ x 36ᶜᵐ.

Engraved throughout.

ca 17–806 Unrev'd   MT885.N28

Il principio, or A regular introduction to playing on the harpsichord or organ, by Dʳ. Nares ... London, Welcker [1759?]

2 p. l., 2–35 p. 24 x 33½ᶜᵐ.

Engraved throughout.
Music: p. 2–35.

ca 17–807 Unrev'd   MT243.A2N2

A treatise on singing in which is exhibited and explained by examples all the known rules of solmisation, or learning to sing by notes with directions for the delivery & management of the voice. drawn from observations on nature as well as art. highly usefull in all societies where singing by notes is necessary, being adapted to make that study easy & clear, by Dʳ. Nares ... London, Printed by Longman and Broderip [ca. 1780?]

1 p. l., 40 p. 18 x 26ᶜᵐ.

Engraved throughout.

17–17453   MT830.A2N2

[Neufville de Brunaubois-Montador, Jean Florent Joseph de]
b. 1707.

Lettre au sujet de la rentrée de la demoiselle Le Maure a l'Opera, ecrite a une dame de province par un solitaire de Paris, avec une Parodie de la quatriéme scene du troisiéme acte de Zaïre; et quelques pieces en vers sur le même sujet. Bruxelles, 1740.

47 p. 15½^{cm}.
42–6137   ML1727.3.N28L3

Neujahrsgeschenk ab dem Musiksaal an die zürchersche jugend. 1778–1812. [Zürich, 1778]–1812.

35 no. in 2 v.   plates.   22½–25^{cm}.
Preceded by Musicalische neu-jahrs-gedichte. 1685–1777.
Title varies:
1778–83, Neujahrsgeschenk ab dem Musiksaal an die zürchersche jugend. Schweizerscenen.   1.–6. stück.
1784–89, —— Zürcher-gegenden.   1.–6. stück.
1790–98, Gesänge zur beförderung vaterländischer tugend. Neujahrs-geschenk ab dem Musiksaal an die zürcherische jugend.   1.–9. stück.
1799–1812, no general title. (Imprint: Zürich, Gedr. bey D. Bürkli) 1802, subtitle Neujahrsgeschenk; 1803–12, Geschenk für die zürchersche jugend von der Gesellschaft auf dem Musiksaal ...
1778–89, 12 no. unpaged.   24 x 30^{cm}.   Vignette on each t.-p.
1790–1812, 23 no. continuously paged (184 p.), each accompanied by an unnumbered plate.
In 1812 the "Gesellschaft auf dem Musiksaal" and the "Musik-gesell-schaft zur Deutschen schule" united to form the "Allgemeine musikgesell-schaft", and a new publication was begun in 1813 under title: Neujahrs-geschenk an die zürcherische jugend, von der Allgemeinen musik-gesell-schaft in Zürich.
10–10100   ML5.N46

Neujahrsgeschenk an die zürcherische jugend, von der Musik-gesell-schaft zur Deutschen-schule in Zürich.   1713–1812.   [Zürich, 1713–1812]

100 no. in 4 v.   plates.   18–22^{cm}.
Issued as follows:
1713–79, (No general title) "Vorgestellt von der Music-gesellschafft ab dem Music-saal auf der Teutschen schul in Zürich: der lieben jugend da-selbsten verehrt."   67 no., continuously paged (538 p.) each accompanied by a numbered plate.
1780–83. Neüjahrsgeschenk für die vaterländische jugend von der Musik-gesellschaft auf der Teütschen schule in Zürich.   4 no.   19½ x 24^{cm}.   Engr. t.-p.
1784–1800, National-kinderlieder für di zürchersche jugend.   1.–17. stück. Zürich, Gedr. bey D. Bürkli, 1784–1800.   17 no. continuously paged (136 p.). 18 x 22^{cm}.   Each number has title vignette.
1801–04, Neujahrs-geschenk für die zürchersche jugend von der Musik-gesellschaft ab der Deutschen schule.   Zürich, Gedr. bey D. Bürkli, 1801–04.   4 no. continuously paged (31, [1] p.), each accompanied by a plate.
Bound with National-kinderlieder, 1784–1800.
1805–11, Väter-tugenden ... Geschenk an die zürchersche jugend von der Musik-gesellschaft der Deutschen schule.   Zürich, Gedr. bey D. Bürkli, 1805–11.   7 no. continuously paged (56 p.)   No. 1 has title vignette; no. 2–7 each accompanied by a plate.
1812, Neujahrsgeschenk an die zürcherische jugend von der Musik-gesell-schaft zur Deutschen-schule in Zürich.   cover-title, 5, [2] p. pl. (Bound with Väter-tugenden, 1805–11.
10–10099   ML5.N47

Neusiedler, Hans, 1508 *or* 9–1563.

Ein Newgeordent Kûnstlich Lau- ‖ tenbuch / In zwentheyl getheylt. Der erst fûr die anfahenden ‖ Schuler / die aus rechter kunst vnd grundt nach der Tabulatur / sich one ‖ einichen Meyster darin zuûben haben / durch ein leicht Exempel dieser ‖ punctlein . .. . wohin man mit einem yedĕ finger recht greiffen ‖ sol. Weyter ist angezeigt / wie mã die Tabulatur auch die men / sur / vñ die gantz Application recht grundtlich lernen vñ versteen sol. ‖ Im andern theyl sein begriffen / vil ausserlessner kunstreicher stuck /‖ von Fantaseyen / Preambeln / Psalmen vnd Muteten / die von den Hochberûmb- ‖ ten vñ besten Organisten / als einen schatz gehaiten / die sein mit sonderm fleiss auff ‖ die Organistich art gemacht vnd colorirt / fûr die geûbten vnd erfarnen di-· ‖ ser kunst / auff die Lauten dargeben. Dergleichen vormals nie im ‖ Truck / Aber yetzo durch mich Hansen Newsidler Lutinisten ‖ vnd Bûrger zu Nûrnberg / offenlich aussgangen. [1. th.] ‖ Mit Rȯm. Keys. vnd Kȯnigk. Ma. freyheit / in ‖ funff iaren nit nach zu trucken / begnadet. [Nûrnberg, 1536]

[171] p. 1 illus., double pl. 15½ x 20½^{cm}.

Colophon (pt. 1) : Getruckt zu Nurmberg bey Johan Petreio / durch angebung vnd ‖ verlegung / Hansen Neusidler Lutinisten / bürtig võ Pressburck ‖ jetzt bûrger zu Nurmburg. Anno Tausent funff ‖ hundert vñ sechs vnd dreyssig.

Signatures: a-x⁴, 2 l. (double pl.), 2 l. (Last 4 leaves unsigned)

Library of Congress copy incomplete: v. 2 wanting.

30–16913   MT640.N3

New and complete instructions for the oboe or hoboy.

See The COMPLEAT tutor for the hautboy.

New and compleat instructions for the violin.

See GEMINIANI, F.

New instructions for playing the harpsichord, piano-forte or spinnet, wherein the Italian manner of fingering is explained by variety of examples. Also concise rules for playing thorough bass, to which is added a collection of choice lessons, marches, airs, songs, &c. Compiled by the most eminent masters for the use of beginners. The most approved method of tuning & a dictionary explaining such words as generally occur in music ... London, Printed & sold at A. Bland's music warehouse [1790?]

1 p. l., 36 p. 2 pl. (1 fold.) 18 x 25^{cm}.

Engraved throughout.

41–10517   MT222.N58

See also The COMPLEAT tutor for the harpsichord.

New instructions for the German flute.

See COMPLEAT instructions for the German flute.

New instructions for the violin.

See GEMINIANI, F.

The **New** musical and universal magazine. Consisting of the most favourite songs, airs, &c., as performed at all public places, adapted for the G. flute, violin, guitar, and harpsichord; also is included ... pages of letter press, of amusing and agreeable subjects. Calculated for the lady, gentleman and musician. v. 1–3; Sept. 1774–[1777?] London, Printed for R. Snagg [etc., 1774–77?]

3 v. in 2. 24½ ^{cm}.

> Title-pages and music engraved.
> Running title of "Literary part", v. 1: The Musical magazine.
> Vol. 1 (printed for R. Snagg) was issued monthly from Sept. 1774 to Dec. 1775; v. 2–3 (printed for I. (*i. e.* J.) French) are undated. In Library of Congress set, "letter press" is wanting in v. 2–3.
> With v. 1 is bound Alexander Malcolm's Treatise of music (London, 1776) which appears to have been issued with the magazine. *cf.* Kidson, British music publishers (London [1900]) p. 51.

ca 14–588 Unrev'd   ML4.N49

Newes from Pauls: containing a relation of the angry disputation betwixt the two church-quarrellers, Orange-Tawnie and Purple: being a contention about the lawfulnesse or unlawfulnesse of organs and other ceremonies. London, Printed in the yeer of discord, 1642.

1 p. l., 6 p. 19 ^{cm}.

20–5440   ML3001.N37

Newte, John, 1655?–1716.

The lawfulness and use of organs in the Christian church. Asserted in a sermon preach'd at Tiverton in the county of Devon upon the 13th of September, 1696. On occasion of an organ's being erected in that parish-church. By John Newte ... 2d ed. London, Printed by F. Collins and are to be sold by W. Rogers; [etc., etc.] 1701.

2 p. l., 31 p. 20½ ^{cm}.

17–31230   ML3001.N38

> *See also* DODWELL, HENRY. A Treatise concerning the lawfulness of instrumental musick.
> A LETTER to a friend in the country, concerning the use of instrumental musick in the worship of God.

Newton, John, *b.* 1712.

The natural, moral, and divine influences of musick. A sermon preach'd in the Cathedral-church of Gloucester, at the anniversary meeting of the choirs of Gloucester, Worcester, and Hereford, September 14, 1748. Published at their joint request. By John Newton ... London, E. Cave; [etc., etc., 1748]

34 p. 18 ^{cm}.

20–14644   ML3001.N39

Niedt, Friedrich Erhardt, 1674–1717.

... Musicalisches A B C. Zum nutzen der lehr- und lernenden. Hamburg, Bei B. Schillern, 1708.

1 p. l., [26], 5–112 p.   illus. (music)   18 x 22½^{cm}.

Signatures: 1 leaf (t.-p.) unsigned, †⁴, ††⁴, †††⁴, A–O⁴ (A₁ wanting)
Contains (p. 35–108) several arias by Niedt, some with oboe obligato and basso continuo.

41–40869   MT7.N67M8

Niger, Franciscus.

Grammatica brevis.   Venetiis, Theodorus Herbipolensis, 1480.

247 l.   8° (21^{cm})

fol. 1 (a[i]) recto–fol. 3 (a iii) recto, line 6, dedicatory letter headed: P. FRANCISCVS NIGER ... LEONARDO BOTTAE ... FOELICITATEM.   fol. 3 (a iii) recto, line 7, caption of grammar: P. FRANCISCI NIGRI. A. VENETI sa ‖ cerdotis: artiūq̃ doctoris: breuis grāmatica ad ‖ splēdidissimū eqtē leonardū bottā ... fol. 247 ([dd vi]) recto, line 17: Santritter helbronna genitus de gente ioannes ‖ Lucilius: prompsit grammata docta nigri. ‖ Herbipolisq̃ satus: socio sudore: lacunis. ‖ Hoc uenetis françus fert theodorus opus. ‖ ANNO SALVTIS, M.CCCC.LXXX. XII. ‖ CAL. APRIL.   Impressū ē hoc opo VENETIIS ‖ DVCE VIRTVTE & COMITE FORTVNA. ‖
Signatures: a–i⁸, k⁹, l–s⁸, s–z⁸, ɔ⁸, &⁸, ℞⁸, aa–cc⁸, dd⁶ (d [viii] signed d ii; sig. ɔ and sig. & transposed) Without pagination or catchwords.
Five musical examples (leaves 199–201, sig. ɔ[vi]–ɔ[viii]), illustrating the section "Harmonia", are probably the oldest specimen of measured music printed from type.   The notes are printed without the staff.   cf. J. Mantuani, Über den beginn des notendruckes (Wien, 1901); C. Wendel, Aus der wiegenzeit des notendruckes (Centralblatt für bibliothekswesen XIX, 1902, p. 569–581)
Hain *11858; Proctor 4498; Panzer III, p. 157, no. 452; Brit. mus.; Pinelli cat. III, no. 7375.
In ms. on fly-leaf: Pinelli Appendix. Ven. 1480, 12th Apr.—5s. 6d. M. Wodhull, Feb. 26th, 1790.

ML171.N4

Nislen, Tobias, *translator.*

See KIRCHER, A.   Neue hall- und thon-kunst.   1684.

Noverre, Jean Georges, 1727–1810.

The works of Monsieur Noverre, translated from the French ... London, G. Robinson; [etc., etc., 1782]–83.

3 v.   front. (port.)   21½^{cm}.

CONTENTS.—v. 1–2. An essay on the art of dancing.—v. 3.   The Danaides. Rinaldo and Armida. Adela of Ponthieu. The Graces. The Horatii and Curiatii. Agamemnon revenged. Apelles and Campaspe, or, The self-conquest of Alexander. The amours of Venus. Alceste.

12–18375 Revised   ML3858.N94

Of the use and abuse of music, particularly the music of the choir. By a friend to church-music ... [n. p.] 1753.

30 p.   16¼^{cm}.

20–14645   ML3001.O3

Orlando, Matteo, *bishop*, 1610–1695.

See CARMELITES.   Directorium chori.   1668.

Oropesa, Tomás de Iriarte y
See IRIARTE Y OROPESA, TOMÁS DE, 1750–1791.

P., N.
See POISSON, NICOLAS JOSEPH, 1637–1710.

Päminger, Leonhard, 1495–1567.
See PÄMINGER, S. Epitaphia Leonarti Pamingeri.

Päminger, Sophonias, 1526–1603.
Epitaphia Leonarti Pamingeri Aschaviensis, viri pietate, ervditione, et virtute præstantis, musici clariss. Patauij in finibus Bauariæ, ad d. Nicolaum secretarij, piè ibidem defuncti, & sepulti, a Sophonia Pamingero Patauino, Leonarti filio, & quibusdam reuerendis, clariss. pijs, ac eruditis viris scripta ... [Ratisponæ? 1568?]

[51] p. woodcut (port.) 18^{cm}.

Signatures: A–F⁴, G² (verso of last leaf blank)
Portrait of L. Päminger on G[ij] recto.
Preface dated: Ratisponæ pridie calend. augusti, anno M.D.LXVIII.

25–21741   ML171.P25

Paisiello, Giovanni, 1741–1816.
Regole per bene accompagnare il partimento; o sia, Il basso fondamentale sopra il cembalo, del signor maestro Giovanni Paisiello. Composte per Sua Altezza imperiale la gran duchessa di tutte le Russie. [S. Pietroburgo] Печатано въ Типографіи Морскаго шляхетнаго кадетскаго корпуса, 1782.

60 p. 27 x 36^{cm}.

22–11232   MT49.A2P14

Paminger, Sophonias.
See PÄMINGER, SOPHONIAS, 1526–1603.

Pancrace, *archevêque de Cythéropolis et patriarche de l'Opéra, pseud.*
See CHEVRIER, FRANÇOIS ANTOINE, 1721–1762.

Paris. Académie royale de musique.
Au corps législatif sur l'Opera, autrement dit le Théatre des arts. [Paris? 178–?]

4 p. 21^{cm}.
Caption title.
Signed: Liébaud.

ML1727.3.L69A9

Compte rendu au public, des conditions auxquelles les administrateurs du Théâtre du Palais royal acceptent de se charger de l'entreprise de l'Opéra. [Paris, Impr. de Cailleau, 1789]

8 p. 21^{cm}.
Caption title.
Signed: Dorfeuille, Gaillard.

ML1727.3.D69C5

Pétition, pour l'Académie royale de musique, a l'Assemblée nationale. [Paris? De l'imp. d'A.-J. Gorsas, 1790?]

8 p. 21^{cm}.

Caption title.

ML1727.8.P2P31

Rapport relatif au mode d'existence de l'Opéra. [Paris, Impr. de L. Potier de Lille, 1790]

4 p. 26½ x 21^{cm}.

Caption title.

At head of title : District des Récolets.

ML1727.8.P2A2

Rapport sur l'Opéra présenté au corps municipal, le 17 août 1791. Par J. J. Leroux ... Paris [Impr. de le Becq] 1791.

2 p. l., 98 p., 1 l. fold. tables. 21^{cm}.

At head of title: Municipalité de Paris. Administration des etablissemens publics.

ML1727.3.L36R2

Parker, William, 1714–1802.

The pleasures of gratitude and benevolence improved by church-musick. A sermon preached at the anniversary meeting of the three choirs of Gloucester, Worcester, and Hereford, in the Cathedral church at Hereford, on Wednesday, Sept. 12, 1753. By William Parker ... Publish'd at the unanimous request of the audience. London, J. Fletcher, 1753.

4 p. l., 31 p. 18^{cm}.

20–14642   ML3001.P17

Pasquali, Giovanni Battista.

See MILIZIA, F. Del teatro. 1773.

Pécourt, Guillaume Louis, 1653–1729.

See FEUILLET, R. A. Recueil de dances. 1709.

Penna, Lorenzo, 1613–1693.

Li primi albori mvsicali per li principianti della musica figurata; distinti in tre' libri: dal primo spuntano li principij del canto figv-rato; dal secondo spiccano le regole del contrapvnto; dal terzo ap-pariscono li fondamenti per suonare l'organo, ò clavicembalo sopra la parte; del p. f. Lorenzo Penna ... Bologna, G. Monti, 1672.

9 p. l., 3–62, [4] p. ; 131, [1] p. ; 89 p. illus. (incl. music) 22^{cm}.

Each part has special t.-p.

22–894   MT6.A2P4

Pepusch, John Christopher, 1667–1752.

See [BROSSARD, S. DE] A musical dictionary. 1769.

Pfenninger, Johann Konrad, 1747–1792.

Briefe an nicht-musiker, ueber musik als sache der menschheit. Von Johann Konrad Pfenninger. Nach seinem tode herausgegeben. Zürich, Gedrukt bey J. K. Näf, 1792.

3 p. l., 140 p. 19½^{cm}.

35–21815   ML3845.P3B7

Pflugg, Eitel Gallus, *respondent.*

See TREW, ABDIAS, *praeses.* Disputatio musica secunda.

Philippineus, Bartholomæus.

See VEGIUS, M. Quae in hoc opere continentur. Maphei Vegij ... Pompeana [etc.] ... [1521]

Philpot, Stephen.

An introduction to the art of playing on the violin, on an entire new plan, calculated for laying a regular foundation for young beginners, explained by such easy rules and principles as will enable a scholar to acquire a proper method for performing on that instrument. By Stephen Philpot, of Lewes in Sussex ... London, Printed and sold for the author by Randall and Abell [etc., 1767?]

14 p., 1 l., 31 p. 37½^{cm}.
Music engraved.

43–33442   MT262.P49I6

Playford, John, 1623–1686?

A brief introduction to the skill of musick: in three books. The first: The grounds and rules of mvsick, according to the gam-ut and other principles thereof. The second: Instructions for the bass-viol, and also for the treble-violin: vvith lessons for beginners. By John Playford Philo-musicæ. The third: The art of descant, or composing musick in parts. By Dr. Tho. Campion. With annotations thereon by Mr. C. Simpson. London, Printed by W. Godbid for J. Playford, 1667.

9 p. l., 151 p. front. (port.) illus. 17½^{cm}.

The illustrations are on prepared ground. Pt. 3 has special t.-p.
The 1st edition was published in 1654 as " Breefe introduction to the skill of musick, for song and viall."
"The tunes of the Psalmes as they are commonly sung in parish-chvrches. With the bass set under each tune": p. 57–73.

16–616   MT7.A2P71

―― An introduction to the skill of musick. In two books. The first: The grounds and rules of mvsick, according to the gam-vt, and other principles thereof. The second: Instructions & lessons for the bass-viol: and instructions & lessons for the treble-violin. By John Playford. To which is added, The art of descant, or composing mvsick in parts. By Dr. Tho. Campion. With annotations thereon, by Mr. Chr. Simpson. The sixt ed. cor. and enl. London, Printed by W. Godbid for J. Playford, 1672.

7 p. l., 117 (*i. e.* 113), [1], 41 (*i. e.* 43) p. front.(port.) illus. (incl. music) 17½^{cm}.

Playford, John—Continued.

"The art of descant" has special t.-p., dated 1671, and separate paging.
"A brief discourse of the Italian manner of singing ... written some years since by an English gentleman, who had lived long in Italy, and being returned, taught the same here": p. 37–56.
"The tunes of Psalms used in parish chvrches": p. 73–81.
24–13340   MT7.A2P716

—— An introduction to the skill of musick, in three books. The first contains the grounds and rules of musick, according to the gam-ut, and other principles thereof. The second, instrvctions and lessons both for the bass-viol and treble-violin. The third, the art of descant, or composing of musick in parts, in a more plain and easie method than any heretofore published. The 10th ed., cor. and enl. By John Playford. London, Printed by A. G[odbid] and J. P[layford the younger] for J. Playford, 1683.

7 p. l., 116, [2], 47 p. front. (port.) illus. (incl. music) 17½^{cm}.

The third part has separate paging and special t.-p.: A brief introduction to the art of descant.
"A brief discourse of the Italian manner of singing ... written some years since by an English gentleman who had lived long in Italy, and being returned taught the same here": p. 34–49.
"The order of performing the divine service in cathedrals and collegiate chappels": p. 78–85.
19–17372   MT7.A2P74

—— An introduction to the skill of musick: in three books: by John Playford. Containing I. The grounds and principles of musick, according to the gamut ... II. Instructions and lessons for the treble, tenor, and bass-viols; and also for the treble violin. III. The art of descant, or composing musick in parts: made very plain and easie by the late Mr. Henry Purcell. The 17th ed. Corrected and done on the new-ty'd note. London, Printed by W. Pearson, for J. and B. Sprint, 1718.

9 p. l., 170 p., 1 l. front. (port.) illus. (incl. music) 16½^{cm}.

Parts 2 and 3 have each special t.-p.
"The order of performing the divine service in cathedrals, & collegiate chappels": p. 53–60.
24–15631   MT7.A2P791

Musick's delight on the cithren, restored and refined to a more easie and pleasant manner of playing than formerly; and set forth with lessons al a mode, being the choicest of our late new ayres, corants, sarabands, tunes, and jiggs. To which is added several new songs and ayres to sing to the cithren. By John Playford Philomusicæ. London, Printed by W. G[odbid] and are sold by J. Playford, 1666.

7 p. l., [96] p. (music) illus. (incl. music) 10½ x 16½^{cm}.

Imperfect: wanting 4 leaves (supplied in manuscript)
17–31236   MT590.A2P5

Musicks hand-maid; new lessons and instructions for the virginals or harpsychord. London, J. Playford, 1678.

4 p. l., [72] p. (music) 15½ x 19½^{cm}.

Engraved throughout, with exception of 3d and 4th prelim. leaves. Illustrated t.-p.

Playford, John—Continued.

Signatures: A⁴, A–F⁴, G², H–I⁴, K² (sig. I irregular in arrangement) Page [48] (F₄ verso) is marked "Finis", p. [52] (G₂ verso) has a tailpiece, and p. [68] (I₂ verso) is marked "Finnis", suggesting that previous editions may have ended with these pages. Contains 75 pieces, numbered as 77. The composers named are B. Sandley, W. Lawes, B. Rogers, M. Locke, J. Mosse, A. Bryan, T. Prat, and J. Jackson. "The tunes of Psalms to the virginal or the organ" : [2] p., appended.

22–13593   MT224.A2P4

Poisson, Nicolas Joseph, 1637–1710.

See DESCARTES, R. Traité de la mécanique. 1668.

Ponterollus, Bartholomæus.

See VEGIUS, M. Quae in hoc opere continentur. Maphei Vegij ... Pompeana [etc.] ... [1521]

Poultier d'Elmotte, François Martin, 1753–1826, *joint author.*

See [MAYEUR DE SAINT PAUL, F. M.] Le vol plus haut.

Prasperg, Balthasar, *16th cent.*

Clarissima plane atq; chora ‖ lis musice interp̄tatio Dñi ‖ Balthasser P₂aspergij Merspurgeñ. ‖ cū certissis regulis atq; Exēplo₇ Ano ‖ tacionib⁹ ₹ figuris multu splēdidis In ‖ Alma Basileo₇ vniversitate exercitata. [Basileae, Michael Furter, 1501]

[38] p.   illus. (music) fold. tab.   21ᶜᵐ.

Colophon: Finis musices ex Orphei lyra et ‖ Saphus cythara manate atq; per venerabi- ‖ lem dñm Balthasser p₂aspergiu₃ Merspur- ‖ geñ. In nobili ac p₂eclaro Basileo₂um stu- ‖ dio p₂oceltico : diligentia exactissima exami ‖ nate. Rogatu tandem audito₂um per proui ‖ dum virum Michaelem Furter Ciuē Basi- ‖ lieñ Imp₂esse. Anno χρ̄iane salutis sup̄ Mil ‖ lesimum quingentesimo p₂imo. [*Printer's mark*]
Signatures: A–B⁸, C⁴ (last leaf, blank, wanting)
Below the title is a large woodcut representing (at left) a music master and (at right) a young woman playing the harp; in the upper section of the cut is a scroll with the hexachord, ut re mi fa sol la. (The editions of 1504 and 1507 have the same title-page illustration)   At end, a folded leaf or table with "Scala greca" and "Scala latina". Gothic type.
First edition ?   Gesner's Bibliotheca, 1574, p. 83, contains the following statement: "Balthassar Praspergius Merspurgensis scripsit de Musica chorali librum, regulis multis ac exemplis varijs refertum, & excusum in quarto, Basileæ anno Domini 1500 ". Maittaire (citing Gesner), Panzer (citing Maittaire), and Hain (13327) list under Prasperg a "De musica chorali ", Basileæ 1500. The notice in Gesner is probably an inexact description of the present edition.

32–7553   ML171.P69

——CLarissima plane ‖ atq; cho₂alis musice interp₂etatio ‖ Dñi Balthasser P₂aspergij Mer ‖ spurgeñ. cum certissimis regulis ‖ atq; Exemplo₇ Annotationib⁹ ‖ ₹ figuris multum splendidis. In ‖ Alma Basileo₂ū vniuersitate ex‖ercitata. [Basileae, Michael Furter, 1507]

[38] p.   illus. (music) fold. tab.   20½ᶜᵐ.

Colophon: Finis musices ex O₂phei lyra et Sa‖phus cythara manate atq; per venerabilem ‖ dominū Balthasser p₂aspergiū Merspur- ‖ geñ. In nobili ac p₂eclaro Basileo₂ū studio ‖ p₂oceltico diligentia exactissima examinate. ‖ Rogatu tandem audito₂um per p₂ouidū vi- ‖ rū Michaelem Furter Ciuem Basilieñ im- ‖ p₂esse. Anno ch₂istiane salutis super millesi- ‖ mo : quingentesimo : septimo. [*Printer's mark*]

Prasperg, Balthasar—Continued.

Signatures: A–B⁶, C⁴ (last leaf blank)
Below the title is a woodcut (*cf.* description of 1501 edition). Between leaves [Aiiii] and [Av] is a folded leaf or table with "Scala greca" and " Scala latina." Gothic type.
Two previous editions were published (Basel, M. Furter, 1501 and 1504, respectively)
13–24940 Revised   ML171.P7

[Prelleur, Peter]

The art of playing on the violin; with a new scale shewing how to stop every note, flat or sharp, exactly in tune, and where the shifts of the hand, should be made. To which is added a collection of the finest rigadoons, almands, sarabands, courants, & opera airs extant. London, Engrav'd, printed and sold at the Printing-office in Bow church-yard [173–?]

1 p. l., 48, 4 p.   front., illus. (music) fold. pl.   23¼ᶜᵐ.

Part 5 of Peter Prelleur's "The modern musick-master", the first edition of which appeared in 1730.
"Airs" by Albinoni, Masciti, St. Helene, Händel and Bononcini, as well as by anonymous composers.
"A dictionary explaining such Greek, Latin, Italian & French words as generally occur in music": 4 p. at end. This is pt. 8 of "The modern musick-master."
Armorial book-plate of Edward Arnold with name added of Andrew W. Arnold, The Grove, Dorking, Surrey.
42–6755   MT262.P88

A brief history of musick; wherein is related the several changes, additions, and improvements, from its origin to this present time. Collected from Aristoxenus, Plutarch, Boetius, Bontempi, Zarlino, Tho: Salmon, and many others. London, Printing-office in Bow church-yard [1738?]

20, 3, [1] p.   front., illus. (music) fold. tab.   23 ᶜᵐ.

Engraved throughout.
A duplicate of pt. [7] of Peter Prelleur's Modern musick-master. 4th ed., 1738.
                                                           MT6.A2P93

Directions for playing on the flute with a scale for transposing any piece of musick to yᵉ properest keys for that instrument. To which is added, a fine collection of minuets, rigadoons, marches and opera airs by judicious masters. London, Engrav'd, printed and sold at the Printing-office in Bow church yard [173–?]

1 p. l., 48, 4 p.   front., fold. pl.   23½ᶜᵐ.

Part 2 of Peter Prelleur's "The modern musick-master," the first edition of which appeared in 1730.
Many of the "airs" are from operas by Händel.
"A dictionary explaining such Greek, Latin, Italian & French words as generally occur in musick": 4 p. at end. This is pt. 8 of "The modern musick master."
With this are bound: The compleat tutor for the hautboy, London, Printed for C. & S. Thompson [17—] and 16 pages of engraved music (principally "airs" by "Mr. Arne", "Mr. Bell", "Dr. Green", "Mr. Attfield" and "Mr. Bryan")
42–6756   MT342.P87

Prelleur, Peter—Continued.

See also The COMPLEAT tutor for the German flute. London [*ca.* 1745]

The COMPLEAT tutor for the harpsichord. London [176–?]

DIRECTIONS for playing on the flute. [London, 173–?]

Printz, Wolfgang Caspar, *of Waldthurn,* 1641–1717.

Compendium musicæ signatoriæ & modulatoriæ vocalis, oder Kurtzer begriff aller derjenigen dinge / so einem / der die vocal-music lernen will / zu wissen von nôthen seyn / auff begehren auffgesetzt / und nunmehro zum andern mahl vermehret und ver-bessert ans licht gegeben von Wolffgang Caspar Printzen / von Waldthurn / Dressden and Leipzig / Bey J. C. Miethen / 1714.

[158] p. illus. (music) 16½^{cm}.
Signatures: A–K⁸ (last leaf blank)
Armorial book-plate of Christian Ernst graf zu Stolberg.

35–21829   MT820.P8C6

Ptolemaeus, Claudius.

See KEPLER, J. Harmonices mundi.

Purcell, Henry, 1658 *or* 9–1695.

See PLAYFORD, J. An introduction to the skill of musick. 1718.

Quercu, Simon de, *15th cent.*

Opusculū musices perq̄ breuissimum: de gregoriana et figuratiua atq̄₃ contrapuncto simplici / vna cum exemplis idoneis / percōmode tractans: omnibus cantu oblectantibus vtile / ac necessarium: p Simonem Brabantinum de Quercu cantorem ducum mediolaneñ. con-fectum ... Dñs Joan. Weyssenburger Nurenberge impressit [1513]

[64] p. 1 illus. 19½^{cm}.

Signatures: A–[H]⁴
Woodcut on t.-p. with "Tetrastichon" below; Guidonian hand on verso of Aij; gothic type; musical examples.
Second edition; 1st edition, Vienna, 1509.
Imperfect; wanting last leaf.

17–17474   ML171.Q4

Rameau, Jean Philippe, 1683–1764.

Dissertation sur les différentes métodes d'accompagnement pour le clavecin, ou pour l'orgue; avec le plan d'une nouvelle métode, établie sur une méchanique des doigts, que fournit la succession fondamentale de l'harmonie: et a l'aide de laquelle on peut devenir sçavant compositeur, & habile accompagnateur, même sans sçavoir lire la musique. Par monsieur Rameau ... Paris, Boivin [etc.] 1732.

2 p. l., 63, [1] p. pl. (music) tab. 24½ x 18½ ^{cm}.

40–21206   MT68.R26D5

A treatise of music, containing the principles of composition. Wherein the several parts thereof are fully explained, and made useful both to the professors and students of that science. By Mr. Rameau ... Translated into English from the original in the French language. London, J. French [1737]

3 p. l., [3]–180 p.   illus. (music)   22½^{cm}.

First edition.
Translation of the third part of Rameau's Traité d'harmonie.
16–24490   MT50.A2R172

See also ALEMBERT, J. LEROND D'. Élémens de musique.

Raspe, Rudolf Erich, 1737–1794, *translator.*
See ALGAROTTI, FRANCESCO, *conte.* Versuche über die architectur [*etc.*]

Ravenscroft, Thomas, 1592?–1635?

A Briefe Discovrse Of the true (but neglected) vse of Charact'-ring the Degrees by their Perfection, Imperfection, and Diminution in Measurable Musicke, against the Common Practise and Custome of these Times. Examples whereof are exprest in the Harmony of 4. Voyces, Concerning the Pleasure of 5. vsuall Recreations.

1 Hunting, }   { 3 Dauncing,
2 Hawking, }   { 4 Drinking,
5 Enamouring.

By Thomas Rauenscroft, Bachelor of Muiske. London, Printed by Edw: Allde for Tho. Adams 1614.

[108] p.   illus. (music)   22^{cm}.

Signatures: ¶⁴, ¶¶⁴, ¶¶¶², A–D⁴, A–G⁴.
The songs (p. [54–107]) are by Ravenscroft, John Bennet, and Edward Pearce (Piers, Peirs, Peirce) "sometimes Maister of the children of Saint Paules in London."
22–13594   ML171.R29

Reeves, John, *joint author.*
See JONES, WILLIAM. Clavis campanalogia. 1788.
                         New campanalogia. [1796]

Reichardt, Johann Friedrich, 1752–1814, *editor.*
See LYCEUM der schönen künste, 1797.

Réponse d'un artiste a un homme de lettres, qui lui avoit écrit sur les Waux-halls. A Amsterdam, et se trouve, a Paris, chez Dufour, 1769.

60 p.   17^{cm}.

With book-plate of Edmond de Goncourt.
42–5445   ML1950.R37

Réponse d'une danseuse de l'Opéra, a une comédienne. (*In* Tréshumbles remontrances adressées à monseigneur le contrôleur général. [Paris, *ca.* 1789] 17^{cm}. p. 18–23)

With [Giraud, Claude Marie] La Pr_____ade. Londres [*i. e.* Paris] 1754.
Caption title.
1–F3703   PQ1985.G58A75

See also LETTRE d'une comédienne, a une danseuse de l'Opera.

[Ribock, Just. Joh. Henr.] *d.* 1784 or 5.

... Bemerkungen über die flöte, und versuch einer kurzen anleitung zur bessern einrichtung und behandlung derselben ... Stendal, D. C. Franzen und Grosse, 1782.

> 1 p. l., 62 p.　7 fold. pl. 24 x 18½ᶜᵐ.
>
> At head of title: J. J. H. R.
>
> 42–306　　　　　　　　　　　　　　　　ML935.R5B3 Miller coll.

Rigoley de Juvigny, Jean Antoine, *d.* 1788.

See TRAVENOL, LOUIS, *plaintiff.* Memoire signifié ... Contre le sieur Arrouet de Voltaire.

[Ritson, Joseph] 1752–1803, *compiler.*

Scotish song ... London, J. Johnson [etc.] 1794.

> 2 v.　18 ᶜᵐ.
>
> Engraved title-pages, with vignettes; engraved head-pieces and tail-piece. With music (unaccompanied melodies)
> Imprint date of v. 1 incorrect (MDCCXIV for MDCCXCIV)
> "A historical essay on Scotish song": v. 1, p. [xi]–cxix.
>
> 16–4678　　　　　　　　　　　　　　　　M1740.R59

A select collection of English songs ... London, J. Johnson, 1783.

> 3 v.　front., illus.　19ᶜᵐ.
>
> CONTENTS.—v. 1. Preface. A historical essay on the origin and progress of national song. Love songs.—v. 2. Drinking songs. Miscellaneous songs. Ancient ballads.—v. 3. Airs to the songs.
> Sprinkled calf binding, by Bedford.
>
> 24–15629　　　　　　　　　　　　　　　　M1740.R6

Robertson, Thomas, *d.* 1799.

An inquiry into the fine arts. By Thomas Robertson ... v. 1. London, Printed for W. Strahan; and T. Cadell, 1784.

> 2 p. l., 461 p.　29ᶜᵐ.
>
> No more published.
>
> CONTENTS.—Introductory discourse. Concerning the principle of the fine arts, and the plan for treating of them.—pt. 1. Of the fine arts which refer to the ear.—Postscript. Concerning the music of the South Sea Islanders.
>
> 22–887　　　　　　　　　　　　　　　　ML3845.A2R62

Rodolphe, Jean Joseph, 1730–1812.

Solfege; ou, Nouvelle méthode de musique, divisée en deux parties. La premiere contient la théorie de cet art, la seconde les leçons avec la basse et les gradation[s] nécessaires pour parvenir aux difficultés. Par Rodolphe. Gravé par F. P. Le Roy ... Paris, Imbault [*ca.* 1790?]

> 1 p. l., 168 p.　fold. pl.　34½ᶜᵐ.
>
> Engraved throughout. Publisher's plate no.: 408.
>
> 29–6575　　　　　　　　　　　　　　　　MT870.R72

Théorie d'accompagnement et de composition, a l'usage des elèves de l'Ecole royale de musique, contenant l'origine des accords, divisée en deux classes, l'harmonie naturelle, et l'harmonie composée; la

base fondamentale de chaque accord, et des leçons de pratique, dédiée
a monseigneur le baron de Breteuil, ministre et secretaire d'etat de
la maison du roy ... par Rodolphe, pensionnaire du roi, maitre de
composition de l'Ecole royale de musique. (Œuvre IIme ... Gravée
par F. P. Le Roy ... Paris, Chez le même [1785?]

2 p. l., 111, [1] p. $33\frac{1}{2}$ x 26^{cm}.

15–11226   MT68.R73

Röllig, Karl Leopold, *d.* 1804.
Über die harmonika. Ein fragment van J. [!] L. Köllig [!]
Berlin, 1787.

1 p. l., 32 p. 22 x $17\frac{1}{2}^{cm}$.

Engraved t.-p., with vignette (a harmonica)
" Ex libris Richard Barth."

32–19109   ML1055.R7

Rousseau, Jean, *17th cent.*
Methode claire, certaine et facile pour aprendre à chanter la
musique sur les tons naturels & sur les tons transposez: à toutes
sortes de mouvemens: avec les régles du port de voix, & de la
cadence, lors mesme qu'elle n'est pas marquée. Et un eclaircissement sur plusieurs difficultez necessaires à scavoir pour la perfection
de l'art. Par Jean Rousseau ... 5. ed., rev., augm. & mise dans un
meilleur état. Amsterdam, P. Mortier [1710?]

87, [1] p. illus. (music) fold. pl. (music) 20 x $11\frac{1}{2}^{cm}$.

Signatures: A–L⁴.
With this are bound: Masson, Charles. Nouveau traité des regles pour la
composition de la musique ... 4. ed. ... Amsterdam [1710?] and Hotteterre,
Jacques. Principes de la flute traversiere, ou flute d'Allemagne ... Amsterdam [1708]

41–26824   MT7.R85 Miller coll.

Rousseau, Jean Jacques, 1712–1778.
Dissertation sur la musique moderne, par m. Rousseau ... Paris,
G. F. Quillau, père, 1743.

1 p. l., xvj, 101, [3] p. illus. (music) fold. tab. 21^{cm}.

Title vignette, representing the annunciation.
"Table générale de tous les tons et de touttes les clefs": folded table at
end.

38–6104   MT6.R86D5

Original letters of J. J. Rousseau, to M. de Malesherbes, M.
d'Alembert, Madame la M. de Luxembourg, &c. &c.; with a facsimile of Rousseau's hand-writing, and an original military air of his
composition. Also, Original letters of Butta Fuoco and David
Hume. Translated from the French. London, Printed by C. Whit-
tingham, for H. D. Symonds, 1799.

vii, 194 p., 1 l., 6, [197]–200 p. front. (facsim.) port. $16\frac{1}{2}^{cm}$. [*With*
Corancez, Olivier de. Anecdotes of the last twelve years of the life of J. J.
Rousseau. London, 1798]

"An essay on military music, by J. J. Rousseau," preceded by "Airs to
be played whilst the corps is marching": 1 l., 6, [197]–200 p.
Facsimile wanting in Library of Congress copy.

PQ2047.A2

[Rousseau, Jean Jacques] 1712-1778.

Traités sur la musique. [Geneve, 1781?]

448 p., 1 l. fold. tab. 15½^{cm}.

Half-title.
The first essay has special title-page with imprint: Geneve, 1781.

CONTENTS.—Projet concernant de nouveaux signes pour la musique.—
Dissertation sur la musique moderne.—Essai sur l'origine des langues, où
il est parlé de la mélodie & de l'imitation musicale.—Lettre a monsieur
l'abbé Raynal au sujet d'un nouveau mode de musique, inventé par m.
Blainville.—Examen de deux principes avancés par· m Rameau, dans sa
brochure intitulée: Erreurs sur la musique, dans l'Encyclopédie.—Lettre a
m. Burney sur la musique, avec fragmens d'observations sur l'Alceste
italien de m. le chevalier Gluck.

31-4471   ML60.R861

See also [BROSSARD, S. DE] A musical dictionary. 1769.

Roussier, Pierre Joseph, 1716-1790?

Observations sur différens points d'harmonie, par m. l'abbe
Roussier ... A Genève et se trouve à Paris, chez d'Houry, 1765.

4 p. l., 170, 79, 25 p. fold. pl. (music) 20^{cm}.

"Extrait du Journal des sçavans ... février 1765" (review of Roussier's
Traité des accords) : 25 p. at end.

41-17404   MT49.R602

[Royal society of musicians of Great Britain, *London*]

The laws and resolutions of several general meetings, for the fu-
ture regulation and management of the fund for the support of
decayed musicians and their families. London, Printed by J. Hughs,
1761.

22 p. 21^{cm}.

Title vignette.
Bound in pig-skin.
Binder's title: The minutes of the Royal society of musicians. 1738-1759.

34-17754   ML28.L8R63 1761

Rudimenta panduristæ, oder: Geig-fundamenta, worinnen die kür-
zeste unterweisung für einen scholaren, welcher in der violin unter-
wiesen zu werden verlanget, sowohl zum behuf des discipuls, als
auch zur erleichterung der mühe und arbeit eines lehrmeisters, auf
die gründlichst- und leichteste art mit beygesetzten exemplen dargethan wird. Von einem aufrichtigen music-freund. Augspurg,
J. J. Lotters seel. erben, 1754.

48 p. illus. (music) 17½ x 20½^{cm}.

"Ernennte music-stück à violino & basso " : p. 17-44.

40-17209   MT262.R93

Ruiz de Ribayaz, Lucas, *17th cent.*

Lvz, y norte mvsical para caminar por las cifras de la guitarra
española, y arpa, tañer, y cantar á compás por canto de organo; y
breue explicacion del arte, con preceptos faciles, indubitables, y expli-

cados con claras reglas por teorica, y practica. Compvesto por d. Lvcas Rviz de Ribayaz ... Madrid, M. Alvarez, 1677.

8 p. l., 144, [6] p. illus. (incl. music) 20½ᶜᵐ.

"Ecos ... en cifras para gvitarra, y arpa": p. 65–144.

17–17467 MT582.A2R9

Sacchini, Antonio Maria Gasparo, 1734–1786.
See CORFE, J. A treatise on singing. [*ca.* 1800]

[Saint Glas, Pierre de] *editor.*
Divers traitez d'histoire, de morale et d'eloqvence ... Paris, Chez la veuve C. Thibovst [etc.] 1672.

5 p. l., 179, [1] p. 15ᶜᵐ.

CONTENTS.—I. La vie de Malherbe [par Ragan]—II. L'orateur [par G. Guéret]—III. De la maniere de vivre avec honneur & avec estime dans le monde.—IV. Si l'empire d'eloquence est plus grand que celuy de l'amour [par G. Guéret]—V. Méthode pour lire l'histoire.—VI. Discours de la musique d'Italie & des opera [par Maugars].

9–9113 AC20.S3

Saint-Lambert, Michel de.
Nouveau traité de l'accompagnement du clavecin, de l'orgue, et des autres instruments. Par monsieur de Saint Lambert. Paris, C. Ballard, 1707.

2 p. l., 64, [2] p. illus. (music) 20 x 26½ᶜᵐ. [*With his* Les principes du clavecin. Paris, 1702]

17–31245 MT224.A2S2

—— Nouveau traité de l'accompagnement du clavecin, de l'orgue, et des autres instruments, par monsieur de Saint Lambert. Amsterdam, E. Roger [ca. 1710]

4 p. l., 134 p. illus. (music) 20½ᶜᵐ.

40–21207 MT68.S15N5

Les principes du clavecin, contenant une explication exacte de tout ce qui concerne la tablature & le clavier. Avec des remarques necessaires pour l'intelligence de plusieurs difficultées de la musique ... Par monsieur de Saint Lambert. Paris, C. Ballard, 1702.

vj, [2], 68 p. illus. (incl. music) 20 x 26½ᶜᵐ.

Second edition; 1st edition published 1697.

17–31244 MT224.A2S2

Salinas, Francisco de, 1513–1590.
Francisci Salinæ Bvrgensis . . . De musica libri septem, in quibus eius doctrinæ veritas, tam quæ ad harmoniam, quàm quæ ad rhythmum pertinet, iuxta sensus ac rationis iudicium ostenditur, & demonstratur. Cvm dvplici indice capitum & rerum. Salmanticæ, excudebant hæredes Cornelij Bonardi. Sumptibus Claudij Curlet, 1592.

8 p. l., 438, [17] p. incl. illus. (music) tab., diagrs. (1 fold.) 29ᶜᵐ.

Curlet's mark on t.-p.

20–10868 ML171.S162

Salmon, Thomas, 1648–1706.

See LOCKE, M. Observations upon a late book.

Salter, Humphry.

The genteel companion; being exact directions for the recorder: with a collection of the best and newest tunes and grounds extant. Carefully composed and gathered by Humphry Salter. London, Printed for Richard Hunt and Humphry Salter, 1683.

2 p. 1., 8 p., 2 1., 42, 6 p., 3 1.   front.   11 x 20½^{cm}.

"Directions for the recorder": 8 p.   The rest of the book is music.

20–10869   MT342.A2S12

Samber, Johann Baptist.

Elucidatio musicæ choralis.   Das ist: gründlich und wahre erläuterung / oder unterweisung / wie die edle und uralte choralmusic fundamentaliter nach denen wolgegründten reglen mit leichter mühe möge erlehrnet werden.   Alles mit vilen ins kupfer gestochenen figuren und exemplen gezieret ... in offenen druck gegeben durch m. Joannem Baptistam Samber ... Salzberg, Gedruckt bey J. J. Mayr, 171[0?]

4 p. 1., 95 p.   illus. (music) 15 pl. (music)   18½ x 24^{cm}.

Last figure in imprint date wanting; 9 supplied in manuscript; "Imprimatur" dated 1710.

26–21063   MT875.A2S16

[Saurin, Didier] *b. ca.* 1692.

L'art de la danse, par m^r * * * * *.   Paris, Impr. de J.-B.-C. Ballard, 1746.

viij, 26 p.   24 x 19^{cm}.   [*With his* La musique theorique et pratique. Paris, 1722]

20–19904   MT6.A2S27

La musique theorique, et pratique, dans son ordre naturel; nouveaux principes par m^r * * * * *.   Paris, Impr. de J.-B.-C. Ballard, 1722.

viij, 100, [4] p.   illus. (music)   24 x 19^{cm}.

Principally exercises.   MT6.A2S27

20–19905

La musique theorique et pratique, dans son ordre naturel: nouveaux principes par m^r * * * * *.   Auteur de l'Art de la danse. Nouv. ed.   Paris, Impr. de J.-B.-C. Ballard, 1746.

viij, 100, [4] p.   25 x 19^{cm}.

Principally exercises.
Imperfect: p. 17–42 wanting (p. 31–42 supplied in manuscript)

29–6573   MT6.A2S28

Scaletta, Orazio, *d.* 1630.

Scala di mvsica molto necessaria per principianti. Di Horatio Scaletta da Crema, dall'istesso corretta, & ampliata con belissimo ordine, & maggior facilità. Accomodata ancora con li essempi per qualsiuoglia parte. Nona impressione, di nvovo corretta, et ampliata con alcuni dvo in fuga facile, & commodi per introdur il discepolo a cantar con il maestro. Milano, A. Ramellati, 1665.

1 p. l., 22 p.   illus. (music) diagr.   22ᶜᵐ.

41–17732   MT44.S284

Scheid, Johann Friedrich.

Io. Friderici Scheid Dissertatio de ivre in mvsicos, singvlari, german. Dienste und obrigkeit der spielleut/Rappolsteinensi comitatvi annexo. Ienae, litteris Croekerianis, 1738.

72 p.   20 x 17ᶜᵐ.

The author's dissertation, Strassburg.
Second edition. The 1st was published in 1719.
"Docvmenta": p. 61–70.

35–7099   ML63.S34 1738

Schiff, Christian, *fl.* 1694.

See MUSCOVIUS, J.   Gestraffter missbrauch der kirchen-music.

Schlegel, Friedrich von, 1772–1829, *editor.*

See LYCEUM der schönen künste.   1797.

Schmid, Christian Heinrich, 1746–1800, *ed.*

Theaterchronick, erstes stück, herausgegeben von Christian Heinrich Schmid ...   Giessen, In Kriegerischen verlag, 1772.

4 p. l., 230 p.   17½ᶜᵐ.

With this is bound the editor's Das parterr. Erfurt, 1771.

35–34182   PN2652.S35

Schmid, Sebastian, 1617–1696, *praeses.*

... Disputatio theologica de musica. Ex dicto Coloss. III. vers. 16 ...   Argentorati, typis Johannis Wilhelmi Tidemanni [1673]

26, [2] p.   20ᶜᵐ.

Diss.—Strassburg ("Joh. Melchior Schöpperlinus, auth. & resp.")

21–7018   ML3001.S25

Schmutzer, Johann Gottfried.

... Ad avdiendas orationes ... invitat cognationem qvae est grammaticae cvm mathesi et mvsica strictim perseqvvtvs Io. Gottfr. Schmvtzer ...   Lipsiae, ex officina Breitkopfia, 1772.

20 p.   20 x 16ᶜᵐ.

Programm—Gymnasium Rossleben.

9–9135   ML64S24

[Schoensleder, Wolfgang] 1570-1651.

Architectonice mvsices vniversalis, ex qua melopoeam per vniversa et solida fvndamenta mvsicorvm, proprio marte condiscere possis. Autore Volvpio Decoro Mvsagete [*pseud.*] ... Ingolstadii, typis Wilhelmi Ederi, 1631.

3 p. l., 235 p.   illus. (music)   19¼ x 16½^{cm}.

In 2 parts; part 2, " Exempla."

13-24946   MT55.A2S27

Schöpperlin, Johann Melchior, *author and respondent.*

See SCHMID, S., *praeses.*   Disputatio theologica de musica.

Schott, Gaspar, 1608-1666.

P. Gasparis Schotti ... Magia universalis naturæ et artis, sive, Recondita naturalium & artificialium rerum scientia, cujus ope per variam applicationem activorum cum passivis, admirandorum effectuum spectacula, abditarumq; inventionum miracula, ad varios humanæ vitæ usus, eruuntur.   Opus quadripartitum ... Herbipoli, sumptibus hæredum Joannis G. Schönwetteri, bibliopol. francofurtens., excudebat H. Pigrin, typographus herbipolensis, 1657-59.

4 v. in. 2.   illus. (music) 88 pl. (part fold.) on 87 l.   20½ x 16^{cm}.

Each volume has added t.-p., engraved.
Title varies: v. 2-3, ... Magiæ universalis naturæ et artis, pars II.[-III.] ... (without alternative title) v. 4, ... Thaumaturgus physicus, sive, Magiæ universalis naturæ et artis, pars IV. et ultima ...
Vols. 2-3 have imprint: Herbipoli ... excudebat T. Hertz, typographus herbipolensis, 1657-58; v. 4 without printer's name.
CONTENTS.—pars I. Optica.—pars II. Acustica.—pars III. Mathematica.—pars IV. Physica.

32-34977   Q155.S38   1657

—— P. Gasparis Schotti ... Magia universalis naturæ et artis ... Bambergæ, sumpt. Joh. Martini Schönwetteri, 1659-77 [v. 4, '59]

4 v.   illus. (music) 88 pl. (part fold.; incl. tables, diagrs., music) on 87 l. 21^{cm}.

Each volume has added t.-p., engraved.
Vol. 4 is of the Wurzburg edition, 1657-59, and has title and imprint: P. Gasparis Schotti ... Thaumaturgus physicus, sive Magiæ universalis naturæ et artis pars IV. et ultima ... Herbipoli, sumptibus hæredum J. G. Schönwetteri, 1659.
CONTENTS.—pars I. Optica.—pars II. Acustica.—pars III. Mathematica.—pars IV. Physica.

11-23431 Revised   Q155.S38   1677

Schultze, Johann Nikolaus Wilhelm, *respondent.*

See WEIDNER, J. J., *praeses.*   De usu musices.

Schwanenberg, Joseph Franz, *editor.*

See [WOLF VON WOLFENAU, A.]   Gründliche abhandlung.   1797.

Schwartzendorf, Johann Paul Aegidius.

See MARTINI, JEAN PAUL ÉGIDE.

[Seccomb, Joseph] 1706–1760.

An essay to excite a further inquiry into the ancient matter and manner of sacred singing ... Boston: N. E. Printed and Sold by S. Kneeland and T. Green, in Queen-Street over against the Prison, 1741.

2 p. l., ii, 16 p., 1 l. 16ᶜᵐ.

15–545 ML3001.S39

A second edition, <with necessary improvements, which now render the sense entirely plain> of The lawfulness, excellency and advantage of instrumental music, in the public worship of God, but chiefly of organs ... Philadelphia: Printed by Andrew Steuart, and sold at his Printing-Office, at the Bible-in-Heart in Second-street. 1763.

iv, [5]–16 p. 15½ᶜᵐ.

Not a bona fide second edition of the pamphlet "The lawfulness, excellency, and advantage of instrumental musick in the public worship of God ... By a Presbyterian" (Philadelphia, W. Dunlap, 1763. [2], 38 p.) but a satirical reply. *cf.* Sonneck's Francis Hopkinson and James Lyon", 1905, p. 131–132.

BV290.L3

Serpilius, Georg, 1668–1723.

GeorgI SerpilI ... Neuverfertigte lieder-concordantz über DC. kirchen- und andre geistreiche gesänge / zu besondern nutzen der lehrer / denen zuhörern zu erbauung des christenthums und zeitlichen vorschmack der ewigen freude nach art der biblischen concordantz mühsam zusammen getragen. Dabey ein dazu gehöriges gesang-buch / und nöthige anweisung / wie das werck füglich soll gebrauchet werden; nebst einer vorrede ... herrn Johann Friedrich Mäyers ... Dresden und Leipzig, J. C. Mieth und J. C. Zimmermann. Pirna, Druckts G. B. Ludewig, 1696.

[1048, 388] p. 21½ x 17ᶜᵐ.

Signatures: front. (engr. half-title), †³, ††–†††⁴, ††††², a–zzzzz,⁴, aaaaaa-mmmmmm⁴, nnnnnn²; title-page, A–Zz⁴, Aaa–Bbb⁴, Ccc¹.
The "Gesang-buch" ([388] p.) has separate signature numbering and special t.-p.: Verneuert und vermehrtes christliches gesang-buch ... Dresden und Leipzig, 1696.

31–4482 ML3168.S4

Simpson, Christopher, *d.* 1669.

Chelys, minuritionum artificio exornata: sive, Minuritiones ad basin, etiam ex tempore modulandi ratio. In tres partes distributa. The division-viol, or, The art of playing ex tempore upon a ground. Divided into three parts. Pars ı. Chelyos tractandæ præcepta. Pars ıı. Melothesiæ compendium. Pars ııı. Minuritiones ad basin aptandi methodus. Part ı. Of the viol it self, with instructions to play upon it. Part ıı. Use of the concords, or A compendium of descant. Part ııı. The method of ordering division to a ground. Authore Christophoro Simpson. Editio secunda. London, Printed by W. Godbid for H. Brome, 1667.

6 p. l., 67 p. incl. illus., pl., diagrs. front. (port.) 32½ᶜᵐ.

First edition, 1659, published under title: The division-violist.
Numerous musical examples and exercises. "Minuritiones, tyronum exercitationi, accommodae [Divisions for the practice of learners]": p. [52]–67 (engraved)

19–12401 MT49.A2S42

The principles of practical mvsick delivered in a compendious, easie, and new method: for the instruction of beginners, either in singing or playing upon instruments. To which are added, some short and easie ayres designed for learners. By Chr. Simpson. London, Printed by W. Godbid for H. Brome, 1665.

4 p. l., 84 p.   illus. (music)   17½ᶜᵐ.

Signatures: A⁴, B–F⁸, G².
Some of the musical illustrations are engraved.
First edition.
Subsequently published under titles "A compendium of practical musick" and "A compendium: or, Introduction to practical musick".
"Short and easie ayres designed for learners": p. 45–84.

38–4302   MT40.S58

—— A compendium: or, Introduction to practical musick. In five parts. Teaching ... 1. The rudiments of song. 2. The principles of composition. 3. The use of discords. 4. The form of figurate descant. 5. The contrivance of cannon. By Christopher Simpson. The 5th ed. with additions: much more correct than any former, the examples being put in the most useful cliffs ... London, Printed by W. P. for J. Young, 1714.

7 p. l., 144 p.   front. (port.) illus. (music) tables.   17½ᶜᵐ.

41–18175   MT40.A2S65

See also PLAYFORD, J.   A brief introduction to the skill of musick. 1667.
                         An introduction to the skill of musick. 1672.

Sinn, Christoph Albert, b. ca. 1680.

Die aus mathematischen gründen richtig gestellete musicalische temperatura practica, das ist: Grundrichtige vergleichung der zwölff semitoniorum in der octave, wie dieselbe nach anweisung der arithmetic und geometrie ad praxin, fürnemlich in die orgel-wercke / können gebracht werden / nebst denen dazu gehörigen figuren, gründlich und deutlich vorgestellet von Christophoro Alberto Sinn ... samt einer Vorrede herrn Caspari Calvoers ... Wernigeroda / Druckts M. A. Struck [1717?]

24 p. l., 136 p.   2 fold. pl. (diagrs.)   19ᶜᵐ.

"Vorrede" dated: Claussthal den 16ten decemb. 1717.
Armorial book-plate of Christian Ernst graf zu Stolberg.

35–21825   ML3809.S61

Sotos, Andrés de, b. ca. 1730.

Arte para aprender con facilidad, y sin maestro, á templar y tañer rasgado la guitarra de cinco órdenes, ó cuerdas; y tambien la de cuatro ó seis órdenes, llamadas guitarra española, bandurria y vandola, y tambien el tiple. Demuéstrase con grande claridad la formacion de los 12 puntos naturales, y 12 b. mollados con láminas, y principalmente se pone una tabla, que por ella se puede cifrar cualquiera tono, tocarle y cantarle por doce modos distintos, sacado de las mejores obras y maestros: dispuesto, recopilado y aumentado por Andrés de Sotos.   [Madrid] Impr. de Lopez y compañía [1764]

63 p.   illus.   16ᶜᵐ.

Title vignette.

13–24942   MT582.A2S7

Spangenberg, Johann, 1484–1550.

Qvæstiones mvsicae in vsvm scholæ Northusianæ, per Ioannem Spang. Hordess. collectæ. Coloniæ, excudebat Petrus Horst, anno 1563.

[62] p. illus. (music) 15^{cm}.

Title vignette.
Signatures: A–D³ (last leaf blank)
"De arte canendi ex libro decimo-sexto De subtilitate Hieronymi Cardani Mediolanensis": p. [56]–[57]
Armorial book-plate of J. H. Beaufoy.

40–21469 ML171.S83 1563

Spataro, Giovanni, d. 1541.

See VEGIUS, M. Quae in hoc opere continentur. Maphei Vegij ... Pompeana [etc.] ... [1521]

Speer, Daniel, d. 1693 or 4.

Grund-richtiger kurtz- leicht- und nôthiger / jetzt wol-vermehrter unterricht der musicalischen kunst. Oder / Vierfaches musicalisches kleeblatt / worinnen zu ersehen / wie man fûglich und in kurtzer zeit I. Choral- und figural-singen. II. Das clavier und general-bass tractiren. III. Allerhand instrumenta greiffen / und blasen lernen kan. IV. Vocaliter und instrumentaliter componiren soll lernen. Denen lehr- und lernenden zu beliebigem gebrauch zum andernmahl herausgegeben von Daniel Speeren ... Ulm / In verlag G. W. Kûhnen / gedruckt bey C. B. Kûhnen seel. erben. / 1697.

3 p. l., 289, [1] p. illus. (music) IV pl., fold. tab. 17½ x 21½^{cm}. [*With his* Choral gesang-buch. Stuttgart, 1692]

32–19111 M2138.S73

Sperling, Johann Peter Gabriel.

Principia musicæ, das ist: Gründliche anweisung zur music. Wie ein music-scholar vom anfang instruiret und nach der ordnung zur kunst oder wissenschafft der figural-music soll geführet und gewiesen werden, vorgestellet von Johann Peter Sperling ... Budissin, Gedruckt bey A. Richtern, 1705.

2 p. l., 148 p. illus. (music) 17½ x 21^{cm}.

41–40868 MT6.S76

Stanesby, Thomas.

A new system of the flute a' bec, or common English flute ... By Tho: Stanesby jun^r. [n. p., 1732?]

4 p. 1 illus. (music) 21½ x 16½^{cm}.

Caption title. Engraved throughout.
Prospectus advocating the use of a C flute.
"A scale in C for the flute a' bec, or common English flute": p. 4.

42–1529 ML936.S72 Miller collection

Stearns, Charles, 1753–1826.

A sermon: preached at an exhibition of sacred musick, in Lincoln, on the nineteenth of April, 1792. By Charles Stearns ... Printed at Boston, by Isaiah Thomas and Ebenezer T. Andrews, At Faust's statue, no. 45, Newbury street. 1792.

15 p. 20^{cm}.

24–24667   ML64.S83

Steffani, Agostino, 1654–1728.

D. A. Steffani ... send-schreiben / darinn enthalten wie grosse gewiss-heit die music aus ihren principiis, und grundsåtzen habe / und in wel-chen werthe / und wûrckung sie bey denen alten gewesen / aus dem ita-liånischen ins hochdeutsche befôrdert; dann um der wûrde / und nutzen so darinnen enthalten / mit einigen anmerckungen erlåutert / und dem druck ûbergeben von Andr. Werckmeister ... Qvedlinburg und Aschersleben, G. E. Struntz, 1699.

101, [1] p. 16^{cm}.

41–23957   ML3800.A2S8

See [HAWKINS, *Sir* JOHN] *supposed author.* Memoirs of the life of Sig. Agostino Steffani.

Steinbart, Gotthilf Samuel, 1783–1809.

Grundbegriffe zur philosophie ûber den geschmack, von Gotthilf Samuel Steinbart. Erstes heft, welches die allgemeine theorie såmtlicher schônen kûnste, und die besondere theorie der tonkunst enthålt. Zûllichau, Waysenhaus- und Frommannische buchhand-lung, 1785.

xvi, 236 p. 22^{cm}.

No more published.

5–19179†   BH183.S8

Stella, Giuseppe Maria, *fra, d.* 1678.

Breve instrvttione alli giovani per imparare con ogni facilità il canto fermo, divisa in dve parti. Nella prima s'assegnano le regole svccinte d'esso canto, col vero modo di pratticarle. Il canto francescano, con vna regola al chorista per ben regger' il choro, ed vn' altra all' organista per lasciar in tono con l'organo i canti, ch' occorrono in tutto l'anno. Nella seconda si pone tvtt' il canto della Settimana santa con quello per la processione della purificatione della B. V. e quattro credi nel fine. Del p. f. Gioseppe Maria Stella della Mirandola ... Roma, Nella stamparia di Iacomo Fei d'Andr. f., 1665.

149, [11], 111 (*i. e.* 119), [1] p.   1 illus.   23½^{cm}.

Signatures: A–V⁴, a–p⁴.

Nos. 65–72 repeated in paging of 2d part.

36–23942   MT860.S86B8

Stiles, *Sir* **Francis Haskins Eyles,** *bart.*

An explanation of the modes or tones in the antient Græcian music. By Sir Francis Haskins Eyles Stiles, bart., F. R. S. Read at several meetings of the Royal society. London, 1761.

1 p. 1., 5–83 p. fold. tab., 2 fold. diagr. 23¼ x 18^{cm}.

22–7976   ML169.A2S74

Strozzi, Gregorio, *17th cent.*

Elementorvm mvsicæ praxis.   Vtilis non tantùm incipientibus, sed proficientibus, & perfectis ...   Accedit Nexus, & sympatya musicæ, & astronomiæ. Avtore rev. ac regio abb. d. Gregorio Strozzio ... Pars prima, & secunda, opus tertium.   Neapoli, typis Nouelli de Bonis, 1683.

4 p. l., 95, [1] p.   front.   22½ᶜᵐ.

Half-title: Sancta crvx mvsicæ.
Tenor. (Gaspari describes 2 vols.: "Cantus" and "Tenor.")
Contrapuntal singing exercises.
This vol. does not contain the " Nexus."

7–13026   MT870.A2S92

Symmes, William, 1731–1807.

The duty and advantages of singing praises unto God.   A discourse delivered at an occasional lecture in Andover, on Tuesday, April 6, 1779.   Appointed to promote and encourage the religious art of psalmody.   By William Symmes ...   Danvers, near Boston: Printed and sold by E. Russell, at his printing-office, next the Bell-tavern, M, DCC, LXXIX.

24 p.   20ᶜᵐ.

Half-title: Mr. Symmes's discourse on the duty and advantages of singing praises unto God.

41–9086   BV290.S9

Synopsis of vocal musick: containing the rudiments of singing rightly any harmonical song, delivered in a method so solid, short and plain, that this art may now be learned more exactly, speedily and easily, than ever heretofore.   Whereunto are added several psalms and songs of three parts.   Composed by English and Italian authors for the benefit of young beginners.   By A. B. Philo-Mus. London, Printed for Dorman Newman, at the Kings Arms in the Poultrey, 1680.

5 p. l., 135, [7] p.   diagrs.   11 x 20½ᶜᵐ.

On verso of t.-p.: John Lever, bookseller, stationer and printseller, at Little Moorgate, near Moorfields.
"A very rare book. 3 copies only known to be extant, one in the British museum, one in the Royal library of Belgium at Brussels, and this copy."— Ms. note on fly-leaf.

CONTENTS.—Synopsis of vocal musick.—Twelve most usual tunes of psalms: in three parts. Treble, mean, and bass.—Twelve selected English tunes in three parts. Two trebles and a bass.—Twelve selected English catches. A. 3. voc.—Fourteen Italian songs composed by Giovanni Giacomo Castoldi [*i. e.* Gastoldi] da Carravaggio.

Ex libris William Hayman Cummings.
Bound in full brown levant morocco, inside gilt borders, by Zaehnsdorf, 1895.

20–10871   MT830.A2S9

Tacet, Joseph, *fl.* 1750.

See COMPLEAT instructions for the German flute.

Tartini, Giuseppe, 1692–1770.

L'arte del arco, ou L'art de l'archet, contenant 38 variations composées sous la plus belle gavotte de Corelly. Par Giusepe Tartini ... Gravées par m^me. Leclair ... Paris, M. Leclerc [1780?]

16 p. 21 x 30^cm.

Engraved throughout.

29–6574 MT267.T172

A letter from the late Signor Tartini to Signora Maddalena Lombardini, (now Signora Sirmen.) Published as an important lesson to performers on the violin. Translated by Dr. Burney. London, Printed for R. Bremner by G. Bigg, 1779.

2 p. l., 7 (*i. e.* 11) p. illus. (music) 26^cm.

Added t.-p. in Italian; Italian and English on opposite pages.
18–17819 ML410.A2T18

Taswell, William, 1709?–1775.

The propriety and usefulness of sacred musick. A sermon preach'd in the Cathedral-church of Gloucester, at the anniversary meeting of the three choirs of Gloucester, Worcester, and Hereford, September 8, 1742. And published at their joint request, (for the use of their charity) by William Taswell ... Gloucester, C. Hitch; [etc., etc., 1742]

31 p. 18^cm.

20–14641 ML3001.T15

Tate, Nahum, 1652–1715.

See WEEDON, C., *ed.* The oration, anthems and poems, spoken and sung at the Performance of divine musick. [1702]

Taubert, Gottfried, *fl.* 1700.

... Rechtschaffener tantzmeister / oder Gründliche erklärung der frantzösischen tantz-kunst / bestehend in drey büchern, deren das erste historice des tantzens / ursprung / fortgang / verbesserung / unterschiedlichen gebrauch ... untersuchet; das andere methodice des so wol galanten als theatralischen frantzösischen tantz-exercitii grundsätze ethice, theoretice und practice ... deutlich zeiget; anbey wird / nebst einer ausführlichen apologie für die wahre tantz-kunst / der haupt-schlüssel zu der chorégraphie ... zu finden seyn; und das dritte discursive derer maitres, scholaires, assemblées, balls, hochzeittäntze / und anderer tantz-compagnien requisita ... zulänglich erörtert. Endlich ist ein vollständiges register aller eingebrachten sachen beygefüget worden. Leipzig, Bey F. Lanckischens erben, 1717.

5 p. l., 1176 (*i. e.* 1173), [55] p. incl. plates (diagrs.) front. 21¼^cm.

Nos. 662, 798, 916 omitted in paging.
The plates are included in the pagination, each numbered as one page.
"Chorégraphie, das ist, Die kunst einen tantz durch characteres, figuren und andere zeichen zu beschreiben ... von mons. Feüillet ... Ins teutsche übersetzet ... von dem authore dieses buches" (p. 745–915) has reproduction of title-page of French edition of 1701.
Book-plate: Friederici Nicolai et amicorum.

13–4473 GV1590.T4

Tenducci, Giusto Ferdinando, *fl.* 1760–1790.

Instruction of Mr. Tenducci, to his scholars. [London] Longman & Broderip [1785?]

1 p. l., 48 p. 23 x 31½^{cm}.

Engraved throughout.
Portrait of Tenducci at head of t.-p.
"Necessary rules for students and dilettanti of vocal music": p. 2. Exercises: p. 3–48.
"Musical publications, printed and sold by Longman & Broderip, at the Apollo, n° 26, Cheapside, & n° 13, Hay-market, London": p. [1]
Four pages of manuscript music (4 marches) and "Glee. Sung by Mr. Wathen, Mr. Suett, and Mr. Bannister" (2 leaves, numbered 6–7) inserted at end.

Terrasson, Antoine, 1705–1782.

Mélanges d'histoire, de littérature, de jurisprudence littéraire, de critique, &c. Par m. Terrasson ... Paris, Chez la veuve Simon & fils, 1768.

vii, 6, 438 p., 1 l. illus., vi plans. 17 x 10^{cm}.

"Dissertation historique sur l'instrument nommé la vielle": p. [173]–254.

Teutsche filarmonische gesellschaft.

See DEUTSCHE filarmonische gesellschaft.

Theodor *von Würzburg.*

See THEODORUS *Herbipolensis.*

Theodorus *Francus.*

See THEODORUS *Herbipolensis.*

Theodorus *Herbipolensis, printer.*

See NIGER, FRANCISCUS. Grammatica brevis.

Thorowgood, Henry, *fl.* 1760–1770.

A description of the æolian-harp, or harp of Æolus, from the earliest account to the present time, as approved by the late D^r. Hales & Ja^s. Oswald, esq^r. (some time chamber composer to His Majesty) which are made on the truest mechanical principles by Henry Thorowgood, musical instrument maker and musick printer at the Violin & guitar ... London, H. Thorowgood [1754?]

1 p. l., 4 p. front. 24^{cm}.

26–18519   ML1005.T5

Thoughts on the use and advantages of music, and other amusements most in esteem in the polite world, and the means of improving them to make our proper happiness and our pleasures but one object. In nine letters. In answer to a letter relating to modern musical entertainments, &c. London, J. Dodsley, 1765.

2 p. l., 116 p. front. 20½^{cm}.

18–4318   ML60.A2T4

Tieck, Johann Ludwig, 1773–1853.

Phantasien über die kunst, für freunde der kunst. Herausgegeben von Ludwig Tieck. Hamburg, F. Perthes, 1799.

1 p. l., iv p., 1 l., [5]–283 p. 17^{cm}.

"Ein theil dieser aufsätze ist ein vermächtniss meines verstorbenen freundes W. H. Wackenroder ... sie sollten eine fortsetzung des buchs: 'Herzensergiessungen eines kunstliebenden klosterbruders' seyn."—p. [i]

"Von Wackenroder ist in der ersten abtheilung die erste und fünfte nummer geschrieben, unter Berglingers aufsätzen gehören mir die vier letzten an."—p. iii.

CONTENTS.—1. abschnitt. I. Schilderung wie die alten deutschen künstler gelebt haben: wobei zu exempeln angeführt werden Albrecht Dürer, nebst seinem vater Albrecht Dürer dem alten. II. Eine erzählung, aus einem italienischen buche übersetzt. ·III. Rafael's bildniss. IV. Das jüngste gericht, von Michael Angelo. V. Die Peterskirche. VI. Wateau's gemählde. VII. Über die kinderfiguren auf den Rafaelschen bildern. VIII. Ein paar worte über billigkeit, mässigkeit und toleranz. IX. Die farben. X. Die ewigkeit der kunst.—2. abschnitt. Anhang einiger musikalischen aufsätze von Joseph Berglinger: Vorerinnerung. I. Ein wunderbares morgenländisches mährchen von einem nackten heiligen. II. Die wunder der tonkunst. III. Von den verschiedenen gattungen in jeder kunst, und insbesondre von verschiedenen arten der kirchenmusik. IV. Fragment aus einem briefe Joseph Berglingers. V. Das eigenthümliche innere wesen der tonkunst, und die seelenlehre der heutigen instrumentalmusik. VI. Ein brief Joseph Berglingers. VII. Unmusikalische toleranz. VIII. Die töne. IX. Symphonien. Der traum: eine allegorie.

10–8859   N7445.T5

Tomlinson, Kellom.

The art of dancing explained by reading and figures; whereby the manner of performing the steps is made easy by a new and familiar method: being the original work, first design'd in the year 1724, and now published by Kellom Tomlinson, dancing-master ... London, Printed for the author, 1735.

12 p. l., [3]–159, [1] p. front. (port.) 37 pl. 29½ x 23^{cm}.

The frontispiece is dated 1754.
Many of the plates contain tunes for the dances which they illustrate.
[*Real name:* Kenelm Tomlinson]

20–10890   MT950.A2T6

Torres, Melchior de.

Arte ingeniosa de musica, con nueua manera de auisos breues y compēdiosos sobre toda la facultad della. Agora nueuamente reformada y corregida por su mesmo autor. Assi para canto llano y canto de organo: como para contrapunto: donde se hallará reglas en breue cōprehendidas y declaradas por Melchior de Torres ... Alcala, P. de Robles y I. de Villanueua. Vendese en casa de L. Gutierrez, 1566.

xxxv numb. l. illus. (music) 20^{cm}.

Colophon: Esta presente obra breue y muy compendiosa de Musica pratica ... fue impressa en la muy noble villa de Alcala de Henares en casa de Juan de Villanueua y Pedro de Robles ... Año de mil y quinienios [!] y sesenta y seys años.

Signatures: A–D⁸, E⁴ (last leaf blank)
Vignette (coat of arms) at head of title. Title and vignette within historiated side-borders and horizontal borders of printer's ornaments. Gothic type (except title-page.)
At least two earlier editions were published, in 1544 and 1559 respectively.

30–3283   MT860.T7

Torres y Villarroel, Diego de, 1693?–1770.

Montante christiano, y politico, en pendencia musica-medica-diabolica. Lo desembaynò don Diego de Torres ... [Salamanca?] J. de Moya [1726?]

3 p. l., 25 p. 14½^{cm}.

Polemic occasioned by v. 1 of Feijóo y Montenegro's "Theatro critico universal".

27–25045 ML3001.F28T7

See also COROMINAS, J. F. DE. Cantaridas amigables.

Tosi, Pietro Francesco, *ca.* 1650–*ca.* 1732.

Observations on the florid song; or, Sentiments on the ancient and modern singers. Written in Italian by Pier. Francesco Tosi ... Translated into English by Mr. Galliard ... To which are added, explanatory annotations, and examples in musick ... London, J. Wilcox, 1742.

xviii, [2], 184 p. VI fold. pl. (music) 17½^{cm}.

"A prefatory discourse, giving some account of the author": p. [vii]–xiii.

19–17367 MT820.A2T728

Travenol, Antoine, *plaintiff.*

Memoire signifié, pour le sieur Antoine Travenol, maître de danse à Paris, demandeur en intervention. Contre le sieur Arrouet de Voltaire ... deffendeur. [Paris, Impr. de J. Bullot, 1746]

13 p. 26½ x 21^{cm}.

Caption title.
Signed: Antoine Travenol. Mᵉ. Lemarié, avocat.

42–6750 ML1727.3.A2T728

[Travenol, Louis] *d.* 1783.

Arrest du conseil d'etat d'Apollon, rendu en faveur de l'orchestre de l'Opera. Contre le nommé J. J. Rousseau, copiste de musique, auteur du Devin du village, & de l'ecrit intitulé, Lettre sur la musique françoise, &c. Sur le mont Parnasse; de l'Imprimerie divine. [Paris?] 1753.

14 p. 15½^{cm}.

The "Arrest" is in verse, with "Remarques" in prose. A revision of this pamphlet is included in the author's Œuvres mêlées, 1775.
With autograph of Edmond de Goncourt.

41–25462 ML1727.3.T72A7

Requeste d'un acteur de l'Opera, à monseigneur le prevost des marchands. [n. p., 1758]

8 p. 15½^{cm}.

Caption title.
In verse.
With autograph and book-plate of Edmond de Goncourt.

41–27530 ML1727.3.T72R4

Travenol, Louis, *d.* 1783, *plaintiff.*

Memoire signifié. Pour Louis Travenol, de l'Académie royale de musique. Contre le sieur Arrouet de Voltaire, de l'Académie françoise. [Paris, Impr. de J. Bullot, 1746]

14 p. 26½ x 21ᶜᵐ.

Signed: Louis Travenol. Mᵉ. Rigoley de Juvigny, avocat.

ML1727.3.T72M3

Trew, Abdias, 1597–1669, *praeses.*

Disputatio musica prima De natura musicæ ... Altdorphi, e chalcographéo Scherffiano, 1645.

[16] p. 19½ x 15½ᶜᵐ.

Diss.—Altdorf (Eitel Gallus Pflugg, respondent)

ML3800.T73

Disputatio musica secunda, De natura soni et auditus, quatenus eorum notitia musicæ scientiæ conducit ... Altdorphi, e chalcographéo Scherffiano, 1645.

[16] p. 19½ x 15½ᶜᵐ. [*With* Trew, Abdias, *praeses.* Disputatio musica prima. Altdorphi, 1645]

Diss.—Altdorf (Martinus Joannis, Chittinga-Francus, respondent)
42–5447 ML3800.T73

Trew, Abdias, 1597–1669.

Lycei musici theorico-practici intimatio et epitome latino-germanica, hoc est: Explicatio tredecim divisionum monochordi, earumq́; ad veteris & novæ musicæ jucundam & scientificam cognitionem ac collationem, & in genere ad usum theorico-practicum componistarum, cantorum & organopœorum accomodatio. Kurtzes musicalisches kunstbûchlein / in welchem auss erklârung vnd abtheilung dess monochordi der rechte grund / so wol die alte bissher vnbekandte / als heutige musicam grûndlich zu verstehen / vnd kûnstlich im componirn vnd musicirn anzubringen vnd zu ûben / auch orgel pfeiffen auss solchen vnd der geometriæ fundamentis in gute proportion zu bringen / vnd so wol als anderè instrumenta zu stimmen gewiesen wird. Durch m. Abdiam Trevv ... Rotenbvrgi ad Tvb., ex officina chalcographica Jacobi Mollyni, 1635.

2 p. l., 92 p. illus. (music) fold. pl. 20½ᶜᵐ.

"Die demonstrationes lateinisch / vnd die applicationes ad praxin teutsch."

Second edition. The 1st edition appeared the same year under title: Janitor lycei musici intimatio, et epitome (Rotenburg, 1635) *cf.* Mendel, Musikalisches konversations-lexikon.

25–21739 ML3809.A2T81

Troyes. Académie de musique.

See ACADÉMIE DE MUSIQUE DE TROYES.

Trümper, Michael, 1603–1670.

Epitome oder Kurtzer ausszug der musik / für die anfahende / so da wollen singen lernen; auffgesetzet durch Michaelem Trumperum ... Gotha / typis Reyherianis, gedruckt durch J. M. Schalln, 1668.

[16] p. illus. (music) 16ᶜᵐ.

Signature: A⁸.

32–5348   MT7.T88

Turner, William, *fl.* 1677.

Sound anatomiz'd, in a philosophical essay on musick. Wherein is explained the nature of sound, both in its essence and regulation, &c. Contrived for the use of the voice in singing, as well as for those who play on instruments. Together with a thorough explanation of all the different moods used in musick, for regulating time in the different divisions of measures used therein ... To which is added, a discourse, concerning the abuse of musick. By William Turner. The 2d ed. London, Printed by W. Pearson for the author [172–]

4 p. l., 80, 7 p. illus. (music) fold. pl. (music) 21 x 17ᶜᵐ.

First published, 1677, under title: A philosophical essay on musick, directed to a friend.

22–889   MT7.A2T96

Twining, Thomas, 1735–1804, *editor and translator.*

See ARISTOTELES. Aristotle's treatise on poetry. 1789.

Vaginarius, Joannes, *pseud.*

See SPATARO, GIOVANNI, *d.* 1541.

Valla, Giorgio, *d.* 1500.

Georgii Vallae Placentini viri clariss. De expetendis, et fvgiendis rebvs opvs ... [*Colophon:* Venetiis in aedibvs Aldi Romani, impensa, ac stvdio Ioannis Petri Vallae filii pientiss: mense decembri. M.D.I.]

2 v. diagr. 43 x 28ᶜᵐ.

Title followed by contents; v. 2, caption title only; colophon at end of v. 2. Both volumes unpaged.

CONTENTS.—[t. 1] De arithmetica libri .III. ubi quædam a Boetio prætermissa tractantur. De musica libri .v. ... De geometria libri .VI. ... De tota astrologia libri .IIII. ... De physiologia libri .IIII. ...—[t. 2] De medicina libri .VII. ... Problematum liber unus. De grammatica libri .IIII. De dialectica libri .III. De poetica liber unus. De rhethorica libri .II. De morali philosophia liber unus. De oeconomia, siue administratione domus libri .III. ... Politicon unicum uolumen ... De corporis commodis, & incommodis libri .III. ... De rebus externis liber unus, ac ultimus, ubi de gloria, amplitudine, & cæteris huiusmodi.

6–39618   AC14.V3

Vandenbroeck, Othon Joseph, 1759–1832.

Traité général de tous les instrumens a vent a l'usage des compositeurs. Dédié a son ami Rodolphe par Othon Vandenbrock. Cette methode traite de l'etendue du cor dans tous les tons majeurs et mineurs, avec un violon unisson. On y trouve tous les traits et passages que cet instrument peut faire, tous les solo qu'un compositeur peut et doit employer à commencer par le si en bas jusqu'au si en haut. Elle indique aussi la maniere de placer les clarinettes, les trompettes, tromboni, timballes, et tous les autres instrumens à vent dans leurs tons naturels ...   Paris, Chez Boyer [1793]

1 p. l., 2–65 p.   35ᶜᵐ.
Engraved throughout.
Label of Louis, Paris, mounted over imprint on t.-p.
13–33569   MT70.V28

Vegius, Mapheus, *d.* 1458.

Qvae in hoc ‖ opere continentur. ‖ Maphei Vegij Laudeñ Pom ‖ peana. ‖ Epigrammata in rusticos. ‖ Conuiuium Deorum. ‖ Barth. Pōterolli iureconsulti ‖ Laudeñ Albula. ‖ Bartho. Philippinei. Gaphu- ‖ riani Nominis Assertoris in. ‖ Io. Vaginarium Bononieñ ‖ Apologia ‖ Ad. Præstantiss. Virum. Ant. ‖ de Fantis Theologum ac Phi ‖ losophum Taruisinum ‖ [Mediolani (2d pt.: Taurini) 1521]

[106] p.   21½ᶜᵐ.

In two parts.   Signatures: A–H⁴; a–d⁴, e⁶.
Sig [Hiij] verso, line 16, colophon of 1st part: Impressum Mediolani per Ioannem de Ca‖stiliono impensis andree calui Anno ‖ Dñi. M.D.XXI. Die. XI. octobris. ‖ Registrum omnes sunt duerni ‖ [Hiiij] blank. [ai], title of 2d part: Apologia ‖ Barto. Philippi‖nei Gaphuriani. Nominis ‖ Asserto. in Ioan. Vaginarium ‖ Bononieñ. ‖ Ad Ant. de Fätis Taruisinū. ‖ Theologum ac Philosophū ‖ Prestantiss. ‖ [eᵛⁱ] verso, colophon of 2d part: Taurini per Frañ de sylua impen‖sis Andreæ Calui tertio Kl' ‖ Septembris. M.D.XXI.
The two title-pages have the same floreated border.   Initials.
For an account of the controversy between Gaffurio and Spataro which occasioned Filippini's pamphlet, *cf.* Fétis. Biog. univ. des musiciens, 2d ed., v. 3, p. 378–379 (art. Gafori) "Joannes Vaginarius" is the contemptuous name bestowed upon Spataro by Gaffurio.
27–7063   ML171.V33

Verdizotti, Giovanni Mario, 1525–1600, *translator.*

See Falletti, G.   Le lodi della mvsica.   1563.

Verhandeling, over de muziek; waer in men tracht, de zelve tot meerder klaerheit te brengen ... als mede hoe men de klawier instrumenten tot volkoomenheit kan brengen, met eene beschryving van een nieuw uitgevonden klavesimbel ... en eindelyk ... eene lyst van konstwoorden der muziek ... en 8 plaeten. 's Gravenhage, J. A. Bouvink, 1772.

v, [3], 379 p.   8 fold. pl. (incl. music)   21ᶜᵐ.
17–8853   MT6.A2V27

Villarroel, Diego de Torres y
See Torres y Villarroel, Diego de.

Viotti, Giovanni Battista, 1753–1824.

See Franches et courtes réflexions sur un mémoire au roi; publié nouvellement par m. Viotti.

Vogler, Georg Joseph, *abt,* 1749–1814.

Georg Joseph Vogler's ... Tonwissenschaft und tonsetzkunst. Mannheim, Gedruckt in der Kuhrfürstlichen hofbuchdruckerei, 1776.

5 p. 1., 86 p. 2 fold. tab. 16½^{cm}.

Added t.-p., engraved: Tonwissenschaft und tonsetzkunst vom abt Vogler.
Ein für sich bestehender haupttheil seiner Tonschule. Offenbach a/M, Bey
J. André [n. d.]

26–224   MT40.V87

Vogüé, Jacques Joseph François de, *bp.*, 1740–1787.

Catalogue de la musique et des instrumens dépendans de la succes-
sion de m. de Vogüé, évêque de Dijon, dont la vente commencera, au
Palais épiscopal de la même ville, le mercredi 21 novembre 1787
... Dijon, J. B. Capel, 1787.

24 p. 16^{cm}.

40–21186   ML138.D55C2

Voltaire, François Marie Arouet de, 1694–1778.

See TRAVENOL, ANTOINE, *plaintiff*. Memoire signifié ... Contre le
    sieur Arrouet de Voltaire.
    TRAVENOL, LOUIS, *plaintiff*. Memoire signifié ... Contre le sieur
    Arrouet de Voltaire.

Volupius Decorus, *Musagetes, pseud.*

See SCHOENSLEDER, WOLFGANG, 1570–1651.

W., B. von.

See WIESE, C. L. G., *freiherr* VON.

Wackenroder, Wilhelm Heinrich, 1773–1798.

See TIECK, J. L. Phantasien über die kunst.

Walter, Thomas, 1696–1725.

The grounds and rules of musick explained: or, An introduc-
tion to the art of singing by note. Fitted to the meanest capacities.
By Thomas Walter, M. A. Recommended by several ministers ...
Boston, Printed by Benjamin Mecom for Thomas Johnston [1760?]

1 p. 1., iii, [1], 25 p.; 20 1. (music) illus. (music) 12 x 18^{cm}.

Contains "Thoughts on poetry and musick: by Dr. Watts" (verso of
t.-p.) "A recommendatory preface," dated Boston, April 18, 1721, and
signed by Increase and Cotton Mather and 13 other ministers, the name
of Peter Thacher heading the list (iii p.) Explanation of musical
characters ([1] p.) "Some brief and very plain instructions for singing
by note" (25 p.) Music (engraved) consisting of "Rules for tuning the
voice" (leaf 1) followed by hymn tunes arranged for 3 parts (leaves 2–20)

16–24482   M2116.W22

Warren, Ambrose, *b. ca.* 1656.

The tonometer: explaining and demonstrating, by an easie method,
in numbers and proportion, all the 32 distinct and different notes,
adjuncts or suppliments contained in each of four octaves inclusive,
of the gamut, or common scale of musick. With their exact difference and distance. Whereby the practitioner on any key'd, or
fretted instrument, may easily know how to tune the same. And

also, with great exactness, how to transpose any musick from one key to another, sharp or flat, higher or lower; with proper sharps or flats thereto. Never before published. By Ambrose Warren ... [London] Printed by J. Cluer and A. Campbell, and sold by B. Creake, 1725.

3 p. l., [5]–24 p.   front., illus. (music) 3 fold. pl. (incl. music)   24½ x 19ᶜᵐ.

17–31251   MT165.A2W2

Warton, Thomas, 1728–1790.

Ode for music, as performed at the theatre in Oxford, on the second of July, 1751. Being the anniversary appointed by the late Lord Crew, bishop of Durham, for the commemoration of benefactors to the university ... By Tho. Warton ... Set to music by Dr. Hayes ... Oxford, R. Clements and J. Barrett; [etc., etc., 1751]

11 p.   28 x 23ᶜᵐ.

Without the music.
With this is bound the author's poem, The triumph of Isis.

25–15588   ML54.2.O3H2

Weaver, John, 1673–1760.

A collection of ball-dances perform'd at court: viz. the Richmond, the roundeau, the rigadoon, the favourite, the Spanheim, and the Britannia. All compos'd by Mr. Isaac, and writ down in characters, by John Weaver, dancing-master. London, Printed for the author, and sold by J. Vaillant, 1706.

3 p. l., 41 pl. on 32 l.   26½ᶜᵐ.

Plates contain diagrams of dance figures; each has, at head, tune for figure represented.

20–10872   MT950.A2 I 7

Weaver, John, 1673–1760, *translator.*

See FEUILLET, R. A.   Orchesography.   [1715?]

Weber, Jeremias, 1600–1643.

Hymnologia sacra, das ist: Geistliche und liebliche singe kunst / darinnen einfeltiger bericht geschicht vom vrsprung / nothwendigkeit / fůrtreffligkeit vnd vielfeltigem nutz der geistlichen lieder / vnd insonderheit / wie derer viel / so in etlichen versen von dem gemeinen volck vnrecht gesungen werden / zu corrigiren sind / etc. In zweyen predigten der christlichen gemeine zu Leipzig vorgetragen von m. Ieremia Webern ... Leipzig / In verlegung G. Grossen / buchhendlers.   Gedruckt bey J. A. Mintezeln / 1637.

1 p. l., [18], 3–197, [13] p.   13ᶜᵐ.

35–21821   ML3168.W4H8

Weedon, Cavendish, *fl.* 1700, *editor.*

The oration, anthems and poems, spoken and sung at the Performance of divine musick. For the entertainment of the Lords spiritual & temporal, and the honourable House of commons. At Stationers-Hall, January the 31st 1701. Undertaken by Cavendish Weedon, esq; London, Printed for H. Playford, and are to be sold by J. Nutt, MDCII [!] [*i. e.* 1702]

> 23 p. 19ᶜᵐ.
>
> Signatures: A–C⁴.
> Contains poems by Nahum Tate and anthems by William Turner and John Blow.
> Without music.
>
> 27–7948   PR3729.T115O7

Weidner, Johann Joachim, 1672–1732, *praeses.*
De usu musices in ecclesia christiana ... Rostochii, typis Nicolai Schwiegerovii [1728]

> 3 p. l., 133, [1] p. 19½ᶜᵐ.
>
> Diss.—Rostock (J. N. W. Schultze, respondent)
>
> 32–5349   ML3001.W4

Wenk, August Heinrich.
Beschreibung eines chronometers oder musikalischen taktmessers und seines vortheilhaften gebrauchs für das musikliebende publikum, von A. H. Wenk. Magdeburg, G. C. Keil, 1798.

> 30 p. fold. pl. (music) 17½ᶜᵐ.
>
> 24–13308   ML1080.W36

Werckmeister, Andreas, 1645–1706, *translator.*
See STEFFANI, AGOSTINO. Send-schreiben.

Wetzel, Johann Caspar, 1691–1755, *editor.*
See MÜLLER, H. Hymnologia sacra ... 1728.

[Wiese, Christian Ludwig Gustav, *freiherr* von] 1732–1800.
Anweisung der mechanischen behandlung das clavier nach einer vorgeschlagenen neuen temperatur zu stimmen. B. v. W. Dresden, Im Hilscherschen musick-verlage [1790]

> [4] p. illus. (music) 20 x 26 ᶜᵐ.
>
> Music engraved.
>
> 29–11865   ML3809.W62

Wöchentliche nachrichten und anmerkungen die musik betreffend.
See MUSIKALISCHE nachrichten und anmerkungen.

> 37–35294

[Wolf von Wolfenau, Anton]
Gründliche abhandlung über die unnütz- und unschicklichkeit des H im musikalischen alphabete; nebst einer anmerkung, die kunstlichen töne betreffend. Herausgegeben von J. F. Schwanenberg. Mit einer kupfertafel. Wien, C. F. Wappler und L. Hochenleitter; [etc., etc.] 1797.

> xvi, 140, [19] p. illus. (music) fold. tab., fold. diagr. 19½ᶜᵐ.
>
> Engraved title vignette, head and tail pieces.
>
> 22–903   ML432.A2W65

[Wollick, Nicolas]

Opus Aureum. ‖ Musice castigatissimū. ‖ de Gregoriana. et Figuratiua atq̄ con / ‖ trapūcto simplici percōmode tra / ‖ ctans om̄ib⁹
cantu oblectan ‖ tibus vtile et necessa / ‖ rium e diuersia exerptum
‖ Fata regunt finem, spero dij cepta secundent ‖ Qui ducis vultus
et non legis ista libenter ‖ Omnibus inuideas, liuide nemo tibi: ‖
[Colonie, H. Quentel, 1501]

[78] p. 1 illus., diagr. 20ᶜᵐ.

Colophon (H[ᵥ]ʳᵉᵒᵗᵒ): ❰Explicit opusculū musices omnibus volentib⁹
cantū ‖ vtrūq̄ scire necessariū fausto fine Impressum Colonie p ‖ honestū
virū Henricū Quentel ciuem famatū eiusdem ‖ Anno missionis in carnē diuini
verbi. millesimo quingē ‖ tesimo vno addito.

Signatures: A⁶, B⁴, C⁶, D–E⁴, F⁶, G⁴, H⁶ (last leaf blank)

Only the staves are printed for the musical examples of the third and
fourth parts; the notes are filled in in manuscript.

In four parts, of which only the first two, treating of the Gregorian choral,
are by Wollick; the last two, dealing with florid song, are by Malcior of
Worms ("At Malcioris de Wormatia figuratiuū") as appears from a letter
on the last page, headed: Nicolaus Wollick de Serouilla Ārtiū magister. dño
Ade Popardiensi sacre pagine licentiato ac in gymnasio Corneliano regenti
Salutē. P. D. The letter ends: Vale p̄sidiū ꝯ decus Nicolai galli.

The treatise by Malcior of Worms was also published in Gregor Reisch's
Margarita philosophica. *cf.* Eitner's Quellen-lexikon.

40–21470   ML171.W748

Zarlino, Gioseffo, 1517–1590.

See GALILEI, V.   Discorso.   1589.
                    Dialogo.   1602.

INDEX TO AUTHORS OF WORKS ISSUED ANONYMOUSLY

Works of unknown authorship are not listed here; title entries will be found in their alphabetical place in the body of the catalogue.

Anweisung der mechanischen behandlung das clavier nach einer vorgeschlagenen neuen temperatur zu stimmen. *See* Wiese, Christian Ludwig Gustav, *freiherr* von.

Architectonice musices universalis. *See* Schoensleder, Wolfgang.

Arithmetique des musiciens. *See* Gallimard, Jean Edme.

Arrest du conseil d'etat d'Apollon. *See* Travenol, Louis.

L'art de la danse. *See* Saurin, Didier.

The art of playing on the violin. *See* Prelleur, Peter.

Au corps législatif sur l'Opera. *See* Paris. Académie royale de musique.

The battle of the fiddles. *See* Baretti, Giuseppe Marco Antonio.

Bemerkungen über die flöte. *See* Ribock, J. J. H.

A brief history of musick. *See* Prelleur, Peter.

Cantus, songs and fancies. *See* Forbes, John.

Compte rendu au public. *See* Paris. Académie royale de musique.

La constitution de l'Opera. *See* Chevrier, François Antoine, *supposed author.*

Déclamation théâtrale. *See* Dorat, Claude Joseph.

Declaration du roy. *See* France.

Del teatro. *See* Milizia, Francesco.

Il Desiderio, overo, De' concerti di uarij strumenti musicali. *See* Bottrigari, Ercole.

Dialogue sur la musique des anciens. *See* Châteauneuf, François de Castagnères, *abbé* de.

Dictionnaire portatif des beaux-arts. *See* Lacombe, Jacques.

Dictionnaire portatif des théatres. *See* Léris, Antoine de.

Directions for playing on the flute. *See* Prelleur, Peter.

Directorium chori. *See* Carmelites; *see also* Guidetti, Giovanni.

Discours sur la musique d'Italie. *See* Maugars, André.

Divers traitez d'histoire, de morale et d'eloqvence. *See* Saint Glas, Pierre de, *ed.*

Editto per le donne. *See* Catholic church. *Pope, 1700–1721 (Clemens xi)*

Editto sopra la musica. *See* Catholic church. *Pope, 1691–1700 (Innocentius xii)*

Efemeridi letterarie di Roma, Risposta al giudizio delle. *See* Eximeno y Pujades, Antonio.

Effets de l'air sur le corps humain. *See* Béthisy, Jean Laurent de, *supposed author.*

Essai sur les révolutions de la musique, en France. *See* Marmontel, Jean François.

An essay to excite a further inquiry into the ancient matter and manner of sacred singing. *See* Seccomb, Joseph.

Este es un excelente tractado dela musica llamado Lux bella. *See* Duran, Domingo Marcos.

Extrait de l'arrest definitif de la Cour de Parlement. *See* France.

La Galliade (by G. Le Fèvre de la Boderie) *See* Mersenne, M. Qvæstiones celeberrimæ in Genesim. 1623.

Georg Friedrich Hándels lebensbeschreibung. *See* Mainwaring, John.

Gründliche abhandlung über die unnütz- und unschicklichkeit des H im musikalischen alphabete. *See* Wolf von Wolfenau, Anton.

In hoc opere contenta Arithmetica decem libris demonstrata. Musica libris demõstrata quatuor. *See* Le Fèvre, Jacques, *d'Étaples.*

Instruction du procès, entre les premiers sujets de l'Académie royale de musique et de danse. *See* Ginguené, Pierre Louis.

An introduction to the knowledge and practice of the thoro' bass. *See* Baillie, Alexander, *supposed author.*

The laws and resolutions of several general meetings, for the . . . regulation . . . of the fund for the support of decayed musicians. *See* Royal society of musicians of Great Britain, *London.*

Lettre à une dame d'un certain âge sur l'état présent de l'opéra· *See* Holbach, Paul Henri Thiry, *baron* d'.

Lettre au sujet de la rentrée de la demoiselle Le Maure a l'Opera. *See* Neufville de Brunaubois-Montador, Jean Florent Joseph de.

Lettre critique et historique sur la musique françoise, la musique italienne, & sur les Bouffons. *See* Jourdan, Jean Baptiste.

Lettre de madame * * *. . . sur les spectacles. *See* Du Boccage, Marie Anne (Le Page) Fiquet.

Lettre sur les Bouffons. *See* Jourdan, Jean Baptiste. Lettre critique.

Lettres d'un academicien de Bordeaux sur le fonds de la musique. *See* Castel, Louis Bertrand.

Lux bella. *See* Duran, Domingo Marcos.

Mémoires anecdotes des avantures galantes de M. Duliz. *See* Desforges.

Memoirs of the life of Sig. Agostino Steffani. *See* Hawkins, *Sir* John, *supposed author.*

Memoirs of the life of the late George Frederic Handel. *See* Mainwaring, John.

The most pleasant companion, or Choice new lessons for the recorder. *See* Banister, John, *supposed author.*

Musica libris quatuor demonstrata. *See* Le Fèvre, Jacques, *d'Étaples.*

A musical dictionary. 1769. *See* Brossard, Sébastien de.

Musicks hand-maid. *See* Playford, John.

La musique theorique, et pratique. *See* Saurin, Didier.

Pétition, pour l'Académie royale de musique, a l'Assemblée nationale. *See* Paris. Académie royale de musique.

Point de vue de l'Opera. Fragment anonyme. (By Bernis.) *See* Meusnier de Querlon, Anne Gabriel. Reglement pour l'Opera.

Projet concernant de nouveaux signes pour la musique. *See* Rousseau, Jean Jacques. Traités sur la musique.

Rapport relatif au mode d'existence de l'Opéra. *See* Paris. Académie royale de musique.

Rapport sur l'Opéra présenté au corps municipal, le 17 août 1791. *See* Paris. Académie royale de musique.

Reglement pour l'Opera de Paris. *See* Meusnier de Querlon, Anne Gabriel.

Requeste d'un acteur de l'Opera. *See* Travenol, Louis.

Risposta al giudizio delle Efemeridi letterarie di Roma. *See* Eximeno y Pujades, Antonio.

Saggio sopra l'opera in musica. *See* Algarotti, Francesco, *conte.*

Scotish song. *See* Ritson, Joseph.

Select collection of English songs. *See* Ritson, Joseph.

Il teatro alla modo. *See* Marcello, Benedetto.

Thoughts on the use and advantages of music. *See* Hanway, Jonas.

Three treatises. The first concerning art. The second concerning music [etc.] *See* Harris, James.

Traité contre les danses et les mauvaises chansons. *See* Gauthier, François Louis.

Traités sur la musique. *See* Rousseau, Jean Jacques.

Le triomphe de l'intérêt. (By Louis de Boissy.) *See* Desforges.

A vade mecum for the lovers of musick. *See* Hudgebut, John.

Versuch über das schöne. *See* André, Yves Marie.

The voice of discord. *See* Baretti, Giuseppe Marco Antonio.

La voix de la discorde. *See* Baretti, Giuseppe Marco Antonio.

Le vol plus haut. *See* Mayeur de Saint Paul, François Marie.

Le Waux-hall populaire. *See* Cailleau, André Charles.

BOOKS ON EAST ASIATIC MUSIC
IN THE
LIBRARY OF CONGRESS

(Printed before 1800)

I. Works in Chinese

Compiled and annotated by K. T. Wu
Division of Orientalia

FOREWORD

The origin of Chinese music is generally traced to remote antiquity, but no credence can be placed in the usual accounts that the legendary Emperor Huang-ti originated it. That music was very well developed by the time of Confucius (*551–479 B. C.*), however, is undisputed—it was an integral part of all ritual and was taught as one of the six fundamental arts. It is generally believed that, after the so-called First Emperor ordered the Burning of the Books in 213 B. C., the music of antiquity became a lost art, although a few works on the subject survived this literary inquisition.

In the Han Dynasty (*206 B. C.–221 A. D.*) music maintained its religious character but became entangled with mystical and philosophical speculation, which hampered rather than facilitated its development. About the same time new influences began to filter into China through the opening of trade routes and invasions by foreign peoples. Different scales were introduced, together with a number of foreign musical instruments, some of which are in use today. The ancient outlook gradually altered and the old musical tradition vanished. To trace the link with the remote past is a very difficult task.

Modern Chinese music is said to date from the T'ang Dynasty (*618–907*), during which it attained a very high degree of development. Emperor Hsüan-tsung, who reigned from 712 to 756, was himself a great patron of music and drama. In the seventeenth and eighteenth centuries the elements of Western music were brought to the attention of educated Chinese by the Catholic missionaries then living in Peking. Although this knowledge had no perceptible effect on the music of China, it was incorporated in several officially compiled works of the time. Some missionaries in turn became interested in Chinese music and wrote in the eighteenth century a few treatises on the subject. One of the earliest works of this kind was a monograph, written by the French Jesuit, Joseph Marie Amiot (1718–1793), entitled "Mémoire sur la Musique des Chinois." It was published in 1779 as part of the monumental work, *Mémoires concernant l'Histoire, les Sciences, les Arts, les Moeurs, les Usages, etc., des Chinois.* Since then a number of other studies have appeared in Western languages, most of them providing only a limited introduction to the subject.

Within the last century, Chinese music has undergone very important changes. The modern theatrical music-drama, *p'i-huang* 皮黄, familiar to most Western residents of China, must not be considered as representative of all Chinese music, for it is of comparatively modern origin, being chiefly a development of the last half of the nineteenth century. Still more recently, Western methods of performance, voice-production and harmonization have been introduced,

121

primarily through mission-established schools. For an understanding of the peculiar character of Chinese musical tradition, however, it is necessary to give attention to the theory and practice of earlier times, and it is for this purpose that the following bibliography has been compiled.

Among the terms used in this bibliography there are several that deserve a brief explanation.

The term *lü-lü* 律呂 derives from the name of an ancient musical instrument which was used, in the manner of a pitch-pipe, to determine the twelve chromatic semitones of the octave. It consisted of twelve bamboo tubes of graduated lengths, six tubes representing the positive tones (*yang*), called *lü* 律, and six representing the negative tones (*yin*), called *lü* 呂. Hence this instrument received the name *lü-lü*, meaning "law," or "principle." The first and longest of the tubes measured nine inches and was called *huang-chung* 黃鐘. The sound it produced, known as *kung* 宮, was the keynote of the chromatic scale. In time the term *lü-lü* became more or less synonymous with music in general.

The *ch'in* 琴 is the most celebrated classical instrument of China. The name *ch'in* is generally translated into English as " lute," but actually the instrument resembles the psaltery or zither. It consists of an oblong, convex sounding board, over which are stretched seven silk cords of equal length but of differing thickness, tuned GACDEGA. It was used formerly in state ceremonies and was played exclusively by the educated classes. Owing to the fact that it is a very difficult instrument to master, the *ch'in* was never widely popular and today there are even fewer players. The tablature is especially complicated. Each note is made up of several simple symbols indicating for each tone the pitch, string, finger position and direction of plucking.

Ch'in-p'u 琴譜 are musical compositions written expressly for the lute. They have been handed down for several hundred years and the composers are now unknown. The same compositions appear in most of the collections listed below and vary slightly according to the interpretations of the editors.

A companion instrument of the *ch'in* is the *sê* 瑟. It is larger than the *ch'in*, having twenty-five strings, but is similar to it in principle. It is tuned in the pentatonic scale and is played in octaves. Notation is similar to that for the *ch'in*, but the" notes " in a score are doubled to indicate the octaves. Owing to the fact that it is even more difficult to play than the *ch'in*, it is more rare today.

[In cases where there are two or more editions of the same work in the Library of Congress, only the earliest appears in the following list. Works from collectanea are described only when this Library does not possess them in separate editions.]

WORKS ON MUSICAL THEORY

Ch'ing-shan yüeh-lu 覲山樂錄 (" Ching-shan's Book of Music "), 4 *chüan*, compiled by Mao Ch'i-ling (see *Shêng-yü yüeh-pên chieh-shuo* below), printed in Mao's collected works in 1796. The first two words in the title constitute the courtesy name of the author's father, to whom the book is dedicated. This work on musical theory is based on a treatise concerning flutes by Chu Ch'üan 朱權 (d. 1448), a son of the first Ming Emperor. The latter work in turn treats the music of the T'ang period (618–907 A. D.), with the result that Mao's book has some valuable information on the music of that time.

Huang-chung t'ung-yün 黃鐘通韻 (" The Theory of Music "), 2 *chüan*, 2 v., by Tu Ssŭ-tê 都四德 (18th century), printed in 1744. This work, divided into ten sections, deals entirely with the principles of music, illustrated by tables and diagrams. Seventy or eighty percent of the material is credited to Ts'ai Yüan-ting, author of the *Lü-lü hsin-shu*, mentioned below.

Huang-yen ting-shêng lu 皇言定聲錄 ("Notes to the Emperor's Talks on Music "), 8 *chüan*, compiled by Mao Ch'i-ling (see *Shêng-yü yüeh-pên chieh-shuo*) and printed in 1796 in his collected works, *Hsi-ho ho-chi*. The Emperor referred to is Shêng-tsu, who ruled as K'ang-hsi in the years 1662–1723. The author also expounds his own theories concerning the nine tones and the seven notes. Having decisive views of his own, he took issue with the theories of many musicologists of earlier times. The last *chüan* deals with musical instruments of all types.

Ku-chin yüeh-lu 古今樂錄 ("Notes on Ancient and Contemporary Music "), 1 *chüan*, by Chih-chiang 智匠, a monk of the sixth century. In the *Han-Wei i-shu ch'ao* 漢魏遺書鈔 printed in 1800. Compiled in 568, this work is a collection of anecdotes relating to Chinese music from antiquity down to the author's lifetime. It contains a great deal of useful information and has been frequently quoted by later writers.

Li-shih hsüeh-yüeh lu 李氏學樂錄 (" Li's Notes on Music "), 2 *chüan*, by Li Kung (1659–1733), printed in 1796 in the collected works of Mao Ch'i-ling (see *Shêng-yü yüeh-pên chieh-shuo* below). A collection of notes, tables and diagrams on musical theory, supposedly written when the author was a pupil of Mao Ch'i-ling, though some critics regard Mao as the real author. The book holds that all tunes, however complex, evolved from the twelve semitones of the octave.

Li-yüeh ho-pien 禮樂合編 (" Collected Treatises on Rites and Music "), 30 *chüan*, 16 v., by Huang Kuang 黃廣 (17th century), printed in 1633. These essays were extracted from various sources, but unfortunately these sources are not given. Irrelevant material is sometimes included and the whole is rather poorly organized.

Lü-lü 律呂 (" Principles of Music "), 1 *chüan*, author unknown. In the musical collectanea entitled *Hsiao-yü p'u* 嘯餘譜, or "Song Manual," printed in 1622. This treatise is devoted in part to a discussion of the respective lengths of the twelve pitch-pipes, but chiefly to the general principles of Chinese music.

Lü-lü chêng-i 律呂正義 (" The True Principles of Music "), 5 *chüan*,
5 v., compiled by imperial order of 1713 and printed in 1724 from
movable copper type at the Wu Ying Palace. It constitutes the
third section of a tripartite work on the calendar, mathematics and
music, bearing the collective title, *Lü-li yüan-yüan* 律歷淵源. The
musical treatise is divided into three parts, as follows: (1) the
theory of music, including the proportional dimensions of musical
instruments, (2) a discussion of eight kinds of musical instruments
in China and (3) a description of Western music and its notation,
compiled in large part by two Catholic missionaries, Thomas
Pereira (1645–1708) and Theodore Pedrini (1670–1746). The work
is provided throughout with charts, diagrams and tables.

Lü-lü chieh-chu 律呂解註 (" Comments on the *Lü-lü hsin-shu* "), 2
chüan, 6 v., by Têng Wên-hsien 鄧文憲 (16th century), printed in
1523. The author of these notes was a teacher in the Ch'üan-shan
Academy at Amoy. The book has illustrations which are not in
the *Lü-lü hsin-shu* (see below).

Lü-lü hsin-shu 律呂新書 (" A New Book of Music "), 2 *chüan*, 1 v., by
Ts'ai Yüan-ting 蔡元定 (1135–1198). This work comprises chap-
ters 22–23 in the collectanea of philosophical items, *Hsing-li ta-
ch'üan* 性理大全, compiled in 1415 by Hu Kuang and others. The
Hsing-li ta-ch'üan in the Library of Congress was printed in 1553.
The first part of the *Lü-lü hsin-shu* deals with the origin and general principles of music; the second part is devoted to quotations
illustrating the principles, together with comments by the author.
The work has a preface written by the famous philosopher, Chu
Hsi (1130–1200), in 1187, in which he pays high tribute to its value
as a musical treatise.

Shêng-yü yüeh-pên chieh-shuo 聖諭樂本解說 (" A Commentary to
Emperor Shêng-tsu's Discourses on Music "), 2 *chüan*, by Mao
Ch'i-ling 毛奇齡 (1623–1716), in his collected works, printed in
1796. In 1692 Emperor Shêng-tsu gathered a number of scholars
to discuss the mathematical principles of music. Mao presented
his elucidations to the Emperor in 1699. They relate chiefly to
the ratios of the pitch-pipes and the method of determining them.

T'ai-yüeh lü-lü yüan-shêng 大樂律呂元聲 (" The Basic Principles of
Music "), 6 *chüan*; and *T'ai-yüeh lü-lü k'ao-chu* (考註, "Comments
on the Principles of Music"), 4 *chüan*, 2 v., by Li Wên-li 李文利 (*chü-
jên* of 1480, *d.* 1498), printed in 1535. This work was presented
to the throne in 1524 and was printed eleven years later by Fan
Yung-luan 范永鑾, a censor in Szechwan and a pupil of the author.
The first part of this work is largely devoted to a discussion of the
length of the standard pitch-pipe, known as *huang-chung*, the
author taking it to be 3.9 Chinese inches, instead of the nine inches
given by the historian, Ssŭ-ma Ch'ien (*b.* 145 B. C.). The length
of the other eleven pitch-pipes, of course, varied proportionately.
It is not indicated which of the varying foot-measures is the one
referred to. The first of these two treatises is preceded by a bibliography of twenty-five titles. The second part, aside from comments on the works quoted, deals with the principles of music, the
relation of music to government, musical instruments and the art
of playing.

Yüan-lo chih-yüeh 苑洛志樂 (" Yüan-lo's Book of Music "), 20 *chüan*, 12 v., by Han Pang-ch'i 韓邦奇 (1479–1555), printed in 1549. The author was Secretary of the Board of War during the Chia-ching period (1522–1567). Yüan-lo was his sobriquet. The first two *chüan* are Han's commentaries to the *Lü-lü hsin-shu* mentioned above. From the third *chüan* onward, Han expounds his own principles, with many illustrations of musical instruments and ceremonial dancing. This work is generally considered to be one of the best treatises on music written in the Ming period (1368–1644).

Yüeh-lü ch'üan-shu 樂律全書 (" A Compendium of Music "), 38 *chüan*, 40 v., by Chu Tsai-yü (1536–1611), printed in 1606 by the Prince of Chêng and presented to the throne in the same year. This is a collection of twelve treatises dealing with the theory and mathematical principles of music, including a discussion of the instruments, scores, ceremonial dancing and related topics. It was written by a sixth-generation descendant of the Ming Emperor Jên-tsung, who reigned for one year in 1425. It is illustrated with woodcuts showing various musical instruments and postures in dancing. This work is considered one of the most authoritative and comprehensive treatises on Chinese music. The author, who devoted his whole life to the subject, is credited with having been the first person to determine accurately (1596) the exact figures for the calculation of a tempered intonation, nearly one hundred years before Werkmeister published his *Musikalische Temperatur* (1691). He realized the importance of the harmonic values of the first and last tones in themes and theoretically confirmed the method current at that time of indicating tonality in a musical score.

Yüeh-lü piao-wei 樂律表微 (" An Exposition of the Theory of Music "), 8 *chüan*, 2 v., by Hu Yen-shêng 胡彥昇 (*chin-shih* of 1730), printed in 1762. This is a general treatise on music by a grandson of the celebrated historical critic, Hu Wei 胡渭 (1633–1714). The work was presented to Emperor Ch'ien-lung in 1761, when the latter was making a tour of the South. Illustrated by diagrams and tables, the book is divided into four parts: (1) theory of music, (2) musical tones, (3) composition and (4) musical instruments. The author revised many theories upheld by ancient musicologists.

Yüeh-tien 樂典 (" Canons of Music "), 36 *chüan*, 10 v., by Huang Tso 黃佐 (1490–1566), printed in 1682. This is a general work on music by a Supervisor of Instruction, who asserts that he spent fifteen years in composing it. It is divided into five parts: (1) *chüan* 1–12 treat the determination of scales, (2) *chüan* 13–21, the meaning of music, (3) *chüan* 22–24, the duties of the Minister of State Music, (4) *chüan* 25–55, the history of music, (5) *chüan* 36, the music of the *Classic of Poetry*. Special emphasis is given to the perfect regulation of tones for the attainment of balance.

Yüeh-yüan 樂原 (" Origin of Music."), 1 *chüan*, 1 v., by Hsiao-hsiao tzŭ (*pseud.*) 囂囂子. The identity of the author has not been established, but the book probably was written and printed in the Ch'ien-lung period (1735–1796). It treats first the general principles of music, illustrated by diagrams and tables. The major portion is devoted to quotations from old works, with sources given, and to historical data to show the development of music in China.

The Chinese Lute, or *Ch'in*

Ch'êng-chien t'ang ch'in-p'u chih-fa 澄鑒堂琴譜指法 (" Ch'êng-chien Studio Manual of Fingering "), 2 *chüan*, 1 v., by Hsü Ch'ang-yü 徐常遇 (17th century), printed in 1773. Edited and first published in 1702 by a son of the author, Hsü I 徐褘, this manual forms an introduction to thirty-eight music scores for the lute. A second edition appeared in 1718. This is the third edition, published by a grandson. The first *chüan* consists of explanation for fingering with the right hand; the second *chüan* gives the same for the left hand and in addition a few other pointers for playing the instrument.

Ch'êng-i-t'ang ch'in-t'an 誠一堂琴談 (" Ch'êng-i Studio Discourses on the Lute "), 2 *chüan*, 2 v., by Ch'êng Yün-chi 程允基 (18th century), printed in 1705. The first part of this treatise is devoted to a general discussion of the lute, the technique of playing, including fingering, and the symbols used for tablature. Excerpts from earlier works are given, as well as the twenty-four desired tonal qualities listed in Hsü Hung's *Ta-huan ko ch'in-p'u* (see below). Finally the author gives his own theories on how one should be taught to play. The second part is devoted to the historical aspects of the *ch'in*. Episodes relating to it or to celebrated personages are quoted from a variety of works, with the sources indicated.

Ch'in-chien t'u-shih 琴箋圖式 (" The Ch'in Illustrated "), by T'ao Tsung-i 陶宗儀, who lived about the years 1320–1399. In his collectanea, *Shuo-fu*, printed in 1647. The first three illustrations show the lute, or *ch'in*, in three dimensions. There are twenty-six illustrations, with brief descriptions, of lutes supposed to have been owned by famous men of history.

Ch'in-chih 琴旨 (" Essentials of the Lute "), 2 *chüan*, 2 v., by Wang T'an 王坦 (18th century), printed in 1747. This work, completed after long study under competent masters of the lute, is based principally on the *Lü-lü chêng-i* (see above) and is illustrated with tables and diagrams. The editors of the *Imperial Catalog* (*Ssŭ-k'u ch'üan-shu*) characterize it as one of the best treatises on the principles of music as applied to the lute.

Ch'in-hsüeh pa-tsê 琴學八則 (" Eight Rules for Learning to Play the Lute "), 1 *chüan*, by Ch'êng Hsiung 程雄 (17th century), in the second series of the *T'an-chi ts'ung-shu* 檀几叢書, printed in 1697. This work was written in 1684. The eight rules deal with the following subjects: stringing the instrument, adjusting the stand which holds the instrument, tuning, function of the finger-nails, plucking, fingering, interpretation and dynamics.

Ch'in-p'u ho-pi 琴譜合璧 ("Two Manuals for Playing the Lute "), 3 *chüan*, 8 v., compiled by Yang Lun 楊掄 (early 17th century), printed in the seventeenth century. The manuals comprise the *T'ai-ku i-yin* 太古遺音 (" Melodies Bequeathed by Remote Antiquity "), 2 *chüan*, and the *Po-ya hsin-fa* 伯牙心法 ("The Methods of Po-ya"), 1 *chüan*. Both of these works contain music scores. The first has explanatory matter regarding the lute, such as its use and care, technique and general principles. Parts of the instrument are illustrated. The illustrations portray the compiler accompanied by a servant carrying a lute; they show the different positions for the fingers and picture forty-four instruments used by famous personages of Chinese history. Each score has a brief introductory paragraph. The second of these works, edited in 1609, contains only music scores.

Ch'in-p'u ta-ch'üan 琴譜大全 ("Complete Manual for Playing the Lute"), 10 *chüan*, 10 v., by Yang Piao-chêng 楊表正 (16th century), printed by the Fu-ch'un-t'ang 富春堂, Nanking, 1585. This is a reprint, revised and enlarged, of the first edition, printed in 1573. It is principally a collection of old music scores for the lute, re-edited by Yang, who himself played the instrument. The introductory part, constituting the first two *chüan*, gives the general principles, technique and fingering. There is also a list of musicians and famous masters of the *ch'in*. The different positions for the fingers are illustrated by thirty-two woodcuts. *Chüan* 3–10 contain the music scores of one hundred compositions, each with a brief introduction.

Ch'in-shêng shih-liu fa 琴聲十六法 (" Sixteen Rules Governing the Tonal Qualities of the Lute "), originally formulated by a musician in the Board of Music named Lêng Ch'ien 冷謙 (late 14th century), who styled himself Lung-yang-tzǔ 龍陽子. It was reproduced in 1697 in the collectanea *T'an-chi ts'ung-shu*, but in that work was attributed wrongly to Chuang Chên-fêng 莊臻鳳 (17th century). The "sixteen rules" are translated in detail in R. H. van Gulik's *The Lore of the Chinese Lute*, pp. 105–113.

Ch'in-ts'ao 琴操 (" Lute Motifs "), 2 *chüan*. A list of forty-seven *ch'in* melodies, with stories showing the circumstances that motivated their composition, the author being the scholar and musician, Ts'ai Yung 蔡邕 (132–192 A. D.). In the *Tu-hua-chai ts'ung-shu* 讀畫齋叢書, printed in 1799. This is the oldest extant list of *ch'in* tunes. Though its authorship has on occasion been attributed to other scholars who lived before or after Ts'ai Yung, his connection with it is now hardly questioned, thanks to the critical studies of Ma Jui-ch'ên 馬瑞辰 (1782–1853) and Sun Hsing-yen 孫星衍 (1753–1818) in the latter's *P'ing-ching kuan ts'ung-shu* (1812). For an analysis of the titles of these early songs and the elaborate ideology which they built up concerning the lute, see R. H. van Gulik, *op. cit.*, chapter 4.

Ch'in-yüan hsin-ch'uan ch'üan-pien 琴苑心傳全編 ("Complete Handbook for the Lute"), 20 *chüan*, 8 v., by K'ung Hsing-yu 孔興誘 (17th century), a descendant of Confucius in the sixty-sixth generation. Begun in 1636, completed in 1667 and printed in 1670. The book, which treats the *ch'in* in all its aspects, begins with a list of 132 persons closely associated with the lute or who composed music for it, the contributions of each being indicated and the sources of quotations given. Among the topics treated are the general principles of music; the standard keynotes; methods of manufacturing the instrument; the lutes used by famous persons, with illustrations; historical episodes relating to the *ch'in* and its players; fingering, with thirty-three illustrations, etc. *Chüan* 9–20 are devoted to music scores, with brief explanatory notes.

K'ao-p'an yü-shih 考槃餘事 ("Jottings of a Scholar in his Retreat "), 4 *chüan*, by T'u Lung 屠隆 (*chin-shih* of 1577). In the collectanea, *Pao-Yen-t'ang mi-chi*, a work compiled by Ch'ên Chi-ju (1558–

1639) and printed about 1606. The remarks dealing with the lute are in *chüan* 2. They relate to the care and use of the instrument and its parts, the studio in which it was kept and played and similar topics.

Ku-ch'in lun 古琴論 ("A Discussion of Ancient Lutes"), 1 *chüan*, written by Ts'ao Chao 曹昭 (late 14th century) and incorporated in 1388 in his *Ko-ku yao-lun* 格古要論. The edition in the Library of Congress was printed in the Wan-li reign-period (1573–1620). This essay contains valuable information for identifying antique lutes by ornamental designs, color and shape. It also describes their construction and gives hints concerning their use and care.

Ku-ch'in shu 古琴疏 ("Comments on Antique Lutes"), by Yü Ju-ming 虞汝明 (Sung dynasty), in the collectanea, *Shuo-fu*, printed in 1647. A collection of anecdotes on lutes from remote antiquity down to the sixth century. The musician, Ts'ai Yung (132–192 A. D.; see under item, *Ch'in-ts'ao*), is said to have obtained his lute in the following manner. Seeing some people using a bough of the *t'ung* tree for cooking, he said, as he heard the crackling sound of the fire, " This is excellent material [for the *ch'in*]." Salvaging a half-burnt piece, he made for himself a lute which was called " the scorched end."

Li-hsing yüan-ya 理性元雅, 4 *chüan*, 8 v., by Chang T'ing-yü 張廷玉, (*chin-shih* of 1610), printed about the 1620's. This is a collection of seventy-one scores for the *ch'in*, accompanied by words. The introduction contains instructions regarding plucking and fingering. The author had a *ch'in* and a *sê* made according to his own specifications.

Ta-huan-ko ch'in-p'u 大還閣琴譜 (" The Ta-huan Studio Manual for Playing the Lute"), 6 *chüan*, 4 v., by Hsü Hung (*d. ca.* 1665), printed posthumously in 1673. The book is also known as *Ch'ing-shan* (青山) *ch'in-p'u*, after the author's courtesy name. The first volume contains twenty illustrations for fingering, each accompanied by a highly metaphorical title, as in the *Wên-hui-t'ang ch'in-p'u* (see below), but, unlike the latter, the accompanying titles are not themselves illustrated. A section in this volume, entitled *Wan-fêng-ko chih-fa pi-chien* 萬峯閣指法祕箋, which sometimes circulates separately, gives directions for reading the notes and fingering. Another section, entitled *Hsi-shan ch'in-k'uang* 溪山琴況, which also circulates separately, lists twenty-four desired tonal qualities, which may be compared with those listed in the *Ch'in-shêng shih-liu fa* (see above). They are harmony, tranquility, clarity, remoteness, classic simplicity, placidity, quietness, ease, elegance, beauty, sonority, brilliance, purity, smoothness, fullness, firmness, loudness, softness, polish, vigor, lightness, heaviness, deliberation and speed. The last three volumes contain scores for thirty-one compositions.

T'ai-yüeh yüan-yin 大樂元音 ("Basic Principles of Music"), 7 *chüan*, 5 v., by P'an Shih-ch'üan 潘士權 (18th century), printed in 1745. This work deals principally with the fundamentals of music, as illustrated by the *ch'in*. It is based on Ts'ai Yüan-ting's *Lü-lü hsin-shu* and the *Lü-lü chêng-i* (for both, see above). In the first five *chüan* the author discusses the *ch'in*, its construction, etc. He includes some songs composed for the *ch'in* and expounds the

mathematical principles upon which such music is based. Fingering
and technique, illustrated with scores, are also discussed. *Chüan*
6 takes up the *sê* and includes a few scores. The last *chüan* is
devoted to rhymes.

Tê-yin-t'ang ch'in-p'u 德音堂琴譜 ("The Tê-yin Studio Manual for
Playing the Lute"), 10 *chüan*, 4 v., by Kuo Yung-ying 郭用英
(17th century), printed in 1691. In the first *chüan* is a list of 143
famous persons associated directly or indirectly with the *ch'in*.
Chüan 2 describes, with illustrative woodcuts, fifty-one lutes owned
by prominent personages of history. *Chüan* 3 contains quotations
from old works regarding the instrument, its care and use. *Chüan*
4 explains the notation used in scores for the *ch'in* and in *chüan* 5–10
there are thirty-two scores for that instrument.

Tsa-shu ch'in-shih 雜書琴事 ("Miscellaneous Notes on the Lute"),
by Su Shih 蘇軾 (1036–1101), in the collectanea, *Shuo-fu*, printed
in 1647. This is a collection of historical episodes and personal
reminiscences by the famous Sung poet and essayist, better known
by his courtesy name, Su Tung-p'o. He describes a *ch'in* in his
possession called *Lei-ch'in* 雷琴 which was then more than three
centuries old, having been made in 722.

Tsun-shêng pa-chien 遵生八箋 ("Eight Essays on Living in Harmony
with Nature"), 19 *chüan*, 12 v., by Kao Lien 高濂 (16th century),
printed in 1591. This book is devoted chiefly to physical hygiene
from the Taoist point of view, but in the sixth essay there is a section
on the lute and the lore associated with it. The author discusses
music scores, gives fifteen pointers for the care and preservation of
the lute and tells how to distinguish between old and new instruments.

Wên-hui-t'ang ch'in-p'u 文會堂琴譜 ("The Wên-hui Studio Manual
for Playing the Lute"), 6 *chüan*, 8 v., by Hu Wên-huan 胡文煥
(16th century), printed in 1596. This manual discusses the lute
(*ch'in*) from eighteen aspects: method of constructing the instrument, materials, strings, repair, care and preservation, history,
shapes of famous ancient instruments, technique of playing, points
to be observed when playing, how to obtain enjoyment when
playing, the theory of music, list of tones, list of compositions under
the tones, movement of the hand, fingering, names of famous players,
scores of 53 compositions (nine of which are accompanied by words),
appendix. There are woodcuts depicting standard lutes, with
explanations of the parts and their dimensions, the lutes used by
famous personages of history and the ways of carrying the instrument and stringing it. There are thirty-three illustrations on
fingering, each with a highly metaphorical title, suggesting the
nature of the movement. Some of these titles read as follows:
the dragon-fly skimming the water, the shrieking crane about to
take flight, the wild goose alighting with a reed in its bill, the mantis
seizing the cicada, the waterfall in a deep gorge, the wind chasing
the fleeting clouds, etc. The illustrations are unique in depicting
not only the hand as it makes the movement, but the act suggested
in the title—for example, a dragon-fly actually skimming the water.
The author took for his sobriquet the words 抱琴居士, or "The
Recluse Embracing the *Ch'in*". Two lutes were made by him in
1586, according to his own specifications, from the wood *pawlonia*

imperialis. Because they were pieced together from many parts, he called them Pai-na ch'in 百衲琴, " Lutes of a Hundred Pieces." *Wu-chih-chai ch'in-p'u* 五知齋琴譜 (" The Wu-chih Studio Manual for Playing the Lute "), 8 *chüan*, 6 v., written by Hsü Ch'i 徐祺 (17th century), edited by the latter's son, Hsü Chün 徐俊, and by Chou Lu-fêng 周魯封 and printed in 1737. The first *chüan* gives the general principles, fingering, care of the instrument, etc., together with the names of 165 persons who made contributions to the art. There are also illustrations, with descriptive notes, of fifty-one lutes once owned by some of the persons named. Other illustrations show the parts of the instrument, etc. Sixteen desired tonal qualities of the *ch'in* are explained, these being more or less like those given by Lêng Ch'ien (see under *Ch'in-shêng shih-liu fa*). *Chüan* 2–8 contain thirty-three music scores, all with words and explanations concerning tempo, expression, etc.

Ying-yang ch'in-p'u 潁陽琴譜 ("Ying-yang Manual for Playing the Lute "), 4 *chüan*, 4 v., by Li Chiao 李郊 (18th century), printed in 1751. Ying-yang was the native town of the author, who was a *ch'in* instructor. The first two *chüan* deal with general principles for the technique, care and use of the *ch'in*. The last two *chüan* contain twelve music scores, each preceded by an introductory paragraph giving the historical background.

MISCELLANEOUS WORKS

Chieh-ku lu 羯鼓錄 ("Notes on the Deerskin Drum "), 1 *chüan*, by Nan Cho 南卓 (9th century), in the collectanea, *Shuo-fu*, printed in 1647. This work is divided into two parts: the first, completed in 848, the second in 850. The first deals with the introduction of this drum to China (probably from Central Asia), its shape, and stories relating to it since the time of T'ang Hsüan-tsung (ruled 712–756 A. D.), in whose reign Chinese music—in particular, music for the theater—reached its greatest development. The second part deals with the story of Sung Ching (663–737), whose faculty for identifying the tones emitted from various instruments seems to have been phenomenal. It also contains a list of compositions for the drum.

Hsiao-chih 嘯旨 ("Elements of Singing "), 1 *chüan*, by Sun Kuang 孫廣 (T'ang dynasty), in the collectanea, *Shuo-fu*, printed in 1647. This is probably the oldest work in Chinese on the subject of voice culture. According to the author, " breath impelled from the throat, being muffled, is called speech; whereas breath impelled from the tip of the tongue, being clear, is called singing." The subject is treated under fifteen heads, the first dealing both with the origin of singing and with voice control, including the use of the tongue and lips, the others explaining types of songs composed by masters of the past.

P'an-kung li-yüeh ch'üan-shu 頖宮禮樂全書 (" Complete Handbook of Ritual and Music for the Confucian Academy "), 16 *chüan*, 8 v., by Chang An-mao 張安茂 (*chin-shih* of 1647), printed in 1656. This work, based primarily on the *P'an-kung li-yüeh shu* (疏), by Li Chih-tsao 李之藻 (1570?–1630), and the *Wên-miao* (文廟) *li-yüeh shu*, by Wang Huan-ju 王煥如 (17th century), was intended to serve as a handbook for *literati* in the ceremonies honoring Confucius. The first seven *chüan* deal with methods of instruction, utensils and paraphernalia used in the ceremonies, the history of Confucian worship and the arrangement of the worship hall—all illustrated by woodcuts. *Chüan* 8–16 deal with the musical aspects of the ceremonies, the arrangement of the orchestra, the history of ceremonial music and the general principles and development of music. Musical instruments of all types are described, with excellent illustrations. Directions on how to play the various instruments are also given. The last *chüan* is devoted to dance music, with illustrations showing dancing positions and postures.

P'i-p'a lu 琵琶錄 ("Notes on the *P'i-p'a*"), 1 *chüan*,by Tuan An-chieh 段安節 (9th century), in *Shuo-fu*, printed in 1647. The *p'i-p'a*, a Chinese instrument of unknown origin, is a kind of guitar with four strings. Though the *ch'in* is now seldom played, the *p'i-p'a* is still popular. This work consists of tales concerning the instrument, some of them more amusing than authentic.

T'ang-yüeh ch'ü-p'u 唐樂曲譜 ("Titles of Tunes Composed in the T'ang Dynasty"), compiled by Kao Ssŭ-sun 高似孫 (*chin-shih* of 1184). In the collectanea, *Shuo-fu*, printed in 1647. The list comprises fifty-five tunes composed during the reigns of eight T'ang emperors. Thirty-four are attributed to the reign of the famous Emperor Hsüan-tsung (or Ming Huang), who ruled in the years 712–756.

Yüeh-fu chieh-t'i 樂府解題 ("Explaining the Titles of Tunes"), by Liu Su (8th century). In the collectanea, *Shuo-fu*, printed in 1647. This is a collection of short articles explaining the titles and origin of certain tunes.

Yüeh-fu tsa-lu 樂府雜錄 ("Miscellaneous Notes on Music"), 1 *chüan*, by Tuan An-chieh (see above). Incorporated in the *Ku-chin i-shih* 古今逸史, the latter a work edited by Wu Kuan 吳琯 (*chin-shih* of 1571) and printed in the sixteenth century. A series of notes on ceremonial music, musical instruments and their decoration, dancing and theatrical music, together with some anecdotes. Since the author lived toward the close of the T'ang dynasty (618–907 A. D.), the material relates to a very important period in the history of Chinese music.

Yüeh-fu yüan-t'i 樂府原題 (" On the Proper Classification of Songs "), 1 *chüan*, by Chêng Ch'iao 鄭樵 (1104–1162 A. D.), in the *Hsiao-yü p'u* (see under the work called *Lü-lü*) printed in 1662. This is the first of a two-*chüan* work by Chêng Ch'iao known as *Yüeh-lüeh* 樂略 ("Musical Sketches "), the title having been incorrectly altered. Believing that music in his day was often played on the wrong occasions because the pieces were given inaccurate titles, Chêng divided songs and melodies into four main categories as follows: (1) *fêng* and *ya*, songs for national and court uses, respectively; (2) *sung*, songs for religious and ceremonial use; (3) *pieh-shêng*, songs for non-official and private uses; (4) *i-shêng*, songs whose melodies had been lost. The first two categories included music for the seven-stringed lute, or *ch'in*, and the third category included music for dancing. Under most of the titles treated there are notes on the authorship, origin and history of the songs.

II. Works in Japanese

Compiled and annotated by Shio Sakanishi,
formerly of the Division of Orientalia

Abe no Munetô matsura no kinugasa. Text by Sôsuke Namiki (1695–1751) and music by Toyotake Echizen no Shôjô I (1681–1764). Osaka, Shôhonya Kyûzaemon, 1736, 96 leaves. This is a *jôruri,* or historical romance, chanted to the accompaniment of the *samisen.* Toyotake Echizen no Shôjô, popularly known as Kawachiya Kanzeamon, founded a new *jôruri* school, called the Toyotake-ha. This work was chanted by Echizen no Shôjô himself, accompanied by a large orchestra, in the Toyotake theater in 1736. The manuscript text, with his musical notations, was cut in wood blocks and published in the same year.

Gi shi gakki zu 魏氏樂器圖 (" Illustrated Treatise on Wei Hao's Musical Instruments "), selected and explained by Kagechika Tsutsui. Kyoto, Keibunkan, 1780, 21 leaves. Wei Hao 魏皓 was a musician in the Ming Court, but after the collapse of the Ming dynasty (1644) he fled to Nagasaki with his musical instruments and scores. Before his death, he requested one of his followers, Kagechika Tsutsui, to record his teachings. The treatise contains two diagrams showing the arrangement of the orchestra, drawings of fourteen musical instruments and Wei's portrait.

Kaden-sho 花傳書, by Seami Motokiyo (1363–1443), 8 v. This is a rare movable-type edition, printed probably during the Genna and Kanei periods (1615–1643). Being a collection of aesthetic treatises by Seami on the Nô play, it discusses in detail such matters as music for the chorus and orchestra (consisting of drums and flutes), the training of actors and musicians, the interrelation of the music, the chanted word and the movements of the actors.

Kin-kyoku shi-fu 琴曲指譜 (" Music for the *Koto,* with Instructions "), by Gensui. Edo, Umemura Saburôbei and others, 1780, 5 v. This is one of the earliest collections of *koto* scores in Japan. Gensui was a teacher of music in Kyoto who collected twenty-seven popular pieces and transcribed them in proper notation, with instructions.

Ôiso Tora osana monogatari 大磯虎稚物語, author anonymous, music by Takemoto Chikugo no Jô (d. 1705). Osaka, Yamamoto Kyûbei, 1702, 15 leaves. This old *jôruri* belongs to the large cycle based on the Soga vendetta and probably was composed especially for the famous master and composer, Takemoto Chikugo no Jô. It was first presented at his theater, Takemoto-za, in Osaka in 1702. During his life Takemoto Chikugo no Jô composed music for more than 140 *jôruri.* His genius and originality enabled him to free these chants from the domination of the puppet plays and give them a more independent position under the new name, *gidayû.* The later Toyotake school of *jôruri* was influenced by his work.

Onkyoku gyokuen shû 音曲玉淵集 (" Language and its Relation to Voice "), by Tsuguyasu Miura and Yoshifuku Imamura. Osaka, Kashiwabara Seiuemon, 1762, 5 v. Each sound in the Japanese language is carefully analyzed and, with the Nô texts as illustrations, the authors discuss voice training in chanting and intoning. They emphasize especially the significance of the beat in Japanese music.

Shô-kyoku taii shô 箏曲大意鈔 (" Music for the *Koto* and Its Study "), by Shôkoku Yamada. Edo, Fûgetsu Sôzaemon, 1780, 7 v. The author, a successful physician in Edo, transcribed with copious notes the forty-two most representative pieces of *koto* music of the Ikuta school. The last volume contains the history of the *koto* in China and Japan, references to it in Japanese literature, a discussion of technique, and descriptions of the various types and the construction of the *koto*.

Tai-gen shô 體原鈔, by Sumiaki Toyohara (1450–1524), eighteenth century manuscript, 13 books in 20 v. The author, a native of Kyoto, came from a long line of Court musicians and in 1518 succeeded his father as head of the Imperial Music Bureau. Fearing that the tradition of classical music might be lost, as in the Shogun's court the Nô drama was taking the place of ancient music, he wrote an informal essay about the *gagaku*, the music of the court. The *Tai-gen shô* is an encyclopaedic work which treats of the origin and evolution of music and musical instruments, the significance of various ceremonial pieces performed in the Court, scales and modes, and also includes transcriptions of a number of famous compositions.

Tomonaga 朝長, text and music by Seami Motokiyo. Kyoto, Sumikura Soan, middle seventeenth century, 32 p. This is the text of a Nô play, with musical notations for choral and orchestral accompaniment. The movable wooden types were cut after a manuscript by Koetsu Honami and the format was also designed by that famous artist.

A List of Books from the

DAYTON C. MILLER COLLECTION

(bequeathed to the Library of Congress in 1941)

From the Catalog of the Collection
Compiled by Mr. Miller

NOTE.—The titles have not been revised, for the reason that the books themselves had been placed in protective storage for the duration of the war.

Dayton C. Miller Collection

(*Anonymous Tutors for the flute*. Many of the early tutors for the flute were published without any designation of authorship or editorship. These are listed below as being Anonymous. The names of authors of other 17th and 18th century instruction books are given under *Recorder* and *Tutor*.)

Anon.—Lessons for the German Flute with an Explanation of ye largest Scales extant Easy and Instructive for Learners The Lessons compos'd in ye Several Keys proper for the Instrument. London Printed for I: Walsh Sevrt. to his Majesty at the Harp and Hoboy in Catherine Street in the Strand: & I: Hare at the Viol & Flute in Cornhill, near the Royal Exhange. *n. d. c.* 1730. *Obl. 8vo. Title* + 21 *leaves of music* + 2 *folded charts of fingerings.*

Anon. Michel Corrette.—Methode Pour apprendre aisèment à joüer de la Flute Traversiere. Avec des Principes de Musique, et des Brunettes a I. et II. parties. Ouvrage utile et Curieux, Qui conduit en très peu de tems à la parfaite connoissance de la Musique et a joüer a Livre ouvert les Sonates et Concerto. A Paris, Chez Me. Boivin ... A Lyon, Chez Mr. de Bretonne ... Avec Privilege du Roy, *n. d. c.* 1730. *Sm. 4to,* IX + 50 *pp.* + *Privilege, frontispiece.*

Anon.—The Compleat Tutor For the Flute. Containing The Best and Easiest Instructions for Learners to Obtain a Proficiency. To which is Added A Choice Collection of the most Celebrated Italian English and Scotch Tunes Curiously adapted to that Instrument. Printed for & Sold by Thompson & Son at the Violin, Hautboy, and German Flute the West end of St. Paul's Church Yard. London. Where Books of Instructions for any Single Instruments may be had. *n. d., between 1758 and 1761. 8vo,* 32 *pp.*

(**Anon.**—The Compleat Tutor For the German Flute, Containing the Best and Easiest Instructions for Learners to Obtain a Proficiency. Translated from the French. To which is Added a Choice Collection of ye most Celebrated Italian, English, & Scotch Tunes Curiously adapted to that Instrument. London: John Johnson, (*ante* 1760. *8vo,* II + 36 *pp., frontispiece of flute player. Already in Library of Congress collection but see next item.*)

Anon.—The Compleat Tutor For the German Flute, ... (With exactly the same title as the preceding work, and a similar frontispiece; but with slight variations in the text, and with a different selection of tunes.) London: John Johnson (*c.* 1760). *8vo,* II + 36 *pp., frontispiece.*

Anon.—The Compleat Tutor For the German Flute, ... (With exactly the same title as the preceding work; but with a different frontispiece, with slight variations in text and with a different selection and added pages of tunes.) Printed for and Sold by Chas. & Saml. Thompson, Musical Instrument Makers, at the

Violin Hautboy and German Flute the West-end of St. Pauls Church Yard London. Where Books of Instructions for any Single Instrument may be had. Price 1s, 6d, *c*. 1764. *8vo*, II+32+20+4 *pp*.

Anon.—The Compleat Tutor For the German Flute ... (With exactly the same title as the two preceding works, but with a different frontispiece, slight variations in text, and a different selection of tunes.) London: Maurice Whitaker, (1765). *8vo*, II+36 *pp*.

Anon.—The Compleat Tutor for the German-Flute. Containing the easiest and most modern Methods for Learners to play, To which is Added a favorite Collection of Song Tunes, Minuets, Marches, Duets, &c. Also The method of double Tongueing and a concise Scale and description of a new invented German-Flute with additional Keys—such as play'd on by the two celebrated Masters, Tacet and Florio. London: Printed for C. & S. Thompson. (*c*. 1770). *Obl. 8vo, frontispiece,* II+36 *pp., with* 22 *pp. engraved music, and* 65 *leaves of MSS. music.*

Anon.—The Compleat Tutor, For the German Flute ... (With the same title as the three preceding works, but with a different frontispiece and slight variations in the text and with a different selection of tunes. At the bottom of the title page there is the following sentence.) The Second Addition with Alterations and the Method of Double Tongueing. (Under the Frontispiece) N. B. To This Tutor is added a Complete Scale and Description of the Additional Notes of Florio and Tacet's new invented German Flute with all the Keys. London: Johnathan Fentum. (1770). *4to,* II+32 *pp.,* 2 *pp. on Double Tongueing, frontispiece.*

Anon.—The Compleat Tutor for the German-Flute. Containing the easiest and most modern Methods for Learners to play, To which is Added a favorite Collection of Song Tunes, Minuets, Marches, Duets, & c. Also The method of double Tongueing and a concise Scale and description of a new invented German-Flute with additional Keys—such as play'd on by the two celebrated Masters, Tacet and Florio. London: S. A. & P. Thompson. (1780?). *Obl. 4to,* II+36+2 *pp., frontispiece.*

Anon.—New Instructions for the German-Flute, Containing the Easiest & most modern Methods for Learners to play, to which is Added a favorite Collection . . . Also The method of double Tongueing And a complete Scale & description of A new invented German Flute with the additional Keys such as play'd on by two eminent Masters, Florio and Tacet. London, Preston and Son. *c*. 1790. *obl. 4to,* 21. + 30 *pp., frontis.*

Anon.—New Instructions for the German Flute, Containing the easiest & most modern methods for Learners to Play, To which is added A Favorite Collection of Song-Tunes, Marches, Dances, Duetts, &c. Also The method of double Tongueing and a concise Scale & Description of Potters Patent German-Flute with additional Keys. London: Thompson. (1790). *Obl. 4to,* II + 32 *pp., chart.*

Anon.—New and Modern Preceptor for the Flute. Wherein every Instruction relative to that Instrument is elucidated in the most clear and simple manner, to which is annexed a series of select Airs, & c., best calculated for improvement. London: C. Wheatstone. (1800?) *Obl. 4to*, II + 22 *pp.*

Anon.—The Pocket Preceptor for the German Flute. (Bound with The German Flute & Violin Pocket Magazine.) London: Thos. Tegg. (*c*. 1800). *Obl.* 16*mo*, 54 *pp., frontispiece.*

Anon.—The Compleat Tutor for the German Flute Containing The best and easiest Instructions for Learners to obtain a Proficiency To which is added . . . Dublin, J. Delany, *c.* 1800. *Obl. 4to*, II + 32 *pp.*

Anon.—Anweisung die Flöte zu blasen, nebst Tabellen und Uebungen. Nach den Schulen der besten Meister. Hamburg: Rudolphus. (1800?) *Sm. 4to*, 20 *pp. text* + 16 *pp., music.*

Arnold, Dr. (Samuel).—New Instructions for the German-Flute. Containing . . . with Easy Directions for Playing . . . Also, A plain and concise Description of Mr. Potter's, New-invented Patent German-Flute; Accompanied by a very curious, large, and complete Scale, on an entire new Plan, fully explaining the Use of all the additional Keys. To which is added . . . London: Harrison & Co. 1787. *Obl. 4to*, 98 *pp., frontispiece, chart.*

Bernoulli, Daniel.—Sur le son & sur les tons des tuyaux d'Orgues différement construits. Recherches Physiques, Mécaniques et Analytiques. Paris, Mémoires de l'Académie Royale des Sciences, Année 1762. *4to pages* 431–485, 2 *plates.*

Bonanni, Filippo.—Gabinetto Armonico Pieno d'Istromenti Sonori Indicati, e Spiegati. Roma: Giorgio Placho. 1722. *4to*, XXII + 177 *pp.*, 2 *frontispieces,* 148 *plates.*

Corrette, Michel.—Methode Pour apprendre aisèment à joüer de la Flute Traversiere. Paris, *c.* 1730. *See full description under* **Anon. Michel Corrette.**

Delusse, (Charles).—L'Art de la Flûte Traversiere. Paris: . . . (1760). *Sm. 4to*, 12 + 41 *pp.*

Devienne, F.—Nouvelle Méthode Théorique et Pratique Pour la Flûte. Dans laquelle il est traité . . . et 6 Sonates graduées . . . Paris: Naderman. (1795). *Folio*, 77 *pp.*

Devienne, F.—Nouvelle Méthode pour la Flute. Francais & Allemand. Hambourg: Jean August. (1795?). *Folio*, 42 *pp.*

Devienne, (Francois).—Méthode de Flute. augmentée de trois tablatures, pour la gamme diatonique, les notes diésées et bémolisées et les demitones altérées, sur la flute à patte d'ut. Paris: Benoit. (1795). *Folio*, II + 77 *pp., music.*

Devienne, (Francois).—Nouvelle méthode de Flute pour apprendre sans maitre. Renfermant les principes de musique, les Tablatures pour la Flute ordinaire et celle a 4 clefs, des gammes et exercices dans tous les tons, des airs faciles, et un air varie. Nouvelle édition. Revue et augmentée par A. Brulon. Paris: Joly. (1800?). *Obl. 4to*, II + 33 *pp.*

Dordau, Cot.—Extrait d'une Lettre de Lille en Flandre, au sujet de l'Addition à la Flûte Traversiere proposée dans la Feuille du 25

Août dernier. Signé Cot Dordau, 1ʳ Septemb. 1773. Paris, Bureau des Affiches, Trentehuitieme Feuille Hebdomadaire, 22 Sept. 1773. *page* 151. *Extract.*

Granom, Lew. C. A.—Plain and Easy Instructions for Playing on the German-Flute. London: T. Bennett. 1766. (1st edition.) *4to,* IV + 18 + 157 *pp., frontispiece.*

Granom, Lew. C. A., Esqr.—Plain and Easy Instructions for Playing on the German-Flute. Third edition with Additions. London: T. Bennett, *c.* 1770. *4to,* IV + 138 *pp., frontispiece.*

Gunn, John.—The School of the German-Flute, or Principles & Practice for attaining a Command of that Instrument in all Keys . . . With an accompaniment for a second flute. London: Birchall. 1794. *Folio,* II + 39 *pp.*

Heron, Luke.—A Treatise on the German Flute, containing An Account of the Ancient Music, its Modes, their Application and Effects: Instructions for Playing the Flute; wherein The Common Objections to that Instument are obviated, and Any Defects that may be attributed to it are demonstrated to arise from an Improper Method in the Performance: The Diatonique and Chromatique Scales, with the Shakes, laid down in the most obvious Manner: The Method of Playing in Time exemplified by Figures, ascertaining the Proportion the Notes bear to each other. With Directions for Accompanying; interspersed with Musick selected from the most favourrite Authors, and adapted to The German Flute. Sold . . . at all the Music Shops in London; by Luke Heron, at his House in Great Britain-street, Dublin . . . London: W. Griffin. 1771. *4to,* XII + 52 *pp.* text + 37 *pp. music.*

Hotteterre le Romain.—Methode pour apprendre a jouer en très peu de tems De la Flute traversiere, de la Flute à bec et du Haut-bois. Divisée en differents traités. Nouvelle Edition Augmentée des Principes de la musique et des Tablature de la Clarinette et du Basson Suive d'un Recueil . . . par Mr. Bailleux. Paris: Chez Mr. Bailleux Md. de Musique. *c.* 1765. *Large 4to,* II+79 *pp., frontis. portrait.*

La Grange, Louis De.—(*a*) Recherches sur la Nature, et la Propagation du Son (*With a chapter on* Théorie des Cordes de Musique et des Flutes). X+112 *pp.,* 2 *pp.* errata, 2 *plates.* (*b*) Lettre de M. Euler à M. De La Grange. 10 *pp.* (*c*) Nouvelles Recherches sur la Nature et la Propagation du Son (*With a chapter on* La Théorie des Instrumens à Vent). 162 *pp.,* 3 *plates.* (*d*) Addition a la premiere partié des Recherches sur la Nature et la Propagation du Son. 14 *pp. From* Miscellanea Philosophico-Mathematica Societatis Privatae Taurinensis, Tomus Primus, Tomus Alter. Turin, de l'Imprimerie Royale, 1759, 1760–1761. *4to.*

Lenotre, G.—Descoteaux, Le Joueur de Flûte. (Depuis 1662 l'emploi de flûte douce de la chambre du roi, Louis XIV.) Paris, *n. d.* 12*mo,* 7 *pp., clipping.*

Longman and Lukey.—Longman and Lukey's Art (in Miniature) of blowing or playing on ye German Flute. Illustrated with proper Examples and other requisites for playing with a good Taste, Tone,

&c. To which is Added, select Airs, Duets, Minuets, & Marches from the most eminent Italian and English Masters. London: Printed and Sold at No. 26, Cheapside. N. B. Variety of New Invented G. Flutes for Concerts. *c.* 1775. (Two volumes, in one.) *Obl.* 32*mo, miniature. Frontis., two titles,* 56+56 *pp.*

Mahaut, A.—Nieuwe Manier om Binnen Korten Tyd op de Dwars-fluit te Leeren speelen.—Nouvelle Méthode pour Apprendre en Peu de Tems a Jouer de la Flûte Traversière. Seconde Édition. (Text in Dutch and French). Amsterdam: J. J. Hummel. n. d. (1st ed. 1759). *Obl.* 8*vo.,* II+36 *pp.*

Mahaut, A.—Nieuwe Manier om binnen korten tyd op de Dwars-fluit te leeren speelen, Tot gebruik van aanvangers en meer gevor-derden opgesteld. Nieuwe Druk. Voorzien met 12 Nooten Tabula's. Te Amsteldam, By J. J. Hummel, Musiekdrukker en Verkooper. (Title and text in Dutch and French, in parallel columns.) *n. d.* (1st ed., 1759). *Obl.* 8*vo,* II+36 *pp.*

Mercurin, Ludovicus Stephanus.—Tentamen Physico-Medicum de Musice seu de influxu musices in corpus humanum. Monspelii: Joannis Francisci Picot. 1782. *Sm.* 4*to,* 29 *pp.*

Merian, Emanuel.—Tibiae Germanicae Pervestigatio Physico-Mathematica. Basiliae: Typis Johan. Jacobi Thurneisen. 1790. 4*to,* 12 *pp.* 1 *table.*

Modern Musick-Master, The.—The Modern Musick-Master or, The Universal Musician, containing, I. An Introduction to Sing-ing, after so easy a Method, that Persons of the meanest Capacities may (in a short Time) learn to sing (in Tune) any Song that is set to Musick. II. Directions for playing on the Flute; with a Scale for Transposing any Piece of Musick to the Properest Keys for that Instrument. III. The Newest Method for Learners on the German Flute, as Improv'd by the greatest Masters of the Age. IV. Instructions upon the Hautboy, in a more Familiar Method than any extant. V. The Art of Playing on the Violin, . . . VI. The Harpsichord . . . In which is included a Large Collection of Airs and Lessons, adapted to the several Instruments . . . With a Brief History of Musick . . . To which is Added, A Musical Dictionary . . . Curiously Adorn'd with Cuts representing the Manner of Performing on every Instrument. Finely Engrav'd on above 320 Plates. (Edited by Peter Prelleur.) Engrav'd, Printed, and Sold (by Cluer, or Dicey) at the Printing-Office in Bow Church Yard, London: 1731. 8*vo. Each part has an engraved frontispiece and title page, and is separately paged; total pages "above 320."*

Modern Musick-Master, The.—(This is a second set of the parts of "The Modern Musick-Master," on "The Art of Playing on the Violin," "Directions for Playing on the Flute," "The Newest Method for Learners on the German Flute," and two copies of "A Dictionary," bound together in fine red morocco binding, gilt edges, and in perfect condition. The texts are the same as in the other set, but the frontispiece and some of the music for the violin instructions are different. The flute section bears the imprint of "D. Wright," the other parts that of "the Printing Office, in Bow Church-Yard.") London: (1731). *Three frontispieces; five titles, three charts, and* 136 *pp., texts and music.*

Quantz, Jean Joachim.—Essai d'une Methode pour apprendre à jouer de la Flute Traversiere, avec plusieurs remarques pour servir au bon gout dans la Musique. Le tout eclairci par des exemples et par XXIV. tailles douces. Berlin: Chretien Frederic Voss. 1752. 4*to*, XVI+336+18 *pp.*

Quantz, Johann Joachim.—Grondig Onderwys Van den Aardt en de regte Behandeling der Dwarsfluit; Verzeld met eenen treffelyken Regelenschat van de Compositie En van de Uitvoering der voornaamste Muzyk-stukken, op de gebruikelykste Instrumenten; Door *lange ondervinding* en *schrandere opmerking*, in der Groote Muzykaale Wereld. Uit het *Hoogduitsche* vertaald door Jacob Wilhelm Lustig. Amsteldam: A. Olofsen. 1754. 4*to*, XVI+240+16 *pp.*, XXI *tables*.

Quantz, Johann Joachim.—Grondig Onderwys Van den Aardt en regte Behandeling der Dwars-Fluyt, door lange ondervindinge en schrandere opmerkinge in de groote Muzykaale Waereld. Met eene voortreffelyke Inleidinge, nopens de Hoedanigheid in iemand die zich tot de Muziek denkt te begeven, vereischt werdt. Uit het Hoogduits na het echte Origeel door den Kenner der Muziek J. W. L. vertaalt. Met 21 Cierlyke op Koopere gesnedene Plaaten. Amsterdam: A. Olofsen. *c.* 1765. 4*to*, II+80 *pp.*, XXI *pls.*

Quantz, Johann Joachim.—Versuch einer Anweisung die Flöte traversiere zu spielen; mit . . . Zweyte Auflage. Breslau: Johann Friedrich Korn. 1780. 4*to*. XIV+334+18 *pp.*, XXIV *plates*.

Quantz, Johann Joachim.—Versuch einer Anweisung die Flöte traversiere zu spielen; mit . . . Dritte Auflage. Breslau: Johann Friedrich Korn. 1789. 4*to*, XII+18 *pp*. *Title*, XXIV *plates*.

Quantz, John Joachim.—Easy and Fundamental Instructions Whereby either vocal or instrumental Performers unacquainted with Composition, may from the mere knowledge of the most common intervals in Music, learn how to introduce Extempore Embellishments or Variations; as also Ornamental Cadences, with Propriety, Taste, and regularity. Translated from a famous Treatise on Music, written by John Joachim Quantz, Composer to his Majesty the King of Prussia. London: Printed by Longman and Broderip No. 26 Cheapside. Music Sellers to the Royal Family. *n. d.* (1790?). *Folio, title and 32 pages, engraved throughout.*

Rousseau, J. J.—Lettres originales de J. J. Rousseau . . . *There is one letter on* "Musique Militaire", *referring to the use of the .fife.* Paris, Charles Pougens, 1798. 24*mo*. 15*cm.*, 206 *pp.*, 6 *pages of engraved music for fife and military band.*

Wieland, C. M.—Die Erfindung der Flöte und die Bestrafung des Marsyas. Attische Mythen und Sprichwörter. In *Attisches Museum*, herausgegeben von C. M. Wieland. I Bandes. Zürich: Heinrich Gessner. 1796. 12*mo*, *pp*. 279–365.

Wragg, J.—The Flute Preceptor; or The whole Art of Playing the German Flute Rendered easy to all Capacities. Wherein every Instruction relative to that instrument, is elucidated in the most clear and simple Manner, and by which any one may, Without the

Assistance of a Master, Learn to play with Taste & Judgment in a short time. To which is added an Easy Method of acquiring the Double Tongue; and a valuable Selection of Favorite Airs, Songs, Tunes, & Duets. Opus III, 13th Edition with Additions, July 4, 1795. By J. Wragg, Teacher of the German Flute and Oboe. London: The Author, 1795. *Obl. 4to*, V+102 *pp., folded chart of " Chromatic Scale " for a four-keyed flute. This Collection also contains copies of the 14th Edition, dated 1795, and of the 16th Edition, dated September 1, 1798, having the same title-page as the 13th Edition, but slight rearrangements of pages V, 3, 4, and 80.*